GONZAGA
UNIVERSITY

Published for the **Institute of International Education**
809 United Nations Plaza
New York NY 10017
Tel: 212-984-5374
Fax: 212-984-5496
Email: membership@iie.org
Web: www.iie.org/iienetwork

Daniel Obst
Executive Editor

Svetlozara Trocheva
Editor

Jon Grosh
Editor

Published by
NAYLOR
ASSOCIATION SOLUTIONS
5950 NW 1st Place
Gainesville FL 32607
Tel: 800-369-6220
Fax: 352-332-3331
Web: www.naylor.com

Publisher
Tracy Tompkins

Editor
Carter Davis

Project Manager
Amanda Goodwin

Sales Manager
James Ream

Advertising Sales Director
Jeff Bunkin

Advertising Sales
Erik Henson

Marketing Account Specialist
Kent Agramonte

Design and Layout
Birendra Kumar

Printed in the United States of America

ISBN-978-0-87206-373-0

Contents

NOTE: The information contained in this book was submitted by sponsoring institutions at the invitation of IIE and Naylor Association Solutions. IIE has reviewed, but cannot guarantee the accuracy of, the information contained in this book. Sponsoring institutions submitted information in a Web-based form. This information was used to create the www.fundingusstudy.org online guide to grants, awards, scholarships, and fellowships and to produce this book. Any information submitted after August 30, 2014, will appear in the next edition of *Funding for US Study.*

IIE would like to thank all the institutions, foundations, governments, and other organizations that so generously provide scholarships and grants that allow students and scholars from other countries to come to the U.S. for study and research, and thereby keep America's doors open to talented academics from around the world. Our classrooms and research labs are enriched by their knowledge, and American students benefit from their global perspectives.

IIE thanks the Bureau of Educational and Cultural Affairs of the U.S. Department of State for generously allowing us to reprint information on financial assistance and EducationUSA advising centers around the world. Special thanks go to Nichole Johnson (Director of Global EducationUSA Services), and Nancy W. Keteku (Regional Educational Advising Coordinator for Africa West and Central) for contributing articles on financial assistance and the cost of a U.S. education, and to the College Board.

To order *Funding for United States Study: A Guide for International Students and Professionals*, please go to www.iiebooks.org.

Published December 2014/IIE-D0214/4308

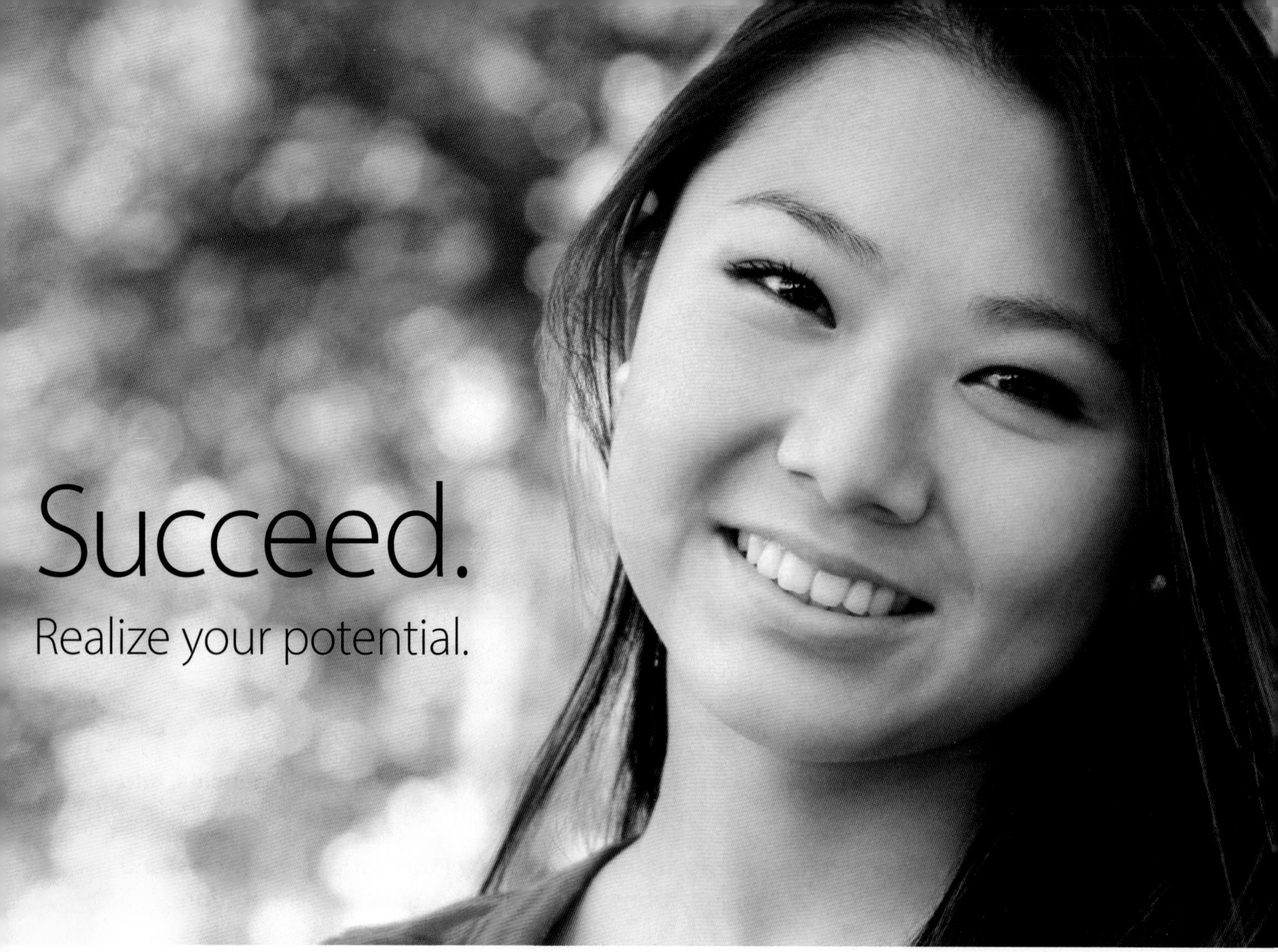

INDIANATECH
Live. Learn. Lead.
TECH
WARRIORS
A perfect place to start your lifelong journey
business, computer sciences, criminal justice
engineering, education, leadership, and more
to learn more, visit
www.IndianaTech.edu/International

WESTERN
WYOMING COMMUNITY COLLEGE
• 2+2 agreements with universities
• Campus residences
• Estimated cost: $13,000 per year
• Scholarships available
ADMISSIONS
2500 College Drive, Rock Springs, WY 82901 USA
Phone: 307-382-1647 Fax: 307-382-1636
admissions@wwcc.wy.edu westernwyoming.edu

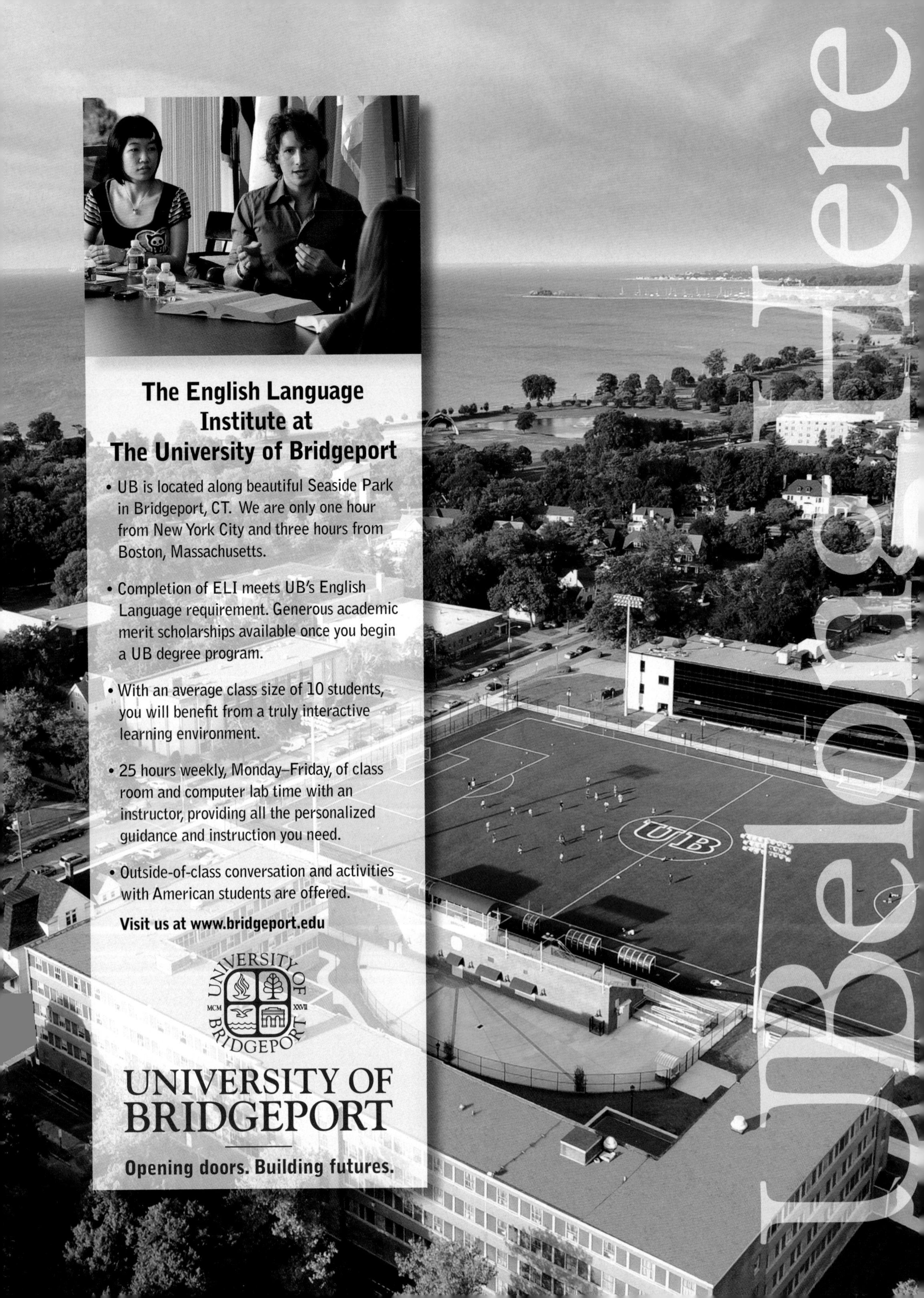
The English Language Institute at The University of Bridgeport
• UB is located along beautiful Seaside Park in Bridgeport, CT. We are only one hour from New York City and three hours from Boston, Massachusetts.
• Completion of ELI meets UB's English Language requirement. Generous academic merit scholarships available once you begin a UB degree program.
• With an average class size of 10 students, you will benefit from a truly interactive learning environment.
• 25 hours weekly, Monday–Friday, of class room and computer lab time with an instructor, providing all the personalized guidance and instruction you need.
• Outside-of-class conversation and activities with American students are offered.
Visit us at www.bridgeport.edu
UNIVERSITY OF BRIDGEPORT
MCM XXVII
UNIVERSITY OF BRIDGEPORT
Opening doors. Building futures.

Introduction

About this Book

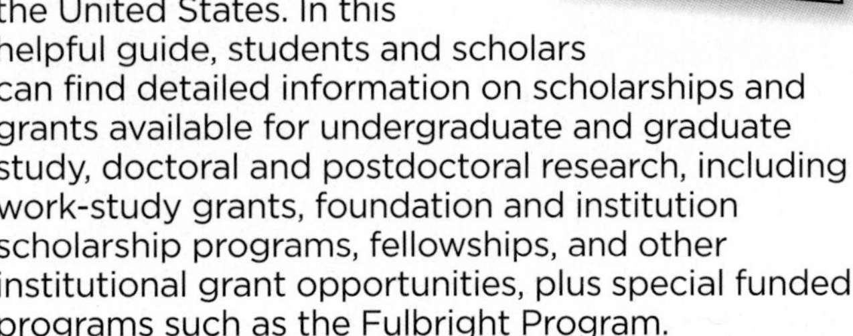

Funding for United States Study: A Guide for International Students and Professionals is a reference directory designed to be a descriptive guide to financial assistance for prospective international students interested in studying or conducting research in the United States. In this helpful guide, students and scholars can find detailed information on scholarships and grants available for undergraduate and graduate study, doctoral and postdoctoral research, including work-study grants, foundation and institution scholarship programs, fellowships, and other institutional grant opportunities, plus special funded programs such as the Fulbright Program.

Listings will include grants and scholarships available through:

- U.S. and foreign governments
- Colleges and universities
- Educational associations
- Libraries
- Research centers
- Foundations
- Corporations
- Other organizations

In addition, the guide provides informative articles on funding U.S. education at the graduate and undergraduate levels, as well as information on EducationUSA educational advising centers around the world, where students can go for educational counseling and to further research university and funding opportunities.

Funding for U.S. Study Online: The listings included in this directory are also available online at **www.fundingUSstudy.org**. Funding for U.S. Study Online includes all types of funding programs, for all levels of postsecondary study, across the full range of academic areas. The extensive database of scholarships, fellowships, and grants is searchable by Area of Study, Country/ Region of Origin, Location in the United States, and Name of Program.

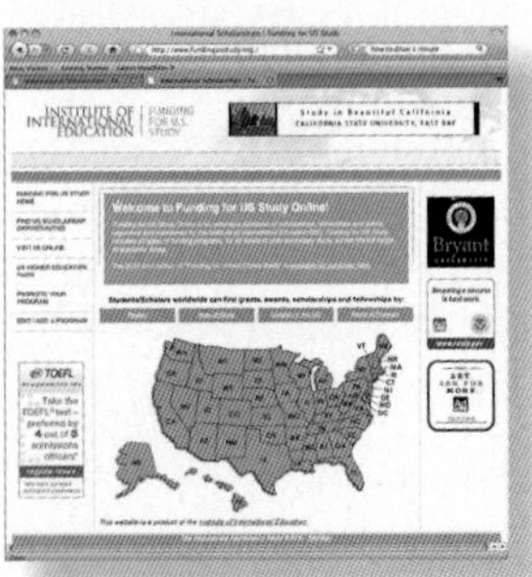

About the Institute of International Education

An independent not-for-profit founded in 1919, the Institute of International Education (IIE) is among the world's largest and most experienced international education and training organizations. IIE helps to solve global problems by building the mutual understanding and international competence necessary to forge collaborative solutions. Each year, more than 30,000 men and women from 175 countries received scholarships and professional training through our programs, assisted by more than 600 IIE staff at 18 offices around the globe.

IIE has joined with many partners—governments, foundations, corporations, and generous donors—to find the most talented people around the world and to provide them with the means to acquire greater knowledge and to share their knowledge with others outside of their country. IIE designs and administers more than 250 programs that reach Americans in all 50 states and serve all the member nations of the United Nations.

Among IIE-administered programs are the Fulbright and Humphrey Programs, administered on behalf of the U.S. Department of State and the Brazil Scientific Mobility Program, administered on behalf of the Brazil Government. IIE also designs and implements scholarship programs on behalf of corporations, including the GE Foundation's Scholars-Leaders Program. IIE's Scholar Rescue Fund, launched in 2002, institutionalizes the Institute's commitment to the rescue of threatened scholars, providing them with fellowships at host universities outside of their country so that they can continue their academic work in freedom and safety.

IIE's annual *Open Doors Report on International Educational Exchange* is a long-standing, comprehensive statistical report on international students and scholars in the United States and on U.S. students studying abroad (www.iie.org/opendoors).

For more information about IIE, please visit IIE online at www.iie.org.

Map of the United States of America

State Abbreviations

Alabama	AL
Alaska	AK
Arizona	AZ
Arkansas	AR
California	CA
Colorado	CO
Connecticut	CT
Delaware	DE
District of Columbia	DC
Florida	FL
Georgia	GA
Hawaii	HI
Idaho	ID
Illinois	IL
Indiana	IN
Iowa	IA
Kansas	KS
Kentucky	KY
Louisiana	LA
Maine	ME
Maryland	MD
Massachusetts	MA
Michigan	MI
Minnesota	MN
Mississippi	MS
Missouri	MO
Montana	MT
Nebraska	NE
Nevada	NV
New Hampshire	NH
New Jersey	NJ
New Mexico	NM
New York	NY
North Carolina	NC
North Dakota	ND
Ohio	OH
Oklahoma	OK
Oregon	OR
Pennsylvania	PA
Rhode Island	RI
South Carolina	SC
South Dakota	SD
Tennessee	TN
Texas	TX
Utah	UT
Vermont	VT
Virginia	VA
Washington	WA
West Virginia	WV
Wisconsin	WI
Wyoming	WY

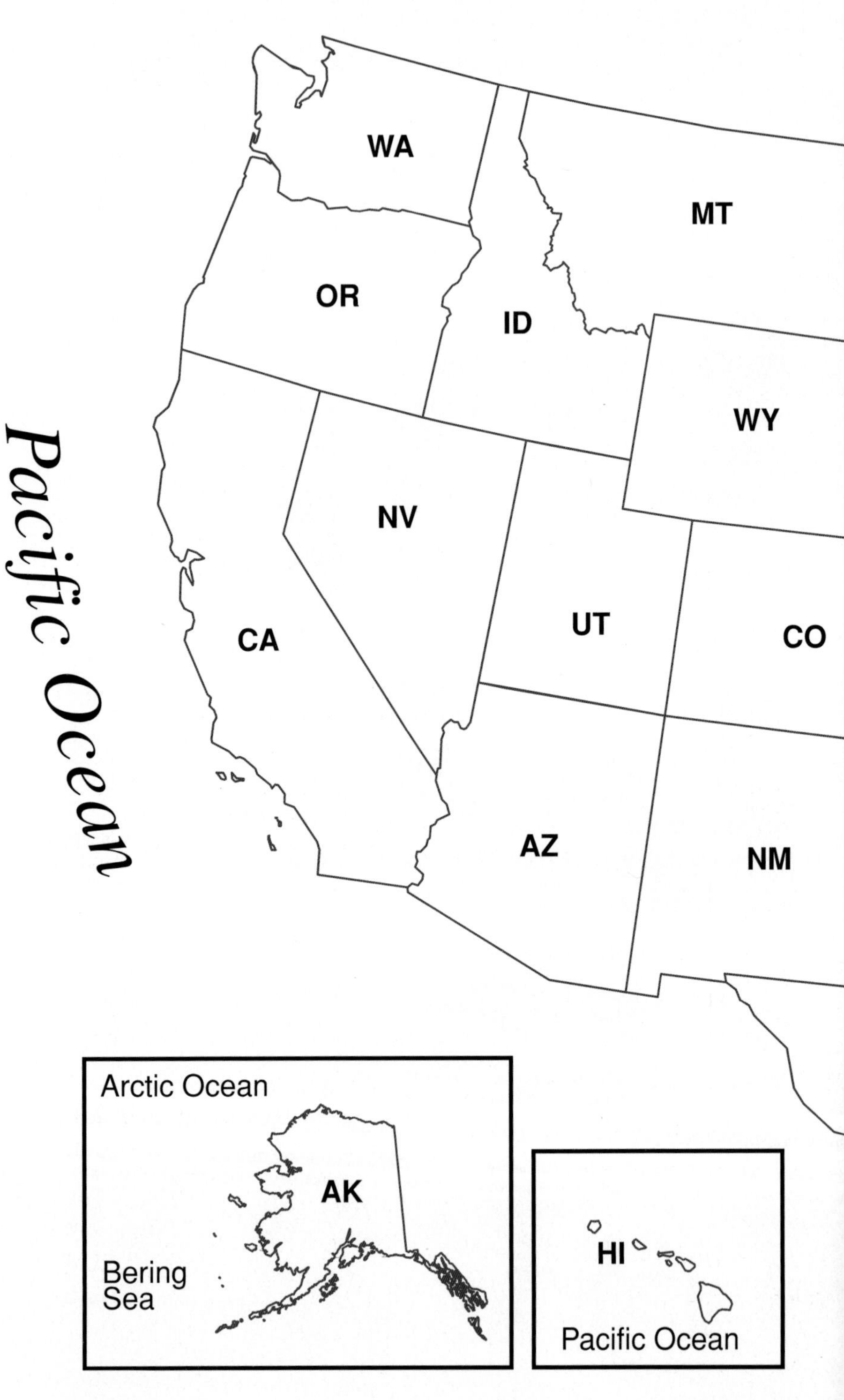

The map shows the geographic location of the 50 states of the United States, where the grants and scholarships described in *Funding for United States Study* are located. The states are identified by their two-letter U.S. Post Office abbreviations throughout this book. Use this map for reference in identifying the geographical location of programs of interest to you.

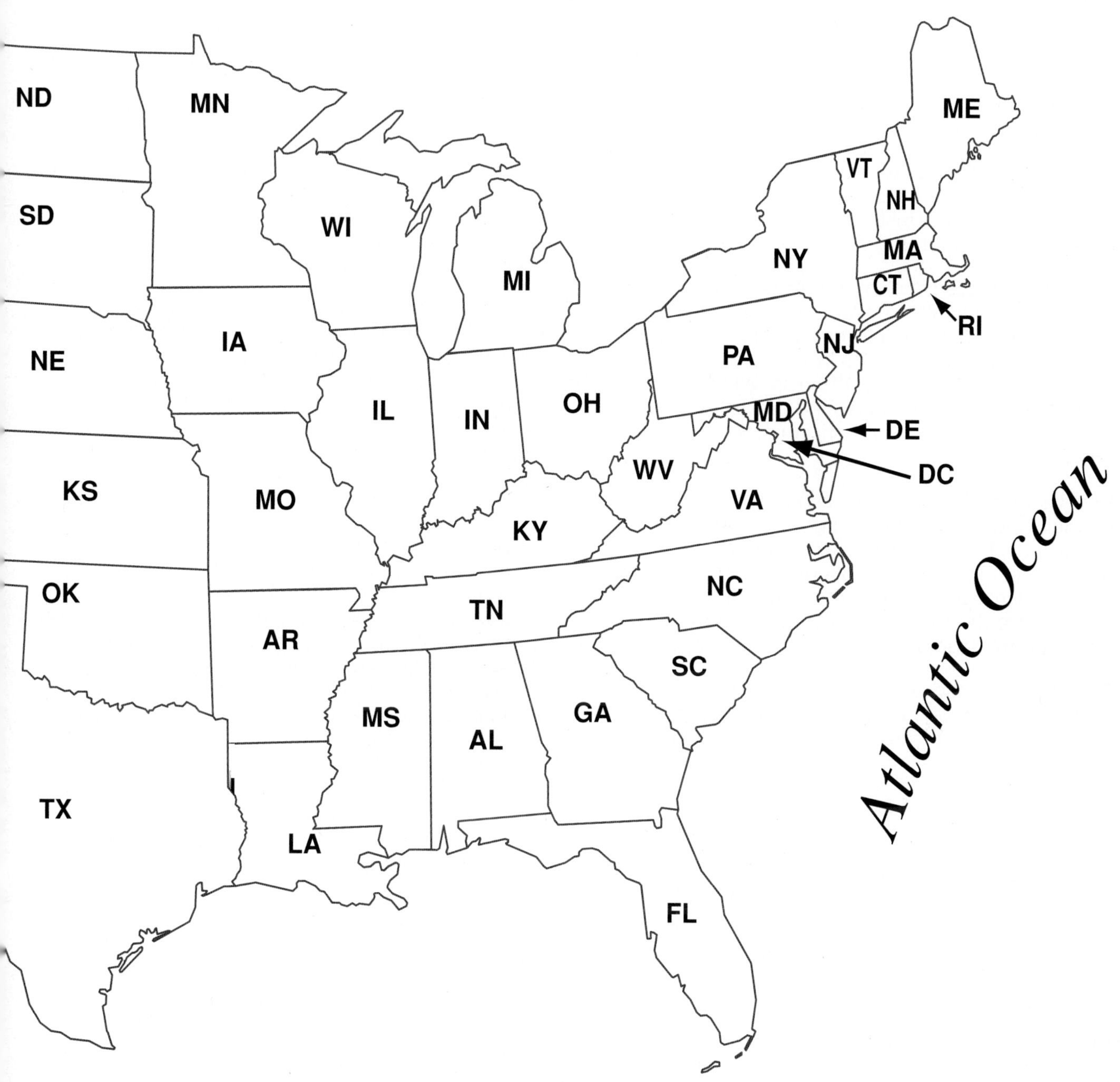

Funding Undergraduate Education: Fast Facts

By Nancy Keteku, EducationUSA Regional Educational Advising Coordinator for Africa West & Central

Pursuing an undergraduate degree at a U.S. institution is an expensive investment, but it will pay off for the rest of your life. Because studying in the United States will cost more than study in your own country, it is important to start your financial planning at least 12 months before you intend to begin your studies, and research thoroughly to find all possible sources of funding. Here are some points to keep in mind:

1. Financial assistance from universities and colleges is awarded at the beginning of the academic year (August/September) and is rarely available for students entering at other times.

2. Full scholarships covering the entire cost of your education are extremely rare, and extremely competitive. To get a full scholarship, you must be one of the top students in your country. There are 10-20 top students from all over the world competing for each scholarship, so you must distinguish yourself among a pool of outstanding students.

3. Private liberal arts colleges award the most financial aid to undergraduate international students, followed by private research universities. The private colleges and universities with the largest endowments and a global outlook are the most likely to award funding to international students.

4. Public (state) and two-year institutions (community colleges) are less expensive than private universities, but also less likely to award significant financial aid to international students.

5. About 80 percent of students at the undergraduate level paid for their U.S. education primarily from personal and family funds, according to IIE's Open Doors Report on International Educational Exchange 2013. Nine percent of international undergraduates were supported primarily by funds from their U.S. college or university.

6. Many students save thousands of dollars in tuition by attending two-year or community colleges for their first two years and then transferring to four-year institutions to complete their degree. Before embarking on this route, make sure to plan your course selection and finances to ensure a smooth transfer.

7. Another way to save money is to master English and take the TOEFL in your home country, so that you can go directly into your academic program in the United States, where English courses are more expensive than at home.

8. To reduce the cost of your education, apply to be a hall counselor or resident adviser, which provide free housing and sometimes a small stipend (but also a lot of distractions). If you speak a language that's in demand on college campuses, you can serve as a language tutor. Immigration law permits international students to work part-time on campus, but don't expect to earn more than $4,000 a year from working.

9. You can reduce the time it takes to complete your degree if you take the maximum course load or if you can receive U.S. college credit for courses taken in your home country. Completing a four-year bachelor's degree in three years saves thousands of dollars. Students can accelerate their programs by (a) taking one additional course each semester (in selected cases); (b) attending summer school; (c) taking courses at a nearby community college, if tuition is lower and credits are transferable; and (d) earning credit for college-level studies (such as A-levels, Baccalaureate) completed in the home country.

10. Application for aid will not prejudice your chances of admission to a chosen program of study, but the more you need, the lower your chances of admission with funding. Because most scholarships cover only a part of your educational costs, you need to state the amount of money you do have available for study, rather than asking for a full scholarship. Don't ask for more money than you genuinely need, because this will reduce your chances of admission.

Visit your local EducationUSA Advising Center for comprehensive and up-to-date information on financial aid and scholarships from colleges and universities in the United States.

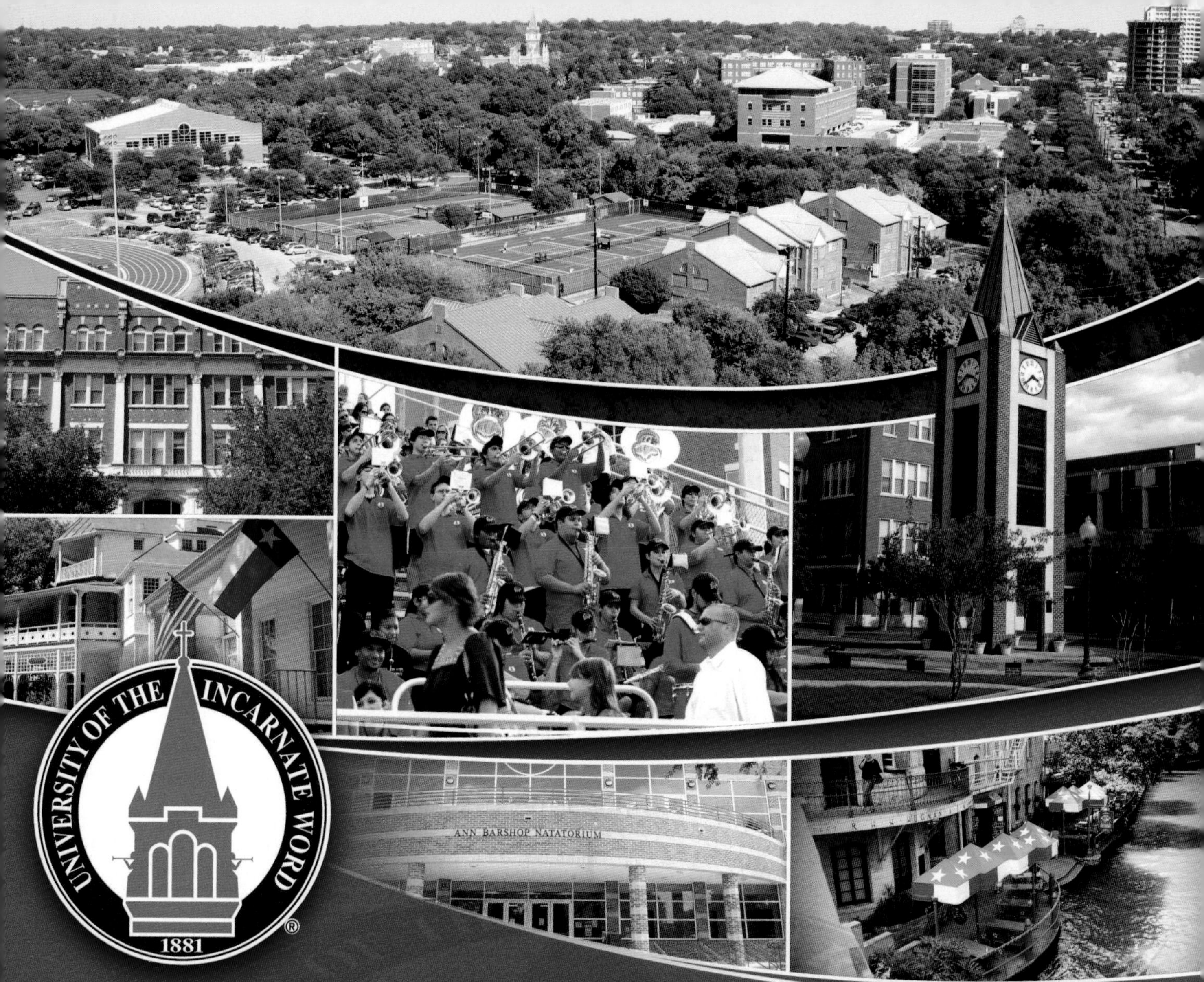
UNIVERSITY OF THE INCARNATE WORD
1881
ANN BARSHOP NATATORIUM

Funding Graduate School: Fast Facts

By Nancy Keteku, EducationUSA Regional Educational Advising Coordinator for Africa West & Central

Graduate study—the pursuit of a master's or doctoral degree—in the United States offers you much more than expertise in a particular field of study. The U.S. graduate education system allows you to tailor programs to your individual goals, and gives you the opportunity to build lifelong professional networks through conference attendance and cooperative projects. U.S. education not only emphasizes practical experience and applications of your field of study, but also fosters the development of leadership, communication, and interpersonal skills to help you adapt to varied working conditions throughout your career. As you investigate graduate education, keep the following funding tips in mind:

1. Funding for graduate school is competitive. The key to being awarded funding is to distinguish yourself from the competition by thoroughly researching each department's program and building a compelling application that demonstrates your potential as a scholar.
2. Financial aid for graduate studies is based on academic merit. Admissions committees seek applicants who attract attention because of their strong academic performance, well-written essays, recommendations, and research or teaching experience. If your qualifications are not yet fully developed, consider taking additional time to strengthen yourself before applying.
3. According to IIE's Open Doors Report on International Educational Exchange, 40 percent of international graduate students were primarily financed by their U.S. universities, while 51 percent relied primarily on personal and family funds in 2012-13.
4. Availability of funding varies by field: science, technology, engineering, and mathematics (known as the STEM fields) have the most funding, followed by the social sciences and the humanities. Professional fields such as business, health, law, and education have comparatively less funding available, and many students take out loans to finance their education.
5. More funding is available for Ph.D. programs than for master's programs. If you are interested in eventually pursuing a doctorate, state this on your application, as it will increase your chances of getting funding.
6. Graduate school funding comes primarily through teaching and research assistantships. Universities with strong research and doctoral programs are able to attract research funds to finance more graduate students. In 2012-13, $65.8 billion was spent on university research in the United States. Identify the departments that have the most research funds and the greatest number of assistantships, and apply to them.
7. Teaching assistantship (TA) positions are found at large institutions with a high number of undergraduate classes in science, math, English, economics, psychology, or languages. International students with particular language skills may be able to get language teaching positions even if they are studying in a different department.
8. Some public (state) universities offer out-of-state tuition waivers to graduate students, thus considerably reducing the cost of attendance.
9. Some departments will expect graduate students to bear the costs of the first year, so that the professors can observe their performance and evaluate their suitability for TAs and RAs in the second year.
10. Graduate departments are small, and the work is intense. Therefore, admissions committees pay close attention to applicants' personal qualities in addition to their academic potential. Your graduate admissions essays should illustrate your personal strengths, such as leadership, originality, motivation, commitment, self-discipline, work habits, adaptability, and team work. At the same time, they evaluate specific skills, especially writing, research, teaching, computer use, and the use of English in academic settings. You can greatly strengthen your chances of admission with funding by composing essays that thoroughly demonstrate your academic interests, experiences, and abilities.

Visit your local EducationUSA Advising Center to learn how to research graduate programs and build strong applications. EducationUSA offers expertise from professional advisers who provide accurate, comprehensive, and current information on all accredited universities in the United States.

Looking Beyond University-Based Funding Sources

By Nichole Johnson, Director of Global EducationUSA Services, Institute of International Education

In the United States, tuition, fees, and living costs vary greatly between institutions, making U.S. higher education affordable to hundreds of thousands of international students each year. It is important to start your financial planning as early as possible. With the right amount of planning and research, it can be made affordable with high returns on your investment. International students may receive significant amounts of financial assistance toward their studies, and this can come from a combination of different sources. In addition to U.S. college and university scholarships, students should also look to organizations that offer financial assistance under the following categories:

- **Academic/Professional Associations:** There is a wide range of member-based associations, composed of practitioners sharing the same profession or academic field. Many of these associations offer scholarships, fellowships, and awards to promising students and young professionals to encourage continuing education and development in the profession. Typically, prospective applicants must become members of the association to be eligible for the scholarship. For example, the Inter American Press Association offers scholarships for Latin America and Caribbean college graduates to study journalism in the U.S., and the American Psychological Association assists with funding dissertation research for science-oriented doctoral students of psychology.

- **Advocacy Associations:** There are many organizations and community groups that advocate for equal rights of underrepresented groups of people and offer financial support to students who are members of the group for which they advocate. For example, the Association for Women in Science and the Hispanic Association of Colleges and Universities award scholarships to make certain that students from these respective communities gain equal access to higher education.

- **Corporations or Corporate-Sponsored Foundations:** In an effort to engage in community development and build recognition for their philanthropic and educational investments, many large corporations and corporate foundations offer funding to students, associations, and nonprofit organizations. Corporate-sponsored scholarship programs are aimed at increasing access to education for citizens of the countries where the corporation is operating to foster global advancement of the industry as well as expand their future pool of qualified U.S.-trained international employees. ExxonMobil and General Electric are examples of corporate foundations that sponsor programs promoting international education and global leadership.

- **Employer/Parents' Employers:** In addition to traditional employment benefits, many corporations offer tuition reimbursement programs or academic training for employees and their dependents. As corporations expand their operations overseas and train a global workforce, many support employees' interests in language immersion and cross-cultural communication programs. Several large multinational corporations such as Chevron Corporation, Lockheed Martin Corporation, and Verizon Communications also offer scholarships to children of employees.

- **Foreign Governments:** Increasingly, many foreign governments award scholarships for their citizens to study abroad. Funding for these scholarship programs is most often made available through the Ministry of Education or the Secretariat of Foreign Relations. For example, the Brazilian government's Science Without Borders Program provides scholarships to undergraduate students from Brazil for one year of study in the Science, Technology, Engineering, and Mathematics (STEM) fields at colleges and universities in the United States.

- **Foundations:** Private foundations, established with funding from an individual, family, or company, award grants with their endowment to support various charitable causes. For example, through its Ambassadorial Scholarships program, the Rotary Foundation aims to further international understanding and friendly relations among people of different countries. International students should also research foundations in their home country that may sponsor student exchange programs and provide scholarships for study abroad.

- **Institution-Affiliated Foundations:** Some private foundations, such as the Houston Endowment and New York Academy of Sciences (NYAS), are affiliated with specific universities and offer scholarships to students at those particular institutions. Typically, the student must apply for these scholarships through the college or university. Other foundations may offer grants to specific academic programs within a university, thereby supporting students participating in those programs.

- **Loans:** In order to pay for their studies, many students must complement scholarships with other types of financial aid, such as a bank loan. International students who wish to obtain a loan from a U.S. bank are usually required to have an eligible co-signer who will pay reimbursement fees should students fail to pay their loans. Some colleges and universities will serve as a co-signer on behalf of their international students. However, in these cases, there are greater chances of higher interest rates and limited funding. International students should also consider applying for loans offered by banks in their home country or by international loan programs, such as the Leo S. Rowe Fund administered by the Organization of the American States.

- **U.S. Government:** To promote cultural understanding throughout the world and support future world leaders and scholars who may contribute to the progress of their home countries, U.S. government agencies, such as the Department of State and the Agency of International Development (USAID), sponsor professional and educational exchange programs at U.S. higher education institutions. Often these government-sponsored programs are administered in partnership with a nonprofit organization and in collaboration with another organization in the foreign country. For example, the Fulbright Program is administered in partnership with the Institute of International Education and with 50 Fulbright commissions around the world.

- **Nonprofit Organizations:** There are several nonprofit organizations experienced in managing educational exchange programs aimed at international community development, social justice, global leadership, and fostering mutual understanding. With sponsorship from corporations, foundations, and governments, nonprofit organizations such as the Institute of International Education (IIE) administer customized scholarship programs including program promotion, applicant screening and selection, student placement, funds disbursement, and student monitoring. As you explore the many financial aid listings in this directory, consider that most students cover the costs of higher education in the United States by combining scholarships, grants, and loans from multiple sources. Consult with the EducationUSA Adviser closest to you to identify the various financial aid programs for which you may be eligible.

TIP: The first step to studying in the United States is researching your choices to find a college or university that best fits your needs. Every student is different, and it is important to think about your own reasons for wanting to study at a college or university in the United States. This process should begin at least one year prior to U.S. study. Begin your search today by visiting the EducationUSA Your 5 Steps to U.S. Study website at: www.educationusa.info/5_steps_to_study.

FAST FACTS OVERVIEW

Brazil Scientific Mobility Undergraduate Program in the U.S.

About the Program (as of August 22, 2014)

The Brazil Scientific Mobility Undergraduate Program in the U.S., launched in 2011, is administered by IIE, and sponsored by the Government of Brazil.

- **17,244** grantees have been placed in academic programs
- **11,278** grantees have been placed in intensive English programs
- **475** U.S. institutions have applied to participate
- **429** U.S. institutions have hosted grantees (academic and IEP)
- **72%** of the grantees major in Engineering and Computer Science
- **39%** of the grantees are female, and **61%** are male

The program is part of the Brazilian government's larger effort to grant 100,000 scholarships for the best students from Brazil to study abroad at the world's best universities.

Total Grantees Placed in Academic Programs by Academic Year

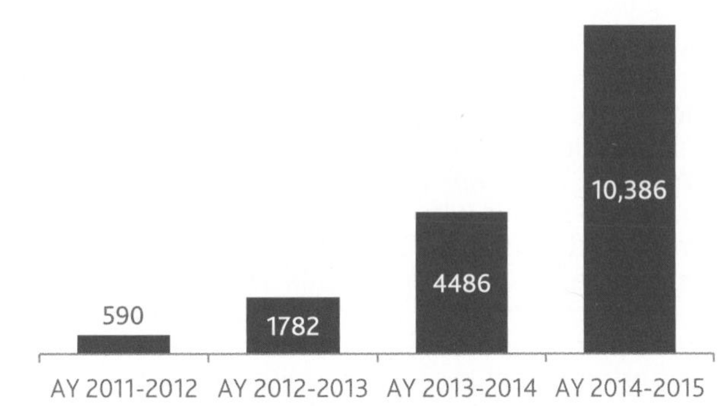

Top Fields of Study and Number of Grantees

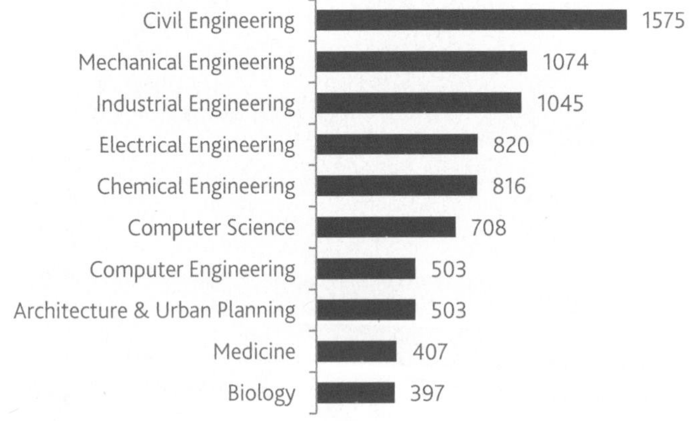

Broad Field of Study Breakdown

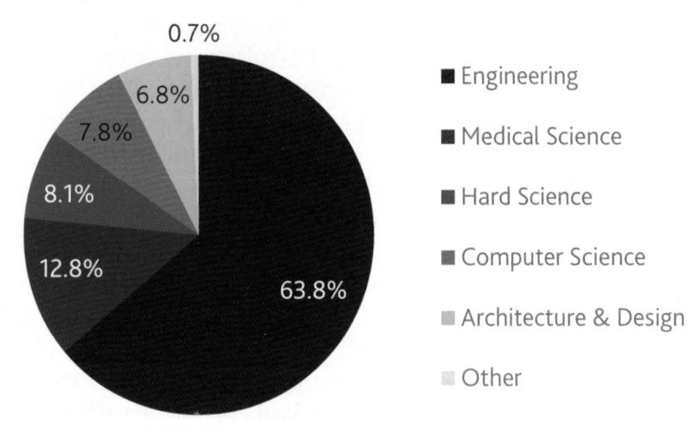

Sample Academic Placement U.S. Host Institutions and Number of Grantees

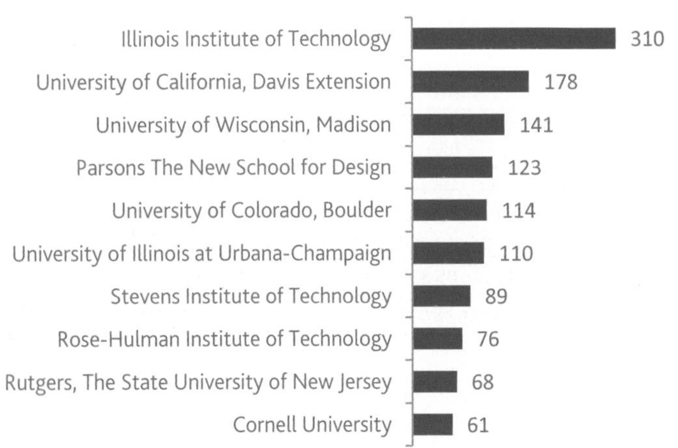

Total Grantees Placed in Intensive English Programs by Cohort

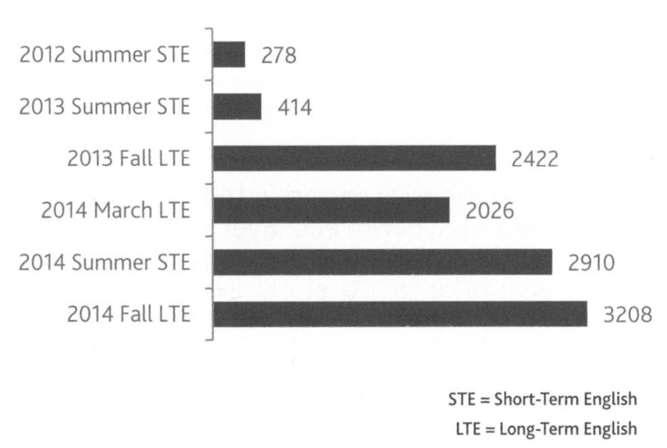

Breakdown of GPAs*

Below 2.0	2.0-2.49	2.5-2.99	3.0-3.49	3.5 or higher
1.2%	6.8%	14.6%	27.8%	49.5%

Academic Training (AT) Overview**

Academic Training is an important component of the Brazil Scientific Mobility Undergraduate Program (BSMP).

In summer 2014:

- IIE assisted in coordinating AT opportunities for **2,090** BSMP grantees
- Over **400** companies hosted grantees
- Over **1300** university research departments hosted grantees
- Grantees participated in AT in **47** states and **Washington, DC**

Student Satisfaction with Academic Host Institution*

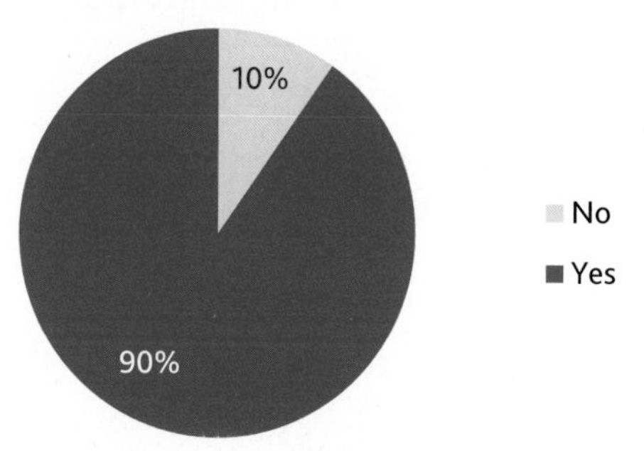

Student Satisfaction with AT**

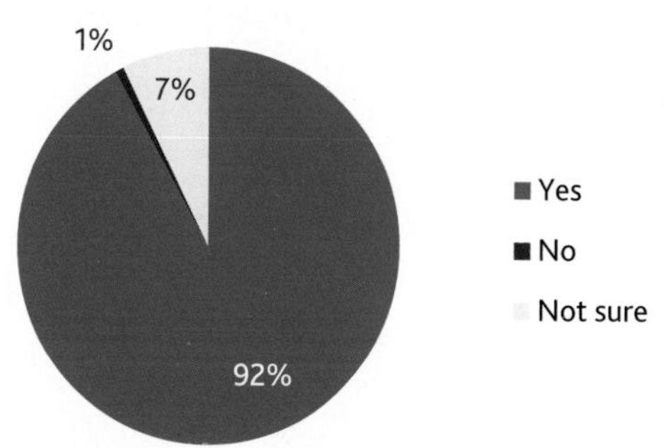

Post-Graduation Plans*

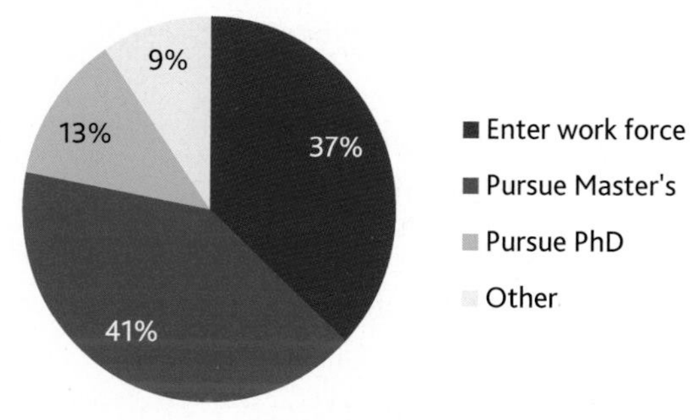

*Data collected from grantees who completed their program in August 2014

Top AT Host Sites & Number of Grantees**

Host Site	Grantees	Host Site	Grantees
Boeing	25	Embraer	11
Pfizer	23	Praxair (Making our planet more productive)	10
Intelligensia International	18	Rama Business Solutions	10
abbvie	15	DuPont	9
Cargill	13	LexisNexis	9

**Data collected from grantees who completed AT in Summer 2014

Student Feedback

"The host institution that was chosen for me fit perfectly well into my expectations. It provided me the courses I was thinking of taking according to my major and the path I want to take in my major. It helped me to decide what the field I want to work in the future is. Plus the fact the professors, classmates and staff are great! They are really friendly and helped me in everything that I needed. It couldn't have been a better choice."

- Mechanical Engineering student from Ohio University

"I believe that this program is a clear indicator that the Brazilian government is giving more attention to education in general. Me and some colleagues are now considering continue our career in the academic field, after taking part in the BSMP. I have also noticed that programs of this kind can serve as some kind of motivation to students in high school and in the beginning of college."

- Industrial Engineering student from The Pennsylvania State University

"When you are in a different culture, you have to think out of the box. Everytime, everywhere. That helps you to expand your networking, to express ideas more clearly, you understand the challenges that other people have to overcome because you have to overcome yourself day after day. A lot of feeling happen, from homesickness to amusement in each situation, and it's another task to keep all of them aligned to the person you are. Every student had the "Brazilian way" of thinking, a way that demands a lot of creativity to perform a job, and the US way demands less resources and less time used as possible. Adding the two of them make me a better student and professional, more prepared for the challenges that I might go through."

- Mechanical Engineering student from North Carolina State University

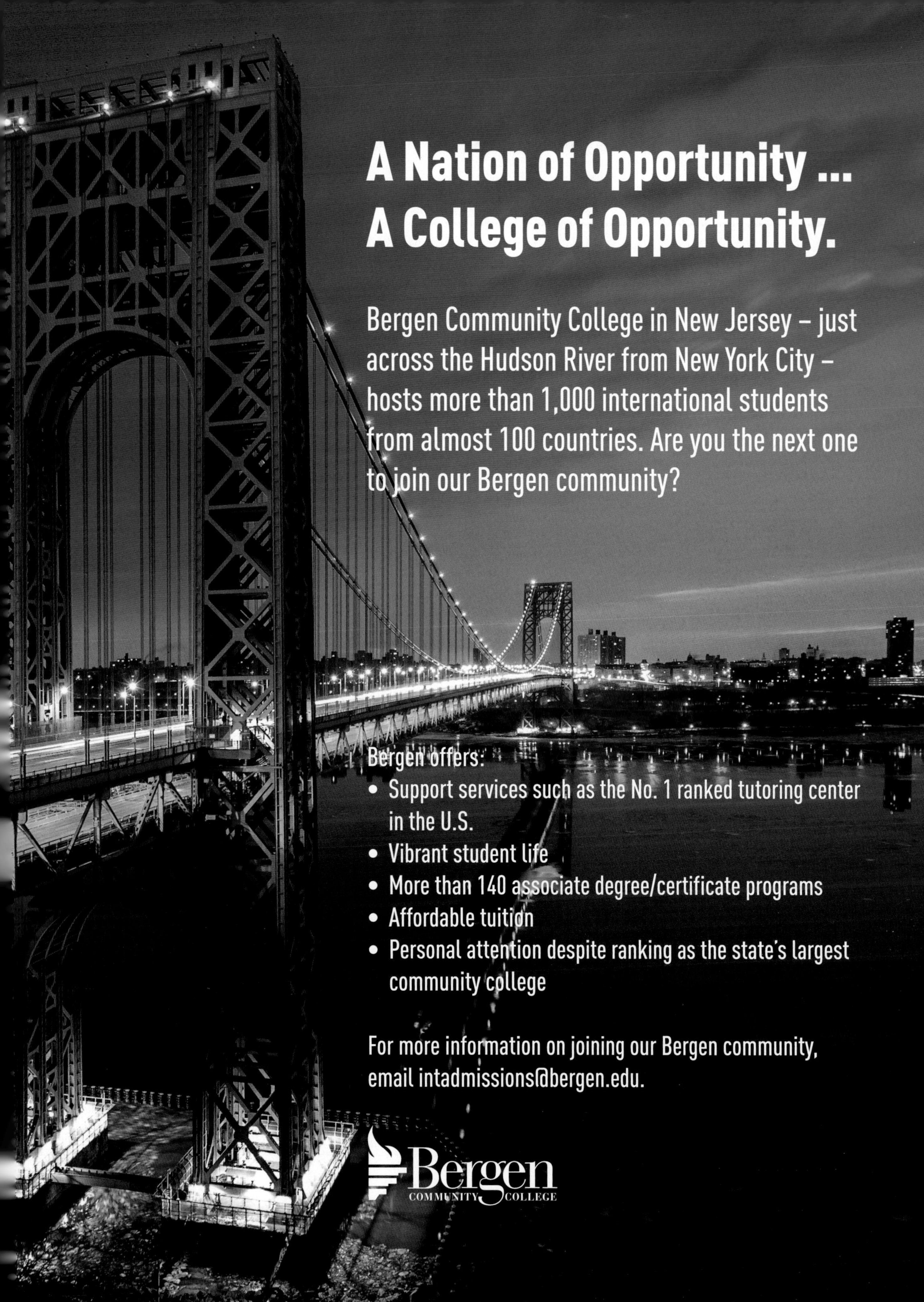

EducationUSA Advising Centers

EducationUSA is a U.S. Department of State-supported network of hundreds of advising centers around the world. Each year, EducationUSA advisers provide millions of international students with accurate, comprehensive, and current information about how to apply to U.S. colleges and universities. EducationUSA staff also work with U.S. higher education professionals to promote recruitment of international students. Advisers guide students in their search for institutions or programs of study in the United States that meet their individual needs. Advisers can help you understand the application process, establish timelines, prepare to take required tests, learn about the U.S. student visa process, and make a smooth transition to a U.S. campus.

EducationUSA advisers work in U.S. embassies and consulates and in a variety of partner institutions, including Fulbright commissions; bi-national cultural centers; U.S. nongovernmental organizations (NGOs) such as AMIDEAST and American Councils/ACCELS; foreign NGOs; foreign universities; and libraries. These institutions share a common goal of assisting students in accessing U.S. higher education opportunities. To find the center nearest you, visit www.educationusa.state.gov/centers.

Whether you plan to pursue an undergraduate, graduate, English language, or short-term program, EducationUSA's "Your 5 Steps to U.S. Study" provides free online advice that helps you:

- Research Your Options
- Finance Your Studies
- Complete Your Application
- Apply for Your Student Visa, and
- Prepare for Your Departure

Visit www.educationusa.state.gov for information about the free EducationUSA mobile app, as well as EducationUSA social media profiles to stay connected with the network.

EducationUSA Opportunity Funds

The EducationUSA Opportunity Funds program assists highly qualified students who are likely to be awarded full financial aid from U.S. colleges and universities but lack the financial resources to cover the up-front costs of obtaining admission, such as testing, application fees, or airfare. Opportunity funds are provided through EducationUSA Advising Centers in the following countries as of this printing:

- **Asia:** Bangladesh, Cambodia, Kazakhstan, Mongolia, Nepal, Pakistan, Sri Lanka, Tajikistan, Turkmenistan, Uzbekistan, Vietnam
- **Europe:** Belarus, Bosnia, Russia, Serbia, Ukraine
- **Middle East & North Africa:** Egypt, Lebanon
- **Sub-Saharan Africa:** Ethiopia, Ghana, Malawi, Mauritius, Namibia, Nigeria, South Africa, Togo, Uganda, Zambia, Zimbabwe
- **Latin America:** Argentina, Bolivia, Brazil, Chile, Colombia, Costa Rica, Ecuador, El Salvador, Guatemala, Honduras, Nicaragua, Panama, Paraguay, Peru, Venezuela

If you live in one of these countries, contact the advising center nearest you for more information about Opportunity Funds.

ehman College has been ranked by U.S. News & World Report as a Tier 1 institution and a Top 50 iblic College among Regional Universities in the Northeast for three consecutive years. Our students me from more than 90 countries and speak over 60 languages. Wherever you are from, you will feel ght at home at the College and in New York City!

cademic Excellence

hman College offers undergraduate and graduate programs with over majors and career paths and 11 doctoral programs in conjunction with CUNY Graduate Center.

hman College has been acclaimed by the National Institutes of Health d National Science Foundation for programs in biological sciences, ychology, mathematics and computer science, physics, and astronomy. amples of other notable degree majors include:

- ccounting
- conomics
- Business Administration
- Nursing
- Dietetics
- Social Work
- Speech Pathology
- Mass Communication
- Multimedia Journalism

idents' classroom and lab experience is enhanced through internships with major companies and organizations.

tensive English

r many international students, our Intensive English Program (IEP) is the first step to a degree program. The IEP fully mplies with the F1 visa requirements and provides courses in Grammar/Reading/Writing and Listening/Speaking. addition, there are classes that focus on specific skills such as pronunciation and college writing. Students who complete our IEP d meet all other academic requirements may be eligible for Lehman undergraduate admission without the TOEFL test.

see our beautiful campus and explore academic, tural and sporting activities, please visit our b site: http://www.lehman.cuny.edu
ntact email: InternationalPrograms.
balPartnerships@lehman.cuny.edu

Facebook: http://www.facebook.com/pages/Lehman-College/186133461418370
Twitter: https://twitter.com/@LehmanCollege
YouTube: http://www.youtube.com/lehmancollege
News: http://wp.lehman.edu/lehman-today/

Program Name and Address:
International Programs & Global Partnerships,
Carman Hall 128,
250 Bedford Park Boulevard West,
Bronx, NY 10468

The Fulbright Program

Established by the U.S. Congress in 1946, the Fulbright Program supports educational exchanges that strengthen mutual understanding among the United States and more than 155 participating countries. A partnership in which the U.S. and foreign governments jointly set priorities, the program also promotes leadership development for students through learning and international cooperation. The program's success is based on its binational character. Sponsored by the Bureau of Educational and Cultural Affairs of the U.S. Department of State, the program is also supported by additional funding from partner governments, corporations, foundations, and academic institutions.

Each year, approximately 4,500 foreign students (new and renewed grants) and 850 visiting scholars and teachers arrive in the United States to study, conduct research, or teach.

"Fulbrighters" range from young professionals who return to their home countries to positions of increasing responsibility to faculty selected for the Fulbright Visiting Scholar Program. Fulbright alumni serve inleadership positions in government, academia (including primary, secondary, and tertiary education), business, the arts, science, media, and other professional fields.

Fulbright Award Descriptions

- **Fulbright Student Program**
  The Foreign Fulbright Student Program is designed to provide individuals from over 150 nations around the world an opportunity to pursue graduate-level studies in the United States. The program provides grants of up to five years to foreign students for graduate-level study at U.S. universities in selected fields. Full and partial grants are offered. Competitive test scores and strong academic records are required.

- **Foreign Language Teaching Assistant Program (FLTA)**
  The FLTA Program enables young educators to refine their teaching skills and increase their English language proficiency while assisting in foreign language instruction and serving as cultural ambassadors on campuses in the United States. The program provides both native speaking student teachers and Americans with an opportunity to learn about each other's cultures and customs, thereby enhancing mutual understanding. Only foreign nationals residing in their home countries are eligible to apply. Participating countries: Afghanistan, Algeria, Argentina, Austria, Bahrain, Bangladesh, Belgium, Brazil, Canada, Chile, China, Colombia, Egypt, Finland, France, Germany, India, Indonesia, Iraq, Ireland, Israel, Italy, Jordan, Kazakhstan, Kenya, South Korea, Kuwait, Kyrgyzstan, Lebanon, Libya (L.A.R.), Malaysia, Mauritania, Mexico, Mongolia, Morocco, Nigeria, Oman, Pakistan, Palestinian Authority, Philippines, Portugal, Qatar, Russia, Saudi Arabia, Senegal, Spain, Syria, Taiwan, Tajikistan, Tanzania, Thailand, Tunisia, Turkey, United Arab Emirates, Uruguay, Uzbekistan, and Yemen.

- **Fulbright Visiting Scholar Program**
  Each year the Fulbright Foreign Scholar Program brings approximately 850 faculty and professionals from more than 150 partner countries to the U.S. to teach and conduct advanced research.

- **Fulbright Scholar-in-Residence Program**
  Designed for institutions historically underrepresented in international academic exchange, the Fulbright Scholar-in-Residence Program allows scholars outside the United States to gain experience in U.S. higher education, specifically at small liberal arts colleges, Minority-serving Institutions, and Community Colleges.

- **Fulbright Visiting Scholar Programs for Iraq and Libya**
  The Fulbright Visiting Scholar Programs for Iraq and Libya are designed to bring junior scholars to U.S. host institutions for faculty development, mentoring, and cultural exchange activities. The intent of the ten-week programs is to equip scholars with the knowledge and tools needed to build the capacity of universities at home and to advance the education of future generations of Iraqis and Libyans. In addition, it lays the foundation for scholars and their U.S. hosts to develop long-term institutional relationships and to identify areas of cooperation that can be sustained beyond the grant period.

- **Fulbright NEXUS Regional Scholar Program**
  The Fulbright Regional Network for Applied Research (NEXUS) Program brings together a network of junior scholars, professionals, and mid-career applied researchers from the United States and other Western Hemisphere nations for a series of three seminar meetings and a Fulbright exchange experience. The Program fosters collaborative and multidisciplinary research to

address challenging regional issues and produce tangible results. More information is available at www.iie.org/cies.

- **Fulbright Teacher Exchange Programs**
  Fulbright Teacher Exchange Programs are designed for highly qualified full-time teachers, primarily at the secondary level. The Fulbright Classroom Teacher Exchange Program provides teachers from Czech Republic, France, Hungary, India, Mexico, Switzerland, and the United Kingdom with the opportunity to participate in a direct one-to-one exchange of classrooms with colleagues in the U.S. for a semester or academic year, to gain practical experience in an international classroom, and to share best practices of teaching, school administration, and curriculum development. The Distinguished Fulbright Awards in Teaching Program brings teachers from Argentina, Finland, India, Israel, Mexico, Morocco, Singapore, and South Africa to the United States and sends U.S. teachers to these countries, in addition to the United Kingdom, for a semester or summer to pursue individual projects, conduct research, take courses for professional development, and lead master classes or seminars in participating countries.

- **Hubert H. Humphrey Fellowship Program**
  The Hubert H. Humphrey Fellowship Program brings accomplished professionals from designated countries to the United States at a midpoint in their careers for a year of study and related professional experiences. Fellowships are granted competitively to professional candidates with a commitment to public service in both the public and private sectors. For participating countries and additional information, please check website at www.humphreyfellowship.org.

How to Apply

Applications for all the programs listed above must be submitted through the Fulbright Commission or Public Affairs Section of the U.S. Embassy in the applicant's home country. The Fulbright Commissions will also be able to give you more information on the exact requirements, specific needs, other types of Fulbright awards, or the specific number of awards available.

Fulbright Commissions: Contact Information

Please review the following list of Fulbright Commissions; in approximately 90 countries, the competition is run by the public affairs section of the U.S. embassy. Please contact the commission or U.S. embassy in your home country to obtain further information or Fulbright grant application materials.

ARGENTINA
Commission for Educational Exchange
Viamonte 1653, Piso 2
Buenos Aires, C1055ABE, ARGENTINA
Tel: 54-11-4814-3561,3562
Email: info@fulbright.com.ar
Web: www.fulbright.edu.ar

AUSTRALIA
Australian-American Fulbright Commission
Executive Director - Dr. Tangerine Holt
PO Box 9541
Deakin ACT, 2600, AUSTRALIA
Tel: 61-2-6260-4460
Email: programmanager@fulbright.com.au
Web: www.fulbright.com.au

AUSTRIA
Austrian-American Educational Commission
Quartier 21/MQ, Museumplatz 1, Hof 2
Stiege 8, Top 4
Vienna, A1070, AUSTRIA
Tel: 43-1-236-7878-0
Email: LJohnson@Fulbright.at
Web: www.fulbright.at

BELGIUM & LUXEMBOURG
Commission for Educational Exchange Between the United States, Belgium & Luxembourg
Royal Library of Belgium
Boulevard de L'Empereur, 4, Keizerslaan
Brussels, B-1000, BELGIUM
Tel: 32-2-519-57-70
Email: adviser@fulbright.be
Web: www.fulbright.be

BRAZIL
Commission for Educational Exchange
Edificio Casa Thomas Jefferson
SHIS Q1 09-CONJ 17-Lote L
Brasilia DF, 71625170, BRAZIL
Tel: 55-61-3248-8600
Email: fulbright@fulbright.org.br
Web: www.fulbright.org.br

BULGARIA
Bulgarian-American Commission for Educational Exchange
Ministry of Culture
17 Alexander Stamboliiski Blvd
Sofia, 1000, BULGARIA
Tel: 359-2-981-8567
Email: fulbright@fulbright.bg
Web: www.fulbright.bg

CANADA
Foundation for Educational Exchange
350 Albert Street, Suite 2015
Ottawa, K1R1A4, CANADA
Tel: 613-688-5540
Email: info@fulbright.ca
Web: www.fulbright.ca

CHILE
Fulbright Commission - Chile
Providencia 2331, Piso 9 Oficina 901
Providencia, Santiago, CHILE
Tel: 56-2-334-4368
Email: becas@fulbrightchile.cl
Web: www.fulbrightchile.cl

COLOMBIA
Commission for Educational Exchange
Calle 38 #13-37, Piso 11
Bogota, COLOMBIA
Tel: 57-1-287-7831
Email: amason@fulbright.edu.co
Web: www.fulbright.edu.co

CYPRUS
J. William Fulbright Center
2 Egypt Avenue P.O. Box 24051
CY 1700 Nicosia, CYPRUS
Tel: 357-22669757
Email: cfc@fulbright.org.cy
Web: www.fulbright.org.cy

CZECH REPUBLIC
J.William Fulbright Commission for Educational Exchange
Karmelitska 17
Prague 1, 118 00, CZECH REPUBLIC
Tel: 420-2-2271-8452
Email: fulbright@fulbright.cz
Web: www.fulbright.cz

DENMARK
Denmark-America Foundation
Fiolstraede 24
3 sal DK-1171 Copenhagen K., DENMARK
Tel: 45-33-12-82-23
Email: advising@daf-fulb.dk
Web: www.daf-fulb.dk

ECUADOR
Fulbright Commission - Ecuador
Diego de Almagro N25-41 y Avenue Colon
Quito, ECUADOR
Tel: 593-2-222-2103
Email: programs@fulbright.org.ec
Web: www.fulbright.org.ec

EGYPT
Binational Fulbright Commission in Egypt
21 Amer Street
Messaha, Dokki
Giza, 12311, EGYPT
Tel: 20-23-3359717
Email: lohof@bfce.eun.eg
Web: www.fulbright-egypt.org

FINLAND
Fulbright Center
Hakaniemenranta 6
Helsinki, 530, FINLAND
Tel: 358-9-5494-7400
Email: Executive.Director@fulbright.fi
Web: www.fulbright.fi

FRANCE
Franco-American Commission
9, Rue Chardin
Paris, 75016, FRANCE
Tel: 33-1-4414-5360
Email: cfa@fulbright-france.org
Web: www.fulbright-france.org

GERMANY
German-American Fulbright Commission
Oranienburger Str. 13-14
Berlin, 10178, GERMANY
Tel: 49-30-284443-0
Email: gpu@fulbright.de
Web: www.fulbright.de

GREECE
Fulbright Commission
6 Vassilissis Sofias Avenue
Athens, 10674, GREECE
Tel: 30-210-724-1811
Email: info@fulbright.gr
Web: www.fulbright.gr

HUNGARY
Hungarian-American Fulbright Commission
Baross u. 62
Budapest, H-1082, HUNGARY
Tel: 36-1-462-8040
Email: info@fulbright.hu
Web: www.fulbright.hu

ICELAND
Iceland-United States Educational Commission
Laugavegur 59
Reykjavik, 101, ICELAND
Tel: 354-551-0860
Email: adviser@fulbright.is
Web: www.fulbright.is

INDIA
United States-India Educational Foundation (USINEF)
Fulbright House
12 Hailey Road
New Delhi, 110001, INDIA
Tel: 91-11-2332-8944
Email: info@usief.org.in
Web: www.usief.org.in

INDONESIA
American-Indonesian Exchange Foundation (AMINEF)
CIMB NIAGA Plaza, 3rd Floor
Jl. Jend. Sudirman Kav. 25
Jakarta, INDONESIA
Tel: 021-529-61966
Email: mike_mccoy@aminef.or.id
Web: www.aminef.or.id

IRELAND
The Ireland- United States Commission for Educational Exchange (The Fulbright Commission)
Brooklawn House, Crampton Avenue
Shelbourne Road, Ballsbridge
Dublin, 4, IRELAND
Tel: 353-1-660-7670
Email: admin@fulbright.ie
Web: www.fulbright.ie

ISRAEL
United States-Israel Educational Foundation
One Ben Yehuda Street 10/F
Tel Aviv, 63801, ISRAEL
Tel: 972-3-5172392
Email: info@fulbright.org.il
Web: www.fulbright.org.il

ITALY
The United States-Italy Fulbright Commission
Via Castelfidardo, 8
Rome, 00185, ITALY
Tel: 39-06-48-88-211
Email: fulbright@fulbright.it
Web: www.fulbright.it

JAPAN
The Japan-United States Educational Commission
Sanno Grand Building #207
2-14-2 Nagata-Cho, Chiyoda-Ku
Tokyo, 1000014, JAPAN
Tel: 81-3-3580-3231
Email: program@fulbright.jp
Web: www.fulbright.jp

JORDAN
Jordanian-American Commission for Educational Exchange
19, Mahdi Bin Barakah Street, Shmeisani
Amman, 11185, JORDAN
Tel: 962-6-568-4760
Email: info@fulbright.org.jo
Web: www.fulbright-jordan.org

KOREA, SOUTH
Korean-American Educational Commission
168-15 Yomni-Dong, Mapo-Gu
Seoul, 121-874, KOREA
Tel: 82-2-3275-4000
Email: admin@fulbright.or.kr
Web: www.fulbright.or.kr

MALAYSIA
The Malaysian-American Commission on Educational Exchange
18th Floor Menara Yayasan Tun Razak
200 Jalan Bukit Bintang
Kuala Lumpur, 50200, MALAYSIA
Tel: 60-3-2166-8878
Email: coffmanjm@macee.org.my
Web: www.macee.org.my

MEXICO
Comision Mexico - Estados Unidos
Berlin 18, 2do. piso, Col. Juarez
C.P. 06600, México D.F.
Mexico City, 6600, MEXICO
Tel: 52-5-555-92-2861
Email: marcecruz@comexus.org.mx
Web: www.comexus.org.mx

MOROCCO
The Moroccan-American Commission for Educational and Cultural Exchange (MACECE)
7, rue d'Agadir
Rabat, 10000, MOROCCO
Tel: 212-537-760-468
Email: info@macece.ma
Web: www.macece.org

NEPAL
Commission for Educational Exchange Between the United States and Nepal
The American Center
Gyaneswor, Kathmandu, NEPAL
Tel: 977-1-441-5845
Email: fulbcomm@fulbrightnepal.org.np
Web: www.fulbrightnepal.org.np

NETHERLANDS
Fulbright Commission
The Fulbright Center
Herengracht 430 Amsterdam, 1017 BZ, NETHERLANDS
Tel: 31-20-5315930
Email: info@fulbright.nl
Web: www.fulbright.nl

NEW ZEALAND
Fulbright New Zealand
Level 8, 120 Featherston Street
Wellington, 6140, NEW ZEALAND
Tel: 64-4-472-2065
Email: info@fulbright.org.nz
Web: www.fulbright.org.nz

NORWAY
United States-Norway Fulbright Foundation for Educational Exchange
Arbinsgate 2
Oslo, 0253, NORWAY
Tel: 47-22-01-4010
Email: fulbright@fulbright.no
Web: www.fulbright.no

PAKISTAN
United States Educational Foundation in Pakistan
P.O. Box 1128, Islamabad 44000, Pakistan
Islamabad, PAKISTAN
Tel: 92-51-2877075
Email: info@usefpakistan.org
Web: www.usefpakistan.org

PERU
Commission for Educational Exchange
Juan Romero Hidalgo 444
San Borja
Lima, 41, PERU
Tel: 511-475-3083
Email: info@fulbrightperu.pe
Web: www.fulbrightperu.pe

PHILIPPINES
The Philippine-American Educational Foundation
10/F Ayala Life/FGU Center
Makati 6811 Ayala Avenue
Makati City, 1226, PHILIPPINES
Tel: 63-2-812-0919
Email: fulbright@paef.org.ph
Web: www.fulbright.org.ph

POLAND
Polish-United States Fulbright Commission
ul. Konstantego Ildefonsa Galczynskiego 4
Warsaw, 00-362, POLAND
Tel: 48-22-10-10-040
Email: fulbright@fulbright.edu.pl
Web: www.fulbright.edu.pl

PORTUGAL
Luso-American Ed. Commission
Avenida Elias Garcia, 59-5th floor
Lisbon, 1000148, PORTUGAL
Tel: 351-21-799-6390
Email: fulbright@fulbright.pt
Web: www.fulbright.pt

ROMANIA
Romanian-United States Fulbright Commission
Inginer Nicolae Costinescu, 2, Sector 1
Bucharest, 11878, ROMANIA
Tel: 4021-2315500
Email: office@fulbright.ro
Web: www.fulbright.ro

SLOVAK REPUBLIC
J. William Fulbright Commission
Levicka 3
Bratislava, 82108, SLOVAK REPUBLIC
Tel: 421-2-5937-4639
Email: office@fulbright.gov.sk
Web: www.fulbright.sk

SPAIN
Commission for Cultural,
Educational and Scientific Exchange between the
United States of America and Spain
Calle General Oráa, 55, Planta Baja
Madrid, 28006, SPAIN
Tel: 34-91-702-7000
Email: postmaster@comision-fulbright.org
Web: www.fulbright.es

SRI LANKA
United States-Sri Lanka Fulbright Commission
7 Flower Terrace
Colombo, 7, SRI LANKA
Tel: 94-1-1256-4176
Email: fulbright@isplanka.lk
Web: www.fulbrightsrilanka.com

SWEDEN
Fulbright Commission
Vasagatan 15-17, 4th Floor
Stockholm, S-11120, SWEDEN
Tel: 46-8-534-818-85
Email: fulbright@fulbright.se
Web: www.fulbright.se

TAIWAN
Foundation for Scholarly Exchange
2 F., 45 Yanping S. Rd.
Taipei, 10043, TAIWAN
Tel: 886-2-2388-2100
Email: wvocke@fulbright.org.tw
Web: www.fulbright.org.tw

THAILAND
Thailand-United States Educational Foundation
21/5 Thai Wah Tower I, 3rd Floor, South Sathorn Road
Bangkok, 10120, THAILAND
Tel: 66-0-2285-0581
Email: tusef@fulbrightthai.org
Web: www.fulbrightthai.org

TURKEY
The Turkish Fulbright Commission
Eskişehir Yolu 9. Km. Tepe Prime İş Merkezi B Blok
No:124 06800 Çankaya/Ankara, TURKEY
Tel: 90-312-427-1360
Email: trprog@fulbriht.org.tr
Web: www.fulbright.org.tr

UKRAINE
Fulbright Program in Ukraine
20 Esplanadna Street, 9th floor, office No 904
Kyiv, 01001, UKRAINE
Tel: 380-44-287-0777
Email: student@fulbright.com.ua
Web: www.fulbright.org.ua

UNITED KINGDOM
United States-UK Fulbright Commission
Battersea Power Station
188 Kirtling Street
London, SW8 5BN, UNITED KINGDOM
Tel: 44-20-7498-4010
Email: programmes@fulbright.co.uk
Web: www.fulbright.co.uk

URUGUAY
Fulbright Commission - Uruguay
JUNCAL 1327 D, APT. 401
Montevideo, 11100, URUGUAY
Tel: 598-2-901-4160
Email: comision@fulbright.org.uy
Web: www.fulbright.org.uy

How to Use this Book

There are many different types of scholarships available to you to study in the United States. *Funding for United States Study* is a guide to financial assistance for prospective students interested in studying and conducting research in the United States. This book was compiled by the Institute of International Education, one of the largest higher educational exchange agencies in the United States. The information contained in the scholarship profiles was collected in 2011 from U.S. and foreign governments, colleges and universities, educational associations, libraries, research centers, foundations, corporations, and other organizations.

IIE has made every effort to ensure that the information in this directory is as accurate as possible. Keep in mind that contact information may change. Whenever possible please take a look at the web address provided, to confirm the correct or updated contact information for scholarship administrators. You can also take a look at *Funding for U.S. Study Online* (www.FundingUSstudy.org), this book's companion website, which is continually updated.

Organization of the Scholarship Profiles

The scholarship profiles are organized in three main sections:

- Funding Opportunities Provided by Foundations, Agencies, and Other Organizations: For Study at Any Institution
- Funding Opportunities Provided by Foundations, Agencies, and Other Organizations: For Study at a Specified Institution
- Funding Opportunities Provided by U.S. Colleges and Universities

The profiles are alphabetized by name of sponsoring or administering agency.

About half of the scholarship profiles contained in this directory are open to students, scholars, or professionals from any country or nationality. The remaining funding opportunities are open to students from particular countries or regions, and often apply only for certain fields of study. Use the index in the back to find scholarship listings that pertain to your particular field of study.

Roughly 25 percent of all international students studying in the United States receive funding directly from U.S. colleges or universities. The listings contained in the *Funding Opportunities Provided by U.S. Colleges and Universities* section represent only a snapshot of the scholarships that are available to you through U.S. colleges and universities. They often are limited to certain fields of study or degree programs, and vary greatly in terms of the size of the financial award. If you do not find a scholarship from a particular college or university in this book, be sure to check with the college or university directly to determine whether special scholarships or other forms of financial assistance are offered to international students.

Each individual scholarship profile has four key information clusters:

1. Program Information
2. Award Information
3. Eligibility Requirements
4. Application Information

1. Program Information

Program/Scholarship Sponsoring or Administering Agency
Names the sponsoring or administering institution or foundation.

Program/Scholarship Title
Names the specific scholarship or program opportunity.

Program Description
Provides an overview of the purpose and goals of the grant program.

Level of Study
This refers to the academic level of study the student will be pursuing under the scholarship program. In this field you will find the options listed below:

Undergraduate usually refers to students pursuing a bachelor's degree.

Graduate generally describes students who hold a bachelor's degree and usually refers to students pursuing a master's degree program.

Doctorate usually refers to students pursuing a doctoral (Ph.D.) degree. This category refers to students who may or may not have completed their research and/or dissertation, and have yet to receive their degree.

Postdoctorate refers to students that already hold the doctoral degree.

Professional refers to individuals with professional experience in the field. This category can also refer to students seeking a professional degree in fields such as law or medicine.

Field of Study
Many scholarship programs are restricted to certain fields of study. This listing can range from a very specific topic to a general field of study. Some programs may be listed as unrestricted, meaning there is not a required concentration in a particular field. Up to 10 specific fields of study offered by the program are listed in this profile. If you are looking for grants in particular fields of study, consult the index in the back on page 278 to locate programs in a specific field of study.

Nationality
This field describes who may apply for the scholarship program. Some programs may be applicable only to students from a particular country or region. You may see the following listed:

Specific country name(s) refers to students from a particular country or list of countries.

Specific region name(s) refers to students from countries within a particular region or regions.

Any refers to students from any nationality.

Location of Study
For funding opportunities that are limited to specific regions, states, or cities in the United States.

2. Award Information

Award Type
This section identifies the type of financial award provided through the program, such as a fellowship, grant, assistantship, internship, scholarship, or other type of grant for a specific purpose.

Average Amount
This section refers to the average amount that recipients are awarded. This number can vary for recipients depending on the degree program pursued, the educational institution costs, and the estimated living expenses for the location of study. The amount listed is the amount awarded per year unless otherwise noted.

Number of Awards
This section refers to the number of awards granted per year through the program. If a program grants only one award, it does not necessarily mean the program is more or less competitive than a program that grants 45 awards.

Award Coverage
This section lists the types of costs that are covered by the award. Common costs are: tuition, cost of living, books, health insurance, and research costs.

Award Duration
This refers to the length of the award period. Students may or may not be eligible to apply for subsequent years. Some awards are listed as renewable.

3. Eligibility Requirements

This section lists the prerequisites for applicant eligibility. Examples of requirements here include minimum admission test scores, academic standing, academic and/or professional experience. Up to five requirements are listed in the scholarship profiles. For a complete list of requirements for a specific program, check the program website.

Some programs require a minimum score on the written or computer-based TOEFL. PBT refers to the paper-based (or written) test, and CBT refers to computer-based test. For example: "Must have minimum TOEFL score of 550 PBT/213 CBT" means "Must score a minimum of 550 on written TOEFL or 213 on computer-based TOEFL."

4. Application Information

Application Deadline
This refers to the closing date for the receipt of application materials. It is understood that these dates may change annually, therefore only the month has been included. Check the program website for exact application deadlines.

Instructions
This field describes the application process and where applicants can find application materials.

Some examples include: apply online, contact to request application materials, apply through University.

Note: "Common Application"
Some of the scholarship profiles refer students to use the "Common Application." The "Common Application" is a general application form that is used by over 250 colleges and universities in the United States for undergraduate admission to these institutions. Check the website to verify which application is required. For more information about the Common Application, check www.commonapp.org.

Contact Information
The contact information in the scholarship profiles generally includes name, mailing address, telephone and fax numbers, email, and program website. In some cases, sponsoring or administering agencies have not provided complete contact information. If contact information is missing or incomplete, please check the program website for contact information.

Name
If a name has been provided, it is usually the name of the program administrator. This information may change.

Mailing Address
The address listed in the scholarship profiles generally refers to the mailing address of the primary contact or program administrator at the administering or sponsoring agency. This is not necessarily the address where you will need to send your grant application. It is the address used for written inquiries.

Telephone/Fax/Email
Most scholarship profiles include telephone and fax numbers and email address. If an email address is not listed, then it has not been supplied or there is an online contact form available on the website. You should check the website to determine the best way to contact the program sponsor.

Program Website
Program website is where you can find more details and information on the scholarship program. Usually, program websites include more detailed information regarding requirements as well as downloadable application forms.

Helpful Acronyms

ACT	American College Testing Program
AUD	Australian Dollars
BA	Bachelor's of Arts
BS	Bachelor's of Science
CBT	Computer-Based Test (TOEFL)
ECA	Bureau of Educational and Cultural Affairs, U.S. Department of State
Ed.D.	Doctor of Education
ESL	English as a Second Language
EU	European Union
GMAT	Graduate Management Admission Test
GPA	Grade Point Average
GRE	Graduate Record Examinations
IB	International Baccalaureate
IBT	Internet-Based Test (TOEFL)
IELTS	International English Language Testing System
IIE	Institute of International Education
LL.M.	Master of Laws
LSAT	Law School Admission Test
MA	Master's of Arts
MBA	Master of Business Administration
MXN	Mexican Pesos
PBT	Paper-Based Test (TOEFL)
Ph.D.	Doctor of Philosophy
SAT	Scholastic Aptitude Test
TESL	Teaching English as a Second Language
TOEFL	Test of English as a Foreign Language
UK	United Kingdom
U.S.	United States

Funding Opportunities Provided by Foundations, Agencies, and Other Organizations:

For Study at Any Institution

Admittedly

Admittedly Improve Your Chances Scholarship

PROGRAM INFORMATION

Description: The Improve Your Chances scholarship is an ongoing, monthly scholarship open to all high school students. Once you apply, you are entered to win each month.

Nationality: Any Region

AWARD INFORMATION

Award Type: Scholarship

Average Amount: $500

Number of Awards: 1 per month

Award Coverage: Winners must use the $500 for college or to fund a program that will help enhance your resume to improve your chances for college

ELIGIBILITY REQUIREMENTS

- Open to all high school and college students, and those planning to enroll within 12 months
- Applicant must be a legal resident of the US; international students with valid student visas are also eligible
- Winners must use the $500 for college or to fund a program that will help enhance your resume to improve your chances for college
- Students must apply on the website to be considered for a scholarship
- Only 1 entry allowed per person per month, a new winner will be chosen every month

APPLICATION INFORMATION

Instructions: Visit our website to complete the application form

CONTACT

Web: admitted.ly/scholarship

Alexander von Humboldt Foundation (AvH)

Feodor Lynen Research Fellowships

PROGRAM INFORMATION

Description: Feodor Lynen Research Fellowships provide opportunities for highly qualified German postdoctoral researchers (who have completed their doctorates less than 4 years ago) and experienced German researchers (who have completed their doctorates less than 12 years ago) to conduct research abroad with a former Humboldt fellow or award winner of the Alexander von Humboldt Foundation.

Levels of Study: Post Doctorate

Field of Study: All

Nationality: Germany

AWARD INFORMATION

Award Type: Fellowship

Average Amount: Approx €2,500-€2,800 per month

Number of Awards: Varies

Award Coverage: Benefits for families, travel expenses

Award Duration: Approx 6-24 months

ELIGIBILITY REQUIREMENTS

- Must have successfully completed a doctorate less than 12 years ago
- Must be able to demonstrate work published in recognized academic journals
- Applicants wishing to study in the US must have working knowledge of the English language

APPLICATION INFORMATION

Award Deadline: Rolling

Instructions: For more information, please visit our website

CONTACT

Alexander von Humboldt Foundation
Jean-Paul-Str. 12
D-53173 Bonn
Germany
Tel: +49 (228) 833-0
Fax: +49 (228) 833-114
Email: info@avh.de
Web: www.humboldt-foundation.de

American Antiquarian Society

Short-Term Visiting Academic Research Fellowships

PROGRAM INFORMATION

Description: The American Antiquarian Society offers short-term visiting academic research fellowships tenable for 1 to 3 months each year. The fellowships are available for scholars holding a PhD and for doctoral candidates engaged in dissertation research. Candidates holding a recognized degree appropriate to the area of proposed study, such as a master's degree in library science, are also eligible to apply.

Levels of Study: Graduate, Doctorate, Post Doctorate

Field of Study: All

Nationality: Any Region

AWARD INFORMATION

Award Type: Fellowship

Average Amount: $1,000-$3,000

Number of Awards: Varies

Award Coverage: Varies

Award Duration: 1-3 months

APPLICATION INFORMATION

Award Deadline: Jan

Instructions: For more information on how to apply, please visit the website

CONTACT

American Antiquarian Society
185 Salisbury Street
Worcester, MA 01609
Tel: +1 (508) 755-5221
Fax: +1 (508) 754-9069
Email: academicfellowships@mwa.org
Web: www.americanantiquarian.org/acafellowship.htm

American Association of Petroleum Geologists

AAPG Foundation Grants-in-Aid

PROGRAM INFORMATION

Description: The purpose of the AAPG Foundation's Grants-in-Aid program is to foster research in the Geosciences. Grants are made to provide financial assistance to graduate students (currently enrolled in master's or postdoctorate programs) whose thesis research has application to the search for and development of petroleum and energy-mineral resources or related environmental geology issues. Grants are based on merit, and in part on the financial needs of the applicant.

Levels of Study: Graduate, Doctorate, Post Doctorate

Field of Study: Earth Science, Minerals Industry, Natural Sciences, Oceanography, Paleontology

Nationality: Any Region

AWARD INFORMATION

Award Type: Grant

Average Amount: $1,000-$3,000

Number of Awards: Varies

Award Coverage: Field work, laboratory analyses

Award Duration: 1 year

ELIGIBILITY REQUIREMENTS

- Must be enrolled in a master's or postdoctorate Geosciences program
- Some grants have individual restrictions
- Official transcripts from your last 2 years or 4 semesters of schooling are required

APPLICATION INFORMATION

Award Deadline: Jan

Instructions: Apply online, all applications are scored by a committee of 60 persons

CONTACT

AAPG Foundation
Grants-in-Aid Coordinator
PO Box 979
Tulsa, OK 74101
Email: jterry@aapg.org
Web: www.foundation.aapg.org/gia/index.cfm

American Association of University Women-Educational Foundation

AAUW International Fellowships

PROGRAM INFORMATION

Description: Fellowship awarded for full-time study or research at accredited institutions, to support community-based projects designed to improve the lives of women and girls in the fellow's home country.

Levels of Study: Graduate, Doctorate, Post Doctorate, Professional

Field of Study: All

Nationality: Any Region

AWARD INFORMATION

Award Type: Fellowship

Average Amount: $18,000-$30,000

Number of Awards: Approx 58

Award Coverage: Writing, field research.

Award Duration: Academic year

ELIGIBILITY REQUIREMENTS

- Must study within the US
- Female applicants only
- Must have applied to proposed institution of study at time of application
- Must hold an undergraduate degree
- Must have minimum of TOEFL 550 PBT/213 CBT

APPLICATION INFORMATION

Award Deadline: Dec

Instructions: For more information on how to apply, please visit the website

CONTACT

American Association of University Women
Educational Foundation
1111 Sixteenth St., NW
Washington, DC 20036
Tel: +1 (800) 326-2289
Fax: +1 (202) 872-1425
Email: info@aauw.org
Web: www.aauw.org/what-we-do/educational-funding-and-awards/international-fellowships

American Council of Learned Societies ACLS

Mellon/ACLS Dissertation Completion Fellowships

PROGRAM INFORMATION

Description: The Mellon/ACLS fellowships support a year of research and writing to help advanced graduate students in the humanities and related social sciences in their last year of PhD dissertation writing.

Levels of Study: Doctorate

Field of Study: Humanities, Social Science

Nationality: Any Region

AWARD INFORMATION

Award Type: Fellowship

Average Amount: Up to $38,000

Number of Awards: 65

Award Coverage: Stipend ($30,000), university fees (up to $5,000), research costs (up to $3,000).

Award Duration: Academic year

ELIGIBILITY REQUIREMENTS

- Must be a PhD candidate in a humanities or social science department in the US
- Must have completed all requirements for the PhD except the dissertation, and obtained ABD status by the application deadline
- Must be no more than 6 years in the degree program; awardees can hold this fellowship no later than their 7th year.
- Unsuccessful applicants may reapply to this program only once
- Graduate students who currently hold or have previously held a dissertation completion fellowship are not eligible for the Mellon/ACLS Dissertation Completion Fellowship

APPLICATION INFORMATION

Award Deadline: Oct 22

Instructions: Completed applications must be submitted through the ACLS Online Fellowship Application system (https://ofa.acls.org)

CONTACT

American Council of Learned Societies
633 Third Avenue, 8th floor
New York, NY 10017
Tel: +1 (212) 697-1505
Email: fellowships@acls.org
Web: www.acls.org

American Hygienists' Association, Institute for Oral Health

ADHA Institute Grants

PROGRAM INFORMATION

Description: Fellowships awarded to individuals to support study and research in dental hygiene.

Levels of Study: Professional

Field of Study: Health Professions

Nationality: Any Region

AWARD INFORMATION

Award Type: Fellowship, Grant

Average Amount: $1,000-$2,000

Number of Awards: Varies

Award Coverage: Varies

ELIGIBILITY REQUIREMENTS

- Must be a registered dental hygienist or pursuing a degree in the field

APPLICATION INFORMATION

Award Deadline: Feb

Instructions: See website for application information

CONTACT

Institute for Oral Health
ADHA Executive Administrator
444 N. Michigan Avenue, Suite 3400
Chicago, IL 60611
Tel: +1 (312) 440-8909
Email: institute@adha.net
Web: www.adha.org/ioh/

American Society for Microbiology

ASM International Fellowships

PROGRAM INFORMATION

Description: Fellowships are awarded to encourage international collaborations in microbiological research and training worldwide. In addition, the fellowships provide the opportunity for promising young investigators throughout the world to travel to another country or a distant site to obtain expertise in a method, procedure, or specific topic.

Levels of Study: Doctorate, Post Doctorate

Field of Study: Biology

Nationality: Latin America

AWARD INFORMATION

Award Type: Fellowship

Average Amount: Up to $5,000

Number of Awards: Varies

Award Coverage: Travel, living expenses

Award Duration: Maximum of 6 months

ELIGIBILITY REQUIREMENTS

- Must have obtained, or be in the process of obtaining, a master's, PhD, or other equivalent academic degree within the last 5 years
- Preference will be given to applicants from developing countries traveling to visit a MIRCEN (Microbiology Resource Center) laboratory
- For Travel Awards, both the home country and host country must be UN/UNESCO members
- Must be a member of ASM or any other national microbiological society
- Must be actively involved in research in the microbiological sciences

APPLICATION INFORMATION

Award Deadline: Apr, Oct

Instructions: Application forms available online or by request from contact, visit the website for more information

CONTACT

American Society for Microbiology
Awards Committee
International Affairs
1752 N Street NW
Washington, DC 20036
Tel: +1 (202) 942-9368
Fax: +1 (202) 942-9328
Email: international@asmusa.org
Web: www.asm.org/index.php/international/grants-fellowships

American Society of International Law

Arthur C. Helton Fellowship Program

PROGRAM INFORMATION

Description: Funded in part by contributions from ASIL members, Helton Fellowships provide financial assistance in the form of "micro-grants" for law students and young professionals to pursue field work and research on significant issues involving international law, human rights, humanitarian affairs, and related areas. Helton Fellowship micro-grants are intended to ensure that these individuals have access to modest amounts of funding that can often stand between them and their first professional opportunities to become effective practitioners, experts, and scholars of international law. Fellows will undertake their project in association with an established educational institution, international organization, or nongovernmental organization working in areas related to international law, human rights, and humanitarian affairs. ASIL does not assist in securing organizational sponsoring for fellows.

Levels of Study: Professional

Field of Study: Human Rights, International Law, Law

Nationality: Any Region

AWARD INFORMATION

Award Type: Grant

Award Coverage: Logistics, housing and living expenses, other costs related to the fellow's fieldwork and research

ELIGIBILITY REQUIREMENTS

- Must be a current law student or have graduated from law school within the past 3 years
- The successful applicant's proposal will involve affiliation with an NGO or human rights organization
- Applicants should have contacted the sponsoring organization to discuss their proposal prior to applying for the Helton Fellowship
- In acknowledgment of Arthur Helton's commitment to human rights advocacy in the field, preferential consideration may be given to proposals demonstrating a significant fieldwork component

APPLICATION INFORMATION

Award Deadline: Jan

Instructions: Only the first 50 completed applications submitted online and received in full by the submission deadline will be reviewed. A notice that the application process has closed will be posted on the ASIL website once 50 completed applications have been received.

CONTACT

The American Society of International Law
ASIL Director of Research and Outreach Programs
2223 Massachusetts Avenue, NW
Washington, DC 20008
Tel: +1 (202) 939-6000
Email: fellowship@asil.org
Web: www.asil.org/resources/helton-fellowship-program

Amity Institute

Amity Intern Program

PROGRAM INFORMATION

Description: The Intern Program provides language assistants the opportunity to serve as models of language and culture in US schools at all levels, from preschool to university. Interns assist in the classroom for up to 25 hours per week, take personal study classes, and live with American host families.

Levels of Study: Undergraduate, Graduate, Professional

Field of Study: Education, Foreign Languages

Nationality: Central America/Mexico, Argentina, Austria, Belgium, Bolivia, Canada, Chile, China, Colombia, Dominican Republic, Ecuador, Fiji, France, French Guiana, French Polynesia, Germany, Guadeloupe, Guyana, Haiti, Hong Kong, Japan, Liechtenstein, Luxembourg, Martinique, Montserrat, Paraguay, Peru, Russia, San Marino, Spain, Taiwan, Uruguay, Vatican City, Venezuela

AWARD INFORMATION

Award Type: Internship

Average Amount: Varies

Number of Awards: Varies

Award Coverage: Room and board

ELIGIBILITY REQUIREMENTS

- Must be 20 years of age or older
- Must be currently enrolled in an academic institution (college/university) pursuing studies granting a degree or have graduated no more than 12 months prior to program start date
- Must have a career goal in education
- Must have sufficient proficiency in the English language to participate in the program
- Must be enthusiastic about sharing culture and native language with US students

APPLICATION INFORMATION

Instructions: For more information on how to apply, please visit the website

CONTACT

Amity Institute
3065 Rosencrans Place
Suite 104
San Diego, CA 92110
Tel: +1 (619) 222-7000
Fax: +1 (619) 222-7016
Email: mail@amity.org
Web: www.amity.org/new-cultural-exchange-page/

Asian Cultural Council

Asian Cultural Council Individual Grants

PROGRAM INFORMATION

Description: Asian individuals in the visual and performing arts seeking grant assistance to conduct research, study, receive specialized training, undertake observation tours, or pursue creative activity in the US are eligible to apply for fellowship support from the Council.

Levels of Study: Graduate

Field of Study: Archaeology, Architecture and Environmental Design, Art History, Dance, Film, Fine Arts, Literature, Music, Photography, Theater, Visual and Performing Arts

Nationality: Asia

AWARD INFORMATION

Award Type: Grant

Average Amount: Varies

Number of Awards: Varies

Award Coverage: Living costs, international travel.

Award Duration: Up to 1 year, nonrenewable

ELIGIBILITY REQUIREMENTS

- Contact or visit our website for more information regarding requirements

APPLICATION INFORMATION

Award Deadline: Nov

Instructions: Visit our website for application information

CONTACT

Asian Cultural Council
6 West 48th Street, 12th floor
New York, NY 10036-1802
Email: acc@accny.org
Web: www.asianculturalcouncil.org

Association for Women in Science

AWIS Predoctoral Awards

PROGRAM INFORMATION

Description: The Association for Women in Science offers scholarships and fellowships for women in the sciences. Several of the awards are named in honor of the achievements of women scientists.

Levels of Study: Undergraduate, Doctorate

Field of Study: Astronomy, Biochemistry, Biology, Chemistry, Computer Science, Earth Science, Ecology, Engineering, Environmental Studies, Information Technology, Life Sciences, Mathematics, Molecular Biology, Natural Sciences, Oceanography, Physical Sciences, Physics, Science

Nationality: Any Region

AWARD INFORMATION

Award Type: Award

Average Amount: Varies

Number of Awards: Varies

Award Coverage: Books, travel, meeting registration, publication costs, etc

ELIGIBILITY REQUIREMENTS

- Must be a female undergraduate or graduate student. Undergraduates must be planning to get a 4-year degree, and be in their second or third year of study. Doctoral students must have passed their qualifying (eligibility) exams and be considered PhD candidates
- Non-US residents or citizens must be enrolled in a US educational institution. US residents/citizens can study anywhere. Field of study must be a STEM field (science, technology, engineering, math)
- Generally not eligible: students studying for a medical or clinical degree, e.g., physician, dentist, veterinarian

APPLICATION INFORMATION

Award Deadline: Jan

Instructions: For more information on how to apply, please visit our website

CONTACT

Association for Women in Science
1321 Duke Street, Suite 210
Alexandria, VA 22314
Tel: +1 (703) 894-4490
Email: awis@awis.org
Web: www.awis.org

Australian-American Fulbright Commission

Fulbright Postdoctoral Scholarship

PROGRAM INFORMATION

Description: Fulbright Postdoctoral Scholarships are available to Australian citizens to engage in 3 - 10 months of postdoctoral research or professional training in the US. A Postdoctoral Scholarship is also available in the field of Cultural Competence sponsored by the University of Sydney. Please refer to our website for more details.

Levels of Study: Post Doctorate

Field of Study: All

Nationality: Australia

AWARD INFORMATION

Award Type: Scholarship

Average Amount: Varies

Number of Awards: Up to 6

Award Coverage: Travel allowance, monthly stipend, accident and health insurance (ASPE); dependent allowance (if applicable)

Award Duration: Up to 10 months

ELIGIBILITY REQUIREMENTS

- The scholarship is generally offered to applicants who are no more than 3 years post-PhD, however, applicants who are 4 to 5 years postdoctoral and present a strong case will be considered
- Applicants must be Australian citizens by birth or naturalization
- Applicants holding dual US/Australian citizenship or US green card are ineligible to be considered
- Postgraduate and postdoctoral applicants are required to attend an interview in South Australia if short listed
- To be eligible, your thesis must be lodged prior to submitting your Fulbright application and your results known by the time of assessment – see website for timeline

APPLICATION INFORMATION

Award Deadline: 1 Aug

Instructions: Please refer to the Australian-American Fulbright Commission website for further information

CONTACT

Australian-American Fulbright Commission
Senior Manager Scholarships
PO Box 9541
2600 Deakin ACT
Australia
Tel: +61 (2) 6260-4460
Fax: +61 (2) 6260-4461
Email: program@fulbright.com.au
Web: www.fulbright.com.au

Australian-American Fulbright Commission

Fulbright Senior Scholarship

PROGRAM INFORMATION

Description: Fulbright Senior Scholarships are available to Australian citizens who are at Associate or Professorial level. There are several scholarships in the General Category open to any academic field or discipline. There are also several sponsored Scholarships. Applicants should be: Scholars of established reputation working in an academic institution who teach and undertake research. Senior members of academically-based professions who are currently engaged in the private practice of their profession. Recognized academics or professionals who have been invited to the US by a tertiary institution, learned society, or professional organization for a significant purpose that will build strong partnerships and linkages into the future.

Levels of Study: Doctorate, Professional

Field of Study: All

Nationality: Australia

AWARD INFORMATION

Award Type: Scholarship

Average Amount: Varies - please refer to website

Number of Awards: Up to 6 or 7 per year

Award Coverage: Return travel to and from the US plus monthly stipend, baggage, and establishment allowances.

Award Duration: 3 - 4 months

ELIGIBILITY REQUIREMENTS

- Must be at a Senior Level (Assoc Prof or Prof)
- Applicants must be Australian citizens by birth or naturalization
- Applicants holding dual US/Australian citizenship or US green card are ineligible to be considered
- Shortlisted applicants must be available to attend an interview to be considered
- Any field or discipline for the General Category. Also sponsored Senior Scholarships are available in Nuclear Science and Technology; for the States of NT and TAS; and an Indigenous Scholarship

APPLICATION INFORMATION

Award Deadline: 1 Aug

Instructions: For further information please refer to the Australian-American Commission website www.fulbright.com.au

CONTACT

Australian-American Fulbright Commission
Senior Manager Scholarships
PO Box 9541
2600 Deakin ACT
Australia
Tel: +61 (2) 6260-4460
Fax: +61 (2) 6260-4461
Email: programmanager@fulbright.com.au
Web: www.fulbright.com.au

Australian-American Fulbright Commission

Fulbright Postgraduate Scholarship

PROGRAM INFORMATION

Description: Enables promising postgraduate students to undertake study in any field; to complete their Australian postdoctorate; or to support enrollment in a US postgraduate program. This scholarship supports an 8-10 month program.

Levels of Study: Graduate

Field of Study: All

Nationality: Australia

AWARD INFORMATION

Award Type: Scholarship

Average Amount: Up to $39,000

Number of Awards: Up to 9

Award Coverage: Travel entitlement, monthly stipend, and accident and health insurance (ASPE)

Award Duration: Up to 10 months

ELIGIBILITY REQUIREMENTS

- Must have a bachelor's degree, preferably with first class honors or equivalent, or a research master's degree from a recognized university
- Must be an Australian citizen by birth or naturalization
- Applicants holding dual US/Australian citizenship or US green card are ineligible to be considered
- Postgraduate and postdoctoral applicants are required to attend an interview in their state if shortlisted

APPLICATION INFORMATION

Award Deadline: 1 Aug

Instructions: Please refer to our website for further information www.fulbright.com.au

CONTACT

Australian-American Fulbright Commission
Senior Manager Scholarships
PO Box 9541
2600 Deakin ACT
Australia
Tel: +61 (02) 6260-4460
Fax: +61 (02) 6260-4461
Email: ruth.leemartin@fulbright.com.au
Web: www.fulbright.com.au

Australian-American Fulbright Commission

Fulbright Professional Scholarship

PROGRAM INFORMATION

Description: Fulbright Professional Scholarships are available to Australian citizens poised for advancement to a senior role from the private, public and not-for-profit sectors (outside academe), or mid-career academics whose professional focus is industry related and whose research and sharing of results within the industry is clearly outlined. The scholarship supports a 3-4 month program of professional development in the US.

Levels of Study: Professional

Field of Study: All

Nationality: Australia

AWARD INFORMATION

Award Type: Scholarship

Average Amount: Varies - please refer to website

Number of Awards: Up to 9 - 10

Award Coverage: Travel entitlement, stipend, dependent's allowance (if applicable); accident and health insurance (ASPE)

Award Duration: 3 - 4 months

ELIGIBILITY REQUIREMENTS

- These Scholarships are aimed at professionals working with an organization from the sectors of government, business, leadership, vocation, education (with a focus on practical application of educational training), or non-profit. Also includes mid-career academics (Senior Lecturer Level) with industry focus. While the program may include attending a conference, this does not fulfill the educational requirements of the scholarship. The Professional Scholarship does not fund postgraduate study.
- Applicants must be Australian citizens by birth or naturalization
- Applicants holding dual US/Australian citizenship or green card holders residing abroad are ineligible and will not be considered
- Postgraduate and postdoctoral applicants are required to attend an interview in Queensland if they are shortlisted
- A General Professional Scholarship is available in any field; also sponsored Scholarships in a variety of fields. Please refer to website for full listing. www.fulbright.com.au

APPLICATION INFORMATION

Award Deadline: 1 Aug

Instructions: For further information please refer to the Australian-American Fulbright Commission www.fulbright.com.au

CONTACT

Australian-American Fulbright Commission
Senior Manager Scholarships
PO Box 9541
2600 Deakin ACT
Australia
Tel: +61 (02) 6260-4460
Fax: +61 (02) 6260-4461
Email: program@fulbright.com.au
Web: www.fulbright.com.au

Australian-American Fulbright Commission

Fulbright-Anne Wexler Scholarship in Public Policy

PROGRAM INFORMATION

Description: The aim of the Fulbright-Anne Wexler Scholarships is to grow Australian-American educational linkages by building the network of public policy experts and to encourage ongoing policy exchange between both countries. The scholarship will enable an Australian with strong academic credentials and leadership potential to undertake a 2 year Master's degree in the US in an area that supports Mrs. Wexler's binational interests in the field of public policy. These may include key areas such as health, sustainability, energy, climate change, regional security, education, political science, history or governmental relations.

Levels of Study: Graduate

Field of Study: All, Public Policy

Nationality: Australia

AWARD INFORMATION

Award Type: Scholarship

Average Amount: Up to $140,000

Number of Awards: 1

Award Coverage: Travel entitlement, stipend, tuition fees (up to a set limit), accident and health insurance (ASPE)

Award Duration: Up to 2 years

ELIGIBILITY REQUIREMENTS

- Must be Australian citizen by birth or naturalization
- Must have a bachelor's degree with honors or equivalent
- Applicants are required to attend an interview if shortlisted
- Degree must be primarily in the area of Public Policy

APPLICATION INFORMATION

Award Deadline: 1 Aug

Instructions: Please refer to Australian-American Fulbright Commission website for detailed information www.fulbright.com.au

CONTACT

Australian-American Fulbright Commission
Senior Manager Scholarships
PO Box 9541
2600 Deakin ACT
Australia
Tel: +61 (02) 6260-4460
Fax: +61 (02) 6260-4461
Email: program@fulbright.com.au
Web: www.fulbright.com.au

British Association for American Studies

BAAS Short-Term Travel Grants

PROGRAM INFORMATION

Description: The BAAS Grant is for scholars in the UK who need to travel to conduct research, or who have been invited to read papers at conferences on American studies topics. The resources available are normally modest. Grants should be supplemented by funds from other sources.

Levels of Study: Graduate, Doctorate, Post Doctorate

Field of Study: American History, American Literature, American Politics, American Studies

Nationality: United Kingdom

AWARD INFORMATION

Award Type: Grant

Average Amount: Up to €750

Number of Awards: Varies

Award Coverage: Travel.

Award Duration: Varies

ELIGIBILITY REQUIREMENTS

- Preference will be given to those who have had no previous opportunities for research-related visits to the US, and to young scholars, including postgraduate students
- Must be normal resident of the UK and/or working at or registered in postgraduate studies at a UK institution of higher education
- Must provide a brief report of research trip for publication in American studies in Britain once travel is completed

APPLICATION INFORMATION

Award Deadline: Dec

Instructions: Download application materials from our website

CONTACT

Keele University
American Studies, School of Humanities
ST5 5BG Keele
United Kingdom
Email: awards@baas.ac.uk
Web: www.baas.ac.uk/index.php?option=com_content&view=article&id=54%3Abaas-postgraduate-short-term-travel-awards-2009-&catid=6&Itemid=12

BUNAC

BUNAC BEST Scholarship

PROGRAM INFORMATION

Description: The BUNAC Educational Scholarship Trust offers scholarships to UK passport holders who are looking to study in graduate courses in the US or Canada. Preference is given to those whose proposed study is likely to further transatlantic understanding or to those who are required to study in the US for specific coursework.

Levels of Study: Graduate, Doctorate

Field of Study: All

Nationality: United Kingdom

AWARD INFORMATION

Award Type: Scholarship

Average Amount: $5,000-$10,000

Number of Awards: 5-10

Award Coverage: Varies.

Award Duration: 1 academic year

ELIGIBILITY REQUIREMENTS

- Must be a UK passport holder
- Must be currently enrolled, or have been enrolled in the last 5 years, in full-time studies at a higher education institution in the UK
- Must be planning to undertake a graduate course at a recognized American or Canadian institution. Cannot be part of a UK course of study
- Must not be currently engaged in a course of study in the US or Canada

APPLICATION INFORMATION

Award Deadline: Mar

Instructions: For more information on how to apply, please visit the website

CONTACT

BUNAC
Scholarship Dept
16 Bowling Green Lane
EC1R 0QH London
United Kingdom
Tel: +44 (0) 2072-513472
Fax: +44 (0) 2072-510215
Email: scholarships@bunac.org.uk
Web: www.bunac.org.uk/uk/awards

Commonwealth Fund

Commonwealth Fund
Harkness Fellowships

PROGRAM INFORMATION

Description: The Commonwealth Fund's Harkness Fellowships in Health Care Policy provide a unique opportunity for mid-career health services researchers, and practitioners to conduct original research and work with leading health policy experts in the US The Commonwealth Fund supports projects in the areas of: improving health insurance coverage, access to care, and improving the quality of health care services to underserved populations. Fellowships are not awarded to support study for academic degrees.

Levels of Study: Professional

Field of Study: Health Studies

Nationality: Australia, Canada, Germany, Netherlands, New Zealand, Norway, Sweden, Switzerland, United Kingdom

AWARD INFORMATION

Award Type: Fellowship

Average Amount: Up to $119,000

Number of Awards: Varies

Award Coverage: Living stipend, research expenses, tuition, health insurance, round-trip airfare.

Award Duration: Maximum of 1 year

ELIGIBILITY REQUIREMENTS

- Must show significant promise as a policy-oriented, health services researcher or practitioner
- Must have demonstrated expertise in health policy issues and a record of informing health policy through research, health services, or clinical leadership
- Must hold a master's or doctoral degree in healthcare services or related field

APPLICATION INFORMATION

Award Deadline: Sep

Instructions: Download application materials

CONTACT

The Commonwealth Fund
Director, International Program in Health Policy and Practice
1 East 75th Street
New York, NY 10021
Tel: +1 (212) 606-3809
Fax: +1 (212) 606-3875
Email: ro@cmwf.org
Web: www.commonwealthfund.org/Fellowships/Harkness-Fellowships.aspx

Consejo Nacional de Ciencia y Tecnologia (CONACYT)

CONACYT Fellowships for Foreign Study

PROGRAM INFORMATION

Description: Assists Mexican students with the pursuit of graduate studies outside Mexico.

Levels of Study: Graduate

Field of Study: Anthropology, Economics, Education, Engineering, Linguistics, Philosophy and Religion, Political Science, Science

Nationality: Mexico

AWARD INFORMATION

Award Type: Fellowship

Average Amount: Varies

Number of Awards: Approx 200

Award Coverage: Partial or full tuition, health insurance, university fees

Award Duration: 2 years for master's, 4-5 years for doctorate

ELIGIBILITY REQUIREMENTS

- Must have a minimum 80/100 GPA
- Must hold immediate preceding degree by Jun of the next year application

APPLICATION INFORMATION

Instructions: Visit our website or contact us for more information

CONTACT

Consejo Nacional de Ciencia y Tecnologia
Department Head Assignment Foreign Scholarships
Av. Constituyentes 1046
Col. Lomas Altas
11950 Mexico DF
Mexico
Tel: +52 (55) 327-7400; +52 (55) 322-7700
Fax: +52 (55) 327-7653
Email: ochoa@conacyt.mx
Web: www.conacyt.mx

Conselho Nacional de Desenvolvimento Cientifico e Tecnológico (CNPq)

CNPq Fellowships

PROGRAM INFORMATION

Description: Scholarships for graduate and postgraduate study for Brazilian students.

Levels of Study: Graduate, Doctorate, Post Doctorate

Field of Study: All

Nationality: Brazil

AWARD INFORMATION

Award Type: Fellowship

Average Amount: Varies

Number of Awards: Varies

Award Coverage: Stipend, medical insurance, travel.

Award Duration: 2 years for master's, 4 years for doctoral, 3-12 months for doctorate

APPLICATION INFORMATION

Instructions: Visit our website or contact us for more information

CONTACT

CNPq/SEPRO
Servicio de Protocolo
SEPN 509
Bloco A, Ed. Nazir I
70750-901 Brasilia DF
Brazil
Web: www.cnpq.br

Coordination for Advancement for High Level Personnel CAPES

CAPES Graduate Program

PROGRAM INFORMATION

Description: Fellowships for graduate program of academic studies and industrial strategies for excellent students in the intermediate phase of their education.

Levels of Study: Graduate

Field of Study: Agriculture and Related Sciences, Engineering, Natural Resources and Conservation

Nationality: Brazil

AWARD INFORMATION

Award Type: Fellowship

Average Amount: Varies

Award Coverage: Medical insurance, travel, monthly living expenses.

Award Duration: 1 year

ELIGIBILITY REQUIREMENTS

- Must be studying in the US

APPLICATION INFORMATION

Award Deadline: Varies

Instructions: Visit our website or contact us for more information.

CONTACT

CAPES
Cooperation and Exchange Coordinator
Anexo 1 de MEC, 2o andar, sala 211
Caixa Postal 365
70359-970 Brasilia DF
Brazil
Tel: +55 (61) 410-8875
Fax: +55 (61) 322-9458
Email: cci@capes.gov.br
Web: www.capes.gov.br

Coordination for Advancement for High Level Personnel CAPES

CAPES Fellowships

PROGRAM INFORMATION

Description: Scholarships for graduate and doctoral studies.

Levels of Study: Graduate, Doctorate

Field of Study: All

Nationality: Brazil

AWARD INFORMATION

Award Type: Fellowship

Average Amount: Varies

Number of Awards: Varies

Award Coverage: Tuition assistance

Award Duration: 2 years for master's 4 years for doctorate

APPLICATION INFORMATION

Instructions: Visit our website or contact us for more information

CONTACT

CAPES
Coordenacao de Aperfeicoamento de Pessoal de Nível Superior
Anexo 1 do MEC, 2o Andar, sala 211, CGCI
Caixa Postal 365
70359-970 Brasilia DF
Brazil
Tel: +55 (61) 410-8864; +55 (61) 410-8398
Email: cce@capes.gov.br; cgci@capes.gov.br
Web: www.capes.gov.br

Cultural Services of the French Embassy

Chateaubriand Fellowship - Science, Technology, Engineering & Mathematics (STEM)

PROGRAM INFORMATION

Description: The Chateaubriand Fellowship aims to initiate or reinforce collaborations, partnerships or joint projects by encouraging exchange at the doctoral level. To that end, the OST supports PhD students who are registered in an American university and wish to conduct research in a French laboratory for a 4 to 9 month period of time as part of a co-supervised research project.

Levels of Study: Doctorate

Field of Study: Engineering, Mathematics, Science, Science Technologies

CONTACT

Embassy of France
Office for Science and Technology
4101 Reservoir Road, NW
Washington, DC 20007
Tel: (202) 944-6252
Email: stem.coordinator@chateaubriand-fellowship.org
Web: www.chateaubriand-fellowship.org

Cyprus Fulbright Commission

Cyprus Fulbright Program Scholarships

PROGRAM INFORMATION

Description: This program offers scholarships to Cypriot students wishing to pursue a master's degree in the US

Levels of Study: Graduate

Field of Study: Accounting, Anthropology, Archaeology, Architecture and Environmental Design, Biomedical Humanities, Biotechnology, Business and Management, Conflict Management, Conflict Resolution, Engineering, Finance, Fine Arts, Food Technologies, Horticulture, Human Resource Development, Journalism, Law, Marine Engineering, Metallurgy, Military Technologies, Natural Disaster Research, Neuroscience, Peace Studies, Policy Research, Residency Programs, US Foreign Policy

Nationality: Cyprus

AWARD INFORMATION

Award Type: Scholarship

Average Amount: $25,000 per year

Number of Awards: Approx 3

Award Coverage: Medical insurance, tuition, housing, living expenses

Award Duration: Maximum of 2 years

ELIGIBILITY REQUIREMENTS

- Must hold a Cypriot passport and have at least 1 parent who was born in Cyprus. Must not be a US citizen or hold a green card. Must have done 3 years of secondary schooling in Cyprus
- Must have a minimum of 3.5/4, 8/10 or 2:1 on their undergraduate transcripts, or be ranked in the top 5 percent of their department
- Must hold a bachelor's degree by the time the applicant will depart for the US Must not have taken graduate courses or hold a graduate degree (or the equivalent) by the time they apply for this grant
- Must not be over 45 years old at the time of application
- Must take the GRE (and score a minimum of 300) or GMAT (and score a minimum of 600); Must take the TOEFL (and score a minimum of 100) or IELTS exams (and score a minimum of 7)

APPLICATION INFORMATION

Award Deadline: Jul

Instructions: The application and the instructions are available on the Cyprus Fulbright Commission's website in May of each year

CONTACT

Cyprus Fulbright Commission
Fulbright Coordinator
Marcos Drakos Avenue
UN Buffer Z1 (next to Ledra Palace Hotel, Nicosia
Nicosia
1102
Cyprus
Tel: +357 (22) 669757
Fax: +357 (22) 996151
Email: anna@fulbright.org.cy
Web: www.fulbright.org.cy

Cyprus Fulbright Commission

Cyprus Fulbright Visiting Scholars Program

PROGRAM INFORMATION

Description: Cypriot professionals who already hold a PhD, or will complete their PhD shortly after the application deadline, are invited to apply for a grant to support a 4-month research or teaching program at a US university.

Levels of Study: Post Doctorate

Field of Study: All

Nationality: Cyprus

AWARD INFORMATION

Award Type: Scholarship

Average Amount: Approx $2,900 per month

Number of Awards: 2

Award Coverage: Airfare, monthly stipend, and relocation allowance

Award Duration: 4 months

ELIGIBILITY REQUIREMENTS

- Must have a Cypriot citizenship, and must not be citizens or permanent residents (green card holders) of the US
- Must hold a doctoral degree or equivalent professional training or experience at the time of application. For professionals and artists outside academia, recognized professional standing and substantial professional accomplishment is expected
- Must have proficiency in English appropriate to the proposed lecturing or research project to be carried out in the US
- Must include a detailed statement of proposed activity for research or lecturing at a US institution. The proposed project should contribute to the development of knowledge in your field and must be investigated within 1 academic semester in the US
- Must have 1 parent who was born in Cyprus and at least 3 years of secondary education in Cyprus

APPLICATION INFORMATION

Award Deadline: Late Jul

Instructions: An online application must be completed by the deadline stated on the Fulbright Commission's website. All requested documents should be uploaded with the application

CONTACT

Cyprus Fulbright Commission
Program Consultant
Marcos Drakos Street (UN Buffer Z1)
Nicosia
1102
Cyprus
Tel: +357 (22) 669757
Fax: +357 (22) 669151
Email: anna@fulbright.org.cy
Web: www.fulbright.org.cy

Damon Runyon-Walter Winchell Cancer Research Fund

Research Fellowships for Basic and Physician Scientists

PROGRAM INFORMATION

Description: The foundation encourages all theoretical and experimental research relevant to the study of cancer and the search for cancer causes, mechanisms, therapies, and prevention.

Levels of Study: Graduate, Doctorate, Post Doctorate

Field of Study: Biology, Life Sciences, Medicine, Molecular Biology, Science

Nationality: Any Region

AWARD INFORMATION

Award Type: Fellowship

Average Amount: Varies

Number of Awards: Varies

Award Coverage: Awards are made to the institutions for the support of the fellow under direct supervision of the sponsor.

Award Duration: 3 years

ELIGIBILITY REQUIREMENTS

- Must apply for the fellowship under the guidance of a sponsor, a scientist (tenured, tenure-track or equivalent position) capable of providing mentorship to the fellows
- Must have completed 1 or more of the following degrees or its equivalent: MD, PhD, MD/PhD, DDS, DVM Applicants must include a copy of their diploma to confirm date of conferral
- Basic and physician scientists must have received their degrees no more than 1 year prior to the FAC meeting at with their applications are to be considered and are expected to devote 100 percent of their time and effort to Damon Runyon-supported research activities
- Physician-scientists must have completed their residencies and clinical training no more than 3 years prior to the FAC meeting at which their applications are considered and are expected to devote at least 80 percent of their time and effort to Damon Runyon-supported research activities
- Candidates who have already accepted a postdoctoral research fellowship or who are pursuing a degree are not eligible

APPLICATION INFORMATION

Award Deadline: Aug

Instructions: For more information on how to apply, please visit our website

CONTACT

1 Exchange Plaza
55 Broadway, Suite 302
New York, NY 10006
Tel: +1 (212) 455-0520
Email: awards@damonrunyon.org
Web: www.damonrunyon.org

Daniel Pearl Foundation/Alfred Friendly Press Fellowships

Daniel Pearl Fellowships

PROGRAM INFORMATION

Description: The Daniel Pearl Foundation partners with the Alfred Friendly Press Fellowships and the International Center for Journalists (ICFJ) International Journalism Exchange (IJE) to bring mid-career foreign journalists and editors to work in US newsrooms. It is an invitation to Daniel's former journalism colleagues to continue his mission by writing for the audiences for whom he wrote, working with his colleagues and getting to know the US press from the inside. Journalists from South Asia, the Middle East, and/or North Africa are invited to apply for the Daniel Pearl Fellowship.

Levels of Study: Professional

Field of Study: Journalism

Nationality: Any Region

AWARD INFORMATION

Award Type: Fellowship

ELIGIBILITY REQUIREMENTS

- Visit our website or contact for specific details regarding requirements

APPLICATION INFORMATION

Instructions: Please contact or visit our website for further information

CONTACT

Daniel Pearl Foundation
16161 Ventura Blvd, Suite C, PMB 671
Encino, CA 91436
Tel: +1 (310) 441-1400
Fax: +1 (310) 441-1404
Web: www.danielpearl.org/

Defence Science & Technology Agency

DSTA Scholarship (Undergraduate)

PROGRAM INFORMATION

Description: The undergraduate DSTA Scholarship is a premier scholarship in science and technology for Singapore citizens. We are looking for budding engineers and scientists with a keen passion in science and technology, and with leadership qualities to provide leading-edge technological solutions for our nation's defense and security.

Levels of Study: Undergraduate

Field of Study: Architecture and Environmental Design, Aviation/Aerospace, Biochemistry, Chemistry, Computer Science, Engineering, Mathematics, Physics

Nationality: Singapore

AWARD INFORMATION

Award Type: Scholarship

Average Amount: Varies

Number of Awards: Varies

Award Coverage: Tuition fees, overseas maintenance allowance, annual book allowance, settling-in allowance, warm clothing allowance, computer allowance, interest free computer loan

Award Duration: Varies

ELIGIBILITY REQUIREMENTS

- Must be a Singapore Citizen (Singapore Permanent Residents are required to take up Singapore Citizenship upon accepting the scholarship)
- Must have achieved excellent GCE A-level or Polytechnic Diploma (merit) or equivalent qualifications, such as the international baccalaureate
- Have an exceptional record in co-curricular activities
- Have a passion for science and technology

APPLICATION INFORMATION

Award Deadline: Mar

Instructions: Visit our website or contact us for more information

CONTACT

Defence Science & Technology Agency
Human Resource (Publicity & Scholarship)
71 Science Park Drive
#02-05
118253 Singapore
Singapore
Tel: +65 6879-5123
Email: scholarship@dsta.gov.sg
Web: www.dsta.gov.sg/scholarship-student-outreach/dsta-scholarship---undergraduate

Dog Fence DIY

2nd Annual Dog Fence DIY Scholarship for Veterinary Students

PROGRAM INFORMATION

Description: Our goal is to provide a deserving student the opportunity to have some financial relief that will allow him or her to better focus in their studies and be able to better serve humanity, in particular our best friends.

Field of Study: Biology, Veterinary Medical Technology

Nationality: Any Region

ELIGIBILITY REQUIREMENTS

- Be enrolled in 1 of the following: Doctor of Veterinary Medicine (DVM) program, undergraduate biology or pre-veterinary studies program, or the equivalent
- Must be enrolled full-time and in good standing at an accredited university
- Hold a minimum 3.5 grade point average (GPA) or equivalent
- Submit a 1,000 word essay

APPLICATION INFORMATION

Award Deadline: Sep

Instructions: Apply online www.dogfencediy.com/2014/05/18/2nd-annual-electric-dog-fence-diy-scholarship-for-veterinary-animal-science-students/

CONTACT

Tel: +1 (888) 936-4349
Email: stu@dogfencediy.com
Web: www.dogfencediy.com/2014/05/18/2nd-annual-electric-dog-fence-diy-scholarship-for-veterinary-animal-science-students/

Earthwatch Institute

Earthwatch Field Research Grants

PROGRAM INFORMATION

Description: Earthwatch Institute is an international nonprofit organization that supports scholarly field research worldwide to address critical environmental and social issues in the biological, physical, social, and cultural sciences. Earthwatch works on a system of participant-based funding in which the scientist receives support in the form of motivated, dedicated, paying volunteers. This unique funding model enables us to support research in a variety of disciplines, on the basis of a researcher's need for volunteers and Earthwatch's ability to find them.

Levels of Study: Graduate, Doctorate, Post Doctorate, Professional

Field of Study: Archaeology, Biology, Ecology, Environmental Studies, Geography, Life Sciences, Natural Sciences, Ocean and Resource Management, Oceanography, Paleontology, Public Health, Science, Social Science

Nationality: Any Region

AWARD INFORMATION

Award Type: Grant

Average Amount: $30,000

Number of Awards: 70

Award Coverage: Volunteer and staff food, accommodations, transportation in the field, field equipment, communications costs

Award Duration: 3-20 years

ELIGIBILITY REQUIREMENTS

- Must be doctoral candidate, hold a postdoctorate, or have equivalent scholarship or commensurate experience
- Projects must adhere to the highest standards of scientific practice and address critical conservation issues
- Projects must maximize community engagement, educational potential, and capacity building
- Projects should engage local partner organizations
- Projects must utilize volunteers

APPLICATION INFORMATION

Award Deadline: 18 months in advance of fieldwork

Instructions: Applicants should submit a Concept Note 18 months in advance of fielding. Applicants that pass this preliminary stage will be invited to submit a full proposal, which will be peer reviewed

CONTACT

Earthwatch Institute
Research Department
114 Western Ave.
Boston, MA 02134
Tel: +1 (978) 461-0081, +1 (800) 776-0188
Fax: +1 (978) 461-2332
Email: research@earthwatch.org
Web: www.earthwatch.org

Economic History Association

Economic History Association
Arthur H. Cole Grants-in-Aid

PROGRAM INFORMATION

Description: The Committee on Research in Economic History awards Arthur H. Cole grants-in-aid to support research in economic history, regardless of time period or geographic area.

Levels of Study: Post Doctorate

Field of Study: Economics

Nationality: Any Region

AWARD INFORMATION

Award Type: Grant

Average Amount: $5,000

Number of Awards: Varies

Award Coverage: Varies

ELIGIBILITY REQUIREMENTS

- Must hold a PhD
- Preference given to recent PhD recipients
- Must be a member of EHA

APPLICATION INFORMATION

Award Deadline: Mar

Instructions: Submit application materials by email or postal mail

CONTACT

Committee on Research in Economic History
McClelland Hall, 401GG
PO BOX 210108
Tucson, AZ 85721-0108l
Tel: +1 (520) 621-4421
Email: amusacchio@hbs.edu
Web: eh.net/eha/grants-and-fellowships

Education Vermont USA

EDVTUSA Scholarship

PROGRAM INFORMATION

Description: Education Vermont USA is offering 2 non-renewable $1,000 scholarship to study at its member institutions in Vermont. Who Should Apply? 1. international students (not US passport holders or permanent residents); a. high school students; b. undergraduate students (not graduate students); c. transfer students (not exchange students); d. students starting school in Vermont in the fall of 2014; 2. students who qualify for an F-1 visa

Levels of Study: Undergraduate

Field of Study: All

Nationality: Any Region

AWARD INFORMATION

Award Type: Scholarship

Average Amount: $1,000

Number of Awards: 2

Award Coverage: Any school expenses, the scholarship is paid directly to the school

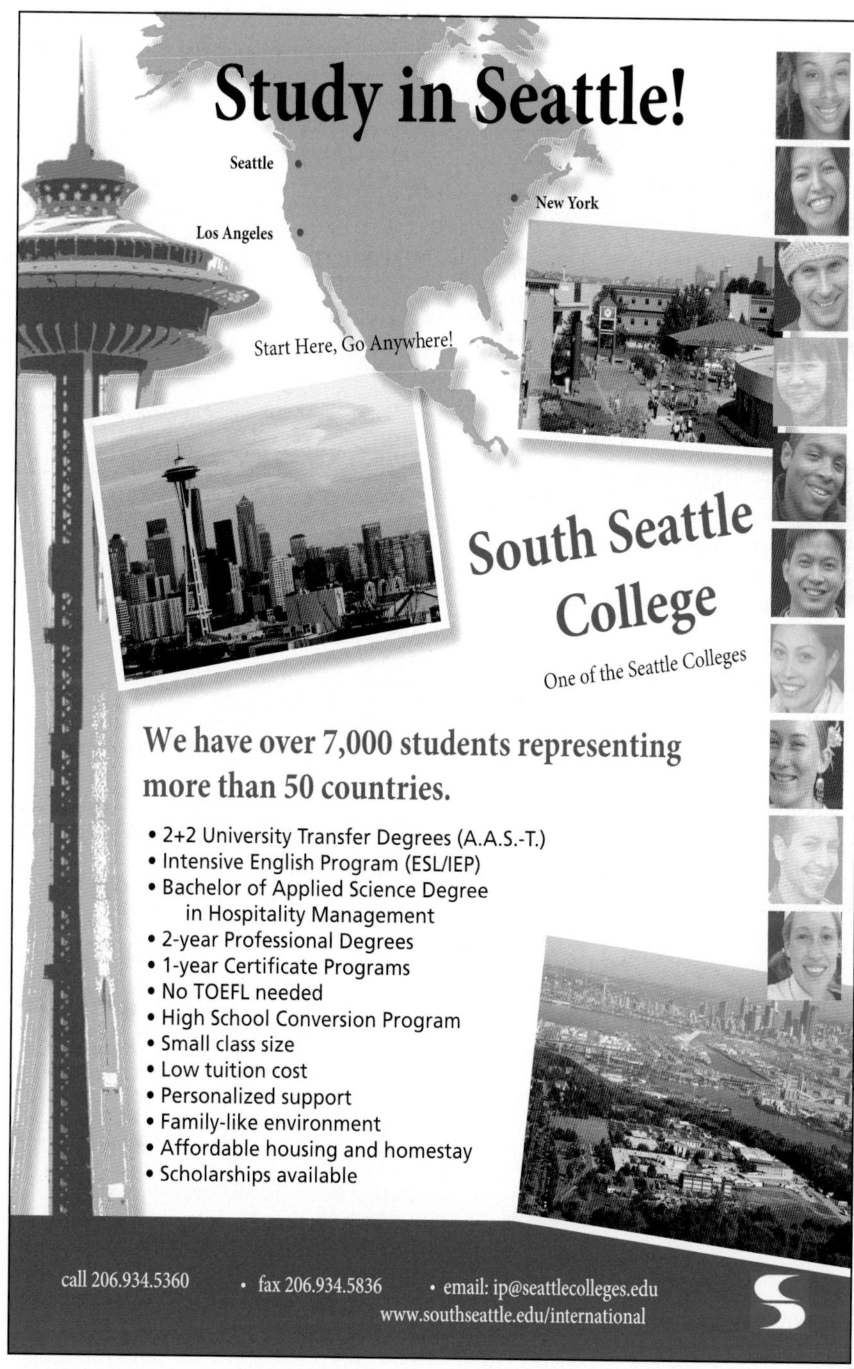

ELIGIBILITY REQUIREMENTS

- The student must have (or be applying for) an F-1 visa
- The student must be a high school or undergraduate student
- The student must be starting an EDVTUSA school (see list at EDVTUSA.org) in the fall of 2015. Transfer students may apply
- The student must attend and pay for the fall semester of 2014. We will submit the scholarship to cover spring expenses

APPLICATION INFORMATION

Award Deadline: Mar

Instructions: Visit the EDVTUSA.org website and click on the link on the left to get to the scholarship form

CONTACT

Education Vermont USA
60 Main Street
Burlington, VT 05401
Tel: +1 (802) 651-5842
Email: edvtusa@gmail.com
Web: www.edvtusa.org

Electrochemical Society

Electrochemical Society Summer Fellowships

PROGRAM INFORMATION

Description: The fellowship is awarded to assist a student during the summer months in the pursuit of work in a field of interest to the Electrochemical Society.

Levels of Study: Graduate, Doctorate

Field of Study: Chemistry

Nationality: Any Region

AWARD INFORMATION

Award Type: Fellowship

Average Amount: $5,000

Number of Awards: Varies

Award Coverage: Varies

Award Duration: 3 months

ELIGIBILITY REQUIREMENTS

- Must plan to continue studies in the fall
- Must be a graduate student pursuing work between the degrees of BS and PhD in a college or university

APPLICATION INFORMATION

Award Deadline: Jan

Instructions: For application instructions, please visit the website or contact by email

CONTACT

Electrochemical Society
65 South Main Street
Pennington, NJ 08534
Tel: +1 (609) 737-1902
Fax: +1 (609) 737-2743
Email: awards@electrochem.org
Web: www.electrochem.org

European Molecular Biology Organization

EMBO Long-Term Fellowships

PROGRAM INFORMATION

Description: The European Molecular Biology Organization (EMBO) awards fellowships that advance training through research. All applicants intending to pursue research in the US must be currently affiliated with a laboratory or institution in 1 of the 27 EMBC Member States listed on the program website.

Levels of Study: Post Doctorate

Field of Study: Life Sciences

Nationality: Austria, Belgium, Croatia, Czech Republic, Denmark, Estonia, Finland, France, Germany, Greece, Hungary, Iceland, Ireland, Israel, Italy, Luxembourg, Netherlands, Norway, Poland, Portugal, Slovakia, Slovenia, Spain, Sweden, Switzerland, Turkey, United Kingdom

AWARD INFORMATION

Award Type: Fellowship

Average Amount: Varies

Number of Awards: Varies

Award Coverage: Living subsistence, travel costs.

Award Duration: Maximum of 2 years

ELIGIBILITY REQUIREMENTS

- Must hold a doctorate degree or equivalent before the start of the fellowship but not necessarily when applying
- Must have at least 1 first author publication in press or published in an international peer reviewed journal at the time of application
- All applications must involve movement between countries

APPLICATION INFORMATION

Award Deadline: Feb, Aug

Instructions: Please visit the website for application instructions

CONTACT

EMBO
Postfach 1022.40
D-69012 Heidelberg
Germany
Tel: +49 (6221) 8891 ext. 116
Email: fellowships@embo.org
Web: www.embo.org/funding-awards/fellowships/long-term-fellowships

EU-US Fulbright-Schuman Program

Fulbright-Schuman Program

PROGRAM INFORMATION

Description: The Fulbright-Schuman Program, administered by the Commission for Educational Exchange between the US and Belgium, with funding from the US Department of State and the Directorate-General for Education and Culture of the European Commission, provides grants to citizens of the member-states of the European Union for study, research, or lecturing on EU affairs, or US-EU relations, integration, and/or political economy at a selected university in the US

Levels of Study: Graduate, Doctorate, Post Doctorate, Professional

Field of Study: European Studies/EU Studies

Nationality: Europe, US

AWARD INFORMATION

Award Type: Grant, Scholarship

Average Amount: $3,000 per month, plus $2,000 for round-trip air transportation and relocation costs (up to a maximum of $30,000 per grantee)

Number of Awards: Varies

Award Coverage: Monthly stipend, round-trip airfare, health insurance, visa sponsorship

Award Duration: Minimum of 3 months; maximum, academic year

ELIGIBILITY REQUIREMENTS

- Must be citizen of the EU
- Must have at least 2 years of work–related experience beyond the bachelor's degree
- Must demonstrate proficiency in English
- Must be a professional, decision-maker, policy-maker; an individual in industry, the media, politics; or involved in academics or public administration in EU affairs

APPLICATION INFORMATION

Award Deadline: Dec 1

Instructions: Download application materials and a preliminary application from our website. Also submit a copy of your CV and a 1-2 page detailed project description. Eligible candidates will then be sent instructions and the final application forms. An official letter of affiliation and/or acceptance from a US university or recognized research institute in the US is required for the application.

CONTACT

Commission for Educational Exchange between the US, Belgium and Luxembourg
Educational Advisor & Program Manager
The Royal Library, Albert 1
Boulevard de l'Empereur, 4 Keizerslaan
B-1000 Brussels
Belgium
Tel: +32 (2) 519-57-72
Email: adviser@fulbright.be
Web: www.fulbrightschuman.eu

ExxonMobil

Esso Angolan Scholars Program

PROGRAM INFORMATION

Description: A competitive scholarship that provides funding for students from Angola to pursue a master's degree in the Geosciences at a university in the US.

Levels of Study: Graduate

Field of Study: Earth Science, Engineering, Environmental Studies, Minerals Industry, Natural Sciences, Oceanography, Physical Sciences, Physics, Science

Nationality: Angola

AWARD INFORMATION

Award Type: Scholarship

Average Amount: Full tuition

Award Coverage: Full tuition for the completion of a master's degree in the field of Geosciences. Housing and living expenses, medical insurance, visa and academic support, an orientation program, as well as textbook and computer allowances are also included

Award Duration: Duration of master's program

ELIGIBILITY REQUIREMENTS

- Hold at least a bachelor's degree in Geosciences from a college or university in the US or the United Kingdom and demonstrate English proficiency
- Hold a valid Angolan passport (applicants do not currently need to reside in Angola) and demonstrate native fluency in Portuguese
- Exhibit exceptional leadership skills, cultural competency and a history of academic excellence
- Be willing and able to travel to Houston, Texas for a final selection activity
- Be willing and able to reside in the US or the UK for the full duration of study; dependents may not accompany scholarship recipients

APPLICATION INFORMATION

Award Deadline: Dec

Instructions: All applications must be submitted online. View additional information, instructions, and access the online application at www.iie.org/EssoAngolanScholars

CONTACT

Institute of International Education
Manager, Corporate Scholarships & Exchange Programs
1800 West Loop South
Suite 250
Houston, Texas 77027
Tel: +1 (832) 369-3482
Fax: +1 (713) 621-0876
Email: EssoAngolanScholars@iie.org
Web: www.iie.org/EssoAngolanScholars

Fight for Sight (FFS)
Fight for Sight Postdoctoral Fellowship

PROGRAM INFORMATION

Description: Post-Doctoral Awards support individuals with a doctorate (PhD, MD, OD, Dr PH, or DVM) who are interested in academic careers in basic or clinical research in ophthalmology, vision or related sciences. This funding is intended to offer those interested in an academic career the opportunity to spend a year engaged in vision and eye research under the supervision of a senior scientist/clinician mentor. Clinical postdoctoral researchers are required to spend sufficient time on the funded research project to carry out the proposed objectives while basic researchers are expected to work full-time.

Levels of Study: Post Doctorate

Field of Study: Medicine, Optics

Nationality: Any Region

AWARD INFORMATION

Award Type: Fellowship

Average Amount: $20,000

Number of Awards: Varies

Award Coverage: Varies.

Award Duration: 1 year

ELIGIBILITY REQUIREMENTS

- Fellowship activities must be conducted within a US institution
- Must be within 3 years of the awarding doctorate

APPLICATION INFORMATION

Award Deadline: Feb

Instructions: If, at the time of application, the applicant does not have a doctorate, a cover letter must be submitted with the application advising that the doctorate will be conferred by the commencement date of the award. Should unanticipated delays occur, FFS reserves the right to postpone the start date or withdraw the award

CONTACT

Fight for Sight
381 Park Avenue South, Suite 809
New York, NY 10016
Tel: +1 (212) 679-6060
Fax: +1 (212) 679-4466
Web: www.fightforsight.org/Grants/Research-Award-Types/

Francis Family Foundation
Parker B. Francis Fellowship in Pulmonary Research

PROGRAM INFORMATION

Description: This fellowship is intended to support the development of outstanding investigators who plan careers in pulmonary research. We seek to help them as they make the transition to independent, self-supporting, faculty members. Parker B. Francis Fellowship grants are awarded to institutions for the purpose of providing stipends, fringe benefits, and modest travel expenses in support of qualified postdoctoral fellows or newly appointed assistant professors.

Levels of Study: Post Doctorate, Professional

Field of Study: Medicine

Nationality: Any Region

AWARD INFORMATION

Award Type: Fellowship

Average Amount: $156,000

Number of Awards: Varies

Award Coverage: Stipend and fringe benefits, plus up to $2,000 for travel

Award Duration: 3 years

ELIGIBILITY REQUIREMENTS

- Must be assured of having at least 75 percent of their time available for research. This means that a total of no more than 3 months per year may be spent on clinical or other non-research activities
- Most successful candidates have 2-5 years of research experience at the time of fellowship application
- Candidates are expected to have participated as an author of a minimum of 2 or 3 research publications
- Applications for fellowships will not be considered for funding if either the mentor or the fellow has a relationship with the tobacco industry as described in the American Thoracic Society (ATS) guidelines

APPLICATION INFORMATION

Instructions: For application guidelines please visit our website

CONTACT

Administrator, PBF Fellowship Program
8427 SE 35th Street
Mercer Island, WA 98040
Tel: +1 (206) 764-2219
Email: dsnapp@uw.edu
Web: www.francisfellowships.org

Fritz Thyssen Stiftung/ German Historical Institute
Jürgen-Heideking Fellowship

PROGRAM INFORMATION

Description: The Fritz Thyssen Stiftung program supports research projects on American, German and international history, as well as the history of German-American relations. The fellows work in Washington, DC or Madison, Wisconsin. Fellows are not only given the opportunity to establish contacts in the academic world during their stay in the US and in Cologne, Germany, but are also enabled to help complete a large scholarly project.

Levels of Study: Post Doctorate

Field of Study: American History, German-American Relations, History

Nationality: Germany

AWARD INFORMATION

Award Type: Fellowship

Average Amount: €1,130-€1,380 per month

Number of Awards: Varies

Award Coverage: Stipend, books, materials

Award Duration: 1 year

ELIGIBILITY REQUIREMENTS

- Highly qualified young academics who have completed their doctorates but who do not yet hold a professorship are the target group of this program

APPLICATION INFORMATION

Award Deadline: Rolling

Instructions: Download application materials from our website

CONTACT

Fritz Thyssen Stiftung
Am Romerturm 3
50667 Cologne
Germany
Tel: +49 (221) 27-74-96-0
Fax: +49 (221) 27-74-96-29
Web: www.fritz-thyssen-stiftung.de/index.php?id=123&L=1&L=1

Fulbright/Commission for Educational Exchange between the US, Belgium and Luxembourg
Fulbright Belgium Grants for Professional Journalists

PROGRAM INFORMATION

Description: This scholarship is designed to aid journalists (specifically those engaged in a career in print or broadcast journalism) to study for a period of 3 to 9 months at an accredited US university.

Levels of Study: Graduate, Professional

Field of Study: Journalism

Nationality: Belgium

AWARD INFORMATION

Award Type: Award
Average Amount: $15,000-$30,000
Number of Awards: Varies
Award Coverage: Intended to cover part of the following expenses: tuition and fees, books and academic supplies, room and board. Visa sponsorship and health/accident insurance are provided
Award Duration: 3-9 months

ELIGIBILITY REQUIREMENTS

- Must be a citizen of Belgium
- Must have completed studies to the level of first masters or equivalent
- Must have ambassadorial qualities and a proven level of academic and/or professional excellence
- Must have at least 2 years of professional journalism experience
- Must have a specific program of study at an American university

APPLICATION INFORMATION

Award Deadline: Oct
Instructions: All interested journalists must download a preliminary application from the Fulbright Commission's website and submit it in order to assess eligibility. If eligible, the commission will forward the final application and supporting documents to the candidate for completion

CONTACT

Commission for Educational Exchange between the US, Belgium and Luxembourg
Educational Adviser & Program Manager
The Royal Library Albert I, 3rd floor
Blvd. de L'Empereur 4, Keizerslaan
1000 Brussels
Belgium
Tel: +32 (519) 57-72
Email: adviser@fulbright.be
Web: www.fulbright.be

Fulbright/Commission for Educational Exchange between the US, Belgium and Luxembourg

Fulbright Belgium Summer Seminar in American Studies

PROGRAM INFORMATION

Description: The Commission for Educational Exchange offers professors and teachers in higher secondary education grants to attend a 2-month summer program in American Studies in the US.
Levels of Study: Graduate, Professional
Field of Study: Education
Nationality: Belgium

AWARD INFORMATION

Award Type: Award, Grant, Scholarship
Average Amount: Varies
Number of Awards: 2
Award Coverage: All expenses paid
Award Duration: 2 months

ELIGIBILITY REQUIREMENTS

- Must be a citizen of Belgium
- Must be teaching in higher secondary education and possess a diploma equivalent to license/licentiaat
- Must have ambassadorial qualities, a proven level of academic and/or professional excellence, and an outstanding record
- Must be proficient in English
- Must be present for a personal interview in English scheduled by the commission

APPLICATION INFORMATION

Award Deadline: Oct 31
Instructions: Interested candidates should download and submit a preliminary application from the commission's website; all eligible candidates will be sent a final application form and the supporting documents for completion

CONTACT

Commission for Educational Exchange between the US, Belgium and Luxembourg
Educational Adviser & Program Manager
The Royal Library Albert I, 3rd floor
Blvd. de L'Empereur 4, Keizerslaan
1000 Brussels
Belgium
Tel: +32 (2) 519-57-72
Fax: +32 (2) 519-57-73
Email: adviser@fulbright.be
Web: www.fulbright.be

Fulbright/Commission for Educational Exchange between the US, Belgium and Luxembourg

Fulbright Belgium Awards for Graduate Study

PROGRAM INFORMATION

Description: The Commission for Educational Exchange awards approx 18 grants-in-aid to students (Belgian citizens only) who are assured admission to an American university or institution of higher education for graduate-level study or pre-doctoral research.
Levels of Study: Graduate
Field of Study: All
Nationality: Belgium, Luxembourg

AWARD INFORMATION

Award Type: Grant, Scholarship
Average Amount: Varies
Number of Awards: Approx 18
Award Coverage: Health and accident insurance, visa sponsorship, partial tuition and academic fees
Award Duration: Academic year

ELIGIBILITY REQUIREMENTS

- Must be a citizen of Belgium
- Must have completed studies to the level of a first master's degree or its equivalent before departure
- Must have ambassadorial qualities, a proven level of academic excellence, and outstanding records
- Must be proficient in English
- Must be present for a personal, mandatory interview in English scheduled by the commission

APPLICATION INFORMATION

Award Deadline: Apr 30
Instructions: All interested candidates must download a preliminary application from the commission's website and submit it to assess eligibility. If eligible, students must submit a letter of acceptance/affiliation from a US university. The final application and supporting documents will then be forwarded to them for completion

CONTACT

Commission for Educational Exchange between the US, Belgium and Luxembourg
Educational Adviser & Program Manager
The Royal Library Albert I, 3rd floor
Blvd. de L'Empereur 4, Keizerslaan
1000 Brussels
Belgium
Tel: +32 (519) 57-72
Fax: +32 (519) 57-73
Email: adviser@fulbright.be
Web: www.fulbright.be

Fulbright/Commission for Educational Exchange between the US, Belgium and Luxembourg

Fulbright Belgium Research Scholars and Lecturers

PROGRAM INFORMATION

Description: The Commission provides grants-in-aid to research scholars and lecturers who are assured of a position at an American institution of higher education.
Levels of Study: Post Doctorate
Field of Study: All
Nationality: Belgium

AWARD INFORMATION

Award Type: Grant
Average Amount: Varies
Number of Awards: 10
Award Coverage: Varies
Award Duration: 3-12 months

ELIGIBILITY REQUIREMENTS

- Must have institutional affiliation in the US
- Must have defended and obtained the doctorate before departure for the US
- Must have ambassadorial qualities and a proven level of academic and/or professional excellence
- Candidates in medicine must have the MD degree prior to the grant period, this award is for research only

APPLICATION INFORMATION

Award Deadline: Mar 1

Instructions: Interested candidates must download a preliminary application from the Fulbright Commission's website and submit it with a letter of invitation/affiliation from a US university or recognized research institute. If candidate is found eligible, final application forms and instructions will be forwarded.

CONTACT

Commission for Educational Exchange between the US, Belgium and Luxembourg
Educational Adviser & Program Manager
The Royal Library Albert I, 3rd floor
Blvd. de L'Empereur 4, Keizerslaan
1000 Brussels
Belgium
Tel: +32 (2) 519-57-72
Fax: +32 (2) 519-57-73
Email: adviser@fulbright.be
Web: www.fulbright.be

Fulbright/Iceland-US Educational Commission

Fulbright Student Grant for Icelandic Students

PROGRAM INFORMATION

Description: This Fulbright Student Grant is an award to Icelandic students about to start their graduate study in the US in the form of a 1-time payment at the onset of studies.

Levels of Study: Graduate

Field of Study: All

Nationality: Iceland

AWARD INFORMATION

Award Type: Award, Grant

Average Amount: Varies

Number of Awards: 6-8

Award Coverage: 1-time payment of award, health and accident insurance

Award Duration: Varies

ELIGIBILITY REQUIREMENTS

- Must be an Icelandic citizen and must have or expect bachelor's degree or equivalent by Jun of the award year
- Must be starting graduate studies in the US

APPLICATION INFORMATION

Award Deadline: Oct

Instructions: Visit our website for more information

CONTACT

Fulbright Commission
Laugavegur 59, 3rd. floor
101 Reykjavik
Iceland
Tel: +354 551-0860
Email: adviser@fulbright.is
Web: www.fulbright.is

Fulbright/Japan-US Educational Commission (JUSEC)

Fulbright Research Grant

PROGRAM INFORMATION

Description: This grant is intended to provide an opportunity for non-degree research in social science and humanities for university faculty and professionals of nonprofit organizations to develop their academic and professional expertise in collaboration with American colleagues and through the auditing of graduate seminars. Younger faculty are encouraged to apply.

Levels of Study: Doctorate, Post Doctorate

Field of Study: Humanities, Social Science

Nationality: Japan

AWARD INFORMATION

Award Type: Grant

Average Amount: Varies

Number of Awards: Approx 10

Award Coverage: Monthly stipend, allowances for settling-in, housing, family and research, roundtrip travel

Award Duration: 3-9 months

ELIGIBILITY REQUIREMENTS

- Must be a full-time assistant, lecturer, associate professor, or professor at a 4-year Japanese university, graduate institution or inter-university research institute; or must be a professional in government or nonprofit
- Must have sufficient English proficiency to conduct research in the US without difficulty
- Invitation from a US research facility must be obtained by May 1

APPLICATION INFORMATION

Award Deadline: May 31

Instructions: Refer to www.fulbright.jp/scholarship/index.html

CONTACT

Japan-US Educational Commission
Fulbright Grant Program
207 Sanno Grand Building
2-14-2 Nagata-cho, Chiyoda-ku
100-0014 Tokyo
Japan
Tel: +81 (3) 3580-3233
Fax: +81 (3) 3580-1217
Email: program@fulbright.jp
Web: www.fulbright.jp/eng/grant/p-kenkyu.html

Fulbright/Japan-US Educational Commission (JUSEC)

Fulbright Graduate Study Grant

PROGRAM INFORMATION

Description: This grant is intended to provide an opportunity for young students who have outstanding academic and personal traits, and fully understand the purpose and objectives of the Fulbright Program, to study at a US institution of higher learning for the purpose of obtaining a Doctoral or a Master's degree.

Levels of Study: Graduate, Doctorate

Field of Study: Humanities, Social Science

AWARD INFORMATION

Award Type: Grant

Average Amount: Varies

Number of Awards: Approx 20 including the Doctoral Dissertation Research Grant category

Award Coverage: Tuition, monthly stipend, allowances for settling-in, books and computer, baggage, housing and family, roundtrip travel

Award Duration: 1-2 years

ELIGIBILITY REQUIREMENTS

- Current graduate students who intend to pursue an academic career as a teacher, professor or researcher with a university-affiliated research center in Japan
- Academicians without a doctoral degree in Japan
- Individuals who are in business, government or other professions in Japan who wish to pursue graduate study in the US
- Applicants must have 1) Bachelor's degree at the time application, 2) an acceptance from a US university by May 1, 3) a minimum TOEFL score of 80 (IBT) or IELTS score of 6.0
- Applicants below 35 years of age at the time of application preferred

APPLICATION INFORMATION

Award Deadline: May 31

Instructions: Refer to www.fulbright.jp/scholarship/index.html

CONTACT

Japan-US Educational Commission
Fulbright Grant Program
207 Sanno Grand Building
2-14-2 Nagata-cho, Chiyoda-ku
100-0014 Tokyo
Japan
Tel: +81 (3) 3580-3233
Fax: +81 (3) 3580-1217
Email: program@fulbright.jp
Web: www.fulbright.jp/eng/grant/p-grad.html

Fulbright/Japan-US Educational Commission (JUSEC)

Fulbright Doctoral Dissertation Research Grant

PROGRAM INFORMATION

Description: This grant is intended to provide an opportunity for outstanding young students and researchers who are seeking a doctoral degree from a Japanese university to conduct doctoral dissertation research at a US institution of higher learning.

Levels of Study: Doctorate

Field of Study: Humanities, Social Science

Nationality: Japan

AWARD INFORMATION

Award Type: Grant

Average Amount: Varies

Number of Awards: Approx 20 including the graduate study category

Award Duration: 6-10 months

ELIGIBILITY REQUIREMENTS

- Must be a current student of a Japanese graduate school who has completed the first year of doctoral studies as of Apr
- Applicants below 35 years of age at the time of application preferred
- Must obtain acceptance from a US research institution by May 1
- Must have a minimum TOEFL score of 80 IBT or 6.0 IELTS score

APPLICATION INFORMATION

Award Deadline: May 31

Instructions: Refer to www.fulbright.jp/scholarship/index.html

CONTACT

Japan-US Educational Commission
Fulbright Grant Program
207 Sanno Grand Building,
2-14-2 Nagata-cho, Chiyoda-ku
100-0014 Tokyo
Japan
Tel: +81 (3) 3580-3233
Fax: +81 (3) 3580-1217
Email: program@fulbright.jp
Web: www.fulbright.jp/eng/grant/p-ron.html

Fulbright/Japan-US Educational Commission (JUSEC)

Fulbright Journalist Grants

PROGRAM INFORMATION

Description: This grant is intended to provide an opportunity for non-degree research to practicing journalists who wish to enhance their professional expertise at a US institution of higher learning or research institution. This grant is not for the study of journalism techniques or theories. Upon returning to Japan, grantees are expected to publish articles in Japanese newspapers/periodicals relating to their US experience.

Levels of Study: Professional

Field of Study: Humanities, Social Science

Nationality: Japan

AWARD INFORMATION

Award Type: Grant

Average Amount: Varies

Number of Awards: Approx 3

Award Coverage: Monthly stipend, allowances for settling-in, housing, family and research, and roundtrip travel

Award Duration: 3-9 months

ELIGIBILITY REQUIREMENTS

- Must be a practicing journalist with at least 5 years' experience in a Japanese-owned print or broadcasting organization
- Must be a writer or critic with at least 5 years' experience who regularly writes for or appears in a Japanese-owned print or broadcast program
- Must have sufficient English proficiency to conduct research in the US without difficulty
- Invitation from a US research facility must be obtained by May 1

APPLICATION INFORMATION

Award Deadline: May 31

Instructions: Refer to www.fulbright.jp/scholarship/index.html

CONTACT

Japan-US Educational Commission
Fulbright Grant Program
207 Sanno Grand Building
2-14-2 Nagata-cho, Chiyoda-ku
100-0014 Tokyo
Japan
Tel: +81 (3) 3580-3233
Fax: +81 (3) 3580-1217
Email: program@fulbright.jp
Web: www.fulbright.jp/eng/grant/p-jour.html

Fulbright/Korean-American Educational Commission

Fulbright International Education Administrator Awards

PROGRAM INFORMATION

Description: This program is intended to give South Korean international education professionals guided exposure to US higher education universities and organizations.

Levels of Study: Professional

Field of Study: International Education

Nationality: Korea, Republic of

AWARD INFORMATION

Award Type: Grant

Average Amount: Varies

Number of Awards: Varies

Award Coverage: Air travel, lodging, daily meal stipend

Award Duration: 3 weeks

ELIGIBILITY REQUIREMENTS

- Must be currently employed in a position with at least 1 year of experience directly related to international education administration at a university or government agency by the beginning of the grant program
- Must have the expectation of serving in the same position for at least 1 year after receipt of this award
- Must have adequate English language proficiency
- Must have completed at least a bachelor's degree
- Must participate in the entire program

APPLICATION INFORMATION

Award Deadline: Oct 16

Instructions: Download application materials from our website

CONTACT

Korean-American Educational Commission
Fulbright Building
23, Baekbeom-ro 28 gil, Mapo-gu
121-874 Seoul
Korea
Tel: +82 2-3275-4018
Fax: +82 2-3275-4028
Email: admin@fulbright.or.kr
Web: www.fulbright.or.kr

Fulbright/Korean-American Educational Commission

Fulbright Graduate Study Awards Non-Degree Study

PROGRAM INFORMATION

Description: Graduate Study Awards are offered to mature and academically superior students whose future career objectives in South Korea would be enhanced by pursuing non-degree study at a US university.

Levels of Study: Professional

Field of Study: Arts and Culture, Business and Management, Humanities, Social Science

Nationality: Korea, Republic of

AWARD INFORMATION

Award Type: Award

Average Amount: Up to $2,065 monthly

Number of Awards: Up to 10

Award Coverage: Roundtrip travel, monthly maintenance stipend, medical insurance coverage, various incidental allowance

Award Duration: 10 months

ELIGIBILITY REQUIREMENTS

- Must be a doctoral candidate enrolled in good standing at an approved Korean university
- Must have adequate English language proficiency. Applicants in the fields of literature or linguistics must have a TOEFL score of 100 iBT or better and 88 iBT or better in other fields
- The required minimum overall undergraduate grade point average is 3.0/4.0, 3.225/4.3, or 3.375/4.5.
- Must have graduated or be eligible to graduate from an accredited university
- Visit www.fulbright.or.kr for detailed information

APPLICATION INFORMATION

Award Deadline: Jul 3

Instructions: Download application materials

CONTACT

Korean-American Educational Commission
Fulbright Building
23, Baekbeom-ro 28 gil, Mapo-gu
121-874 Seoul
Korea
Tel: 02-3275-4018
Fax: 02-3275-4028
Email: admin@fulbright.or.kr
Web: www.fulbright.or.kr

Fulbright/Korean-American Educational Commission

Fulbright Korea Graduate Study Awards Degree Study

PROGRAM INFORMATION

Description: Graduate Study Awards are offered to mature and academically superior students whose future career objectives in Korea would be enhanced by pursuing degree study at an American university.

Levels of Study: Graduate, Doctorate

Field of Study: Arts and Culture, Business and Management, Engineering, Humanities, Science, Social Science

Nationality: Korea, Republic of

AWARD INFORMATION

Award Type: Grant
Average Amount: Varies
Number of Awards: Up to 10
Award Coverage: Round-trip travel, monthly maintenance stipend, full or partial tuition, medical insurance, various incidental allowance
Award Duration: 1 year

ELIGIBILITY REQUIREMENTS

- Must not have been an employee of the Korean-American Educational Commission or a recipient of a US government funded scholarship and completion of military service or exemption (if male)
- Must have adequate English language proficiency. Applicants in the fields of literature or linguistics must have a TOEFL score of 100 iBT or better, and in other fields, 88 iBT or better
- Must have a superior academic record
- Visit www.fulbright.or.kr for detailed information

APPLICATION INFORMATION

Award Deadline: Jul 3
Instructions: Download application materials from our website

CONTACT

Korean-American Educational Commission
Fulbright Building
23, Baekbeom-ro 28 gil, Mapo-gu
121-874 Seoul
Korea
Tel: 02-3275-4018
Fax: 02-3275-4028
Email: admin@fulbright.or.kr
Web: www.fulbright.or.kr

Fulbright/Korean-American Educational Commission

Fulbright Lecturing/Research Awards

PROGRAM INFORMATION

Description: The lecturing and research award is for Korean university faculty in the social sciences, humanities, fine arts, or business who can teach American students about Korea in their discipline. Awardees will be required to teach up to 2 undergraduate courses PER SEMESTER in their academic field but with content which is related to Korea. Awardees will receive placement for their teaching assignments at Korean studies programs at universities in the US in consultation with the KAEC office and with CIES. Applicants must also submit a research project which they intend to pursue while they are teaching in the US The research project can be within their discipline but should be related to either Korea or America or a comparative perspective. Applicants should make research proposals that can be carried out at any university, as they will be at only 1 university, lecturing at the university of their Korean studies during their grant period. Travel to other locations in the US during breaks at the grantee¡¯s expense is, of course, permissible.
Levels of Study: Professional
Field of Study: Arts and Culture, Business and Management, Humanities, Social Science
Nationality: Korea, Republic of

AWARD INFORMATION

Award Type: Award
Average Amount: up to $3,795 per month for maintenance stipend and other allowances
Number of Awards: 2
Award Coverage: Round-trip travel, monthly maintenance stipend, medical insurance coverage, dependent/housing allowances
Award Duration: 4-10 months

ELIGIBILITY REQUIREMENTS

- Must have a minimum of 5 years part-time teaching experience at an accredited Korean university following the receipt of the postdoctoral degree
- Must possess excellent comprehensive English ability

APPLICATION INFORMATION

Award Deadline: Sep
Instructions: Download application materials from our website

CONTACT

Korean-American Educational Commission
Fulbright Building
23, Baekbeom-ro 28 gil, Mapo-gu
121-874 Seoul
Korea
Tel: 02-3275-4018
Fax: 02-3275-4028
Email: admin@fulbright.or.kr
Web: www.fulbright.or.kr

Fulbright/Korean-American Educational Commission

Fulbright Mid-Career Research Award

PROGRAM INFORMATION

Description: Research Awards are offered to faculty members of Korean university research institutes and professionals in education, government, business, the media and other professions in Korea. The purpose of these awards is to provide opportunities for non-degree study and research which will enhance existing academic or professional expertise for future career development and contribution after returning to Korea. Accordingly, the proposed research must entail substantive exchanges of academic and professional expertise between Koreans and Americans, rather than just facilitate observation visits or travel for personal enrichment.
Levels of Study: Professional
Field of Study: Arts and Culture, Business and Management, Humanities, Social Science
Nationality: Korea, Republic of

AWARD INFORMATION

Award Type: Award
Average Amount: Up to $3,795 for maintenance stipend and various other allowances
Number of Awards: Up to 10
Award Coverage: Round-trip travel, monthly maintenance stipend, medical insurance coverage, housing allowance, dependent allowance
Award Duration: 6 months

ELIGIBILITY REQUIREMENTS

- Must have a doctorate or terminal degree for the profession
- Must be a full-time college or university faculty member who has held the maximum rank of associate professor for no more than 6 years at an accredited university
- Must be a full-time researcher at an approved research institute for at least 5 and no more than 10 years
- Must be an employed professional in an eligible field with at least 5 and no more than 10 years of relevant experience beyond the terminal degree

APPLICATION INFORMATION

Award Deadline: Sep
Instructions: Download application materials from our website

CONTACT

Korean-American Educational Commission
Fulbright Building
23, Baekbeom-ro 28 gil, Mapo-gu
121-874 Seoul
Korea
Tel: +82 2-3275-4018
Fax: +82 2-3275-4028
Email: admin@fulbright.or.kr
Web: www.fulbright.or.kr

Fulbright/Korean-American Educational Commission

Fulbright Senior Research Award

PROGRAM INFORMATION

Description: Research Awards are offered to faculty members of Korean university research institutes and professionals in education, government, business, the media, and other professions in Korea. The purpose of these awards is to provide opportunities for non-degree study and research, which will enhance existing academic or professional expertise for future career development and contribution after returning to Korea. Accordingly, the proposed research must entail substantial exchanges of academic and professional expertise between Koreans and Americans, rather than just facilitate observational visits or travel for personal enrichment.
Levels of Study: Professional
Field of Study: Arts and Culture, Business and Management, Humanities, Social Science
Nationality: Korea, Republic of

AWARD INFORMATION

Award Type: Award
Average Amount: Up to $3,795 for maintenance stipend, housing allowance, and dependent allowance
Number of Awards: Up to 5
Award Coverage: Round-trip travel, monthly maintenance stipend, medical insurance coverage, various incidental allowances
Award Duration: 6 months

ELIGIBILITY REQUIREMENTS

- Must have a doctorate or terminal degree
- Must be a tenured faculty member at an accredited university who is a full professor or who has held the rank of associate professor for more than of 5 years
- Must be a full-time researcher who has held an equivalent position in an approved research institute for at least 10 years
- Must be an employed professional in an eligible field with at least 10 years of experience beyond the terminal degree

APPLICATION INFORMATION

Award Deadline: Sep

Instructions: Download application materials from our website

CONTACT

Korean-American Educational Commission
Fulbright Building
23, Baekbeom-ro 28 gil, Mapo-gu
121-874 Seoul
Korea
Tel: +82 2-3275-4018
Fax: +82 2-3275-4028
Email: admin@fulbright.or.kr
Web: www.fulbright.or.kr

Fulbright/Malaysian-American Commission on Educational Exchange

Fulbright Professional Exchange Program

PROGRAM INFORMATION

Description: The purpose of the grant is to enable mid-career Malaysian professionals in the public or private sectors to broaden their experiences through consultation, internship, participation in seminars, workshops, and other professional enrichment programs at relevant organizations in the US for periods of 3 to 6 months. These grants are meant for practitioners rather than scholars; administrators, managers of organizations/associations/ services, journalists, and lawyers are encouraged to apply for these grants.

Levels of Study: Professional

Field of Study: All

Nationality: Malaysia

AWARD INFORMATION

Award Type: Grant

Average Amount: Varies

Number of Awards: Varies

Award Coverage: Monthly stipend, professional research allowance

Award Duration: 3-6 months

ELIGIBILITY REQUIREMENTS

- Must possess a master's degree or equivalent professional qualification in the field of the proposed program
- Must have minimum of 5 years working experience in the relevant field
- Must hold a managerial position in a government organization or the private sector and demonstrate a potential for higher responsibilities
- Must have a good command of English and be willing to share knowledge of Malaysia with social, civic, and other groups while in the US

APPLICATION INFORMATION

Award Deadline: Jul

Instructions: Download application materials from our website

CONTACT

MACEE, 18th floor
Program Officer
Menara Yayasan Tun Razak
200 Jalan Bukit Bintang
55100 Kuala Lumpur Wilayah Persekutuan
Malaysia
Tel: +60 (3) 2166-8878
Fax: +60 (3) 2166-1878
Email: kalis@macee.org.my
Web: www.macee.org.my

Fulbright/Malaysian-American Commission on Educational Exchange

Fulbright Malaysian Graduate Study and Research Program

PROGRAM INFORMATION

Description: As the binational Fulbright Commission for Malaysia, MACEE aims to make the Fulbright program available to qualified graduate-level students whose studies will allow them to contribute to the continued development and progress of Malaysia.

Levels of Study: Graduate, Doctorate, Post Doctorate

Field of Study: All

Nationality: Malaysia

AWARD INFORMATION

Award Type: Grant

Average Amount: Varies

Number of Awards: Varies

Award Coverage: Costs of tuition fees, maintenance based upon projected cost of living, specific allowance, medical insurance

Award Duration: Up to 2 years

ELIGIBILITY REQUIREMENTS

- Must not be more than 35 years of age at the time of application
- Must have a minimum of a bachelor's degree with honors and cumulative grade point average of 3.0 or its equivalent
- Must have a TOEFL score of at least 550 PBT/213 CBT, 79-80 IBT
- Must have a GMAT, GRE, GRE subject test with minimum score as required by the institution of your choice

APPLICATION INFORMATION

Award Deadline: Jul

Instructions: Download application materials from our website

CONTACT

Fulbright/Malaysian American Commission on Educational Exchange
Program Officer
MACEE, 18th floor, Menara Kemayan
200 Jalan Bukit Bintang
55100 Kuala Lumpur
Malaysia
Tel: +60 (3) 2166-8878
Fax: +60 (3) 2166-1878
Email: kalis@macee.org.my
Web: www.macee.org.my

Fulbright/Malaysian-American Commission on Educational Exchange

Fulbright Malaysian Scholar Program

PROGRAM INFORMATION

Description: The Malaysian Fulbright Scholar Program provides opportunities for Malaysian academics to develop or update their research through interaction with distinguished counterparts in the US By providing a mechanism and support for meeting and interacting with the best of American scholars, the program seeks to promote dialogue on subjects of mutual interest to Malaysia and the US

Levels of Study: Post Doctorate

Field of Study: All

Nationality: Malaysia

AWARD INFORMATION

Award Type: Grant

Average Amount: Varies

Number of Awards: Varies

Award Coverage: Varies

Award Duration: 3-8 months

ELIGIBILITY REQUIREMENTS

- Must possess a postdoctoral degree (or in exceptional cases a master's or professional degree with outstanding achievement in professional activities)
- Must possess a minimum working experience of 5 years in the relevant field
- Must be affiliated with a university or a higher education institution in Malaysia and be eligible for sabbatical or other leave
- Must possess an excellent record of achievement as indicated by quality publications and professional activities

APPLICATION INFORMATION

Award Deadline: Jul

Instructions: Download application materials from our website

CONTACT

MACEE, 18th floor
Program Officer
Menara Yayasan Tun Razak
200 Jalan Bukit Bintang
55100 Kuala Lumpur Wilayah Persekutuan
Malaysia
Tel: +60 (3) 2166-8878
Fax: +60 (3) 2166-1878
Email: kalis@macee.org.my
Web: www.macee.org.my

Fulbright/Thailand-US Educational Foundation

Fulbright Junior Research Scholarship Program

PROGRAM INFORMATION

Description: In cooperation with the Thailand Research Fund (TRF), Thailand-US Educational Foundation (Fulbright) announces the Fulbright-Thailand Research Fund Junior Research Scholarship Program to qualified Thai university staff members who wish to gain 6 months of research experience in the US as a part of their doctoral dissertation requirements. This scholarship is aimed to help address the severe shortage of highly qualified professionals, to increase doctoral graduates in Thailand, and to build professional growth through contacts with the US professors and scholars.

Levels of Study: Doctorate

Field of Study: All

Nationality: Thailand

AWARD INFORMATION

Award Type: Scholarship

Average Amount: Varies

Number of Awards: Up to 6

Award Coverage: Round-trip international travel expenses, in-transit allowance, books and educational supplies, monthly stipend, insurance

Award Duration: 6 months

ELIGIBILITY REQUIREMENTS

- Must be a Thai citizen in good health
- Must be a university staff member at a tertiary-level institution who is undertaking graduate work at the doctoral level in a university
- Must have completed 2 years of coursework toward the degree, demonstrated strong academic performance at the graduate level, have the agreement of the university doctorate program in which he/she in enrolled
- Must have a minimum TOEFL score of 525 PBT/193 CBT/70 iBT or at least 75 on a CU-TEP
- Must obtain written confirmation from a US professor/scientist at the host institution whom his/her research will be supervised

APPLICATION INFORMATION

Award Deadline: Aug

Instructions: Download application materials from our website

CONTACT

Thailand-US Educational Foundation
Thai Wah Tower 1, 3rd Floor
21/5 South Sathorn Road
10120 Bangkok
Thailand
Tel: +66 (2) 285-0581
Fax: +66 (2) 285-0583
Email: tusef@fulbrightthai.org
Web: www.fulbrightthai.org

Fulbright/Thailand-US Educational Foundation

Fulbright Thailand Open Competition Scholarship Program

PROGRAM INFORMATION

Description: To continue its mission of promoting mutual understanding between the people of the US and Thailand through educational exchange, which has been successfully implemented throughout the past 5 decades, the Thailand-US Educational Foundation (Fulbright) announces its annual competition for Fulbright Scholarships to qualified Thai individuals for study towards the master's degree in the US

Levels of Study: Graduate, Doctorate

Field of Study: All

Nationality: Thailand

AWARD INFORMATION

Award Type: Scholarship

Average Amount: Varies

Number of Awards: Up

Award Coverage: Round-trip international travel expenses, in-transit allowance, tuition and fees, books and education supplies, monthly maintenance allowance, insurance coverage, round-trip international travel expenses, excess baggage allowance

Award Duration: Academic year

ELIGIBILITY REQUIREMENTS

- Must be a Thai citizen in good health. Must have completed all requirements for a bachelor's degree from a university in Thailand at the time of the interview (applicants with working experience are encouraged to apply)
- Must have at least a cumulative GPA of 3.0 or equivalent on the bachelor's degree transcript of academic performance
- Must have a minimum TOEFL score of 550 PBT/213 CBT/80 iBT taken within 2 years from the date of the application deadline
- Must be in Thailand for the interview
- Must not enroll in any degree program in the US prior to the grant year

APPLICATION INFORMATION

Award Deadline: Early Apr

Instructions: Download application materials from our website

CONTACT

Thailand-US Educational Foundation
Thai Wah Tower 1, 3rd Floor
21/5 South Sathorn Road
10120 Bangkok
Thailand
Tel: +66 (2) 285-0581
Fax: +66 (2) 285-0583
Email: tusef@fulbrightthai.org
Web: www.fulbrightthai.org

Fulbright/Vietnam

Fulbright Vietnamese Fulbright Scholar Program

PROGRAM INFORMATION

Description: The US Embassy administers this program to recruit and nominate Vietnamese scholars for placement by CIES as lecturers and researchers in US universities.

Levels of Study: Professional

Field of Study: American Studies, Economics, Education, Environmental Studies, International Relations, Law, Public Administration, Social Service, Urban Planning

Nationality: Vietnam

AWARD INFORMATION

Award Type: Scholarship

Average Amount: Varies

Number of Awards: 5-8

Award Coverage: Stipend, living expenses, transportation

Award Duration: 3-9 months

ELIGIBILITY REQUIREMENTS

- Must hold an MA or a PhD degree
- Must have English skills adequate to conduct research and/or lectures in the US
- Must be a Vietnamese citizen

APPLICATION INFORMATION

Award Deadline: Oct

Instructions: Download application materials from our website

CONTACT

US Embassy, Public Affairs Section
Fulbright Program Assistant
3rd Floor, Rose Garden Tower
170 Ngoc Khanh
Hanoi
Vietnam
Tel: +84 (4) 3850-5000 x6114
Fax: +84 (4) 3831-4601
Email: dohx@state.gov
Web: www.vietnam.usembassy.gov/fvsc.html

Fulbright/Vietnam

Fulbright Vietnamese Student Program

PROGRAM INFORMATION

Description: Through a grant from US State Department's Bureau of Educational and Cultural Affairs to the Institute of International Education (IIE), Vietnamese university graduates with at least 3 years relevant work experience are recruited and nominated for the Vietnamese Student Program, which places them in master's degree programs at universities throughout the US In Vietnam, the US Embassy coordinates with the IIE to encourage the widest possible participation of qualified students in appropriate fields.

Levels of Study: Graduate

Field of Study: American Studies, Business and Management, Communications and Journalism, Economics, Environmental Studies, International Relations, Law, Public Policy

Nationality: Vietnam

AWARD INFORMATION

Award Type: Fellowship

Average Amount: Varies

Number of Awards: 20-25

Award Coverage: Full tuition and fees, a living allowance, international travel, health insurance

Award Duration: Maximum of 2 years

ELIGIBILITY REQUIREMENTS

- Must hold a 4-year bachelor's degree or the equivalent
- Must have at least 2 years of work experience after the date of undergraduate diploma
- Must have a valid minimum TOEFL iBT of 79 or IELTS 6.5
- Must have Vietnamese single citizenship

APPLICATION INFORMATION

Award Deadline: Apr

Instructions: Applications are available between Jan and Apr on the Vietnamese Student Program website

CONTACT

US Embassy, Public Affairs Section
Fulbright Program Assistant
3rd Floor, Rose Garden Tower
170 Ngoc Khanh
Hanoi
Vietnam
Tel: +84 (4) 3850-5000 x5089
Fax: +84 (4) 3831-5120
Email: nguyenHT4@state.gov
Web: www.vietnam.usembassy.gov/fvst.html

Fulbright Center

Fulbright Graduate Grants Netherlands

PROGRAM INFORMATION

Description: The Fulbright Center offers a number of graduate grants for Dutch students to study in the US These can be used to cover part of the costs of a master's degree or the first year of a PhD, or in some cases for non-degree coursework or research.

Levels of Study: Graduate, Doctorate

Field of Study: All

Nationality: Netherlands

AWARD INFORMATION

Award Type: Award, Fellowship, Grant, Scholarship

Average Amount: $12,500

Number of Awards: 16-20

Award Coverage: Apart from the $12,500 maintenance award, application fees for the US visa and basic health insurance are included

Award Duration: Academic year

ELIGIBILITY REQUIREMENTS

- Must be of Dutch nationality
- Must have excellent grades and good references
- Must have a well-rounded personality and extensive extracurricular activities so that he/she can act as an Ambassador for the Netherlands

APPLICATION INFORMATION

Award Deadline: Jan

Instructions: The application consists of an online application form, which also contains 3 references. All information can be found on the website of the Fulbright Center

CONTACT

Fulbright Center
Fulbright Coordinator
Westerdoksdijk 215
1013 AD Amsterdam
The Netherlands
Tel: +31 (20) 5315930
Fax: +31 (20) 6207269
Email: info@fulbright.nl
Web: www.fulbright.nl

Fulbright Center of Finland

Fulbright Center Undergraduate Grant Program

PROGRAM INFORMATION

Description: The Fulbright Center Undergraduate Grants are awarded for 1 academic year for the purpose of pursuing undergraduate studies in the US.

Levels of Study: Undergraduate

Field of Study: All

Nationality: Finland

AWARD INFORMATION

Award Type: Grant

Number of Awards: Varies

Award Coverage: Toward cost of undergraduate studies

Award Duration: Academic year

ELIGIBILITY REQUIREMENTS

- Must be a Finnish citizen who has been admitted to an accredited American college or university but has not yet begun their studies
- The grant will not be awarded to applicants with dual Finnish-US citizenship
- Applicants residing in the US are not eligible

APPLICATION INFORMATION

Award Deadline: Apr

Instructions: 2 letters of recommendation and an admission letter from an accredited American university must accompany the application together with a statement of tuition and fees, visit our website for application forms and information

CONTACT

Fulbright Center
Hakaniemenranta 6
00530 Helsinki
Finland
Tel: +358 (44) 5535-286
Email: office@fulbright.fi
Web: www.fulbright.fi

Fulbright Center of Finland

Fulbright Grant in Photojournalism sponsored by Patricia Seppälä Foundation

PROGRAM INFORMATION

Description: This grant program supports professional development in photojournalism. The grant is intended for all professional photojournalists and press photographers. The grant project may include photographing, further studies in photography, workshops, conferences, visits to organizations in the field, creating networks, research, or other relevant activities. Grantees can take individual courses at American universities, but they cannot be enrolled as full-time students at bachelor's or master's programs.

Levels of Study: Professional

Field of Study: Communications and Journalism, Journalism, Photography, Photojournalism

Nationality: Finland

AWARD INFORMATION

Award Type: Grant

Average Amount: Up to $15,000

Number of Awards: 1 every other year

Award Duration: 3-12 months

ELIGIBILITY REQUIREMENTS

- Must be a Finnish citizen
- An invitation letter from host organization(s) must be included in the application

APPLICATION INFORMATION

Award Deadline: Fall

Instructions: Visit our website for instructions and application forms

CONTACT

Fulbright Center
Program Coordinator
Hakaniemenranta 6
00530 Helsinki
Finland
Tel: +358 (44) 5535-275
Email: office@fulbright.fi
Web: www.fulbright.fi/fi/fulbright-grant-photojournalism

Fulbright Center of Finland

Fulbright Finland Mid-Career Professional Development Program

PROGRAM INFORMATION

Description: Mid-Career Professional Development Grants are awarded for a period of 3-6 months for professional development projects in the US. The grant is intended for professionals in various fields who seek new ideas and approaches in their work. The grant is not awarded for academic research. A Mid-Career Professional Development project can include, for instance, visits to organizations in the applicant's field, lecturing, and/or further studies in the applicant's field of specialization.

Levels of Study: Professional

Field of Study: All

Nationality: Finland

AWARD INFORMATION

Award Type: Grant

Average Amount: Up to $13,500

Number of Awards: Varies

Award Coverage: Grant, health insurance

Award Duration: 3-6 months

ELIGIBILITY REQUIREMENTS

- Must have a letter of invitation from the US host institution
- Must be a Finnish citizen
- Must be preferably over 35 years of age

APPLICATION INFORMATION

Award Deadline: Nov

Instructions: For more information on how to apply, please visit the website

CONTACT

Fulbright Center
Hakaniemenranta 6
00530 Helsinki
Finland
Tel: +358 (44) 5535-286
Email: office@fulbright.fi
Web: www.fulbright.fi/fi/stipendiohjelmat-ammattilaisille-asiantuntijoille-ja-opettajille/mid-career-professional-development

Fulbright Center of Finland

ASLA-Fulbright Research Grant for a Senior Scholar

PROGRAM INFORMATION

Description: The purpose of the grant is to enable the scholar to carry out a research project at an American university or research institution.

Levels of Study: Post Doctorate

Field of Study: All

Nationality: Finland

AWARD INFORMATION

Award Type: Grant

Average Amount: Up to $15,500

Number of Awards: Varies

Award Coverage: Research, health insurance

Award Duration: 3-12 months

ELIGIBILITY REQUIREMENTS

- Must hold a doctoral degree at the time of the application deadline
- The doctorate must have been earned earlier than 4 years prior to the application deadline
- Must have Finnish citizenship
- The ASLA-Fulbright Research Grants for Senior Scholars are cofunded by the Fulbright Center and the applicant's home university. The applicant must hold a position at a university participating in the cost-share program in order to be eligible

APPLICATION INFORMATION

Award Deadline: Oct

Instructions: For more information on how to apply, please visit the website

CONTACT

Fulbright Center
Program Coordinator
Hakaniemenranta 6
00530 Helsinki
Tel: +358 (44) 5535-275
Email: office@fulbright.fi
Web: www.fulbright.fi/fi/node/85

Fulbright Center of Finland

ASLA-Fulbright Pre-Doctoral Research Fellows Program

PROGRAM INFORMATION

Description: ASLA-Fulbright Pre-Doctoral Research Fellows program supports doctoral students wishing to complete a minimum 6 months of doctoral research in the US. The program is meant for advanced Finnish doctoral students whose intention in the US is to solely conduct research for their PhD in Finland. The grant is specifically not meant for taking courses for credit at a university in the US.

Levels of Study: Doctorate

Nationality: Finland

AWARD INFORMATION

Award Type: Grant

Average Amount: $12,000

Number of Awards: Varies

Award Duration: Minimum of 6 months

ELIGIBILITY REQUIREMENTS

- Must attach an invitation letter from a US university to the grant application
- Must be registered in a Finnish University. ASLA-Fulbright Pre-Doctoral Fellows grants are cost-share grants funded by the Finnish university and the Fulbright Center. Applicant's home university must be willing to fund the grant with Fulbright
- Applicants residing in the US are not eligible
- Must be Finnish citizens. The grant will not be awarded to applicants with dual Finnish-US citizenship

APPLICATION INFORMATION

Award Deadline: Oct

Instructions: For more information on how to apply, please visit the website

CONTACT

Fulbright Center
Senior Program Manager
Hakaniemenranta 6
00530 Helsinki
Finland
Email: office@fulbright.fi
Web: www.fulbright.fi/fi/stipendiohjelmat-maisteri-ja-tohtoritason-opintoihin-ja-tutkimukseen/pre-doctoral

Fulbright Center of Finland

ASLA-Fulbright Graduate Grant Program

PROGRAM INFORMATION

Description: ASLA-Fulbright Grants for Graduate Study are awarded for 1 academic year for graduate studies (master's or doctoral level) at an American university. The grant is available for all fields (some exceptions in Medicine). The grant may be awarded for graduate research, studies leading to a degree in the US as well as for non-degree studies. The Fulbright Center's Board of Directors may, in special cases only, award the grant for graduate study conducted in a research institution or other applicable organization in the US.

Levels of Study: Graduate, Doctorate

Field of Study: All

Nationality: Finland

AWARD INFORMATION

Award Type: Grant

Average Amount: Up to $30,000

Number of Awards: Approx 10

Award Duration: Academic year

ELIGIBILITY REQUIREMENTS

- Must be a Finnish citizen with a degree in higher education. Applicants do not have to be enrolled at a Finnish higher education institution
- The grant will not be awarded to applicants with dual Finnish-US citizenship
- Applicants residing in the US are not eligible

APPLICATION INFORMATION

Award Deadline: May

Instructions: Visit our website for application instructions and forms

CONTACT

Fulbright Center
Senior Program Manager
Hakaniemnranta 6
00530 Helsinki
Finland
Tel: +358 (44) 5535-268
Email: office@fulbright.fi
Web: www.fulbright.fi/fi/stipendiohjelmat-maisteri-ja-tohtoritason-opintoihin-ja-tutkimukseen/asla-fulbright-graduate-grants

Fulbright Center of Finland
ASLA-Fulbright Research Grant for a Junior Scholar

PROGRAM INFORMATION

Description: The purpose of the grant is to enable Finnish scholars to carry out a research project at an American university or research institution. The doctorate must have been earned within 4 years of application deadline. In addition to research-only grants it is also possible to award grants that include a limited amount of teaching—up to 2 hrs/week. The research project work carried out in the US must begin with the ASLA-Fulbright grant. The grant will not be awarded to a project the scholar has already started in the US.

Levels of Study: Post Doctorate

Field of Study: All

Nationality: Finland

AWARD INFORMATION

Award Type: Grant

Average Amount: Up to $30,000

Number of Awards: Varies

Award Coverage: Research, health insurance

Award Duration: 4-12 months

ELIGIBILITY REQUIREMENTS

- Must hold a doctoral degree at the time of the application deadline
- Doctorate must have been earned within 4 years of application
- Professionals and artists outside academe must have recognized professional standing and substantial professional accomplishments
- Must have Finnish citizenship
- A number of the ASLA-Fulbright Junior Scholar grants are co-funded by the Fulbright Center and the applicant's home university

APPLICATION INFORMATION

Award Deadline: Nov

Instructions: Visit our website for application instructions and forms

CONTACT

Fulbright Center
Program Coordinator
Hakaniemenranta 6
00530 Helsinki
Finland
Tel: +358 (44) 5535-275
Email: office@fulbright.fi
Web: www.fulbright.fi/fi/stipendit-tohtorintutkinnon-jalkeiseen-tutkimukseen-ja-luennointiin/asla-fulbright-research-grant

Fulbright Center of Finland
Fulbright Finnish Language & Culture Teaching Assistant Program

PROGRAM INFORMATION

Description: The Fulbright Finnish Language and Culture Teaching Assistant (FLTA) program offers Finnish students an opportunity to spend 1 academic year in an American university. The FLTAs study and/or pursue research at an American university while serving as Finnish language and culture teaching assistants on campus. The purpose of the FLTA program is to diversify the teaching of Finnish language and culture in the US, to further strengthen the academic status of Finnish studies at North American universities, and to intensify the cooperation between Finnish and American scholars and universities.

Levels of Study: Graduate, Doctorate

Field of Study: All

Nationality: Finland

AWARD INFORMATION

Award Type: Grant

Award Duration: Academic year

APPLICATION INFORMATION

Award Deadline: Oct

Instructions: Visit the Fulbright Center website for detailed information and application instructions

CONTACT

Fulbright Center
Senior Program Manager
Hakaniemenranta 6, 5th floor
00530 Helsinki
Finland
Tel: +358 (44) 5535-286
Email: office@fulbright.fi
Web: www.fulbright.fi/fi/stipendiohjelmat-maisteri-ja-tohtoritason-opintoihin-ja-tutkimukseen/fulbright-finnish-language-and

Fulbright Center of Finland
Fulbright Distinguished Awards in Teaching

PROGRAM INFORMATION

Description: The Fulbright Distinguished Awards in Teaching is a program intended to recognize and encourage excellence in teaching in the US and abroad. The program sends highly accomplished primary and secondary teachers from the US abroad and brings international teachers to the US for a semester-long program.

Levels of Study: Professional

Field of Study: Education

Nationality: Finland

AWARD INFORMATION

Award Type: Award

ELIGIBILITY REQUIREMENTS

- Must be a Finnish citizen

APPLICATION INFORMATION

Instructions: For more information on how to apply, please visit the website

CONTACT

Fulbright Center
Manager, Teacher Exchange and Education Programs
Hakaniemenranta 6, 5th floor
00530 Helsinki
Finland
Tel: +358 (44) 5535-269
Email: office@fulbright.fi
Web: www.fulbright.fi/fi/node/97

Fulbright Center of Finland
Fulbright-Technology Industries of Finland Grant

PROGRAM INFORMATION

Description: This program offers 2-3 grants annually for candidates from any relevant field related to the technology industries. Grants are available for graduate studies/research and/or postdoctoral research in the US. Potential fields of study include, but are not limited to, pure sciences, applied sciences, and business administration. Relevant projects in other fields such as humanities and social sciences will also be considered. The grant program is funded by the Technology Industries of Finland Centennial Foundation and the Fulbright Center.

Levels of Study: Graduate, Doctorate, Post Doctorate

Field of Study: All

Nationality: Finland

AWARD INFORMATION

Award Type: Grant

Average Amount: Up to $50,000

Number of Awards: 2-3

Award Duration: Academic year

ELIGIBILITY REQUIREMENTS

- Intended for Finnish citizens with a degree in higher education
- Grants are awarded for 1 academic year for graduate studies at the master's or doctoral level at an American university; the grant may be awarded for studies leading to a degree in the US as well as for non-degree studies
- For postdoctoral research, applicants should have completed a doctoral degree in the 4 years prior to the application deadline
- The grant will not be awarded to applicants with dual Finnish-US citizenship
- Applicants residing in the US are not eligible

APPLICATION INFORMATION

Instructions: Visit our website for application instructions and forms

CONTACT

Fulbright Center
Senior Program Manager
Hakaniemenranta 6
00530 Helsinki
Finland
Tel: +358 (44) 5535-286
Email: office@fulbright.fi
Web: www.fulbright.fi/fi/stipendiohjelmat-maisteri-ja-tohtoritason-opintoihin-ja-tutkimukseen/fulbright-technology-industries

Fulbright Commission Ireland

Fulbright TechImpact Award

PROGRAM INFORMATION

Description: The Fulbright TechImpact Awards are grants for Irish citizens or E.U. citizens resident in Ireland for 3 or more years to complete short-term, non-commercial projects and research in the US for a period of 2 weeks to 3 months.

Levels of Study: Post Doctorate, Professional

Field of Study: Arts and Culture, Education, Humanities, Information Technology, Life Sciences, Science Technologies

Nationality: Ireland

AWARD INFORMATION

Award Type: Award, Grant, Study Abroad

Award Duration: 2 weeks - 3 months

ELIGIBILITY REQUIREMENTS

- Applicant must be an Irish citizen or E.U. citizen living in Ireland for 3 or more years
- Preference will be given to early career researchers with PhD conferred since 2009 or a professional with 3 to 5 years' experience in relevant fields
- Proposals welcomed from all disciplines, but applications in Education, Mobile Technology, and Digital Arts, Humanities, and Culture are particularly encouraged
- Leadership qualities and a clear understanding of what it means to be a Fulbrighter
- Are not a dual US-Irish citizen, green card holder, or currently living in the US, or already have extensive experience of studying or living in the US

APPLICATION INFORMATION

Award Deadline: Nov 11

Instructions: If you meet the above criteria, please email info@fulbright.ie during the application period to indicate your interest. In your email please state your full name, area of study or research, and where you intend to research or study; we will then issue you the link to the online application system (known as Embark) and the Irish instructions for application

CONTACT

Fulbright Commission Ireland
info@fulbright.ie
Web: www.fulbright.ie/fulbright-irish-scholar-awards/fulbright-techimpact-award

Fulbright Commission Ireland

Fulbright Schuman Award

PROGRAM INFORMATION

Description: The Fulbright Schuman Awards are grants for study, research, or lecturing in the topics of the European Union, E.U. Policies, and E.U.-US Relations. Areas of interest must relate to E.U. competencies, not just countries of Europe.

Field of Study: European Studies/EU Studies, International Development, International Law, International Relations, Policy Research, Political Science

Nationality: Ireland

AWARD INFORMATION

Award Type: Award

APPLICATION INFORMATION

Instructions: There are 2 different types of Fulbright Schuman grants for Irish applicants. All successful Irish applicants will be required to attend a pre-departure orientation and submit progress reports during the course of their award. All successful applicants must comply with 2-year home rule, which means that awardees will not be eligible for US residency or a visa until the 2-year home rule in Ireland is complete

CONTACT

Fulbright Commission of Belgium
Web: www.fulbright.be/

Fulbright Commission Ireland

Fulbright Student Awards

PROGRAM INFORMATION

Description: Fulbright Student Awards are for postgraduate applicants who intend to enroll in a US master's or PhD degree program or conduct independent research (minimum 6 months) as part of an Irish or European PhD program. The Awards are only available for 1 academic year, but students may remain in the US for the full duration of their academic program if it is greater than the year.

Levels of Study: Graduate, Doctorate

Field of Study: All

Nationality: Europe

AWARD INFORMATION

Award Type: Award

Average Amount: Maximum of $20,000

Number of Awards: Varies

Award Coverage: Stipend, insurance, J-1 visa, and programming

Award Duration: Maximum of 1 year

ELIGIBILITY REQUIREMENTS

- Must have a recognized third-level degree of at least 2:1 honors standard; graduates who have achieved a 2.2 grade in their primary degree and who have achieved at least 2.1 honors in their postgraduate degree are eligible to apply
- Must have leadership qualities and an understanding of the Fulbright program
- Applicants must be either an Irish citizen who is a resident on the island of Ireland, or an EU citizen who is ordinarily resident in Ireland; a person is deemed to be ordinarily resident in the state if s/he has been living here for the past 3 consecutive years
- Must have a clear course of study and an application to a US institution; successful candidates must secure admission to a US college before commencing an award

APPLICATION INFORMATION

Award Deadline: Nov

Instructions: Log on to the Embark system during application period to apply: www.fulbright.ie/fulbright-irish-student-awards

CONTACT

Fulbright Commission Ireland
Communication & Administration Officer
Brooklawn House
Crampton Avenue, Shelbourne Road
Ballsbridge, Dublin 4
Ireland
Tel: +353 (1) 660-7670
Fax: +353 (1) 660-7668
Email: info@fulbright.ie
Web: www.fulbright.ie/fulbright-irish-student-awards

Fulbright Commission Ireland

Fulbright Scholar and Professional Awards

PROGRAM INFORMATION

Description: Fulbright Scholar Awards enable Irish academics, postdoctoral researchers, or professionals with more than 5 years' experience in any discipline including the visual and performing arts to spend 3 to 12 months researching and/or lecturing in the US

Levels of Study: Post Doctorate, Professional

Field of Study: All

Nationality: Austria, Belgium, Bulgaria, Cyprus, Czech Republic, Denmark, Estonia, Finland, France, Germany, Greece, Hungary, Ireland, Italy, Latvia, Lithuania, Luxembourg, Malta, Netherlands, Poland, Portugal, Romania, Slovakia, Slovenia, Spain, Sweden, United Kingdom

AWARD INFORMATION

Award Type: Award

Average Amount: $20,000 for general awards

Number of Awards: Varies

Award Coverage: Stipend, insurance, J-1 visa, programming

Award Duration: 3-12 months

ELIGIBILITY REQUIREMENTS

- Must have a PhD prior to starting the grant; professional candidates must have a minimum of 5 years professional experience in their field of study
- Must demonstrate leadership and an understanding of the Fulbright Program
- Must be either an Irish citizen who is resident on the island of Ireland, or an EU citizen who is ordinarily resident in Ireland, a person is deemed to be ordinarily resident in the State if s/he has been living here for the past 3 consecutive years
- Must have an affiliation with a US institution

APPLICATION INFORMATION

Award Deadline: Nov

Instructions: Please log on to the Embark system to apply: www.fulbright.ie/fulbright-irish-scholar-awards

CONTACT

Fulbright Commission Ireland
Communication & Administration Officer
Brooklawn House
Crampton Avenue, Shelbourne Road
Ballsbridge, Dublin 4
Ireland
Tel: +353 (1) 660-7670
Fax: +353 (1) 660-7668
Email: info@fulbright.ie
Web: www.fulbright.ie/fulbright-irish-scholar-awards

Fulbright Commission Ireland

Foreign Language Teaching Assistantship Awards

PROGRAM INFORMATION

Description: The Fulbright Foreign Language Teaching Assistantship (FLTA) Program offers FLTAs and US students the unique opportunity to learn about each other's culture and to build mutual understanding between the US and other countries. The FLTA Program is a 10-month non-degree program aimed at strengthening foreign language instruction at US colleges and universities, and some secondary schools. The FLTA Program provides current or future teachers with the opportunity to refine their teaching skills and extend their knowledge of US society and culture that they can draw on when they return to Ireland.

Levels of Study: Graduate

Nationality: Austria, Belgium, Bulgaria, Cyprus, Czech Republic, Denmark, Estonia, Finland, France, Germany, Greece, Hungary, Ireland, Italy, Latvia, Lithuania, Luxembourg, Malta, Netherlands, Poland, Portugal, Romania, Slovakia, Slovenia, Spain, Sweden, United Kingdom

AWARD INFORMATION

Award Type: Award

Average Amount: Approx €20,000

Award Coverage: Stipend, insurance, J-1 visa, and programming

Award Duration: 10 months

ELIGIBILITY REQUIREMENTS

- Must be a postgraduate student or recently-qualified teacher with competency in the Irish language and teaching experience
- Must have a recognized third-level degree of at least 2:1 honors standard; applicants will be accepted from outstanding students in their final year of study, graduates who have achieved a 2.2 grade in their primary degree and who have subsequently demonstrated outstanding academic achievement in their postgraduate degree are eligible to apply
- Must demonstrate leadership and have an understanding of the Fulbright Program
- Applicants must be either an Irish citizen who is a resident on the island of Ireland, or an EU citizen who is ordinarily resident in Ireland; a person is deemed to be ordinarily resident in the state if s/he has been living here for the past 3 consecutive years

APPLICATION INFORMATION

Award Deadline: Nov

Instructions: Please log on to the Embark system to apply: www.fulbright.ie/fulbright-foreign-language-teaching-assistantship-awards

CONTACT

Fulbright Commission Ireland
Communication & Administration Officer
Brooklawn House
Crampton Avenue, Shelbourne Road
Ballsbridge, Dublin 4
Ireland
Tel: +353 (1) 660-7670
Fax: +353 (1) 660-7668
Email: info@fulbright.ie
Web: www.fulbright.ie/fulbright-foreign-language-teaching-assistantship-awards

Fulbright New Zealand

Fulbright New Zealand General Graduate Awards

PROGRAM INFORMATION

Description: Fulbright New Zealand General Graduate Awards are for promising graduate students to undertake Postgraduate study or research at US institutions in any field. Approx 6 awards valued at up to $33,000 including travel are granted each year, towards 1 year of study or research in the US

Levels of Study: Graduate, Doctorate

Field of Study: All

Nationality: New Zealand

AWARD INFORMATION

Award Type: Award, Grant, Study Abroad

Average Amount: Up to $33,000

Award Coverage: Return airfare to the US, 1-time payment of $25,000 toward the cost of study or research; the award will be reduced to $15,000 if the recipient takes up a study or research program of less than 9 months duration; a basic health benefit plan covering a max of $100,000 per sickness or injury

Award Duration: Academic year

ELIGIBILITY REQUIREMENTS

- Must have completed the equivalent of 4 years full-time study at tertiary level and obtained a bachelor's degree by the time you take up your award, but not yet hold a doctoral degree
- Must plan to undertake full-time postgraduate study or research at a US institution for a period of at least 6 months
- Must be a New Zealand citizen, not a permanent resident or citizen of the US, not currently living in the US

APPLICATION INFORMATION

Award Deadline: Aug 1

Instructions: Complete and submit an online application and all supporting documents by the deadline

CONTACT

Fulbright New Zealand
PO Box 3465
6001 Wellington
New Zealand
Tel: +64 (4) 494 1504
Fax: +64 (4) 499 5364
Email: info@fulbright.org.nz
Web: www.fulbright.org.nz/awards/nzgraduate/general/

Fulbright New Zealand

Fulbright-Ngâ Pae o te Mâramatanga Graduate Award

PROGRAM INFORMATION

Description: The Fulbright-Ngâ Pae o te Mâramatanga Graduate Award is for a promising New Zealand graduate student to undertake postgraduate study or research at a US institution in the field of indigenous development. The award is available for study or research which fits within 1 of Ngâ Pae o te Mâramatanga's research themes, as stated at www.maramatanga.ac.nz/research/research-themes

Levels of Study: Graduate, Doctorate

Field of Study: Agriculture and Related Sciences, Area and Ethnic Studies, Arts and Culture, Business and Management, Comparative Law, Conflict Resolution, Environmental Policy, Environmental Studies, Family and Consumer Sciences/Human Sciences, Foreign Languages, Human Rights, Humanities, International Development, International Education, Law, Leadership, Master of Business Administration (MBA), Minority Rights, Natural Sciences, Policy Research, Public Administration, Public Health, Science Technologies, Social Justice, Social Movements, Urban Planning

Nationality: New Zealand

AWARD INFORMATION

Award Type: Award, Grant, Study Abroad

Average Amount: Up to $33,000

Number of Awards: 1

Award Coverage: Return airfare to the US A 1-time payment of $25,000 toward the cost of study or research; the award will be reduced to $15,000 if the recipient takes up a study or research program of less than 9 months duration; a basic health benefit plan covering a maximum of $100,000 per sickness or injury

Award Duration: Academic year

ELIGIBILITY REQUIREMENTS

- Must have completed the equivalent of 4 years full-time study at tertiary level and obtained a bachelor's degree by the time you take up your award, but not yet hold a doctoral degree
- Must plan to undertake full-time postgraduate study or research at a US institution for a period of at least 6 months
- Must be a New Zealand citizen and not a permanent resident or citizen of the US and not currently living in the US

APPLICATION INFORMATION

Award Deadline: Aug 1

Instructions: Complete and submit an online application and all supporting documents by the deadline

CONTACT

Fulbright New Zealand
PO Box 3465
6001 Wellington
New Zealand
Tel: +64 (4) 494 1504
Fax: +64 (4) 499 5364
Email: info@fulbright.org.nz
Web: www.fulbright.org.nz/awards/nzgraduate/fulbright-npmgraduate/

Fulbright New Zealand

Fulbright-EQC Graduate Award in Natural Disaster Research

PROGRAM INFORMATION

Description: The Fulbright-EQC Graduate Award in Natural Disaster Research is for a promising New Zealand graduate student to undertake postgraduate study or research at a US institution in the area of natural disaster research. The award is available for research into the risks posed by natural disasters, the hazards they present, their impact, society's vulnerability, mitigation and management measures.

Levels of Study: Graduate

Field of Study: Architecture and Environmental Design, Behavioral Sciences, Construction Trades, Earth Science, Natural Disaster Research, Psychology, Public Policy, Urban Planning

Nationality: New Zealand

AWARD INFORMATION

Award Type: Award, Grant, Scholarship, Student Exchange, Study Abroad

Average Amount: Up to $33,000

Number of Awards: 1 per year

Award Coverage: Return airfare to the US; a 1-time payment of $25,000 toward the cost of your study or research. The award will be reduced to $15,000 if the recipient takes up a study or research program of less than 9 months duration; basic supplemental health and accident insurance up to $100,000

Award Duration: 1 year

ELIGIBILITY REQUIREMENTS

- Must have completed the equivalent of 4 years full-time study at tertiary level and obtained a bachelor's degree by the time you take up your award, but not yet hold a doctoral degree
- Must plan to undertake full-time postgraduate study or research at a US institution for a period of at least 6 months
- Must be a New Zealand citizen, and not be a permanent resident or citizen of the US and not currently live in the US

APPLICATION INFORMATION

Award Deadline: Aug

Instructions: See www.fulbright.org.nz/awards/nzgraduate/fulbright-eqc/for details on how to apply

CONTACT

Fulbright New Zealand
Tel: +64 4 494 1504
Email: shauna@fulbright.org.nz
Web: www.fulbright.org.nz/awards/nzgraduate/fulbright-eqc/

Fulbright New Zealand

Fulbright New Zealand Science and Innovation Graduate Awards

PROGRAM INFORMATION

Description: Fulbright Science and Innovation Graduate Awards are for promising graduate students to undertake Postgraduate study or research at US institutions in areas targeted to support growth and innovation in New Zealand. Approx 16 awards valued at up to $33,000 including travel are granted each year, toward 1 year of study or research in the US.

Levels of Study: Graduate, Doctorate

Field of Study: Aerospace, Agriculture and Related Sciences, Architecture and Environmental Design, Biomedical Humanities, Biotechnology, Chemistry, Cognitive Science, Communication Technologies, Computer Science, Earth Science, Engineering, Engineering-Related Technologies, Food Technologies, Geography, Horticulture, Life Sciences, Marine Engineering, Metallurgy, Military Technologies, Natural Sciences, Neuroscience, Optics, Physical Sciences, Psychology, Science Technologies, Veterinary Medical Technology

Nationality: New Zealand

AWARD INFORMATION

Award Type: Award, Grant, Scholarship, Student Exchange, Study Abroad

Average Amount: Up to $33,000

Number of Awards: Approx 16

Award Coverage: Return airfare to the US; a 1-time payment of $25,000 toward the cost of your study or research. The award will be reduced to $15,000 if the recipient takes up a study or research program of less than 9 months duration; basic supplemental health and accident insurance up to $100,000

Award Duration: Academic year

ELIGIBILITY REQUIREMENTS

- Must have completed the equivalent of 4 years full-time study at tertiary level and obtained a bachelor's degree by the time you take up your award, but not yet hold a doctoral degree
- Must plan to undertake full-time postgraduate study or research at a US institution for a period of at least 6 months
- Must be a New Zealand citizen and not a permanent resident or citizen of the US and not currently living in the US

APPLICATION INFORMATION

Award Deadline: Aug 1

Instructions: Complete and submit an online application and all supporting documents by the deadline

CONTACT

Fulbright New Zealand
PO Box 3465
6001 Wellington
New Zealand
Tel: +64 (4) 494 1504
Fax: +64 (4) 499 5364
Email: info@fulbright.org.nz
Web: www.fulbright.org.nz/awards/nzgraduate/scienceinnovation

Fulbright Program - US Department of State ECA

Fulbright Foreign Student Program

PROGRAM INFORMATION

Description: The Fulbright Foreign Student Program is designed to give master's and doctoral candidates, and developing professionals and artists opportunities for international experience, personal enrichment and an open exchange of ideas with citizens of other nations. The Fulbright Program supports educational exchanges that strengthen understanding and communication between the US and over 140 countries. It is an effective and prestigious form of public diplomacy. The program has brought some of the world's finest minds to US campuses. It offers insight into US society and values to future leaders from around the world. Foreign students apply for Fulbright Fellowships through the Fulbright Commission/Foundation or US Embassy in their home countries.

Levels of Study: Graduate

Field of Study: All

Nationality: Any Region

AWARD INFORMATION

Award Type: Fellowship

Number of Awards: Varies

Award Coverage: Varies

Award Duration: Varies

ELIGIBILITY REQUIREMENTS

- Must possess an undergraduate degree
- Must have citizenship or permanent resident status qualifying the applicant to hold a valid passport issued in the country in which the application is made
- Must demonstrate proficiency in English
- Must be of sound physical and mental health

APPLICATION INFORMATION

Instructions: Foreign students apply for Fulbright Fellowships through the binational Fulbright Commission or US Embassies in their home countries; to find the binational Fulbright Commission nearest you, please go to the website and select "Foreign Student Program"

CONTACT

Web: foreign.fulbrightonline.org

Fulbright Program - US Department of State ECA

Fulbright Visiting Scholar Program

PROGRAM INFORMATION

Description: Each year faculty and professionals from around the world receive Fulbright Scholar grants for advanced research and university lecturing in the US. Individual grants are available to scholars from over 150 countries. Individuals who meet the eligibility requirements apply for grants through the Fulbright Commission/Foundation or public affairs section of the US embassy in their home countries.

Levels of Study: Post Doctorate

Field of Study: All

Nationality: Any Region

AWARD INFORMATION

Award Type: Grant

Number of Awards: Varies

Award Coverage: Varies

Award Duration: Varies

ELIGIBILITY REQUIREMENTS

- Must have citizenship or permanent resident status qualifying the applicant to hold a valid passport issued in the country in which the application is made
- Must have doctoral degree or equivalent professional training or experience at the time of application
- A detailed statement of proposed activity for research or lecturing at a US institution
- Must demonstrate proficiency in English appropriate to the proposed lecturing or research project to be carried out in the US
- Must be of sound physical and mental health

APPLICATION INFORMATION

Award Deadline: Jun

Instructions: To receive an application for advanced research or university lecturing in the US, interested non-US faculty and professionals must contact the Fulbright Commission/ Foundation or public affairs section of the US embassy in their home countries. To find the binational Fulbright Commission nearest you, please visit the website

CONTACT

Web: www.cies.org/vs_scholars/

Fulbright Taiwan/ Foundation for Scholarly Exchange

Fulbright Taiwan Senior Research Grants

PROGRAM INFORMATION

Description: These grants are designed to provide an opportunity for scholars to conduct in-depth research and develop lasting professional contacts at 1 or 2 American institutions. 2 types of grants are offered.

Levels of Study: Post Doctorate

Field of Study: Arts and Culture, Humanities, Social Science

Nationality: Taiwan

AWARD INFORMATION

Award Type: Grant

Average Amount: $7,200-$24,000

Number of Awards: Up to 23

Award Coverage: Monthly stipend, round-trip economy-class air ticket, baggage allowance

Award Duration: 3-10 months

ELIGIBILITY REQUIREMENTS

- Must have held the rank of assistant professor or its equivalent for the least 3 years, if affiliated with a university or research institution in Taiwan
- Must be recommended by the chief administrator, director, or president of the home institution
- Must not have received a Fulbright grant within the past 5 years

APPLICATION INFORMATION

Award Deadline: Oct

Instructions: Download or contact to request application materials

CONTACT

Fulbright Taiwan
2nd Fl., 45, Yanping S. Rd
10043 Taipei
Taiwan
Tel: +886 (2) 2388-2100
Fax: +886 (2) 2388-2855
Email: fse@fulbright.org.tw
Web: www.fulbright.org.tw

Fulbright Taiwan/ Foundation for Scholarly Exchange

Fulbright Taiwan Non-Academic Professional Grant

PROGRAM INFORMATION

Description: Up to 5 Fulbright partial grants for non-academic professionals are offered to mid-career professionals working in government or private organizations who wish to take part in a learning project in order to enhance their professional expertise through visits, observation, and formal study.

Levels of Study: Professional

Field of Study: Arts and Culture, Communications and Journalism, Environmental Studies, International Relations, Law

Nationality: Taiwan

AWARD INFORMATION

Award Type: Grant

Average Amount: $5,000-$11,000

Number of Awards: Up to 5

Award Coverage: Varies

Award Duration: Varies

ELIGIBILITY REQUIREMENTS

- Must be a senior employee of a private or public organization with responsibilities related to the proposed project
- Must be recommended by the employing institution
- Must possess sufficient English proficiency for successful completion of grant activity
- Must show evidence of financial support from personal savings and/or institutional contributions to cover remaining expenses for the duration of the proposed study

APPLICATION INFORMATION

Instructions: Download or contact to request application materials

CONTACT

Fulbright Taiwan
2nd Fl., 45, Yanping S. Rd
10043 Taipei
Taiwan
Tel: +886 (2) 2388-2100
Fax: +886 (2) 2388-2855
Email: fse@fulbright.org.tw
Web: www.fulbright.org.tw

Fulbright Taiwan/ Foundation for Scholarly Exchange

Fulbright Taiwan Graduate Study Grants

PROGRAM INFORMATION

Description: The graduate study grants provide funds for highly qualified and outstanding students to study at the graduate level at an American university.

Levels of Study: Doctorate

Field of Study: Arts and Culture, Humanities, Social Science

Nationality: Taiwan

AWARD INFORMATION

Award Type: Grant

Average Amount: Varies

Number of Awards: Up to 10

Award Coverage: Monthly stipend

Award Duration: 1 year, educational enrichment renewable for second year

ELIGIBILITY REQUIREMENTS

- Must hold a master's degree and be enrolled directly in a doctoral program
- Must be physically present for an oral interview in Sep or Oct at the Foundation (FSE) in Taipei
- Must have a minimum TOEFL score of 240 CBT/95 iBT

APPLICATION INFORMATION

Award Deadline: Nov

Instructions: Download or contact to request application materials

CONTACT

Fulbright Taiwan
2nd Fl., 45, Yanping S. Rd
10043 Taipei
Taiwan
Tel: +02 2332-8188 ext. 112
Fax: +02 2332-8188
Email: fse@fulbright.org.tw)
Web: www.fulbright.org.tw

Fundacao de Ampara a Pesquida do Estado de Sao Paulo (FAPESP)

FAPESP Fellowships

PROGRAM INFORMATION

Description: The State of São Paulo Research Foundation (FAPESP) is 1 of the main funding agencies for scientific and technological research in Brazil. It is linked to the State of São Paulo's Secretariat for Higher Education. FAPESP offers scholarships for graduate and doctoral study.

Levels of Study: Graduate, Doctorate

Field of Study: All

Nationality: Brazil

AWARD INFORMATION

Award Type: Fellowship

Average Amount: Varies

Number of Awards: Varies

Award Coverage: Medical insurance, living expenses

Award Duration: 2 years for master's; 4 years for doctoral

APPLICATION INFORMATION

Instructions: Visit our website or contact us for requirements and information on how to apply

CONTACT

Fundacao de Ampara a Pesquida do Estado
de Sao Paulo (FAPESP)
Rua Pio XI, 1500
Alto de Lapa
05468-901 Sao Paulo
Brazil
Tel: +55 (11) 3838-4000
Fax: +55 (11) 3645-2421
Email: info@trieste.fapesp.br
Web: www.fapesp.br

Garden Club of America

GCA Interchange Fellowship

PROGRAM INFORMATION

Description: The goal of the Interchange Fellowship program is to fund a British recipient to attend a graduate program in the US in horticulture, landscape architecture, and/or related fields. The intent is to foster cultural understanding, promote horticultural studies, and exchange information in the field.

Levels of Study: Graduate

Field of Study: Horticulture

Nationality: United Kingdom

AWARD INFORMATION

Award Type: Fellowship

Average Amount: Up to $30,000

Award Coverage: Tuition and fees, room and board, living expenses

Award Duration: Academic year

ELIGIBILITY REQUIREMENTS

- Must hold undergraduate degree in horticulture, landscape architecture, or a related field

APPLICATION INFORMATION

Award Deadline: Oct

Instructions: Please visit the website for application instructions

CONTACT

The Garden Club of America
14 East 60th Street
New York, NY 10022
Tel: +1 (212) 753-8287
Fax: +1 (212) 753-0134
Email: cyates@gcamerica.org
Web: www2.gcamerica.org/scholarships.cfm

German Academic Exchange Service (DAAD)

DAAD Annual Scholarship for Study in the US

PROGRAM INFORMATION

Description: Individual scholarships for undergraduate or graduate study at an accredited US college or university of the applicant's choice. In some cases, applicants may be placed at a specific college or university by the DAAD.

Levels of Study: Undergraduate, Graduate

Field of Study: All

Nationality: Germany

AWARD INFORMATION

Award Type: Scholarship

Average Amount: Undergraduate: €15,000; graduate: €19,000

Number of Awards: Undergraduate: 110; graduate: 50

Award Coverage: €425 per month living stipend for undergraduates, €975 per month living stipend for graduates, round-trip airfare, tuition coverage from €10,200 to full tuition, health insurance

Award Duration: Academic year

ELIGIBILITY REQUIREMENTS

- Undergraduate applicants must be in at least the second semester of study at the time of application
- For home university undergraduate programs requiring an intermediate exam, exam must be completed before the commencement of the proposed period of study
- Graduate applicants must have completed their undergraduate degree program prior to commencement of proposed period of study, but not more than 2 years prior to the proposed period of study (not more than 3 years for MBA applicants)
- Must submit TOEFL scores (MBA applicants: minimum TOEFL score of 250 CBT and minimum GMAT score of 600)

APPLICATION INFORMATION

Award Deadline: Jun (Aug for MBA)

Instructions: Visit our website or contact us for more information

CONTACT

Deutscher Akademischer Austauschdienst (DAAD)
Referat 315
Kennedyallee 50
53175 Bonn
Germany
Tel: +49 (228) 882-0
Fax: +49 (228) 882-444
Email: Skwara@daad.org
Web: www.daad.de

German Academic Exchange Service (DAAD)

DAAD Scholarship for Doctoral Research in the US

PROGRAM INFORMATION

Description: Individual scholarship for doctoral and postdoctoral research at the university or scientific institute of the applicant's choice.

Levels of Study: Doctorate, Post Doctorate

Field of Study: All

Nationality: Germany

AWARD INFORMATION

Award Type: Scholarship

Average Amount: Varies

Number of Awards: Varies

Award Coverage: Living stipend, round-trip airfare, health insurance

Award Duration: 1-12 months

ELIGIBILITY REQUIREMENTS

- Doctoral applicants must hold degrees that qualify them for admission to a PhD program at a German university
- Postdoctoral applicants must complete doctorate with at least magna cum laude before the commencement of the proposed period of research

APPLICATION INFORMATION

Instructions: Visit website or contact for more information

CONTACT

Deutscher Akademischer Austauschdienst (DAAD)
Referat 315
Kennedyallee 50
53175 Bonn
Germany
Tel: +49 (228) 882-465
Fax: +49 (228) 882-444
Email: skwara@daad.org
Web: www.daad.de

German Academic Exchange Service (DAAD)

DAAD Short-Term Lectureship

PROGRAM INFORMATION

Description: DAAD funds short-term lectureships of 4-6 months at US colleges or universities. Opportunities are also available for long-term lectureships.

Levels of Study: Professional

Field of Study: All

Nationality: Austria, Belgium, Croatia, Czech Republic, Denmark, Finland, France, Germany, Gibraltar, Greece, Hungary, Iceland, Ireland, Italy, Luxembourg, Monaco, Netherlands, Norway, Poland, Portugal, Romania, Slovakia, Spain, Sweden, Switzerland, Ukraine

AWARD INFORMATION

Award Type: Associateship

Average Amount: Varies

Award Coverage: Travel, living expenses

Award Duration: 4-6 months

ELIGIBILITY REQUIREMENTS

- Must have EU nationality, teaching experience, an affiliation with a German university
- Must have the invitation of a host university
- Must demonstrate adequate financial involvement of the host institution regarding the cost of room and board, and other expenses
- Must be concentrated in 1 of the fields of study referred to on our website

APPLICATION INFORMATION

Award Deadline: Varies

Instructions: Download or contact to request application materials

CONTACT

Deutscher Akademischer Austauschdienst (DAAD)
Referat 315
Kennedyallee 50
53175 Bonn
Germany
Tel: +49 (228) 882-0
Fax: +49 (228) 882-444
Email: skwara@daad.org
Web: www.daad.de

German Historical Institute

German Historical Institute Doctoral and Postdoctoral Fellowships

PROGRAM INFORMATION

Description: The German Historical Institute awards short-term fellowships to German and American doctoral students as well as postdoctoral scholars (Habilitanden) in the fields of German history, the history of German-American relations, and the role of Germany and the US in international relations. These fellowships are also available to German doctoral students and postdoctoral scholars (Habilitanden) in the field of American history.

Levels of Study: Doctorate, Post Doctorate

Field of Study: American History, German-American Relations, History, International Relations

Nationality: Germany

AWARD INFORMATION

Award Type: Fellowship

Average Amount: $1,900 per month for doctoral students; $3,200 per month for postdoctoral students

Number of Awards: Varies

Award Coverage: Stipend, roundtrip airfare

Award Duration: 1-6 months

ELIGIBILITY REQUIREMENTS

- Contact the program for further details and requirements

APPLICATION INFORMATION

Award Deadline: Apr, Oct

Instructions: See website for application instructions

CONTACT

German Historical Institute
1607 New Hampshire Ave., NW
Washington, DC 20009
Tel: +1 (202) 387-3355
Fax: +1 (202) 483-3430
Email: fellowships@ghi-dc.org
Web: www.ghi-dc.org

Google

Google Anita Borg Scholarship

PROGRAM INFORMATION

Description: Dr. Anita Borg devoted her adult life to revolutionizing the way we think about technology and dismantling barriers that keep women and minorities from entering computing and technology fields. Her combination of technical expertise and fearless vision continues to inspire and motivate countless women to become active participants and leaders in creating technology. In her honor, Google is proud to honor Anita's memory and support women in technology, and hopes to encourage women to excel in computing and technology and become active role models and leaders in the field.

Levels of Study: Undergraduate, Graduate

Field of Study: Computer and Information Sciences, Computer Science

Nationality: Any Region

AWARD INFORMATION

Award Type: Scholarship

Award Duration: 1 year

ELIGIBILITY REQUIREMENTS

- Must be a female student entering her senior year of undergraduate study or be enrolled in a graduate program at a university in the US
- Must be enrolled in computer science or computer engineering program, or a closely related technical field as a full-time student
- Must maintain a cumulative GPA of at least 3.5 on a 4.0 scale or 4.5 on a 5.0 scale or equivalent in your current program

APPLICATION INFORMATION

Award Deadline: Feb

Instructions: Please see website for scholarship information

CONTACT

Google
Email: anitaborgscholars@google.com
Web: www.google.com/anitaborg

Harry Frank Guggenheim Foundation

Guggenheim Foundation Dissertation Fellowships

PROGRAM INFORMATION

Description: These fellowships are designed to contribute to the support of the doctoral candidate to enable him or her to complete the PhD dissertation in a timely manner. Applicants may be citizens of any country studying at colleges and universities in the US Particular questions that interest the foundation concern violence, aggression, and dominance in relation to social change, the socialization of children, intergroup conflict, interstate warfare, crime, family relationships, and investigations of the control of aggression and violence. The fellowship is strictly limited to PhD dissertation writing.

Levels of Study: Doctorate

Field of Study: Humanities, Natural Sciences, Social Science

Nationality: Any Region

AWARD INFORMATION

Award Type: Fellowship

Average Amount: $20,000

Number of Awards: A minimum of 10

Award Coverage: Contributes toward the cost of dissertation research/writing

Award Duration: 1 year

ELIGIBILITY REQUIREMENTS

- Award is for writing the PhD dissertation
- Both applicant and advisor are asked to assure us that the thesis will be completed within the grant year
- Work must be related to violence, aggression, and/or domination

APPLICATION INFORMATION

Award Deadline: Feb 1

Instructions: Download application materials or contact us to request application

CONTACT

The Harry Frank Guggenheim Foundation
25 W. 53rd Street
New York, NY 10019
Tel: +1 (646) 428-0971
Fax: +1 (646) 428-0981
Email: info@hfg.org
Web: www.hfg.org

Harry Frank Guggenheim Foundation

Guggenheim Foundation Postdoctoral Research Grants

PROGRAM INFORMATION

Description: The Harry Frank Guggenheim Foundation welcomes proposals from individuals for individual projects in any of the natural and social sciences and the humanities that promise to increase understanding of the causes, manifestations, and control of violence, aggression, and dominance. The Foundation does not provide any kind of scholarship for individuals pursuing higher education.

Levels of Study: Post Doctorate

Field of Study: All

Nationality: Any Region

AWARD INFORMATION

Award Type: Grant

Average Amount: Up to $40,000

Number of Awards: Varies

Award Coverage: Salary, employee benefits, research assistantships, supplies and equipment, field work, essential secretarial and technical help, other items necessary for the successful completion of a project

Award Duration: Academic year, renewable for second year

APPLICATION INFORMATION

Award Deadline: Aug 1

Instructions: Download application materials or contact us to request application

CONTACT

Harry Frank Guggenheim Foundation
25 W. 53rd Street
New York, NY 10019
Tel: +1 (646) 428-0971
Fax: +1 (646) 428-0981
Email: info@hfg.org
Web: www.hfg.org/rg/guidelines.htm

Howard Hughes Medical Institute HHMI

HHMI Research Training Fellowships for Medical Students

PROGRAM INFORMATION

Description: The Medical Fellows Program supports a year of full-time biomedical research training for medical and dental students.

Levels of Study: Graduate

Field of Study: Medicine

Nationality: Any Region

AWARD INFORMATION

Award Type: Fellowship

Average Amount: $29,000 annual stipend; $5,500 annual fellow's allowance; $5,500 annual research allowance

Award Coverage: Stipend, research allowance to meet research-related expenses and allowance to be used for health care and tuition

Award Duration: Academic year

ELIGIBILITY REQUIREMENTS

- Must be enrolled in a US medical or dental school

APPLICATION INFORMATION

Award Deadline: Jan

Instructions: Visit website or contact for more information

CONTACT

Howard Hughes Medical Institute
Office of Grants and Special Programs
4000 Jones Bridge Road
Chevy Chase, MD 20815-6789
Tel: +1 (800) 448-4882
Fax: +1 (301) 215-8888
Email: fellows@hhmi.org
Web: www.hhmi.org/grants/individuals/medfellows.html

Hubert H. Humphrey Fellowship Program/US Department of State ECA

Hubert H. Humphrey Fellowship Program

PROGRAM INFORMATION

Description: The Hubert H. Humphrey Fellowship Program is a non-degree program that brings accomplished professionals from designated countries of Africa, Asia, Latin America, the Caribbean, the Middle East, Europe, and Eurasia to the US for a year of professional development and study. The program provides a basis for establishing long-lasting productive partnerships and relationships between citizens of the US and their professional counterparts in other countries, fostering an exchange of knowledge and mutual understanding throughout the world.

Levels of Study: Professional

Field of Study: All

Nationality: Africa, Latin America, Middle East, Eastern Europe, South/Central Asia, Southeast Asia, China, Fiji, Hong Kong, Kiribati, Korea, Republic of, Mongolia, Nauru, Papua New Guinea, Solomon Islands, Tonga, Tuvalu, Vanuatu

AWARD INFORMATION

Award Type: Fellowship

Average Amount: Varies

Number of Awards: 170-200

Award Coverage: International travel to/from US, accident and sickness benefits, monthly maintenance, program costs; funding for books, computer purchase, professional activities, special program seminars also available

Award Duration: Academic year

ELIGIBILITY REQUIREMENTS

- Must have an undergraduate degree
- Must have 5 years of substantial professional experience
- Demonstrated leadership qualities and record of public service
- Must demonstrate sufficient English language skills

APPLICATION INFORMATION

Award Deadline: Varies

Instructions: Contact the US Embassy or Fulbright Commission in your country regarding the application process and deadline

CONTACT

Institute of International Education (IIE)
Humphrey Fellowship Program
1400 K Street, NW
Suite 700
Washington, DC 20005
Tel: +1 (202) 686-8664
Email: hhh@iie.org
Web: www.humphreyfellowship.org

Hungarian American Coalition

Dr. Elemér and Éva Kiss Scholarship Fund

PROGRAM INFORMATION

Description: The Hungarian American Coalition established a scholarship fund in 1997 for the purpose of providing a partial annual scholarship to 2-4 Hungarian students to pursue studies at US colleges and universities.

Levels of Study: Undergraduate, Graduate

Field of Study: All

Nationality: Hungary, Romania, Serbia, Slovakia, Ukraine

AWARD INFORMATION

Award Type: Scholarship

Average Amount: $1,000

Number of Awards: 2-4

Award Coverage: Varies

Award Duration: Academic year

ELIGIBILITY REQUIREMENTS

- Must be a citizen of Hungary or member of an ethnic Hungarian community in Slovakia, Romania, Voivodina, Serbia or Ukraine
- Must have gained admission as a full-time student to a US college or university
- Must have an outstanding academic record.
- Must submit 2 letters of recommendation regarding the applicant's personal and academic achievements

APPLICATION INFORMATION

Award Deadline: Rolling

Instructions: Please see website for application information

CONTACT

Hungarian American Coalition
Dr. Elemér and Éva Kiss Scholarship Fund
1120 Connecticut Avenue, NW
Suite 280
Washington, DC 20036
Tel: +1 (202) 296-9505
Fax: +1 (202) 775-5175
Email: scholarship@hacusa.org
Web: www.hacusa.org

Hungarian-American Enterprise Scholarship Fund HAESF

HAESF Entrepreneurship Development Program

PROGRAM INFORMATION

Description: The Entrepreneurship Development Program, endowed by US Treasury funds, grants fully funded 4-6-month traineeships at prominent American companies to the most accomplished young talent from Hungary. The goal of the program is to provide promising future entrepreneurs of Hungary an opportunity to have a meaningful international training experience, thereby enhancing their contribution to their home country and its development upon their return. Selected participants will be placed in traineeships that further their professional and personal development, provide them with leadership and entrepreneurial acumen, improve their English language acquisition, and help them grow their businesses as they return to their home country.

Levels of Study: Graduate

Field of Study: Biotechnology, Business and Management, Communication Technologies, Computer and Information Sciences, Engineering, Engineering 3-2, Engineering-Related Technologies, Finance, Information Technology, Leadership, Management, Physical Sciences, Science Technologies

Nationality: Hungary

AWARD INFORMATION

Award Type: Award, Internship

Average Amount: Varies

Number of Awards: 2-4 per semester

Award Coverage: Round trip airfare from Hungary to the US, visa fees, insurance, living expenses, local travel and a stipend for each participant

Award Duration: 4-6 months

ELIGIBILITY REQUIREMENTS

- Applicants must be Hungarian citizens with permanent residency in Hungary
- Must have earned full-time Hungarian-accredited MSc/MA degree plus 1 year professional experience post-graduation
- Some form of English language certification (ideally at least B2 level in the CEFR classification system)
- Former HAESF participants who returned more than 5 years ago may apply

APPLICATION INFORMATION

Award Deadline: Feb 15/Sept 15 each year

Instructions: Application process is detailed on our website, required documents must be uploaded online

CONTACT

CIEE EXCHANGES INC. Hungarian Office
HAESF Scholarship Fund
Budapest
Andrássy út 61. I. 5.
1062 Budapest
Hungary
Tel: +36 (1) 413-0018
Email: info@haesf.org
Web: www.haesf.org/entrepreneur/index.html

Hungarian-American Enterprise Scholarship Fund HAESF

HAESF Senior Leaders and Scholars Fellowship Program

PROGRAM INFORMATION

Description: The HAESF Senior Leaders and Scholars Fellowship Program provides significant funding to distinguished mid-level and senior-level Hungarian professionals in business, public administration, nonprofit organizations and academia, enabling them to pursue individual, independently organized projects in the US. The program promotes knowledge and experiential sharing between Hungarian and American leaders, further strengthening ties between the nations and providing invaluable career and personal development opportunities.

Levels of Study: Post Doctorate, Professional

Field of Study: All

Nationality: Hungary

AWARD INFORMATION

Award Type: Fellowship

Average Amount: Up to $60,000

Number of Awards: 1-2 per semester

Award Coverage: Cost of living, professional expenses, health insurance, local travel, roundtrip airfare

Award Duration: 3-12 months

ELIGIBILITY REQUIREMENTS

- Must have a minimum of 5 years professional experience
- Senior Fellows are responsible for independently establishing contacts, securing host organization, and developing and submitting project proposals
- Must demonstrate proficiency in English

APPLICATION INFORMATION

Award Deadline: Oct 15

Instructions: Download application materials from our website

CONTACT

HAESF Budapest
CIEE Exchange, Inc
Andrassy ut 61. I. 5.
1062 Budapest
Hungary
Tel: +36 (1) 413-0018
Email: info@haesf.org
Web: www.haesf.org

Hungarian-American Enterprise Scholarship Fund HAESF

HAESF Professional Internship Program

PROGRAM INFORMATION

Description: The HAESF Professional Internship Program, endowed by US Treasury funds, grants fully funded 6-12 month internships at prominent American companies to the most accomplished young talent from Hungary. The goal of the program is to provide promising future leaders of Hungarian society an opportunity to have a meaningful international training experience, thereby enhancing their contribution to their home country and its development upon their return. Selected fellows will be placed in career-related internships that further their professional and personal development, provide them with leadership and cross-cultural communication skills, improve their English language acquisition, and help them advance as they attend graduate school and enter the work force at home.

Levels of Study: Graduate, Doctorate

Field of Study: Accounting, Agriculture and Related Sciences, Biomedical Humanities, Biotechnology, Business and Management, Chemistry, Communication Technologies, Earth Science, Ecology, Engineering, Engineering-Related Technologies, Finance, Horticulture, International Development, Metallurgy, Natural Disaster Research, Natural Sciences, Neuroscience, Optics, Physical Sciences, Physics, Science Technologies, Transportation and Material Moving, US Foreign Policy, Veterinary Medical Technology, Waste Minimization and Management

Nationality: Hungary

AWARD INFORMATION

Award Type: Fellowship, Internship

Average Amount: Up to $30,000

Number of Awards: Up to 10 per semester

Award Coverage: Cost of living, health insurance, local travel, roundtrip airfare for the duration of program

Award Duration: 6-12 months

ELIGIBILITY REQUIREMENTS

- Must be Hungarian citizens with permanent residency in Hungary
- Must have completed a minimum of 4 years of university education at a Hungarian accredited university.
- Must demonstrate proficiency in English at an advanced level
- Must illustrate clear professional goals, good academic record, and quality recommendations

APPLICATION INFORMATION

Award Deadline: Oct 15

Instructions: For more information on how to apply, please visit the website

CONTACT

HAESF Budapest
CIEE Exchanges, Inc
Andrassy ut 61. I. 5.
Hungary
1062 Budapest
Hungary
Tel: +36 (1) 413-0018
Email: info@haesf.org
Web: www.haesf.org

Hungarian-American Fulbright Commission

Fulbright Program

PROGRAM INFORMATION

Description: The Fulbright Program was established in 1946 under legislation introduced by late Senator J. William Fulbright of Arkansas. The Program offers grants to study, teach, conduct research for US citizens to go abroad and non-US citizens to come to the US. Around 155 countries participate in the program, including Hungary. The Program is open to all the fields of arts and sciences.

Levels of Study: Graduate, Doctorate, Post Doctorate

Nationality: Hungary

AWARD INFORMATION

Award Type: Award, Fellowship, Grant, Scholarship

Average Amount: $25,000 per academic year

Number of Awards: 25-30 awards per academic year

Award Coverage: Tuition up to $15,000, monthly allowance, 50 percent of travel expenses

Award Duration: Maximum of 9 months

ELIGIBILITY REQUIREMENTS

- Must have Hungarian citizenship
- Must have good command of English to pursue proposed activities in the US
- BA/BSc or MA/MSc degree for study grants; PhD degree for lecturing and research grant

APPLICATION INFORMATION

Award Deadline: May

CONTACT

Fulbright Commission US-Hungarian Educational Exchange Programme Committee
Tel: (+ 36-1) 462-8040
Fax: (+ 36-1) 252-0266
Email: info@fulbright.hu
Web: www.fulbright.hu/for-hungarians/

Institute for Humane Studies

Humane Studies Fellowships

PROGRAM INFORMATION

Description: Humane Studies Fellowships are awarded to graduate students and outstanding undergraduates embarking on liberty-advancing careers in ideas. The fellowships support study in a variety of fields, including economics, philosophy, law, political science, history, and sociology. The program is open to full-time and prospective graduate students, including law and MBA students. There are a limited number of fellowships open to undergraduate juniors and seniors with a demonstrated interest in pursuing a scholarly career.

Levels of Study: Undergraduate, Graduate

Nationality: Any Region

ELIGIBILITY REQUIREMENTS

- Applications must be submitted through our online application system

APPLICATION INFORMATION

Award Deadline: Dec

Instructions: Please visit our website for application and eligibility information

CONTACT

Institute for Humane Studies
ATTN: Humane Studies Fellowships
3301 N Fairfax Dr, Ste 440
Arlington, VA 22201
Tel: +1 (703) 993-4880
Fax: +1 (703) 993-4890
Web: www.theihs.org/programs/humane-studies-fellowships

Institute of Electrical and Electronics Engineers

Charles LeGeyt Fortescue Fellowship

PROGRAM INFORMATION

Description: The Institute of Electrical and Electronics Engineer Fellowships are given to individuals who have made outstanding contributions to the electrical and electronics engineering profession.

Levels of Study: Graduate

Field of Study: Engineering, Engineering-Related Technologies

Nationality: Any Region

AWARD INFORMATION

Award Type: Fellowship

Average Amount: $24,000

Award Coverage: Tuition, stipend

Award Duration: 1 year

ELIGIBILITY REQUIREMENTS

- At the time the nomination is submitted, a nominee must be an IEEE Senior Member in good standing and he/she must have completed 5 years of service in any grade of membership

APPLICATION INFORMATION

Award Deadline: Nov 15

Instructions: For more information, please visit our website

CONTACT

445 Hoes Lane
Piscataway, NJ 08854
Tel: +1 (732) 562-3840
Email: fellows@ieee.org
Web: www.ieee.org/about/awards/fortescue.html

Institute of International Education

The DV Gokhale International Grants in Statistics Program

PROGRAM INFORMATION

Description: The DV Gokhale International Grants in Statistics Program provides grants to: 1) Indian undergraduate and graduate students to study statistics in the US; 2) American undergraduate and graduate students to study statistics and related subjects in India; 3) support faculty exchanges in this field between the US and India. Dr. DV Gokhale, Professor Emeritus of Statistics at the University of California at Riverside, established this program in appreciation of his experiences as a Fulbright scholar in the US in the 1960s.

Levels of Study: Undergraduate, Graduate, Doctorate, Professional

Field of Study: Statistics

Nationality: India, US

AWARD INFORMATION

Award Type: Grant

Average Amount: Varies

Number of Awards: Varies

ELIGIBILITY REQUIREMENTS

- Must demonstrate an interest in the study of statistics
- Institutions of interest: University of Pune, University of California at Berkeley, University of California at Riverside, colleges and universities in California. If suitable candidates are not available within the institutions of interest, other candidates may be considered
- Must be a graduate student, undergraduate student, or faculty member at a US or Indian university
- Although students/faculty from India will be given preference, others may also qualify and are encouraged to apply

APPLICATION INFORMATION

Instructions: For more information, or if you are interested in applying for the DV Gokhale International Grants in Statistics Program, please email the listed contact

CONTACT

Institute of International Education
809 United Nations Plaza
New York, NY 10017
Tel: +1 (212) 984-5446
Email: nkim@iie.org
Web: www.amstat.org/education/DVGokhaleInternationalGrants.cfm

Institute of International Education

ExxonMobil Middle East and North Africa Scholars Program

PROGRAM INFORMATION

Description: Through this unique scholarship opportunity, ExxonMobil aims to contribute to the Middle East and North Africa region by helping to develop highly skilled and culturally adept individuals. Scholarship recipients will be placed by the Institute of International Education in a leading university in the US, according to the strengths and research interests of the applicant. Recipients receive full tuition, housing and living expense stipends, medical insurance, and textbook and computer allowances. The award also includes transportation to the US, visa and academic support, an intensive orientation program, and a yearly professional development and networking conference. Summer internships with ExxonMobil are also possible.

Levels of Study: Graduate

Field of Study: Earth Science, Science

Nationality: Algeria, Bahrain, Egypt, Iraq, Jordan, Kuwait, Lebanon, Libya, Morocco, Oman, Qatar, Saudi Arabia, Tunisia, United Arab Emirates

AWARD INFORMATION

Award Type: Scholarship

Award Coverage: Full tuition, housing, living stipend, health insurance, travel. In addition, IIE will secure placement in a university for recipients

Award Duration: Duration of master's program

ELIGIBILITY REQUIREMENTS

- Must be a citizen of Algeria, Bahrain, Egypt, Iraq, Jordan, Kuwait, Lebanon, Libya, Morocco, Oman, Qatar, Saudi Arabia, Tunisia, or the United Arab Emirates (UAE)
- Must submit TOEFL or IELTS exam results. Practice ITP TOEFL is accepted

APPLICATION INFORMATION

Award Deadline: Oct

Instructions: Contact exxonmobilscholars@iie.org if you have questions, the online application is available from our website

CONTACT

MENA Scholars Program
1800 West Loop South
Suite 250
Houston, TX 77027
Tel: +1 (832) 369.3472
Fax: +1 (713) 621.0876
Email: exxonmobilscholars@iie.org
Web: www.iie.org/exxonmobilscholars

Institute of International Education
ExxonMobil Russian Scholars Program

PROGRAM INFORMATION

Description: The program identifies future leaders in the Geosciences who can develop and cultivate global competency, innovative capacities and critical thinking skills to address the needs of Russia and their home communities.

Levels of Study: Graduate

Field of Study: Earth Science, Science, Science Technologies

Nationality: Russia

AWARD INFORMATION

Award Type: Scholarship

Award Coverage: Full tuition, housing, living stipend, health insurance and travel. In addition, IIE will secure placement in a university for recipients

Award Duration: Duration of Master's program

ELIGIBILITY REQUIREMENTS

- Hold at least a bachelor's degree in the Geosciences
- Hold a valid Russian passport (Applicants do not currently need to reside in Russia but must demonstrate citizenship)
- Exhibit exceptional leadership skills and cultural competency
- Demonstrate a history of academic excellence and native fluency in Russian

APPLICATION INFORMATION

Award Deadline: Oct

Instructions: All applications must be submitted online, visit the website: www.iie.org/exxonmobilscholars_russia for detailed information on how to submit a strong application

CONTACT

1800 West Loop South
Houston, TX 77027
Tel: +1 832-369-3470
Email: exxonmobilscholars_russia@iie.org
Web: www.iie.org/Programs/ExxonMobil-Russian-Scholars-Program

Institute of International Education
Global Engineering Education Exchange Program (Global E3)

PROGRAM INFORMATION

Description: Global E3 is a consortium based study abroad exchange program for engineering students from Global E3 member institutions. Engineering students from member institutions can apply to study at any overseas partner university for a semester or an academic year with an option for an internship. The program operates on a tuition-swap basis and is designed to allow students to take courses for credit at their home institution.

Levels of Study: Undergraduate

Field of Study: Computer Science, Engineering, Engineering 3-2, Engineering-Related Technologies

Nationality: Australia, Austria, China, Denmark, Egypt, France, Germany, Hong Kong, India, Indonesia, Israel, Italy, Japan, Korea, Republic of, Malaysia, Mexico, Netherlands, Singapore, Spain, United Kingdom, US

AWARD INFORMATION

Award Type: Study Abroad

Average Amount: Varies

Number of Awards: Varies

Award Duration: Semester or academic year

ELIGIBILITY REQUIREMENTS

- Only students at participating universities may apply for this award
- International students must demonstrate proficiency in English

APPLICATION INFORMATION

Award Deadline: Oct 1 for spring semester, Mar 1 for fall semester/academic year

Instructions: For more information on how to apply, please visit the website: globale3.studioabroad.com

CONTACT

Institute of International Education
809 United Nations Plaza
New York, NY 10017
Tel: +1 (212) 984-5442
Email: ge3@iie.org
Web: www.globale3.org

Institute of International Education Conselho Nacional de Desenvolvimento Científico e Tecnológico (CNPq) and Coordenação de Aperfeiçoamento de Pessoal de Nível Superior (CAPES)
Brazil Scientific Mobility Program

PROGRAM INFORMATION

Description: The Brazilian government's Brazil Scientific Mobility Program will provide scholarships to undergraduate students from Brazil for 1 year of study at colleges and universities in the US. Scholarships will be given primarily to students in the Science, Technology, Engineering and Mathematics fields. Students in the program will return to Brazil to complete their degrees. This program, administered by the Institute of International Education (IIE), is part of the Brazilian government's larger initiative to grant 100,000 scholarships for the best students from Brazil to study abroad at the world's best universities.

Levels of Study: Undergraduate

Field of Study: Engineering, Mathematics, Science, Science Technologies

Nationality: Brazil

AWARD INFORMATION

Award Type: Scholarship

Average Amount: Varies

Number of Awards: Varies

Award Coverage: Full tuition, room and board, transportation, insurance, monthly stipend

Award Duration: 1 year; or up to 18 months for students who qualify for intensive English prior to the start of their academic program

ELIGIBILITY REQUIREMENTS

- Candidates must be citizens of Brazil; candidates must be currently attending college or university in Brazil
- Candidates should have completed 20% but no more than 90% of their required degree in Brazil; candidates must have superior academic abilities and well-rounded personalities
- Candidates must be proficient in English; candidates must submit TOEFL score report; candidates must present official and translated transcripts from an institution recognized by the Ministry of Higher Education
- Candidates must agree to remain in Brazil for double the number of months that they studied in the US when they complete the Program; Candidates that were admitted in HEI through ProUni or Sisu (Unified Selection System) with grades at ENEM higher than 600 have to present the proper documentation to prove participation in the program
- Candidates awarded honors/prizes at Jovem Cientista, CNPq Iniciação Cientifica – PIBIC or CAPES PIBID have to present the proper documentation to prove participation in the program

APPLICATION INFORMATION

Award Deadline: Sept (Spring), Dec (Fall)

Instructions: Candidates must first be nominated by their Brazilian university and approved by CAPES and CNPq to participate in the Brazil Scientific Mobility Program. Candidates should not apply to US institutions independently and can select only 1 country for their program destination. Candidates who apply to schools on their own or to more than 1 country will be disqualified. Visit the website for more information

CONTACT

Institute of International Education
Brazil Scientific Mobility Program
809 United Nations Plaza
New York City, NY 10017
Tel: +1 (646) 308.8870
Email: BSWB_Spring@iie.org, BSWB_Fall@iie.org
Web: www.iie.org/Programs/Brazil-Scientific-Mobility

Institution of Materials, Minerals and Mining
Mining Club Award

PROGRAM INFORMATION

Description: The Mining Club Award will be offered to British subjects who are actively engaged in postgraduate study or employment in the minerals industry. The award may be used for travel purposes such as studying minerals industry operations overseas, presenting a paper at an international minerals industry conference, or to assist the applicant in pursuing a full-time course of study related to the minerals industry outside of the UK.

Levels of Study: Graduate, Doctorate, Professional

Field of Study: Minerals Industry

Nationality: United Kingdom

AWARD INFORMATION

Award Type: Grant

Average Amount: £1,500

Number of Awards: Varies

Award Coverage: Travel

ELIGIBILITY REQUIREMENTS

- Must be between the ages of 21 and 35
- Must be a British citizen

APPLICATION INFORMATION

Award Deadline: Apr
Instructions: Download application materials

CONTACT

The Institute of Materials Minerals and Mining
1 Carlton House Terrace
SW1Y 5DB London
United Kingdom
Tel: +44 (0) 20 7451-7300
Email: graham.woodrow@iom3.org
Web: www.iom3.org/content/scholarships-bursaries

Institution of Materials, Minerals and Mining

Tom Seaman Traveling Scholarship

PROGRAM INFORMATION

Description: The Tom Seaman Traveling Scholarship is awarded annually to a member who is training, or has been trained, for a career in mining and/or related technologies. The scholarship shall be to assist the study for an aspect of engineering in the minerals industry.
Levels of Study: Graduate, Doctorate, Professional
Field of Study: Metal Mining, Metallurgy
Nationality: Any Region

AWARD INFORMATION

Award Type: Scholarship
Average Amount: £5,500
Number of Awards: Varies
Award Duration: Academic year

ELIGIBILITY REQUIREMENTS

- Must not be more than 35 years of age at the time of application

APPLICATION INFORMATION

Award Deadline: Mar
Instructions: Download application materials at the website

CONTACT

The Institute of Materials Minerals and Mining
1 Carlton House Terrace
SW1Y 5DB London
United Kingdom
Tel: +44 (0) 20 7451 7300
Email: graham.woodrow@iom3.org
Web: www.iom3.org/content/scholarships-bursaries

Institution of Materials, Minerals and Mining

Bosworth Smith Trust Fund Award

PROGRAM INFORMATION

Description: Grants are awarded for the assistance of postgraduate research in metal mining, nonferrous extraction metallurgy, or mineral dressing. Applications will be considered for grants toward research expenses.
Levels of Study: Graduate, Doctorate
Field of Study: Engineering, Engineering-Related Technologies, Minerals Industry
Nationality: Any Region

AWARD INFORMATION

Award Type: Grant
Average Amount: £5,000
Number of Awards: Varies
Award Coverage: Research expenses, travel, equipment

ELIGIBILITY REQUIREMENTS

- Must have completed postdoctorate

APPLICATION INFORMATION

Award Deadline: Apr
Instructions: Download application materials at the website

CONTACT

The Institute of Materials Minerals & Mining
1 Carlton House Terrace
SW1Y 5DB London
United Kingdom
Tel: +44 (0) 20 7451 7300
Email: graham.woodrow@iom3.org
Web: www.iom3.org/content/awards

Inter American Press Association

Inter American Press Association Scholarship Fund

PROGRAM INFORMATION

Description: Scholarships to assist Latin American newspaper reporters in undertaking graduate study in journalism.
Levels of Study: Graduate
Field of Study: Journalism
Nationality: Latin America

AWARD INFORMATION

Award Type: Scholarship
Average Amount: $20,000
Number of Awards: 2
Award Coverage: Varies
Award Duration: 1 year

ELIGIBILITY REQUIREMENTS

- Must be journalists or journalism school seniors or graduates with a good command of the language they are to use. Students must have completed their degree before beginning the scholarship year
- Must demonstrate proficiency in English and French
- Must be between the ages of 21 and 35

APPLICATION INFORMATION

Award Deadline: Jan
Instructions: Visit our website or contact for further information

CONTACT

Inter American Press Association
Jules Dubois Building
1801 SW 3rd Avenue
Miami, FL 33129
Tel: +1 (305) 634-2465
Fax: +1 (305) 635-2272
Email: info@sipiapa.org
Web: www.sipiapa.org/en/scholarships/descripcion-becas/

International Federation of University Women

IFUW Fellowships and Grants

PROGRAM INFORMATION

Description: The International Federation of University Women offers a limited number of fellowships and grants to women graduates for advanced research, study, and training. The competitions are normally held every 2 years. The awards are intended to help finance short graduate and postgraduate study, research, and training projects and to serve as complementary funds for longer programs. Women who are interested should contact the national affiliate in their respective country to ask about available funding. Contact information is available on the website
Levels of Study: Doctorate, Post Doctorate
Field of Study: All
Nationality: Any Region

AWARD INFORMATION

Award Type: Fellowship, Grant
Average Amount: Varies
Number of Awards: 15-25
Award Coverage: Varies
Award Duration: 8-12 months

ELIGIBILITY REQUIREMENTS

- Must be a member of the IFUW or 1 of the 67 national affiliates
- Must be well started on the research program to which the application refers
- Must have obtained admission to the proposed place of study prior to applying to IFUW's competition. An official letter of acceptance must accompany the application

APPLICATION INFORMATION

Award Deadline: Varies
Instructions: Members of IFUW's 67 national federations and associations must obtain the application package from and apply through their respective national headquarters; for more information, please visit the website

CONTACT

International Federation of University Women Headquarters
10 rue du Lac
CH-1207 Geneva
Switzerland
Tel: +41 (22) 731-23-80
Fax: +41 (22) 738-04-40
Email: info@ifuw.org
Web: www.ifuw.org/what-we-do/grants-fellowships/

International Monetary Fund and Government of Japan

Japan-IMF Scholarship Program

PROGRAM INFORMATION

Description: Provides scholarships for Japanese citizens to study economics at the doctoral level at a leading university outside of Japan.
Levels of Study: Doctorate
Field of Study: Economics
Nationality: Japan

AWARD INFORMATION

Award Type: Scholarship

Average Amount: Varies

Number of Awards: 7

Award Coverage: Full tuition and fees, living allowance, round-trip airfare, medical insurance and related fees, book allowance, 10-13 week paid summer internship at the IMF after the third or 4th year of graduate study, a 2-day (expenses-paid) orientation program at the IMF in Washington DC where they will meet other scholars selected for the program and engage with IMF staff members and program alumni, and receive special consideration for the IMF's Economist Program (EP)

Award Duration: 2 years

ELIGIBILITY REQUIREMENTS

- Must be a Japanese citizen
- Must be able to obtain PhD by age 34
- Studying at, or applying to, a PhD program in macroeconomics in the US or at a university outside of Japan
- Entering the 1st, 2nd or 3rd year of the PhD program

APPLICATION INFORMATION

Award Deadline: Jan 15

Instructions: Apply online

CONTACT

Institute of International Education (IIE)
Global Scholarship Programs
809 UN Plaza
New York, NY 10017
Email: japanimfscholarship@iie.org
Web: www.iie.org/jisp

Intro America Inc.

Phoenix IntroAmerica Jiangsu Star Students Search

PROGRAM INFORMATION

Description: Offering $4.5 million in partial to full tuition scholarships from 16 US colleges located in different regions of the country, participation is through local high schools, where essays are written, followed by screening of essays and final interviews to find qualified applicants for scholarships.

Levels of Study: Undergraduate

Nationality: China

AWARD INFORMATION

Award Type: Tuition Reduction

Average Amount: Varies

Number of Awards: 97

Award Coverage: Tuition.

Award Duration: Maximum of 4 years

ELIGIBILITY REQUIREMENTS

- Must be a student eligible for undergraduate college during fall 2015
- Must be from Jiangsu province
- Must be able to successfully meet college requirements after they are selected
- Must enroll in college to receive scholarship

APPLICATION INFORMATION

Award Deadline: Sep

CONTACT

Intro America Inc
Founder and CEO
229 E. 85th Street
PO Box 269
New York, NY 10128, US
Tel: +1 (917) 539-5343
Email: betty@introamerica.com
Web: www.introamerica.cn

InTuition Scholarships

InTuition Academic Scholarship Award

PROGRAM INFORMATION

Description: Academic scholarships are awarded based on each student's academic potential and willingness to get involved in the campus community by sharing ideas and experiences with other students on campus from different parts of the world.

Field of Study: All

Nationality: Ireland, United Kingdom

AWARD INFORMATION

Award Type: Award, Scholarship, Study Abroad, Tuition Reduction

Average Amount: Varies

Number of Awards: 20

Award Coverage: Tuition fees, board, lodging

Award Duration: Duration of the degree

ELIGIBILITY REQUIREMENTS

- Must be between 17 and 26 years old
- Must hold A levels, IB, leaving certificate, highers or BTEC equivalents, or be currently attending university (classes can be transferred)

APPLICATION INFORMATION

Award Deadline: Jul and Jan

Instructions: Email for eligibility before applying

CONTACT

InTuition Scholarships
Admissions
4 Ravey Street
EC2A 4QP London
United Kingdom
Tel: +44 (0) 8456-034054
Fax: +44 (0) 8453-704054
Email: info@student-scholarships.com
Web: www.student-scholarships.com/academic-award-scheme.html

InTuition scholarships

InTuition Sports Scholarship Award

PROGRAM INFORMATION

Description: The sports program covers golf, tennis, basketball, and football (soccer). The award is based on participation in our annual 9 day Sports Showcase program in Florida, where the student can show his or her skills. Note that you don't have to be an excellent student or a top-class sports player to apply for our sports scholarships, but it helps if the student is playing at a high level. Students will have the chance to experience life on an American University campus whilst having exposure to US college coaches to ensure they get the scholarship offers needed to continue their studies stateside.

Field of Study: All

Nationality: Ireland, Poland, United Kingdom

AWARD INFORMATION

Award Type: Award, Scholarship, Study Abroad, Tuition Reduction

Average Amount: Varies

Number of Awards: 100

Award Coverage: Tuition, board, lodging

Award Duration: Maximum of 4 years

ELIGIBILITY REQUIREMENTS

- Must practice 1 of the following sports (men and women, only amateur athletes): soccer, tennis, golf, basketball
- Must be in of the following categories: current high school students, high school graduates, currently attending university (classes can be transferred), university graduates (classes can be transferred)

APPLICATION INFORMATION

Award Deadline: May

Instructions: Email for eligibility before applying

CONTACT

InTuition Scholarships
Admissions
4 Ravey Street
EC2A 4QP London
United Kingdom
Tel: +44 (0) 8456-034054
Fax: +44 (0) 8453-704054
Email: info@student-scholarships.com
Web: www.student-scholarships.com

IREX

The Edmund S. Muskie Graduate Fellowship Program

PROGRAM INFORMATION

Description: Established by the US Congress in 1992 to encourage economic and democratic growth in Eurasia, the Edmund S. Muskie Graduate Fellowship Program is a program of the Bureau of Educational and Cultural Affairs of the US Department of State, and administered by IREX. The program provides opportunities for graduate students and professionals from Armenia, Azerbaijan, Belarus, Georgia, Kazakhstan, Kyrgyzstan, Moldova, Russia, Tajikistan, Turkmenistan, Ukraine, and Uzbekistan for 1-year non-degree, 1-year degree, or 2-year degree study in the US

Levels of Study: Graduate

Field of Study: All

Nationality: Armenia, Azerbaijan, Belarus, Georgia, Kazakhstan, Kyrgyzstan, Moldova, Russia, Tajikistan, Turkmenistan, Ukraine, Uzbekistan

AWARD INFORMATION

Award Type: Fellowship
Average Amount: Varies
Number of Awards: Approx 140
Award Coverage: IREX sponsors students' visas, provides generous financial support (travel, stipend, tuition, and books), health coverage
Award Duration: Maximum of 2 years

ELIGIBILITY REQUIREMENTS

- Must be citizen and current resident of an eligible Eurasian country
- Must be a recipient of an undergraduate degree (4- or 5-year program) by the time of the application
- Must submit a complete application and 2 copies (for a total of 3) by the application deadline to be considered
- Must be able to begin the academic exchange program in the US in the summer of the year following the application
- Must be able to receive and maintain a US J-1 visa

APPLICATION INFORMATION

Award Deadline: Oct
Instructions: Please see website for application information

CONTACT

IREX
2121 K St. NW, Ste. 700
Washington, D.C. 20037
Tel: +1 (202) 628-8188
Fax: +1 (202) 628-8189
Email: muskie@irex.org
Web: www.irex.org/programs/muskie/index.asp

J. W. Fulbright Commission for the Educational Exchange in the Slovak Republic

Fulbright Program

PROGRAM INFORMATION

Description: The nature and character of the Fulbright Program were shaped in 1946 under legislation introduced by former Senator J. William Fulbright. Its aim is "to increase the mutual understanding between the people of the US and the people of other countries". The Fulbright Program is 1 of the world's largest and most diversified educational exchange programs, and it currently operates in 140 countries, including 51 countries with binational Fulbright Commissions.
Levels of Study: Graduate, Doctorate
Field of Study: All
Nationality: Slovakia

AWARD INFORMATION

Award Type: Grant
Average Amount: $1,300 - $2,200
Number of Awards: 4
Award Coverage: Monthly maintenance, professional allowance, travel expenses, health insurance, partial tuition
Award Duration: max. 12 months

ELIGIBILITY REQUIREMENTS

- 6 to 12 months of independent research (Visiting Student Researcher) or study (Master's Degree Study) at a US university or institution
- Open to all disciplines except clinical medicine, MBA and LLM

APPLICATION INFORMATION

Award Deadline: Fall Semester
Instructions: Information and application can be found at: bit.ly/1p6DVyK

CONTACT

J. W. Fulbright Commission
Program Officer
Levická 3
821 08 Bratislava
Slovak Republic
Tel: +4212-59374-639
Email: dasa@fulbright.gov.sk
Web: www.fulbright.sk

Jordanian-American Commission for Educational Exchange

Fulbright Program

PROGRAM INFORMATION

Levels of Study: Graduate, Doctorate, Post Doctorate
Nationality: Jordan

AWARD INFORMATION

Award Type: Fellowship
Average Amount: Varies
Number of Awards: Varies
Award Coverage: Varies

APPLICATION INFORMATION

Award Deadline: Apr
Instructions: Visit website for description of funding opportunities and application procedures

CONTACT

Jordanian-American Commission for Educational Exchange (JACEE)
19, Mahdi Bin Barakah Street (Shmeisani)
P.O. Box 850215
11185 Amman
Jordan
Tel: 962-6-(0)79-6444119
Fax: 962-6-568-4820
Email: info@fulbright.org.jo
Web: www.fulbright-jordan.org/

Josephine de Kármán Fellowship Trust

Josephine de Kármán Fellowship Trust

PROGRAM INFORMATION

Description: The Josephine De Kármán Fellowship Trust was established in 1954 by the late Dr. Theodore von Kármán, world-renowned aeronautics expert, teacher, and first director of the Guggenheim Aeronautical Laboratory at the California Institute of Technology, in memory of his sister, Josephine, who passed away in 1951. The purpose of this fellowship program is to recognize and assist students whose scholastic achievements reflect Professor von Kármán's high standards.
Levels of Study: Undergraduate, Doctorate
Field of Study: All, Humanities
Nationality: Any Region

AWARD INFORMATION

Award Type: Fellowship
Average Amount: $22,000 for doctoral students; $14,000 for undergraduates
Number of Awards: 8
Award Duration: Academic year

ELIGIBILITY REQUIREMENTS

- Must be an undergraduate student entering his/her senior year; or must be a doctoral student preparing to defend his/her dissertation by the end of the academic year. Postdoctoral and master's degree students are not eligible for consideration
- Study must be carried out only in the US and all funds must be expended only within this country
- To be competitive, graduate applicants should have outstanding letters of recommendation, significant publications, and have completed several chapters of the dissertation at the time of application. Undergraduate applicants should have exceptional recommendations

APPLICATION INFORMATION

Award Deadline: Jan 31
Instructions: For more information about how to apply visit our website or contact us

CONTACT

Josephine de Kármán Fellowship Trust
Fellowship Secretary
P.O. Box 3389
San Dimas, CA 91773
Tel: +1 (909) 592-0607
Email: info@dekarman.org
Web: www.dekarman.org

Karin Riley Porter Attorney at Law

Karin Riley Porter Attorney at Law Good Works Scholarship

PROGRAM INFORMATION

Description: Karin Riley Porter Attorney at Law believes that it is essential to lead by example and give back to one's community. This is true both for those directly involved in the legal profession, and for those who are employed in other professions that contribute to the growth and success of the Commonwealth. To this end, the firm is dedicated to providing educational opportunities for future lawyers and other college and university students who are also actively engaged in making their community a better place by leading and planning community service projects. We are pleased to announce the annual Karin Riley Porter Attorney at Law Good Works Scholarship. Karin Riley Porter Attorney at Law remains steadfastly dedicated to this calling and to supporting students equally committed to this cause by providing this annual $500 scholarship.
Levels of Study: Undergraduate, Graduate
Nationality: Any Region

AWARD INFORMATION

Award Type: Scholarship
Average Amount: $500
Number of Awards: 1 per year
Award Coverage: Tuition, housing, travel expenses, text books
Award Duration: 1 year

ELIGIBILITY REQUIREMENTS

- The candidate must be in good academic standing with a minimum cumulative GPA of 3.0 or higher
- Applicants must submit a current, unofficial academic transcript from the applicant's school
- Applicants must submit a 500 word letter of intent that identifies the applicant and describes the applicant's drive and dedication to criminal justice issues, or to community service projects. If writing about community service, focus on the importance of leadership in such efforts
- The scholarship program is open to all undergraduate, graduate, and law school students as well as incoming college freshmen

APPLICATION INFORMATION

Award Deadline: Jan 1, 2015

Instructions: To be considered eligible, interested applicants must submit a completed application along with the previously listed requirements via US mail or fax by Jan 1, 2015; the scholarship winner and other applicants will be notified of the results in late Apr or early May

CONTACT

Karin Riley Porter Attorney at Law
Attn: Firm Administrator
10605 Judicial Drive
Suite 200, A-1
Fairfax, Virginia 22030
Tel: (703) 278-2800
Fax: (703) 991-0604
Email: info@virginia-criminallawyer.com
Web: www.virginia-criminallawyer.com

Korean-American Educational Commission

Fulbright Program for Korean Students and Scholars

PROGRAM INFORMATION

Nationality: Korea, Republic of

AWARD INFORMATION

Award Type: Grant, Scholarship

Average Amount: Varies

Number of Awards: Varies

Award Coverage: Varies

Award Duration: Varies

APPLICATION INFORMATION

Instructions: Visit website for funding opportunities and application instructions

CONTACT

Korean-American Educational Commission
Fulbright Building
23 Baekbeom-ro 28-gil, Mapo-gu
121-874 Seoul
Korea
Tel: 02-3275-4000
Fax: 02-3275-4028
Web: www.fulbright.or.kr/xe/index

Kosciuszko Foundation

Kosciuszko Foundation Fellowships and Grants

PROGRAM INFORMATION

Description: The Kosciuszko Foundation annually awards a number of fellowships and grants to Poles for advanced study, research, or teaching at universities and other institutions of higher learning in the US. Fellowships are awarded to doctoral candidates as well as postgraduate scholars, professionals, or artists with masters or doctoral degrees.

Levels of Study: Doctorate, Post Doctorate

Field of Study: All

Nationality: Poland

AWARD INFORMATION

Award Type: Fellowship

Average Amount: $7,650-$25,500

Number of Awards: Varies

Award Coverage: Living stipend, travel, health insurance; funds may not be used to support tuition or fees

Award Duration: 3-10 months

ELIGIBILITY REQUIREMENTS

- Must hold master's degree prior to the commencement date of the award
- Must be affiliated with an academic institution
- Must demonstrate fluency in English
- Must have invitation from host institution
- Must be a Polish citizens residing permanently in Poland

APPLICATION INFORMATION

Award Deadline: Oct

Instructions: Online application available or contact to request application materials

CONTACT

Kosciuszko Foundation
Warsaw Office
ul. Nowy Swiat 4, Room 118
00-497
Warszawa
Poland
Tel: +48 (22) 621-7067
Fax: +48 (22) 621-7067
Email: info@thekf.org
Web: www.thekf.org/scholarships/

Lee Kuan Yew Scholarship Fund

Lee Kuan Yew Scholarship

PROGRAM INFORMATION

Description: The Lee Kuan Yew Scholarship is funded by the Lee Kuan Yew Scholarship Fund, which was set up in 1991 with generous contributions from the public in honor of Minister Mentor Lee Kuan Yew. The scholarship is open to outstanding Singaporeans who aspire to be leaders in their respective fields and in the community.

Levels of Study: Graduate, Doctorate

Field of Study: Health Professions, Health Studies, Medicine, Nursing, Public Health

Nationality: Singapore

AWARD INFORMATION

Award Type: Grant

Average Amount: Varies

Award Coverage: Lump sum bounty, annual allowance

ELIGIBILITY REQUIREMENTS

- Must have outstanding academic records, only those who have at least a Second Class Upper Honors Degree will be considered
- Must demonstrate leadership qualities and be active in social or community services or sports
- Must complete necessary pre-admission tests such as the GRE, TOEFL or GMAT
- Must independently apply for admission to the university of choice

APPLICATION INFORMATION

Award Deadline: Dec

Instructions: Download application materials

CONTACT

c/o Public Service Commission
Lee Kuan Scholarship Fund
3 St. Andrew's Rd., Level 4
City Hall
178958 Singapore
Singapore
Email: psc@psd.gov.sg
Web: www.pscscholarships.gov.sg/content/pscsch/default/scholarshipapplication/otherscholarships/lky_scholarship.html

Magdalena O. Vde. de Brockman Foundation

MOB Scholarships

PROGRAM INFORMATION

Description: The program was formed to foster the development of Mexican citizens and give them the opportunity to live abroad and understand foreign cultures. The foundation promotes high-level education by annually granting as many scholarships as feasible to young Mexicans.

Levels of Study: Graduate

Field of Study: All

Nationality: Mexico

AWARD INFORMATION

Award Type: Scholarship

Average Amount: $25,000

Number of Awards: 20

Award Coverage: Varies

Award Duration: 2 years

ELIGIBILITY REQUIREMENTS

- Must be a Mexican citizen under 36 years of age
- Must hold an undergraduate degree with 85/100 GPA
- Must have a minimum TOEFL score of 80 IBT or IELTS score of 7.0
- Must intend to return to Mexico upon graduation and remain in country for 5 years

APPLICATION INFORMATION

Award Deadline: Pre-Registration: Oct; application: Dec

Instructions: Does not apply to those studying medicine, anthropology, and fine arts; please visit the website for application information

CONTACT

Magdalena O. Vde. de Brockman Foundation
Av. Moctezuma No. 442
Col. Jardines del Sol
45050 Zapopan Jalisco
Mexico
Tel: +52 (33) 3634-6606 ext. 24
Fax: +52 (33) 3632-2872
Email: becasmob@becasmob.org.mx
Web: www.becasmob.org.mx

Magdalena O. Vde. de Brockman Foundation

Convenio Becas MOB/ Gobierno del Estado de Jalisco

PROGRAM INFORMATION

Description: This scholarship program was formed to foster the development of Mexican citizens and give them the opportunity to live abroad and understand foreign cultures. The foundation works to promote high-level education by annually granting as many scholarships as feasible to young Mexicans.

Levels of Study: Graduate

Field of Study: Public Administration

Nationality: Mexico

AWARD INFORMATION

Award Type: Scholarship

Average Amount: Varies

Number of Awards: Varies

Award Coverage: Tuition, living expenses

Award Duration: 2 years

ELIGIBILITY REQUIREMENTS

- Must be a Mexican citizen under 35 years of age
- Must hold an undergraduate degree with 85/100 GPA
- Must have a minimum TOEFL score of 550 PBT/70 IBT, or an IELTS score of 6.5
- Required to work for the State of Jalisco upon return for at least 3 years

APPLICATION INFORMATION

Award Deadline: Oct

Instructions: Visit website or contact for more information

CONTACT

Becas Magdalena O. VDA. de Brockmann, AC
Av. Moctezuma No. 442
Col. Jardines del Sol
45050 Zapopan Jalisco
Mexico
Tel: +52 (33) 3634-6606 ext. 24
Fax: +52 (33) 3632-2872
Email: becasmob@becasmob.org.mx
Web: www.becasmob.org.mx

Margaret McNamara Memorial Fund

Margaret McNamara Memorial Fund Scholarship

PROGRAM INFORMATION

Description: Margaret McNamara Memorial Fund Scholarships are awarded annually to women from developing countries who are currently enrolled at US/Canadian universities, are completing advanced degrees, demonstrate a commitment to women and children, and plan to return to their countries within 2 years of receiving the grant.

Levels of Study: Graduate, Doctorate

Field of Study: All

Nationality: Africa, South/Central Asia, Albania, Argentina, Armenia, Azerbaijan, Belarus, Belize, Bolivia, Bosnia & Herzegovina, Brazil, Bulgaria, Cambodia, Chile, China, Colombia, Commonwealth of the Northern Marianas Islands (CNMI), Dominica, Dominican Republic, Ecuador, Fed. States of Micronesia, Fiji, Georgia, Grenada, Guatemala, Guyana, Haiti, Honduras, Indonesia, Iran, Iraq, Jamaica, Jordan, Kiribati, Korea, Dem. People's Rep., Laos, Latvia, Lebanon, Lithuania, Macao, Macedonia, Malaysia, Marshall Islands, Mexico, Moldova, Mongolia, Montenegro, Myanmar, Nicaragua, Palau, Palestinian Authority, Panama, Papua New Guinea, Paraguay, Peru, Philippines, Poland, Romania, Russia, Samoa, Serbia, Solomon Islands, St. Kitts-Nevis, St. Lucia, St. Vincent, Suriname, Syria, Thailand, Tonga, Turkey, Ukraine, Uruguay, Vanuatu, Venezuela, Vietnam, Yemen

AWARD INFORMATION

Award Type: Scholarship

Average Amount: Approx $12,000-15,000

Number of Awards: 10-15

Award Coverage: Tuition, fees, educational expenses, living expenses, research

Award Duration: Academic year

ELIGIBILITY REQUIREMENTS

- Must be a woman national of lower/middle income country as designated by MMMF Country List
- Must be currently enrolled and in residence at an accredited university in the US or Canada at the time of submitting the application
- Must be at least 25 years of age by the application deadline and not be related to a World Bank Group staff member or his/her spouse
- Must demonstrate (1) a commitment to women and children, (2) financial need, and (3) use of the scholarship to complete her degree scholarship
- Must plan to return to her country or other developing country within 2 - 3 years after receiving the MMMF scholarship

APPLICATION INFORMATION

Instructions: The application must be submitted online. Please visit the MMMF website to apply

CONTACT

Margaret McNamara Memorial Fund
1818 H Street NW, MSN J2-202
Washington, DC 20433
Tel: +1 (202) 473-5804
Fax: +1 (202) 522-3142
Email: mmmf@mmmf-grants.org
Web: www.mmmf-grants.org

Monetary Authority of Singapore

MAS Undergraduate Scholarship

PROGRAM INFORMATION

Description: The MAS Undergraduate Scholarship is a prestigious award that gives the most outstanding individuals the opportunity to pursue their dreams at the world's best universities, and promises them a career dedicated to solving some of Singapore's most challenging problems – with a dynamic, innovative organization at the forefront of its ever-changing financial landscape.

Levels of Study: Undergraduate

Field of Study: All

Nationality: Singapore

AWARD INFORMATION

Award Type: Scholarship

Average Amount: Varies

Award Coverage: Return economy airfare, approved tuition, maintenance allowance, pre-study allowance, book allowance, sponsorship of exchange program

ELIGIBILITY REQUIREMENTS

- A-Level candidates should offer at least 11 academic units
- Students must have obtained at least 36 points from the IB program to be considered
- Application is open from 1st to 30th Sep for Provisional cycle, and 1st Jan to 10 calendar days after the release of the GCE A Level results for the main cycle

APPLICATION INFORMATION

Award Deadline: Sep 30

Instructions: Visit our website or contact for additional information

CONTACT

Monetary Authority of Singapore
10 Shenton Way
MAS Building
79117 Singapore
Singapore
Tel: +65 6225-5577
Fax: +65 6229-9491
Email: recruit@mas.gov.sg
Web: student.brightsparks.com.sg/profile/mas/scholarship.php?schid=5716

National Academies

National Academies Research Associateship Program

PROGRAM INFORMATION

Description: The National Academies administers Postdoctoral and Senior Research Awards through its Associateship Programs, part of the Policy and Global Affairs Division. Research awards are given for the purpose of conducting research at a specific laboratory chosen by the applicant.

Levels of Study: Doctorate, Post Doctorate

Field of Study: Computer Science, Natural Sciences

Nationality: Any Region

AWARD INFORMATION

Award Type: Associateship
Average Amount: Varies
Number of Awards: Varies
Award Coverage: Varies.

ELIGIBILITY REQUIREMENTS

- See website for more information about requirements

APPLICATION INFORMATION

Award Deadline: Feb, May, Aug, Nov
Instructions: Download or contact to request application materials

CONTACT

Keck Center of the National Academies
Research Associate Programs
500 Fifth Street, NW (Keck 586)
Washington, DC 20001
Tel: +1 (202) 334-2760
Fax: +1 (202) 334-2759
Email: rap@nas.edu
Web: sites.nationalacademies.org/PGA/RAP/index.htm

National Academy of Education

Spencer Postdoctoral Fellowship

PROGRAM INFORMATION

Description: The National Academy of Education/Spencer Postdoctoral Fellowship Program supports early career scholars working in critical areas of education research. This nonresidential postdoctoral fellowship funds proposals that make significant scholarly contributions to the field of education. The program also develops the careers of its recipients through professional development activities involving National Academy of Education members.
Levels of Study: Post Doctorate, Professional
Field of Study: Education
Nationality: Any Region

AWARD INFORMATION

Award Type: Fellowship
Average Amount: $27,500 -$55,000
Number of Awards: Up to 20
Award Duration: 1-2 years

ELIGIBILITY REQUIREMENTS

- Must have received their PhD, EdD, or equivalent research degree between Jan 1, 2009, and Dec 31, 2013
- Should have a demonstrated record of research experience in education
- Proposed project must be an education research project
- NAEd funds studies that examine the efficacy of curriculum and teaching methods, however, we do not fund the initial development of curriculum or instructional programs

APPLICATION INFORMATION

Award Deadline: Nov
Instructions: For detailed application information, please visit our website

CONTACT

National Academy of Education
Postdoctoral Fellowship Program
500 Fifth Street NW, #1049
Washington, DC 20001
Tel: +1 (202) 334-2341
Email: info@naeducation.org
Web: www.naeducation.org

National Research Council of the National Academies

Ford Foundation Fellowship Program

PROGRAM INFORMATION

Description: The National Research Council of the National Academies conducts the Ford Foundation Fellowship Programs for research-based study in the arts and humanities. Fellowships are offered at the predoctoral, dissertation and postdoctoral levels. Eligible applicants must be US citizens, nationals, permanent residents, or individuals granted deferred action status under the DACA program.
Levels of Study: Graduate, Doctorate, Post Doctorate
Field of Study: Aerospace, American History, American Literature, American Studies, Anthropology, Archaeology, Area and Ethnic Studies, Art History, Astronomy, Biochemistry, Biology, Chemistry, Computer and Information Sciences, Earth Science, Engineering, Environmental Studies, History, Humanities, Life Sciences, Linguistics, Literature, Marine Engineering, Mathematics, Molecular Biology, Multi/Interdisciplinary Studies, Natural Sciences, Neuroscience, Oceanography, Optics, Pacific Islands Studies, Peace Studies, Philosophy and Religion, Physical Sciences, Physics, Political Science, Psychology, Sociology, Women's Studies
Nationality: US

AWARD INFORMATION

Award Type: Fellowship
Average Amount: $24,000-$45,000
Number of Awards: 120
Award Coverage: Monthly stipend, 1 Ford Fellows conference, mentoring
Award Duration: 1-3 years

ELIGIBILITY REQUIREMENTS

- Must be US citizens, nationals, permanent residents, or individuals granted deferred action status under the DACA program
- Must have record of scholarly achievement
- Must be planning on a career in teaching and research at the college or university levels
- Must provide evidence of supporting diversity in higher education

APPLICATION INFORMATION

Award Deadline: Nov
Instructions: Go to www.nationalacademies.org/ford for online applications

CONTACT

National Research Council of the National Academies
Ford Foundation Fellowship Program
500 Fifth Street NW
Washington, DC
20001 Washington, DC
Tel: +1 (202) 334-2872
Fax: +1 (202) 334-3419
Email: infofell@nas.edu
Web: www.nationalacademies.org/ford

National Research Council of the National Academies

Graduate, Postdoctoral and Senior Research in US Federal Laboratories

PROGRAM INFORMATION

Description: The National Research Council of the National Academies will offer competitive awards 4 times a year for independent graduate, postdoctoral and senior research in all fields of science and engineering. Research is to be conducted in US federal laboratories and affiliated institutions. Awards include a stipend ranging from $42,000 to $80,000 for recent PhD recipients and higher for additional experience. Graduate entry level stipend is $30,000 and higher for additional experience. Awards also include relocation, professional travel and health insurance.
Levels of Study: Graduate, Doctorate, Post Doctorate, Professional
Field of Study: Aerospace, Astronomy, Biochemistry, Biology, Biotechnology, Chemistry, Computer and Information Sciences, Computer Science, Earth Science, Ecology, Engineering, Environmental Studies, Geography, Life Sciences, Marine Engineering, Mathematics, Metallurgy, Molecular Biology, Multi/Interdisciplinary Studies, Natural Sciences, Neuroscience, Oceanography, Optics, Physical Sciences, Physics
Nationality: Any Region

AWARD INFORMATION

Award Type: Associateship, Fellowship
Average Amount: $42,000-$80,000
Number of Awards: Approx 350
Award Coverage: Stipend, programmatic support, relocation, professional travel, health insurance
Award Duration: 1-3 years

ELIGIBILITY REQUIREMENTS

- Must be at the graduate, postdoctoral or senior level
- Must match research interests with that of a sponsoring laboratory
- Awards offered in all fields of science and engineering

APPLICATION INFORMATION

Award Deadline: Feb 1, May 1, Aug 1, Nov 1

Instructions: Apply online at www.nationalacademies.org/rap. Applicants must contact prospective Adviser(s) at the lab(s) prior to application deadline to discuss research interests and funding opportunities

CONTACT

National Research Council of the National Academies
Research Associateship Programs
500 Fifth Street NW
Washington, DC
20001 Washington DC
Tel: +1 (202) 334-2760
Fax: +1 (202) 334-3419
Email: rap@nas.edu
Web: www.nationalacademies.org/rap

Norway-America Association

Norway-America Association Scholarships

PROGRAM INFORMATION

Description: The Norway-America Association works to strengthen the ties between Norway and North America through higher education and culture. The organization offers scholarships to several universities in the U.S and Canada for Norwegian citizens at all levels of study. We also offer scholarships for American students to come study in Norway. Scholarship programs for US students and scholars to Norway include: The Norwegian Marshall Fund; The Norwegian Thanksgiving Fund; The John Dana Archbold Stipend; and the American Civilization Lecture Fund.

Levels of Study: Graduate, Doctorate, Post Doctorate, Professional

Field of Study: All

Nationality: Norway, US

AWARD INFORMATION

Award Type: Scholarship

Average Amount: Varies

Number of Awards: Varies

Award Coverage: Tuition, housing travel expenses

Award Duration: 1 year

APPLICATION INFORMATION

Award Deadline: Varies

Instructions: Review application process at www.noram.no

CONTACT

Norway-America Association
Director of Scholarship Programs
Radhusgaten 23 B
0158 Oslo
Norway
Tel: +47 (23) 35 71 60
Email: info@noram.no
Web: www.noram.no

Nuffic

VSB Foundation

PROGRAM INFORMATION

Description: Individual scholarships for Dutch students with good study results and social involvement, who want to study or do research at a recognized university abroad.

Levels of Study: Graduate

Field of Study: All

Nationality: Netherlands

AWARD INFORMATION

Award Type: Scholarship

Average Amount: up to €10,000

Number of Awards: Over 200

Award Coverage: All study-related costs: monthly allowance, tuition, housing, insurance, study materials, travel expenses

Award Duration: 3 to 24 months

ELIGIBILITY REQUIREMENTS

- Must be a full-time student who graduates as a bachelor or master of a Dutch college or university

APPLICATION INFORMATION

Award Deadline: Mar

Instructions: Visit website for more information

CONTACT

Department for International Academic Relations
P.O. Box 29777
2502 LT Hague
Netherlands
Tel: (070) 4260245
Email: jginter@nuffic.nl
Web: www.vsbfonds.nl/beurzen

Onassis Foundation

Onassis Foundation Scholarships for Hellenes

PROGRAM INFORMATION

Description: Scholarships are awarded to Greek students of higher education institutions for doctoral and postgraduate studies outside of Greece in any field.

Levels of Study: Doctorate, Post Doctorate

Field of Study: All

Nationality: Greece

AWARD INFORMATION

Award Type: Scholarship

Average Amount: Varies

Number of Awards: 130

Award Coverage: Varies

ELIGIBILITY REQUIREMENTS

- Contact the program for further details and requirements

APPLICATION INFORMATION

Award Deadline: Jan

Instructions: Contact for application instructions

CONTACT

Onassis Foundation
Department of Scholarships for Greeks
4, Aeschinou Str.
10558 Athens
Greece
Tel: +30 (210) 371-3050
Fax: +30 (210) 331-5913
Email: schol@onassis.gr
Web: www.onassis.gr

Open Society Institute

Open Society Fellowship

PROGRAM INFORMATION

Description: The Open Society Fellowship supports individuals seeking innovative and unconventional approaches to fundamental open society challenges. The fellowship funds work that will enrich public understanding of those challenges and stimulate far-reaching and probing conversations within the Open Society Institute and in the world. A fellowship project might identify a problem that has not previously been recognized, develop new policy ideas to address familiar problems, or offer a new advocacy strategy. Fellows should take advantage of the considerable intellectual and logistical resources of the Open Society Institute and expect to contribute meaningfully to OSI's thinking in return.

Levels of Study: Professional

Field of Study: All

Nationality: Any Region

AWARD INFORMATION

Award Type: Fellowship, Grant, Scholarship

Average Amount: $60,000-$100,000

Number of Awards: Varies

Award Duration: Varies

ELIGIBILITY REQUIREMENTS

- Contact or visit our website for more information on eligibility requirements
- The fellowship does not fund enrollment for degree or non-degree study at academic institutions, including dissertation research
- This is a fellowship for individuals only; proposals from 2 or more applicants will not be accepted

APPLICATION INFORMATION

Award Deadline: Feb 1

Instructions: All interested applicants should complete the online application form and submit supporting materials for consideration. Please read the FAQs before applying. Applicants may submit a project proposal or other materials in a language other than English, as long as they also submit an English translation. Certified translations are strongly recommended

CONTACT

Open Society Foundations
224 West 57th Street
New York, NY 10019
Tel: +1 (212) 548-0600
Fax: +1 (212) 548-4679
Email: OSFellows@opensocietyfoundations.org
Web: www.opensocietyfoundations.org/grants/open-society-fellowship

Organization of American States - Rowe Fund program

Rowe Fund Student Loan Program

PROGRAM INFORMATION

Description: The Rowe Fund, a student loan program of the Organization of American States (OAS), helps citizens from Latin American and Caribbean OAS member countries finance a portion of their studies or research at accredited universities in the US by awarding interest-free loans.

Levels of Study: Undergraduate, Graduate, Doctorate

Field of Study: All

Nationality: Any Region

AWARD INFORMATION

Award Type: Scholarship

Average Amount: $15,000

Number of Awards: 100

Award Coverage: A portion of tuition or living expenses

Award Duration: Maximum of 2 years

ELIGIBILITY REQUIREMENTS

- Be a citizen of a Latin American or Caribbean member state of the OAS
- Must submit transcripts showing satisfactory academic records. The candidate must possess an overall GPA of 3.0 or higher from their current or most recent academic institution
- Must be able to successfully complete the studies or research for which the loan is being requested within a maximum of 2 years
- Must be accepted as a full-time student in an accredited institution of higher-learning in the US for at least 1 academic period (lasting at least 4 months)
- Must agree to return to country of origin within the time limit allowed by US laws for optional practical training (OPT), if granted, and within 1 year after completion of studies in the US

APPLICATION INFORMATION

Award Deadline: Rolling

Instructions: Loan applications are submitted by the student to the Rowe Fund Secretariat and are reviewed year-round by the Rowe Fund Committee. Application forms and list of documents can be found at www.oas.org/en/rowefund/ListOfDocument.asp

CONTACT

Organization of American States
Coordinator, Rowe Fund loan program
1889 F St NW (769)
Washington, DC 20006
Tel: +1 (202) 370-9760
Fax: +1 (202) 458-3897
Email: rowefund@oas.org
Web: www.oas.org/en/rowefund

Philanthropic Educational Organization PEO International

PEO International Peace Scholarship

PROGRAM INFORMATION

Description: P.E.O. International Peace Scholarship (IPS) Fund was established in 1949 to provide scholarships for international women students to pursue graduate study in the US and Canada.

Levels of Study: Graduate

Field of Study: All

Nationality: Any Region

AWARD INFORMATION

Award Type: Scholarship

Average Amount: Up to $10,000

Award Coverage: Not intended to cover all academic or personal expenses

Award Duration: 1 year

ELIGIBILITY REQUIREMENTS

- A student holding citizenship or permanent residency in the US or Canada is ineligible. Only women qualify for the award
- Must be qualified for admission to full-time graduate study, working toward a graduate degree in the college or university she will attend
- Must submit a witnessed statement certifying that upon completion of her degree program she will return to her own country within 60 days, depending on her visa status
- Must have round-trip or return travel expenses guaranteed
- Must have a contact person who is a citizen of the US and who currently resides there

APPLICATION INFORMATION

Instructions: Contact or visit our website

CONTACT

P.E.O. International Headquarters
3700 Grand Avenue
Des Moines, IA 50312
Tel: +1 (515) 255-3153
Fax: +1 (515) 255-3820
Email: ips@peodsm.org
Web: www.peointernational.org

Price Benowitz LLP

Price Benowitz Public Interest Law Scholarship

PROGRAM INFORMATION

Description: Price Benowitz LLP believes strongly in advancing the cause of social justice and ensuring that all people, regardless of their socio-economic standing, can realize their full potential and, in turn, give back to their communities. A strong component of any successful social justice program is education, and the firm is equally dedicated to providing valuable educational opportunities to future lawyers and other students who are also passionate about affecting positive social change through volunteer and professional work opportunities. As such, we are pleased to sponsor the annual Price Benowitz Public Interest Law Scholarship, which will seek to achieve the goals of championing social justice through quality education.

Levels of Study: Undergraduate

Field of Study: Human Rights, Law, Minority Rights, Policy Research, Public Health, Public Law, Public Policy, Social Justice

Nationality: Any Region

AWARD INFORMATION

Award Type: Scholarship

Average Amount: $1,000

Number of Awards: 1 per year

Award Coverage: Tuition, housing, travel expenses, book expenses

Award Duration: 1 year

ELIGIBILITY REQUIREMENTS

- The scholarship program is open to college sophomores, juniors, and seniors who are to be enrolled in an accredited post-secondary educational institution within the US
- The candidate for scholarship has a proven interest in furthering a social justice agenda through prior educational, professional, and volunteer work experiences
- The candidate must be in good academic standing with a minimum cumulative GPA of 3.0 or higher
- A current resume and a current, official academic transcript from the applicant's school
- A 500 word letter of intent that identifies the applicant and describes the applicant's drive and dedication to social justice causes

APPLICATION INFORMATION

Award Deadline: Sep 30, 2014

Instructions: To be considered eligible, interested applicants must submit their letter of intent, academic transcripts, and resume via US mail or fax no later than Sep 30, 2014

CONTACT

Price Benowitz LLP
Attn: Firm Administrator
409 7th Street, NW
Suite 200
Washington, DC 20004
Tel: (202) 600-9400
Fax: 202-664-1331
Email: hr@pricebenowitz.com
Web: pricebenowitzlaw.com

Prospect Burma

Prospect Burma Scholarships

PROGRAM INFORMATION

Description: Prospect Burma offers scholarship grants to students of Burmese citizenship for study in universities and colleges anywhere in the world.

Levels of Study: Undergraduate, Graduate

Field of Study: All

Nationality: Myanmar

AWARD INFORMATION

Award Type: Grant, Scholarship, Study Abroad

Average Amount: Varies

Number of Awards: Varies

Award Coverage: Tuition fees, academic expenses, living costs

Award Duration: Academic year

ELIGIBILITY REQUIREMENTS

- Must be of Burmese origin
- Application forms must be fully completed and accompanied by required documentation

APPLICATION INFORMATION

Award Deadline: Mar

Instructions: Forms are available from Prospect Burma, or may be downloaded from the website

CONTACT

Prospect Burma
Executive Director
Porters' Lodge, Rivermead Court
Ranelagh Gardens
SW6 3SF London
United Kingdom
Tel: +44 (0) 2073-710887
Fax: +44 (0) 2073-710547
Email: scholarships@prospectburma.org
Web: www.prospectburma.org

Public Service Commission

OMS Overseas Merit Scholarship (Teaching)

PROGRAM INFORMATION

Description: The Overseas Merit Scholarship (Teaching) - OMS (T) is awarded for undergraduate studies tenable at renowned overseas universities. Highly competitive, these are awarded only to outstanding students with strong leadership abilities. Overseas Merit Scholars will be placed in the Management Associates Program upon completion of their studies. They can look forward to a career that will include policy formulation and leadership roles in the larger civil service.

Levels of Study: Undergraduate

Field of Study: Foreign Languages, Humanities, Mathematics, Science

Nationality: Singapore

AWARD INFORMATION

Award Type: Scholarship

Average Amount: Varies

Award Coverage: Tuition fees and other approved charges, maintenance and other allowances, e.g., book, clothing, computer, return economy airfare

Award Duration: Maximum of 6 years

ELIGIBILITY REQUIREMENTS

- Must have GCE "A" Level, Polytechnic Diploma or equivalent, e.g. International Baccalaureate (IB)
- Must be Singapore citizens, or Singapore permanent residents who will eventually take up the Singapore citizenship before their departure for studies
- Must offer at least 11 academic units ("A" Level candidates)
- Must demonstrate strong co-curricular activities record and strong leadership qualities

APPLICATION INFORMATION

Instructions: Download application materials

CONTACT

Public Service Commission
1 North Buona Vista Drive
138675 Singapore
Singapore
Tel: +65 6872-2220
Fax: +65 6775-5826
Email: moe_scholarship@moe.gov.sg
Web: www.moe.gov.sg/careers/teach/career-info/scholarships/overseas-merit-scholarship/

Public Service Commission

Singapore Police Force Overseas Scholarship (SPFOS)

PROGRAM INFORMATION

Description: The SPF Overseas Scholarship is one of the most prestigious scholarships awarded by the Public Service Commission. SPF (Overseas) Scholars are sent to renowned universities in Oxford, Cambridge, and London in the UK, as well as Cornell, Pennsylvania, Chicago, and Yale in the US for undergraduate studies. SPFO Scholars are groomed as leaders through the Management Associate Program (MAP) that starts from day 1 of the scholarship and continues throughout the scholar's studies into the 4-year master's program upon graduation.

Levels of Study: Undergraduate

Field of Study: All

Nationality: Singapore

AWARD INFORMATION

Award Type: Scholarship

Average Amount: Varies

Number of Awards: Unlimited

Award Coverage: Tuition fees and approved charges, maintenance and other allowance, airfare, monthly stipend

ELIGIBILITY REQUIREMENTS

- Must possess strong leadership qualities and interest in a career in the Singapore Police Force
- Must possess good co-curricular activities record
- Must have GCE "A" levels or equivalent, e.g. International Baccalaureate (IB)
- Must be a Singapore citizen or permanent resident with the intention of taking up citizenship

APPLICATION INFORMATION

Award Deadline: Mar

Instructions: Contact or visit our website for more information

CONTACT

138675 Singapore
Singapore
Tel: +65 6338-6000
Email: psc@psd.gov.sg
Web: www.pscscholarships.gov.sg/

Radio and Television Directors Foundation

Radio and Television Directors Foundation Scholarships

PROGRAM INFORMATION

Description: The Radio and Television Directors Foundation (RTNDF) offers a variety of scholarship opportunities for students and young professionals interested in journalism.

Levels of Study: Undergraduate

Field of Study: All

Nationality: Any Region

AWARD INFORMATION

Award Type: Scholarship

Average Amount: $1,000-$10,000

Number of Awards: Varies

Award Coverage: Tuition, travel expenses to annual meeting

ELIGIBILITY REQUIREMENTS

- Must be officially enrolled in college and have at least 1 full academic year remaining
- Must be a currently enrolled college sophomore or higher. Freshmen are not eligible
- Must apply for only 1 scholarship
- May be enrolled in any major so long as your intent is a career in electronic journalism

APPLICATION INFORMATION

Award Deadline: May

Instructions: For more information, please visit the website

CONTACT

The National Press Building
529 14th Street, NW, Suite 425
Washington, DC 20045
Tel: +1 (202) 725-8318
Fax: +1 (202) 223-4007
Email: katies@rtdna.org
Web: w

Research Council of Norway
Leiv Eiriksson Mobility Program

PROGRAM INFORMATION

Description: This program is intended to enhance trans-Atlantic mobility and research cooperation between Norway and the US and Canada. Support is granted to cover the additional costs of research stays of 3 to 10 months at recognized institutions in the US or Canada.

Levels of Study: Graduate, Doctorate

Field of Study: All

Nationality: Norway

AWARD INFORMATION

Award Type: Fellowship

Average Amount: NOK 12,000- NOK 24,000 per month

Number of Awards: Varies

Award Coverage: Monthly living stipend, research stipend, roundtrip airfare

Award Duration: 3-10 months

ELIGIBILITY REQUIREMENTS

- Must submit letters of recommendation from both the home institution and the host institution

APPLICATION INFORMATION

Award Deadline: Mar

Instructions: Apply online

CONTACT

The Research Council of Norway
International Scholarships
PO Box 2700 St. Hanshaugen
N-0131 Oslo
Norway
Tel: +47 (22) 03-70-33
Fax: +47 (22) 03-70-01
Email: ie@forskningsradet.no
Web: www.forskningsradet.no

Scholarbook
Scholarbook Sports Scholarship

PROGRAM INFORMATION

Description: Not everyone is able to pay for support when looking for a sports scholarship in the US. Therefore, once per year we provide our services for a sports scholarship in the US completely free of charge.

Levels of Study: Undergraduate

Nationality: Germany

AWARD INFORMATION

Award Type: Tuition Reduction

Average Amount: € 2000 minimum

Number of Awards: 1 award per year

Award Coverage: Assistance in finding a sports scholarship completely free of charge

Award Duration: 12 months

ELIGIBILITY REQUIREMENTS

- Athletic achievements
- Proven financial need
- Motivation to study in the US and to succeed in sports at the same time
- Participants must actively strive for a sports scholarship in the US

APPLICATION INFORMATION

Award Deadline: Aug 31

Instructions: Applications can be submitted once per year; the registration period ends Aug 31; visit www.scholarbook.net/scholarbook/site/wp-content/uploads/editor/files/stipendium_formular_datenabfrage.pdf to apply

CONTACT

Scholarbook
Am Hang 1a
56335 Neuhäusel Rheinland-Pfalz
Germany
Tel: +49 2620 3293699
Email: team@scholarbook.net
Web: www.scholarbook.net

Sigma Theta Tau International Honor Society of Nursing
Sigma Theta Tau Small Grants

PROGRAM INFORMATION

Description: The purpose of the small grants is to encourage nurses to contribute to the advancement of nursing through research.

Levels of Study: Graduate, Doctorate, Post Doctorate, Professional

Field of Study: Nursing

Nationality: Any Region

AWARD INFORMATION

Award Type: Grant

Average Amount: Up to $5,000

Number of Awards: 10-15

Award Coverage: Varies

Award Duration: 1 year

ELIGIBILITY REQUIREMENTS

- Preference will be given to Sigma Theta Tau members
- Must be a registered nurse with current license
- Must have a master's or doctoral degree or be enrolled in a doctoral program
- Must be ready to implement research project when funding is received

APPLICATION INFORMATION

Award Deadline: Dec 1

Instructions: All applications must be submitted via the online submission system, please visit our website for further information

CONTACT

Sigma Theta Tau International
Grants Administrative Coordinator
550 West North Street
Indianapolis, IN 46202
Tel: +1 (317) 634-8171
Fax: +1 (317) 634-8188
Email: research@stti.iupui.edu
Web: www.nursingsociety.org/Research/Grants/Pages/grant_bloch.aspx

Sigma Theta Tau International Honor Society of Nursing
Sigma Theta Tau International/Doris Bloch Research Award

PROGRAM INFORMATION

Description: The award is meant to encourage nurses to contribute to the advancement of nursing through research.

Levels of Study: Graduate, Doctorate, Post Doctorate, Professional

Field of Study: Nursing

Nationality: Any Region

AWARD INFORMATION

Award Type: Grant

Average Amount: Up to $5,000

Number of Awards: 1

Award Duration: 1 year

ELIGIBILITY REQUIREMENTS

- Must be a registered nurse with current license
- Must hold a master's or doctoral degree or be enrolled in a doctoral program
- Must submit a completed research application package and signed research agreement
- Must be ready to implement research project when funding is received
- Must complete project within 1 year of funding

APPLICATION INFORMATION

Award Deadline: Jul 1

Instructions: All applications must be submitted via the online submission system, please visit our website for more information

CONTACT

Sigma Theta Tau International
Grants Administrative Coordinator
550 W. North St
Indianapolis, IN 46202
Tel: +1 (317) 634-8171
Fax: +1 (317) 634-8188
Email: research@stti.iupui.edu
Web: www.nursingsociety.org/Research/Grants/Pages/grant_bloch.aspx

Sigma Theta Tau International Honor Society of Nursing

Sigma Theta Tau International/ Rosemary Berkel Crisp Research Award

PROGRAM INFORMATION

Description: The allocation of funds is based upon a research project that is ready for implementation in the area of women's health, oncology, or pediatrics; the quality of the proposed research, future potential of the application, appropriateness of the research budget, and feasibility of time frame. Funds are provided by interest from a gift from The Harry L. Crisp, II and Rosemary Berkel Crisp Foundation to the honor society's Research Endowment.

Levels of Study: Graduate, Doctorate, Post Doctorate, Professional

Field of Study: Nursing

Nationality: Any Region

AWARD INFORMATION

Award Type: Grant

Average Amount: Up to $5,000

Number of Awards: 1

Award Duration: 1 year

ELIGIBILITY REQUIREMENTS

- Must be a registered nurse with current license
- Must hold a master's or doctoral degree or be enrolled in a doctoral program
- Must submit a completed research application package and signed research agreement
- Must be ready to implement research project when funding is received
- Must be a member of Sigma Theta Tau International

APPLICATION INFORMATION

Award Deadline: Dec 1

Instructions: All applications must be submitted via the online submission system, please visit our website for more information

CONTACT

Sigma Theta Tau International
Grants Administrative Coordinator
550 W. North St
Indianapolis, IN 46202
Tel: +1 (317) 634-8171
Fax: +1 (317) 634-8188
Email: research@stti.iupui.edu
Web: www.nursingsociety.org/Research/Grants/Pages/grant_bloch.aspx

Slovak-American Foundation

Slovak-American Foundation Professional Internship Program

PROGRAM INFORMATION

Description: Work alongside US citizens at an exciting company in the world's largest economy, build your international network, improve your English and kick-start your career. The SAF Professional Internship Program scholarship is all-inclusive and scholarship recipients receive up to $30,000 for 6-12 month long internships in the US Live and work in places as diverse as New York City, Washington, D.C., Chicago, or San Diego.

Levels of Study: Undergraduate, Graduate

Field of Study: All

Nationality: Slovakia

AWARD INFORMATION

Award Type: Award, Fellowship, Internship, Scholarship

Average Amount: Varies

Number of Awards: 10-12 per fiscal year

Award Coverage: Internship placement at a dynamic US company, round-trip airfare, travel health insurance, appropriate US visa, SAF orientation and reception, SAF enrichment trip, monthly stipend that covers accommodation, meals, transportation to and from work, extra pocket money; additional benefits: 24/7 emergency line, personalized support

Award Duration: 6-12 months

ELIGIBILITY REQUIREMENTS

- Must hold a passport from Slovakia
- Must have certified written and oral English language proficiency sufficient to function in a business setting
- Must be enrolled at an accredited postsecondary university and be in the final year (academic program/ course of study must be at least 3 years in duration and result in some form of degree) or have graduated within 6 months of application deadline, or be enrolled on a full-time basis at an accredited postgraduate university
- Must not have immediate family members that are SAF employees, and/or SAF Board members
- Applicants should agree to uphold the 2-year Home Country Physical Presence Requirement as precondition for applying
- Upon completion of the SAF program, scholarship recipients and participants are required to return to and reside in Slovakia for a minimum of 2 years, and are not permitted to stay or attempt to stay in the US or any other foreign country for any reason

APPLICATION INFORMATION

Award Deadline: Oct 15

Instructions: For more information on the program, please visit our website

CONTACT

Slovak-American Foundation
CIEE Exchanges Inc. Ker. Kepv.
Andrassy ut 61. I. 5.
1062 Budapest
Hungary
Tel: +421 915 613802
Web: www.slovakamericanfoundation.org

Social Sciences Research Council/Andrew W. Mellon Foundation

SSRC/ACLS International Dissertation Research Fellowship (IDRF)

PROGRAM INFORMATION

Description: The International Dissertation Research Fellowship (IDRF) Program supports the next generation of scholars in the humanities and social sciences pursuing research that advances knowledge about non-US cultures and societies. The program administers both the International Dissertation Research Fellowship for graduate students conducting dissertation research outside the US, as well as the SSRC-IDRF Book Fellowship, available to IDRF alumni to assist in the preparation of their first scholarly monograph. The IDRF Program is funded by the Andrew W. Mellon Foundation and administered in partnership with the American Council of Learned Societies.

Levels of Study: Doctorate

Field of Study: Humanities, Social Science

Nationality: Any Region

AWARD INFORMATION

Award Type: Fellowship

Average Amount: Approx $20,000

Number of Awards: Varies

Award Coverage: Living stipend, travel, equipment, workshop

Award Duration: 9-12 months

ELIGIBILITY REQUIREMENTS

- Must be enrolled full-time in a doctoral program in the US
- Applicants should provide evidence of having attained an appropriate level of training to undertake the proposed research, including evidence of a degree of language fluency sufficient to complete the project
- Must complete all PhD requirements except on-site research by the time the fellowship begins
- Proposals that identify the US as a case for comparative inquiry are welcome; however, proposals which focus predominantly or exclusively on the US are not eligible

APPLICATION INFORMATION

Award Deadline: Nov

Instructions: Applications must be submitted electronically using the SSRC's Online Applications Portal

CONTACT

Social Science Research Council
IDRF Program
810 7th Avenue
31st Floor
New York, NY 10019
Tel: +1 (212) 377-2700
Fax: +1 (212) 377-2727
Email: idrf@ssrc.org
Web: www.ssrc.org/fellowships/idrf-fellowship/

Society of Women Engineers
Society of Women Engineers Scholarships

PROGRAM INFORMATION

Description: The Society of Women Engineers provides financial assistance to women admitted to accredited baccalaureate or graduate programs, in preparation for careers in engineering, engineering technology, and computer science.

Levels of Study: Undergraduate, Graduate

Field of Study: Computer Science, Engineering

Nationality: Any Region

AWARD INFORMATION

Award Type: Scholarship

Average Amount: $1,000-$10,000

Number of Awards: Varies

Award Coverage: Varies

Award Duration: Academic year

ELIGIBILITY REQUIREMENTS

- Must be a woman accepted or enrolled in a full-time, degree-bearing, accredited engineering program

APPLICATION INFORMATION

Award Deadline: Varies

Instructions: Download or contact to request application materials

CONTACT
Society of Women Engineers
203 N La Salle Street
Suite 1675
Chicago, IL 60601
Tel: +1 (312) 596-5223
Email: hq@swe.org
Web: www.swe.org

Sons of Norway
King Olav V Norwegian-American Heritage Fund

PROGRAM INFORMATION

Description: The purpose of the fund is to support American students studying Norwegian topics and Norwegian students studying American topics. Norwegian citizens are eligible to apply to further the study of these heritages at recognized educational institutions in the US

Levels of Study: Undergraduate, Graduate

Field of Study: Arts and Culture, Humanities

Nationality: Norway

AWARD INFORMATION

Award Type: Scholarship

Average Amount: $1,000-$1,500

Number of Awards: Varies

Award Coverage: Partial tuition, fees (travel expenses and living expenses do not qualify)

Award Duration: Academic year

ELIGIBILITY REQUIREMENTS

- Must be a Norwegian citizen
- Must be at least 18 years old
- Must be studying in the US

APPLICATION INFORMATION

Award Deadline: Mar 1

Instructions: Download application materials at the website

CONTACT
Sons of Norway Foundation
King Olav V Norwegian-American Heritage Fund
1455 West Lake Street
Minneapolis, MN 55408
Tel: +1 (612) 827-3611
Fax: +1 (612) 827-0658
Email: foundation@sofn.com
Web: www.sofn.com/foundation

Spencer Foundation/ National Academy of Education
National Academy of Education/ Spencer Postdoctoral Fellowship

PROGRAM INFORMATION

Description: Administered by the National Academy of Education (NAEd), the postdoctoral fellowships are designed to promote scholarship in the US and abroad on matters relevant to the improvement of education in all its forms. Scholars anywhere in the world, who have completed their doctorates within the past 5 years, and who wish to conduct research related to education, may apply.

Levels of Study: Post Doctorate

Field of Study: Education

Nationality: Any Region

AWARD INFORMATION

Award Type: Fellowship

Average Amount: $55,000

Number of Awards: Up to 25

Award Duration: 1-2 years

ELIGIBILITY REQUIREMENTS

- Must have completed a doctoral degree within the past 5 years
- Should have a demonstrated record of research experience in education
- Proposed project must be an education research project

APPLICATION INFORMATION

Award Deadline: Nov

Instructions: Complete online application available at www.naeducation.org

CONTACT
National Academy of Education
500 Fifth Street NW
Washington, DC 20001
Tel: +1 (202) 334-2341
Email: info@naeducation.org
Web: www.naeducation.org

Spencer Foundation/ National Academy of Education
National Academy of Education/ Spencer Dissertation Fellowship

PROGRAM INFORMATION

Description: The Dissertation Fellowship Program seeks to encourage a new generation of scholars from a wide range of disciplines and professional fields to undertake research relevant to the improvement of education. These $25,000 fellowships support individuals whose dissertations show potential for bringing fresh and constructive perspectives to the history, theory, or practice of formal or informal education anywhere in the world. This highly competitive program aims to identify the most talented researchers conducting dissertation research related to education.

Levels of Study: Doctorate

Field of Study: Education

Nationality: Any Region

AWARD INFORMATION

Award Type: Fellowship

Average Amount: $25,000

Number of Awards: 30

Award Duration: 1-2 years

ELIGIBILITY REQUIREMENTS

- Applicants need not be citizens of the US, but they must be enrolled at an institution of higher education in the US
- Must have completed all pre-dissertation requirements before Jun 1 of the award year
- Fellowships may not be deferred to a later academic year
- Must be from an individual (no group submissions) and must be a research project
- Fellowships are not applicable to finance data collection or the completion of doctoral coursework - the fellowship funds are intended to support the fellow during their final analysis of their dissertation

APPLICATION INFORMATION

Award Deadline: Oct

Instructions: Apply online in late summer/early fall at www.naeducation.org

CONTACT
National Academy of Education
500 5th St, NW, WS308
Washington, DC 20001
Tel: +1 (202) 334-2093
Email: info@naeducation.org
Web: www.naeducation.org

Study Oregon
Study Oregon Scholarship

PROGRAM INFORMATION

Description: Study Oregon invites future international students who are interested in enrolling in 1 of 26 colleges and universities that are members of Study Oregon to view scholarship information in the e-brochure found on the Study Oregon website.

Nationality: Any Region

CONTACT
Email: info@studyoregon.com
Web: www.studyoregon.com

Sweden-America Foundation

Sweden-America Foundation Fellowship Program

PROGRAM INFORMATION

Description: The Fellowship Program serves to support master's and postdoctoral studies in the US.

Levels of Study: Graduate, Doctorate, Post Doctorate

Field of Study: All

Nationality: Sweden

AWARD INFORMATION

Award Type: Fellowship, Grant

Average Amount: Varies

Number of Awards: Approx 40

Award Coverage: Varies

Award Duration: 6-12 months

ELIGIBILITY REQUIREMENTS

- Must hold undergraduate degree
- See program website for further information about requirements

APPLICATION INFORMATION

Award Deadline: Sep

Instructions: Apply online

CONTACT

The Sweden-America Foundation
Box 5280
SE-10246 Stockholm
Sweden
Tel: +46 (8) 611-4611
Fax: +46 (8) 611-4004
Email: info@sweamfo.se
Web: www.sweamfo.se

Swiss Benevolent Society of New York

Medicus Student Exchange Fund

PROGRAM INFORMATION

Description: Administered by the Swiss Benevolent Society of New York (SBS), the purpose of the fund is to support students who wish to pursue graduate studies at recognized institutions in the US.

Levels of Study: Graduate, Doctorate

Field of Study: All

Nationality: Switzerland

AWARD INFORMATION

Award Type: Grant

Average Amount: $5,000

Number of Awards: Varies

Award Coverage: Partial tuition and fees

Award Duration: Academic year

ELIGIBILITY REQUIREMENTS

- Must be a Swiss citizen (applicants who hold dual citizenship with the US, or are residents of the US, or have a "green card" are not eligible)
- Must hold an undergraduate degree from a university or a university of applied sciences
- Must demonstrate sufficient English language skills
- Applications for studies in medicine, dentistry, veterinary medicine and clinical psychology cannot be accepted, however a master's degree in public health will be accepted

APPLICATION INFORMATION

Award Deadline: Jun for preliminary application; Aug for final application

Instructions: Contact to request application materials

CONTACT

Rectors' Conference of the Swiss Universities CRUS
Service of Scholarships
P.O. Box 607
CH-3000 Berne
Switzerland
Tel: +41 (31) 306-60-56
Fax: +41 (31) 306-60-50
Email: stip@crus.ch
Web: www.crus.ch/information-programme/stipendien-fuer-auslandstudien/grants-for-the-usa.html

The Danish-American Fulbright Commission

Danish-American Fulbright Commission Grants to Danish Graduate Students

PROGRAM INFORMATION

Description: Grants to Danish citizens who wish to complete 1 or more semesters of graduate level study in the US.

Levels of Study: Graduate

Field of Study: All

Nationality: Denmark

AWARD INFORMATION

Award Type: Grant

Average Amount: DKK 50,000-85,000

Number of Awards: Varies

Award Coverage: Tuition, housing, travel expenses, insurance, does not cover expenses for accompanying family members

Award Duration: 1 year

ELIGIBILITY REQUIREMENTS

- Must have Danish citizenship, applicants with dual citizenship are not accepted
- Must be for graduate studies
- Must be for a minimum of 1 semester (3-6 months)
- Studies in the US must not have commenced
- Is not given to first degrees in medicine, veterinary science, dentistry

APPLICATION INFORMATION

Award Deadline: Mar

Instructions: Find instructions and application form on the website

CONTACT

The Denmark-Amerika Foundation and the Fulbright Commission
Senior Program Coordinator
Nørregade 7A, 1 tv.
1165 Copenhagen K
Denmark
Tel: +45 (35) 324545
Email: advising@daf-fulb.dk
Web: www.wemakeithappen.dk

The Danish-American Fulbright Commission

Danish-American Fulbright Commission Joint Grants to Danish Graduate Students

PROGRAM INFORMATION

Description: Grants to Danish citizens who wish to study at the graduate level, at specific institutions in the US Grants are for tuition reduction at the American institution, plus DKK 85,000 from the Fulbright Commission. Conditions vary.

Levels of Study: Graduate

Nationality: Denmark

AWARD INFORMATION

Award Type: Grant, Tuition Reduction

Average Amount: Varies

Number of Awards: Varies

Award Coverage: Tuition, housing, travel expenses

Award Duration: 1 year

ELIGIBILITY REQUIREMENTS

- Only given to students wishing to study at the Fulbright Commission's cooperating joint grant institutions; agreements are renewed yearly and vary from institution to institution; check the website for updated information
- Must have Danish citizenship, applicants with dual citizenship are not accepted
- Must be for graduate studies
- Minimum 1 academic year (2 semesters or 8-10 months)

APPLICATION INFORMATION

Award Deadline: Oct

Instructions: See instructions and application form on the website

CONTACT

The Denmark-America Foundation and the Fulbright Commission
Senior Program Coordinator
Nørregade 7A, 1. tv
1165 Copenhagen
Denmark
Tel: +45 (35) 324545
Email: advising@daf-fulb.dk
Web: www.wemakeithappen.dk

The Fulbright Foundation in Greece

Fulbright Foundation in Greece
Graduate Student Scholarships

PROGRAM INFORMATION

Description: The Fulbright Foundation in Greece will award up to 15 grants to Greek graduate students for a master's or PhD degree at universities in the US. Awards are open to graduate students in all fields of study except medicine, dentistry and veterinary science or to those who wish to enter residency training programs. Architecture applicants: for the 2015-2016 academic year, the Foundation will accept applications only for degrees in urban planning and/or sustainable architecture/ecological design. Candidates should have already applied to US universities when they submit their Fulbright application. Admission to a US university is not required at the time of application, but is mandatory for the award of the grant. Grantees are selected on the basis of merit/academic excellence, professional experience (if applicable), civic engagement, career potential and character. All awards are subject to the Fulbright Foundation policies.

Levels of Study: Graduate, Doctorate

Field of Study: All

Nationality: Greece

AWARD INFORMATION

Award Type: Grant

Average Amount: Varies

Number of Awards: Up to 15 partial grants

Award Coverage: Up to $18,000 for the first year only (non-renewable), health insurance, travel allowance

Award Duration: Academic year

ELIGIBILITY REQUIREMENTS

- Must have a degree from a Greek University (AEI) with a GPA of 8.0/10.00 and above
- Must provide proof of admission from a US university, and have sufficient financial resources in addition to the Fulbright award
- Must have Greek citizenship, candidates with dual citizenship (US/Greek) or permanent residence in the US are not eligible
- A Fulbright selection committee will interview all candidates in person, in English, on specific dates, interviews are mandatory

APPLICATION INFORMATION

Award Deadline: Jan

Instructions: Candidates should register online at the beginning of Oct before they are entitled to receive instructions for the online Embark application

CONTACT

The Fulbright Foundation in Greece
Greek Program Coordinator/Fulbright Scholarships Advisor
6 Vassilissis Sophias Avenue
10674 Athens
Greece
Tel: +30 (210) 724-1811, ext. 203
Fax: +30 (210) 722-6510
Email: greekprogram@fulbright.gr
Web: www.fulbright.gr/greek_graduate.html

The Fulbright Foundation in Greece

Fulbright Foundation in Greece
Visiting Scholars Program

PROGRAM INFORMATION

Description: The Fulbright Foundation in Greece offers Greek professors/researchers the opportunity to lecture and/or conduct research at universities or research centers in the US. Fulbright grants are awarded for a minimum of 3 months. Recipients may continue their project under the Fulbright auspices for up to 6 months (maximum eligible period) if they obtain funding from sources other than the Fulbright Foundation. In that case, proof of funds is required. The grant period may begin as early as Sep 1, and must be completed by May 31. The grant period cannot be divided, and may be conducted at a maximum of 2 host institutions. Awards are open to scholars in all fields and applicants must arrange their own affiliation/invitation to the US. Candidates are selected on the basis of academic and professional excellence, career potential and character. All awards are subject to the Fulbright Foundation policies.

Levels of Study: Post Doctorate, Professional

Field of Study: All

Nationality: Greece

AWARD INFORMATION

Award Type: Grant

Average Amount: Varies

Number of Awards: Up to 7 partial grants

Award Coverage: Up to $2,500 per month stipend, health insurance, travel allowance

Award Duration: 3 months

ELIGIBILITY REQUIREMENTS

- Must have a PhD degree followed by a minimum of 4 years of professional experience in the field of study
- Must have Greek citizenship. Candidates with dual citizenship (US/Greek) or permanent residence in the US are not eligible
- Must be a mid-career scholar with limited recent experience in the US. Preference is given to candidates whose permanent residence is in Greece
- Must submit an official letter of invitation/affiliation from the US university/research center
- Must have adequate English proficiency

APPLICATION INFORMATION

Award Deadline: Nov

Instructions: Candidates should register online at the beginning of Sep before they are entitled to receive instructions for the online Embark application

CONTACT

The Fulbright Foundation in Greece
Greek Program Coordinator/Fulbright Scholarships Advisor
6 Vassilissis Sophias Avenue
10674 Athens
Greece
Tel: +30 (210) 724-1811, ext. 203
Fax: +30 (210) 722-6510
Email: greekprogram@fulbright.gr
Web: www.fulbright.gr/greek_research.html

The Fulbright Foundation in Greece

Fulbright Foundation in Greece
Artist Grants

PROGRAM INFORMATION

Description: This award is open to professional artists in any field of fine arts, creative writing, music, dance, theater, cinematography, photography, performance and digital arts who wish to gain a higher level of proficiency, to enhance their career, to seek advancement opportunities and familiarize themselves with US culture. The Foundation looks for well-defined projects that are innovative, and will have an impact in the respective areas. The grant may begin as early as Sep 15, and must be completed by May 31. Fulbright grants are awarded for a minimum of 6 months. Recipients may continue their project under the Foundation's auspices for more than 6 months and up to 9 months (maximum eligible period) if funding from sources other than the Fulbright Foundation is obtained. In that case, proof of funds is required. This award is NOT for candidates seeking a degree.

Levels of Study: Professional

Field of Study: Arts and Culture, Creative Writing, Dance, Film, Fine Arts, Music, Theater, Visual and Performing Arts

Nationality: Greece

AWARD INFORMATION

Award Type: Grant

Average Amount: Varies

Number of Awards: Up to 3 partial grants

Award Coverage: Up to $2,000 per month stipend, health insurance, travel allowance

Award Duration: 6 months

ELIGIBILITY REQUIREMENTS

- Applications may be submitted only if applicants have received an official letter of invitation or admission from an educational institution and/or cultural organization in the US
- Must have adequate English proficiency
- Must be a Greek citizen. Candidates with dual citizenship (US/Greek) or permanent residence in the US are not eligible
- Preference will be given to candidates between the ages of 28 to 45 at the time of application, with a minimum of 5 years of professional experience in their field of work
- A Fulbright selection committee will interview all candidates in person, in English, on specific dates, interviews are mandatory

APPLICATION INFORMATION

Award Deadline: Feb

Instructions: Candidates should register online at the beginning of Dec before they are entitled to receive instructions for the online Embark application

CONTACT

The Fulbright Foundation in Greece
Greek Program Coordinator/Fulbright Scholarships Advisor
6 Vassilissis Sophias Avenue
10674 Athens
Greece
Tel: +30 (21) 7241-811 ext. 203
Fax: +30 (21) 7226-510
Email: greekprogram@fulbright.gr
Web: www.fulbright.gr/greek_art.html

The General Sir John Monash Foundation
General Sir John Monash Postgraduate Student Awards

PROGRAM INFORMATION

Description: Annually, up to 8 awards may be awarded to outstanding Australian citizens graduating from Australian universities to enable them to undertake postgraduate study abroad at the world's best universities, appropriate to their field of study.

Levels of Study: Doctorate

Field of Study: All

Nationality: Australia

AWARD INFORMATION

Award Type: Award

Average Amount: Up to AUD 50,000 per year

Number of Awards: Up to 8

Award Coverage: Varies

Award Duration: Maximum of 3 years

ELIGIBILITY REQUIREMENTS

- Must have completed or be about to complete an honors degree with a classification of 1 or 2A, or an equivalent degree with outstanding results, by the end of the year of application
- Must demonstrate outstanding leadership ability
- Must show proof of arrangements with a foreign university to conduct a well-defined research project or study program
- Must be an Australian citizen

APPLICATION INFORMATION

Award Deadline: Aug

Instructions: Download application materials from our website

CONTACT

The General Sir John Monash Foundation
Level 1, Bennelong House
9 Queen Street
3000 Melbourne Victoria
Australia
Tel: +61 (03) 9620-2428
Fax: +61 (03) 9654-3411
Email: carol.clark@monashawards.org
Web: monashawards.org

The GET Foundation
GET Foundation Scholarship

PROGRAM INFORMATION

Description: The Gordon Tam & Elsie K. Tam Charitable Foundation was incorporated in California on Sept 28, 1999, as a nonprofit public benefit corporation. The foundation was renamed "The GET Foundation" on Jun 23, 2000. The foundation was formed by Gordon Tam, who serves as its President and Director, and Elsie K. Tam, who serves as its Treasurer, Secretary, and Director. It was established for the purpose of granting and administering scholarships to deserving high school students from Hong Kong, based on financial need, to pursue undergraduate studies at accredited 4-year universities in the US.

Levels of Study: Undergraduate

Field of Study: All

Nationality: Hong Kong

AWARD INFORMATION

Award Type: Scholarship

Average Amount: Up to $5,000

Number of Awards: Up to 2

Award Coverage: Tuition, books, fees, housing, travel

Award Duration: 1 year

ELIGIBILITY REQUIREMENTS

- Must be a Hong Kong resident and Hong Kong high school graduate with demonstrated financial need
- Must be accepted for full-time enrollment in an accredited 4-year US college/university
- Preference is given to applicants with demonstrated educational motivation and leadership skills
- Must have intention to pursue a career in science, engineering, or teaching
- Must reside in a university dormitory during freshman year

APPLICATION INFORMATION

Award Deadline: Apr 15

Instructions: Apply online

CONTACT

The GET Foundation
President
46 Eugenia Way
Hillsborough, CA 94010
Tel: +1 (650) 342-6388
Fax: +1 (650) 342-6388
Email: gordontam@ymail.com
Web: www.thegetfoundation.org

The Global Beca Foundation for San Mateo Colleges
Chicana/Latina Foundation Scholarship

PROGRAM INFORMATION

Description: Each year the Chicana Latina Foundation awards merit-based scholarships to Latina college students, valued at $1,500 dollars each. You must commit to attending the CLF Leadership Institute and to volunteering 10 hours for CLF before Mar the year after being selected. Past CLF awardees may not re-apply until 4 years after receiving our scholarship.

AWARD INFORMATION

Award Type: Scholarship

Average Amount: $1,500

ELIGIBILITY REQUIREMENTS

- Chicana/Latina women who have resided for at least 2 years in 1 of the Northern California counties
- Undergraduate Chicana/Latina students must be enrolled as a full-time college student when applying
- Have completed a minimum of 12 college units after high school graduation for the following academic year
- Have completed a minimum of 12 college units after high school graduation
- Cumulative GPA of 2.5 college coursework

APPLICATION INFORMATION

Award Deadline: Mar

Instructions: Complete the application (www.chicanalatina.org/scholarship/CLF_Scholarship_Application_2014.pdf) and mail to the Chicana Latina Foundation

CONTACT

Chicana Latina Foundation
Scholarship Committee
1419 Burlingame Ave. Suite W2
Burlingame, CA 94010
Tel: +1 (650) 373-1083
Email: CLFinfo@chicanalatina.org
Web: www.chicanalatina.org/scholarship.html

The Rotary Foundation
Rotary Peace Fellowship

PROGRAM INFORMATION

Description: Rotary Peace Fellows are leaders promoting national and international cooperation, peace, and the successful resolution of conflict throughout their lives, in their careers, and through service activities. Fellows can earn either a master's degree in international relations, public administration, sustainable development, peace studies, conflict resolution, or a related field, or a professional development certificate in peace and conflict resolution.

Levels of Study: Graduate

Field of Study: Conflict Management, International Relations, Peace Studies

Nationality: Any Region

AWARD INFORMATION

Award Type: Scholarship

Average Amount: Varies

Number of Awards: Up to 60

Award Coverage: Tuition and fees, room and board, transportation, books and supplies

Award Duration: 24 months

ELIGIBILITY REQUIREMENTS

- Must hold an undergraduate degree from an accredited institution
- Must demonstrate proficiency in English or a second language
- Must have a minimum of 3 years' combined paid or unpaid full-time relevant work experience (master's degree) or 5 years' relevant work experience with current full-time employment in a mid- to upper-level position (professional development certificate)
- Must possess excellent leadership skills and a commitment to peace and international understanding
- Must submit TOEFL and GRE scores

APPLICATION INFORMATION

Instructions: Please see www.rotary.org/myrotary/en/get-involved/exchange-ideas/peace-fellowships

CONTACT

Rotary International
1 Rotary Center
1560 Sherman Ave.
Evanston, IL 60201
Tel: +1 (847) 866-3834
Email: rotarypeacecenters@rotary.org
Web: www.rotary.org

The Turkish Fulbright Commission
STUDENT PROGRAM/Master's Grant

PROGRAM INFORMATION

Description: The Fulbright Master's Grant Program is a graduate degree program. Grants are awarded for 1 or 2 academic years depending on the length of the program in which the grantees are admitted.

Nationality: Turkey

AWARD INFORMATION

Award Type: Grant

Number of Awards: Varies

Award Coverage: $35,000 (including tuition, fees, living expenses), a round-trip plane ticket, health insurance

Award Duration: Maximum of 2 years

ELIGIBILITY REQUIREMENTS

- Must be a Turkish Citizen. US citizens, Green Card holders or US-Turkish dual citizens cannot apply
- Must be a 4-year University graduate or still registered student at a 4-year university, graduating by Jul 2016 at the latest
- Must have graduation cumulative grade point average of at least 3.00 out of 4.00 or 75 out of 100 (depending on the university's official grading system)
- Must demonstrate fluency in English
- Must start their Program in the USA with the start of their Fulbright Grant

APPLICATION INFORMATION

Award Deadline: Mar 2015

Instructions: Application form and detailed instructions are available at www.fulbright.org.tr

CONTACT
Eskisehir Yolu 9. Km. Tepe Prime Is Merkezi
B Blok No:124 Cankaya
Ankara
Turkey
Tel: 90312 427 13 60
Email: advising@fulbright.org.tr
Web: www.fulbright.org.tr

The Turkish Fulbright Commission
STUDENT PROGRAM/PhD Grant

PROGRAM INFORMATION

Description: The Fulbright PhD Grant Program is a graduate degree program. Grants are awarded for 2 academic years.

Nationality: Turkey

AWARD INFORMATION

Award Type: Grant

Number of Awards: Varies

Award Coverage: $35,000 (including tuition, fees, living expenses), a round-trip plane ticket, health insurance

Award Duration: Maximum of 2 years

ELIGIBILITY REQUIREMENTS

- Must be a Turkish Citizen. US citizens, Green Card holders, or US-Turkish dual citizens cannot apply
- Can be a Master's degree holder, a 4-year University graduate or can be registered at a 4-year university and/or master's program graduating by Jul 2016 the latest
- Must have graduation cumulative grade point average of at least 3.50 out of 4.00 or 85 out of 100 (depending on the university's official grading system)
- Must demonstrate fluency in English
- Must start their Program in the USA with the start of their Fulbright Grant

APPLICATION INFORMATION

Award Deadline: Mar 2015

Instructions: Application form and detailed instructions are available at www.fulbright.org.tr

CONTACT
Eskisehir Yolu 9. Km. Tepe Prime Is Merkezi
B Blok No:124 Cankaya
Ankara
Turkey
Tel: 90312 427 13 60
Email: advising@fulbright.org.tr
Web: www.fulbright.org.tr

The Turkish Fulbright Commission
STUDENT PROGRAM/PhD Dissertation Research Grant

PROGRAM INFORMATION

Description: The Fulbright PhD Dissertation Research Grant Program is designed for PhD degree seeking students who would like to conduct 10 months of research in the USA.

Nationality: Turkey

ELIGIBILITY REQUIREMENTS

- Must be a Turkish Citizen. US citizens, Green Card holders or US-Turkish dual citizens cannot apply
- Must be to a PhD program at 1 of the Turkish universities, and at the level of writing a dissertation
- Must be registered PhD students in Turkey at the time of traveling to the USA
- Must demonstrate fluency in English
- Must start their Program in the USA with the start of their Fulbright Grant

APPLICATION INFORMATION

Award Deadline: Mar 2015

Instructions: Application form and detailed instructions are available at www.fulbright.org.tr

CONTACT
Eskisehir Yolu 9. Km. Tepe Prime Is Merkezi
B Blok No:124 Cankaya
Ankara
Turkey
Tel: 90312 427 13 60
Email: advising@fulbright.org.tr
Web: www.fulbright.org.tr

The US - Italy Fulbright Commission
Fulbright Italian Graduate Student Program

PROGRAM INFORMATION

Description: The Program enables Italian graduate students, young professionals and artists to study in the US at graduate level (ie Master & PhD programs).

Levels of Study: Graduate

Field of Study: All

Nationality: Italy

AWARD INFORMATION

Award Type: Scholarship

CONTACT
The US - Italy Fulbright Commission
Via Castelfidardo 8
Rome 00185
Italy
Email: info@fulbright.it
Web: www.fulbright.it

The US - Italy Fulbright Commission
Fulbright Foreign Language Teaching Assistant Program

PROGRAM INFORMATION

Description: The Program provides opportunities for young English teachers from Italy to refine their teaching skills, increase their English proficiency, and expand their knowledge of US society and values while strengthening Italian language instruction at US colleges and universities.

Levels of Study: Graduate

Nationality: Italy

AWARD INFORMATION

Award Type: Scholarship

CONTACT
The US - Italy Fulbright Commission
Via Castelfidardo 8
Rome 00185
Italy
Email: info@fulbright.it
Web: www.fulbright.it

The US - Italy Fulbright Commission
Fulbright Visiting Scholar Program

PROGRAM INFORMATION

Description: The Program brings Italian scholars to conduct research and/or lecture for up to 9 months at US Universities and Research Centers. The Visiting Scholar Program includes the Fulbright Distinguished Chairs awards.

Levels of Study: Post Doctorate, Professional

Field of Study: All

Nationality: Italy

AWARD INFORMATION

Award Type: Scholarship

CONTACT

The US - Italy Fulbright Commission
Via Castelfidardo 8
Rome 00185
Italy
Email: info@fulbright.it
Web: www.fulbright.it

The US Educational Foundation in Pakistan

Fulbright Degree Program

PROGRAM INFORMATION

Description: This program funds graduate study in the US for a Masters' or doctoral degree.

CONTACT

Web: www.usefpakistan.org

The US Educational Foundation in Pakistan

Fulbright Scholar Program

PROGRAM INFORMATION

Description: This program funds up to 12 months lectureship, post-doctoral research, or a combination of 2 at a US college or university.

CONTACT

Web: www.usefpakistan.org

The US Educational Foundation in Pakistan

Fulbright Foreign Language Teaching Assistant

PROGRAM INFORMATION

Description: Teachers of English language will attend a US institution to improve their English teaching skills. In return, these participants will teach Urdu, Pashto or Punjabi at selected US campuses during their 9-month grant.

CONTACT

Web: www.usefpakistan.org

The US Educational Foundation in Pakistan

Hubert H. Humphrey Fellowship Program

PROGRAM INFORMATION

Description: The Humphrey program provides up to 1 year of professional enrichment and non-degree graduate-level study in the US for mid-level professionals.

CONTACT

Web: www.usefpakistan.org

The US Educational Foundation in Pakistan

Community College Initiative Program

PROGRAM INFORMATION

Description: CCIP enables participants from Pakistan to study 1 year at a community college in the US to earn a vocational certificate and immerse themselves in US society and culture.

CONTACT

Web: www.usefpakistan.org

The US Educational Foundation in Pakistan

Near East & South Asia Undergraduate Program

PROGRAM INFORMATION

Description: Outstanding students from Pakistan will attend a 1 year-long program for non-degree undergraduate study at accredited US institutions.

CONTACT

Web: www.usefpakistan.org

The US Educational Foundation in Pakistan

Global Undergraduate Semester Exchange

PROGRAM INFORMATION

Description: Outstanding students from Pakistan attend a 1 semester-long program for non-degree undergraduate study at accredited 2 and 4 year institutions in the US.

CONTACT

Web: www.usefpakistan.org

The US Educational Foundation in Pakistan

Teaching Excellence and Achievement (TEA) Program

PROGRAM INFORMATION

Description: This program provides Pakistani English Language teachers with unique opportunities to develop expertise in their subject areas, enhance their teaching skills, and increase their knowledge of the US. Participants also engage in hot country university-organized 2-week internships at a local secondary school. Trips to US cultural sites, civic activities, and academic support are provided for participants throughout the program.

CONTACT

Web: www.usefpakistan.org

The US Educational Foundation in Pakistan

US - Pakistan Professional Partnership Program for Journalists

PROGRAM INFORMATION

Description: Participants will be placed within relevant, reputable, legally-recognized US organizations where they will gain hands-on experience with the journalism profession in the US. The 4 to 6 week program provides the opportunity to establish relationship with the US professional counterparts for on-going collaboration.

CONTACT

Web: www.usefpakistan.org

US - Sweden Fulbright Commission

Swedish Fulbright Student Program

PROGRAM INFORMATION

Description: Stipends are available for Swedish students who will undertake a partial or complete Master's or PhD degree in the US Stipends are available for all disciplines and can be used at any accredited American university. Stipends are for students planning a minimum of 1 academic year in the US.

Levels of Study: Graduate, Doctorate

Field of Study: All

Nationality: Sweden

AWARD INFORMATION

Award Type: Grant

Average Amount: SEK 25,000- SEK 200,000

ELIGIBILITY REQUIREMENTS

- Must be a Swedish citizen
- Must not yet have started studies in the US
- Must have a bachelor degree by the time the grant begins
- Student must be at an accredited US university

APPLICATION INFORMATION

Award Deadline: Apr

Instructions: Please visit the Fulbright Sweden website for application instructions and information at: www.fulbright.se

CONTACT

Vasagatan 15-17, 4 tr
11120 Stockholm
Sweden
Tel: +46 8 534 818 85
Email: fulbright@fulbright.se
Web: www.fulbright.se

US - Sweden Fulbright Commission

Swedish Fulbright Scholar Program

PROGRAM INFORMATION

Description: The scholar program offers Swedish citizens with a PhD or equivalent degree in any field the opportunity to conduct research and/or teach in the US for a period of 3 to 9 months.

Field of Study: All

Nationality: Sweden

AWARD INFORMATION

Award Type: Grant

Average Amount: SEK 50,000

Award Duration: 3 to 9 months

ELIGIBILITY REQUIREMENTS

- Must be a Swedish citizen
- Must possess a PhD or equivalent terminal degree
- Must have a minimum stay of 3 months in the US

APPLICATION INFORMATION

Award Deadline: Jan

Instructions: Application instructions and information are found on the Fulbright Sweden website: www.fulbright.se

CONTACT

Vasagatan 15-17
11120 Stockholm
Sweden
Tel: +46 8 534 818 85
Email: fulbright@fulbright.se
Web: www.fulbright.se

US Department of State, Bureau of Educational and Cultural Affairs

Fulbright Foreign Language Teaching Assistant Program (FLTA)

PROGRAM INFORMATION

Description: The FLTA Program enables young educators to refine their teaching skills, increase their English language proficiency, and extend their knowledge of the cultures and customs of the US while engaging in nondegree studies at accredited postsecondary US educational institutions. Along with their studies, FLTAs teach language courses, supervise language labs, and lead language table discussions. FLTAs may also act as resource persons in conversation groups, cultural representatives, attendants in language laboratories, coordinators of extracurricular activities, guest speakers in civilization courses, heads of language clubs, houses, tables, and much more.

Levels of Study: Graduate, Doctorate, Professional

Field of Study: All

Nationality: Afghanistan, Algeria, Argentina, Bahrain, Bangladesh, Belgium, Brazil, Canada, Chile, China, Colombia, Egypt, Finland, France, Germany, India, Indonesia, Iraq, Ireland, Israel, Italy, Jordan, Kazakhstan, Kenya, Korea, Republic of, Kuwait, Kyrgyzstan, Lebanon, Libya, Malaysia, Mauritius, Mexico, Mongolia, Morocco, Nigeria, Oman, Pakistan, Palestinian Authority, Philippines, Portugal, Qatar, Russia, Saudi Arabia, Senegal, Spain, Syria, Taiwan, Tajikistan, Tanzania, Thailand, Tunisia, Turkey, United Arab Emirates, Uruguay, Uzbekistan, Yemen

AWARD INFORMATION

Award Type: Associateship, Award, Grant, Scholarship, Student Exchange

Average Amount: $20,000

Number of Awards: 500

Award Coverage: In most cases health insurance coverage, travel grant

Award Duration: Academic year

ELIGIBILITY REQUIREMENTS

- TAs are required to have formal academic training and/or professional experience in teaching English or related field
- Must possess the equivalent of a US bachelor's degree with a good academic record. Master's degrees are highly desirable at many institutions
- Must be no younger than 21 and no older than 29 at the time of application while residing in the home country throughout the matching process
- Must be fluent in English. TOFEL 550 PBT/213 CBT/79-80 IBT, IELTS 6.0
- Must be outgoing and dynamic individuals with a great sense of humor

APPLICATION INFORMATION

Award Deadline: Feb

Instructions: Visit website

CONTACT

Institute of International Education (IIE)
809 United Nations Plaza
New York, NY 10017
Tel: +1 (212) 984-5494
Fax: +1 (212) 984-5484
Email: ftla@iie.org
Web: www.iie.org/Programs/Fulbright-FLTA

US-Spain Fulbright Commission

Fulbright Graduate Study Program

PROGRAM INFORMATION

Description: Up to 25 grants for postgraduate study toward a Master's Degree or PhD in US universities.

Levels of Study: Graduate, Doctorate

Field of Study: All

Nationality: Europe

AWARD INFORMATION

Award Type: Grant

Number of Awards: 25 awards per year

Award Coverage: Tuition, housing/living expenses, roundtrip travel, settling-in allowance, and health/accident insurance

Award Duration: 10 to 12 months, renewable for up to 12 months

ELIGIBILITY REQUIREMENTS

- Spain or EU citizenship
- Undergraduate degree conferred within the last 6 years
- TOEFL or IELTS score required
- Depending on area of study, it may be necessary to take the GMAT

APPLICATION INFORMATION

Instructions: Submit to the Commission the electronic application and all support documentation: www.fulbright.es

CONTACT

US-Spain Fulbright Commission
General Oráa, 55, planta baja
24
28006 Madrid
Spain
Tel: +34 (91) 702 7000
Email: postmaster@comision-fulbright.com
Web: www.fulbright.es

US-Spain Fulbright Commission

Fulbright Study in the Arts

PROGRAM INFORMATION

Description: Artistic studies or cultural management

Levels of Study: Graduate

Field of Study: Arts and Culture, Museum Studies, Music

Nationality: Europe

AWARD INFORMATION

Award Type: Grant

Award Coverage: Tuition, housing/living expenses, roundtrip travel, settling-in allowance, and health/accident insurance.

Award Duration: 6-12 months; no renewal option

ELIGIBILITY REQUIREMENTS

- Spain or EU Citizenship
- Degree conferred by a Spanish university or recognized by the Spanish authorities, only in cases of specialization in artistic creation and interpretation will other levels of education be accepted
- TOEFL or IELTS score required

APPLICATION INFORMATION

Instructions: Submit to the Commission the electronic application and all support documentation: www.fulbright.es

CONTACT

Fulbright Commission
Academic Advisor
General Oráa, 55, planta baja
28006 Madrid
Spain
Tel: +34 (91) 702 7000
Fax: +34 (91) 702 2185
Email: postmaster@comision-fulbright.com
Web: www.fulbright.es

US-Spain Fulbright Commission

Fulbright Ministry of Industry, Energy, and Tourism

PROGRAM INFORMATION

Description: Academic and professional training

Levels of Study: Graduate

Nationality: Europe

AWARD INFORMATION

Award Type: Grant

Award Coverage: Tuition or project expenses, housing/living expenses, roundtrip travel, settling-in and book allowances, health/accident insurance, when applicable, support for dependents

Award Duration: 1-2 years

ELIGIBILITY REQUIREMENTS

- Degree(s) conferred by a Spanish university or recognized by the Spanish authorities
- Must have excellent command of English
- To hold a position within the Ministry of Industry, Energy and Tourism or its agencies for a minimum of the last 2 years

APPLICATION INFORMATION

Instructions: Submit to the Commission the electronic application and all support documentation: www.fulbright.es

CONTACT

US-Spain Fulbright Commission
General Oráa, 55, planta baja
28006 Madrid
Spain
Tel: 91 702 7000
Fax: 91 702 2185
Email: postmaster@comision-fulbright.com
Web: www.fulbright.es

US-Spain Fulbright Commission

Fulbright Master's Degree Study

PROGRAM INFORMATION

Description: Intended for a Master's Degree in the Humanities, Social Sciences or Arts

Levels of Study: Graduate

Field of Study: Arts and Culture, Humanities, Social Science

Nationality: Europe

AWARD INFORMATION

Award Type: Grant

Award Coverage: Partial tuition award, housing/living expenses, roundtrip travel, and health/accident insurance

Award Duration: 10 to 12 months, renewable for up to 12 months more

ELIGIBILITY REQUIREMENTS

- Spain or EU Citizenship
- Undergraduate degree in the Arts, Humanities or Social Sciences within last 6 years
- Excellent command of English

APPLICATION INFORMATION

Instructions: Submit to the Commission the electronic application and all support documentation: www.fulbright.es

CONTACT

US-Spain Fulbright Commission
General Oráa, 55, planta baja
28006 Madrid
Spain
Email: postmaster@comision-fulbright.com
Web: www.fulbright.es

US-Spain Fulbright Commission

Ruth Lee Kennedy Travel Grant

PROGRAM INFORMATION

Description: For college women to enhance their knowledge of US higher education institutions

Nationality: Europe

AWARD INFORMATION

Award Type: Grant

Average Amount: Travel Costs

ELIGIBILITY REQUIREMENTS

- Not currently residing in the US
- Excellent command of English
- Degree(s) conferred within the last 6 years

APPLICATION INFORMATION

Instructions: Submit to the Commission the electronic application and all support documentation: www.fulbright.es

CONTACT

US-Spain Fulbright Commission
General Oráa, 55, planta baja
28006 Madrid
Spain
Tel: +34 (91) 702 7000
Fax: +34 (91) 702 2185
Email: postmaster@comision-fulbright.com
Web: www.fulbright.es

US-Spain Fulbright Commission

Fulbright Foreign Language Teaching Assistants

PROGRAM INFORMATION

Description: Teach Spanish in US colleges and universities

Levels of Study: Graduate

Field of Study: Education, English as a Second Language, Spanish, TESOL

Nationality: Europe

AWARD INFORMATION

Award Type: Grant

Average Amount: $4,000

Award Coverage: $4,000 to cover roundtrip travel and to supplement the host institution financial/in-kind support

Award Duration: 1 academic year

ELIGIBILITY REQUIREMENTS

- Spain or EU Citizenship
- Undergraduate degree in education, Spanish or English language/literature, or closely related fields

APPLICATION INFORMATION

Instructions: Submit to the Commission the electronic application and all support documentation: www.fulbright.es

CONTACT

US-Spain Fulbright Commission
General Oráa, 55, planta baja
28006 Madrid
Spain
Email: postmaster@comision-fulbright.com
Web: www.fulbright.es

US-Spain Fulbright Commission

Fulbright Ministry of Public Administration

PROGRAM INFORMATION

Description: Academic and professional training

Levels of Study: Graduate

Nationality: Europe

AWARD INFORMATION

Award Type: Grant

Award Coverage: Tuition or project expenses, housing/living expenses, roundtrip travel, settling-in and book allowances, health/accident insurance, when applicable, support for dependents

Award Duration: 9-12 months, no renewal option

ELIGIBILITY REQUIREMENTS

- Degree(s) conferred by a Spanish university or recognized by the Spanish educational authorities
- Excellent command of English
- To hold a position within the Ministry of Public Administration or its agencies for a minimum of the last 2 years

APPLICATION INFORMATION

Instructions: Submit to the Commission the electronic application and all support documentation: www.fulbright.es

CONTACT

US-Spain Fulbright Commission
General Oráa, 55, planta baja
28006 Madrid
Spain
Tel: +34 (91) 702 7000
Email: postmaster@comision-fulbright.com
Web: www.fulbright.es

US-Spain Fulbright Commission

Fulbright Ministry of Public Works

PROGRAM INFORMATION

Description: Academic and professional training

Levels of Study: Graduate

Nationality: Europe

AWARD INFORMATION

Award Type: Grant

Award Coverage: Tuition or project expenses, housing/living expenses, roundtrip travel, settling-in and book allowances, health/accident insurance, when applicable, support for dependents

Award Duration: 6 - 12 months, no renewal option

ELIGIBILITY REQUIREMENTS

- Degree(s) conferred by a Spanish university or recognized by the Spanish educational authorities
- Excellent command of English
- To hold a position within the Ministry of Public Works or its agencies for a minimum of the last 2 years

APPLICATION INFORMATION

Instructions: Submit to the Commission the electronic application and all support documentation: www.Fulbright.es

CONTACT

US-Spain Fulbright Commission
General Oráa, 55, planta baja
28006 Madrid
Spain
Tel: +34 (91) 702 7000
Email: postmaster@comision-fulbright.com
Web: postmaster@comision-fulbright.com

US-UK Fulbright Commission

Fulbright Fight for Sight Research Award

PROGRAM INFORMATION

Description: This award in partnership with the Fulbright Commission will support pioneering research into the prevention of sight loss and the treatment of eye disease at any accredited US institution chosen by the awardee. Grants are awarded for projects of 9-12 months.

Levels of Study: Post Doctorate, Professional

Field of Study: Biology, Biomedical Humanities, Biotechnology, Cognitive Science, Communication Technologies, Health Professions, Health Studies, Imaging Science/Color Science, Information Technology, Medicine, Minority Rights, Optics, Photonics, Physical Sciences, Public Health, Social Science

AWARD INFORMATION

Award Type: Award, Grant, Scholarship

Average Amount: $120,000, prorated for shorter projects

Number of Awards: 1

Award Coverage: $ equivalent of £75,000 (converted using the prevailing rate), paid in installments directly to the grantee, the first of which is typically given just prior to departure from the UK; this funding is intended as a contribution toward any institutional fees, travel to/from the US, general maintenance costs while in the US

Award Duration: 1 year

ELIGIBILITY REQUIREMENTS

- Must be a UK citizen
- Must hold a PhD
- Projects that involve direct patient clinical contact are not permitted
- Awards are not available for peripatetic visits or attendance at conferences only

APPLICATION INFORMATION

Award Deadline: Oct 31

CONTACT

US-UK Fulbright Commission
Fulbright Awards Programme
188 Kirtling Street
London SW8 5BN
UK
Tel: +44 (0) 207 498 4010
Email: programmes@fulbright.org.uk
Web: www.fightforsight.org.uk/fulbright-and-fight-for-sight-research-award

US-UK Fulbright Commission

Fulbright Royal College of Surgeons of England Research Award

PROGRAM INFORMATION

Description: Each year, 1 award is offered in conjunction with Royal College of Surgeons of England, to a surgeon, trainee surgeon, or specialist to pursue research (that does not include clinical work, laboratory-based or otherwise) into the development of new operative techniques, improvements in patient care and recovery, and/or the causes of surgical conditions and how to treat them, at any accredited US higher education institution. As an applicant for this award you should be a member of The Royal College of Surgeons of England at the time of applying.

Levels of Study: Graduate, Doctorate, Post Doctorate, Professional

Field of Study: Biology, Biomedical Humanities, Biotechnology, Health Professions, Health Studies, Medicine, Neuroscience, Optics, Science, Science Technologies, Veterinary Medical Technology

AWARD INFORMATION

Award Type: Award, Grant, Scholarship

Average Amount: £2,275 per month

Number of Awards: 1

Award Coverage: Institutional fees, travel to/from the US, accommodation, general maintenance costs

Award Duration: 3-12 months

ELIGIBILITY REQUIREMENTS

- Must be a UK citizen (resident anywhere)
- Must be a member of The Royal College of Surgeons of England
- Must hold or expect to receive a Bachelor of Medicine, Bachelor of Surgery, master's, PhD, or equivalent professional training or experience in a relevant area before departure to the US
- Projects that involve direct patient clinical contact are not permitted
- Awards are not available for peripatetic visits or attendance at conferences only

APPLICATION INFORMATION

Award Deadline: Oct 31

CONTACT

US-US Fulbright Commission
Fulbright Awards Programme
188 Kirtling Street
London SW8 5BN
UK
Tel: +44 (0) 207 498 4010
Email: programmes@fulbright.org.uk
Web: www.fulbright.org.uk

US-UK Fulbright Commission

Fulbright Scottish Studies Award

PROGRAM INFORMATION

Description: Up to 3 awards are offered to an outstanding UK professional or academic to undertake lecturing, carry out research relating to Scottish studies, and develop institutional links with any accredited US institution.

Levels of Study: Post Doctorate, Professional

Field of Study: Area and Ethnic Studies, Art History, Arts and Culture, European Studies/EU Studies, History, International Relations

Nationality: United Kingdom

AWARD INFORMATION

Award Type: Award, Grant, Scholarship

Average Amount: $5,000 per month

Number of Awards: 1

Award Duration: 3-8 months

ELIGIBILITY REQUIREMENTS

- Must be a UK citizen (resident anywhere)
- Must hold or expect to receive a PhD (or equivalent professional training or experience) in a relevant area before departure to the US
- Projects that involve direct patient clinical contact are not permitted
- Awards are not available for peripatetic visits or attendance at conferences only

APPLICATION INFORMATION

Award Deadline: Nov 15

CONTACT

US-UK Fulbright Commission
Fulbright Awards Programme
188 Kirtling Street
London SW8 5BN
UK
Tel: +44 (0) 207 498 4010
Email: programmes@fulbright.co.uk
Web: www.fulbright.co.uk

US-UK Fulbright Commission

Fulbright Research and/or Lecturing Awards

PROGRAM INFORMATION

Description: The Fulbright Commission seeks applications from outstanding professionals or academics in any field, to undertake lecturing, research, and/or professional development in the US for 3 to 10 months. Up to 5 awards are granted each year in this category.

Levels of Study: Post Doctorate, Professional

Field of Study: All

Nationality: United Kingdom

AWARD INFORMATION

Award Type: Award, Grant, Scholarship

Average Amount: $5,000 per month

Number of Awards: Up to 5

Award Coverage: Stipend, accident and sickness benefit coverage, visa processing, and participation in a number of Fulbright Scholar events

Award Duration: 3-10 months

ELIGIBILITY REQUIREMENTS

- Must be a UK citizen (resident anywhere)
- Must hold or expect to receive a PhD in a relevant area before departure to the US
- Applicants must draw up a detailed project outline and provide evidence that a US institution will agree to act as host and supervisor
- Preference will be given to those who do not have extensive, recent experience in the US (6 months or more)

APPLICATION INFORMATION

Award Deadline: Oct 31

Instructions: Applications are made online; you will need to register with the online application site which can be accessed via the US-UK Fulbright website; you will be able to log in and out of your application account and will not be required to complete the application in 1 sitting

CONTACT

The US-UK Fulbright Commission
Fulbright Awards Programme
188 Kirtling Street
SW8 5BN London
United Kingdom
Email: programmes@fulbright.org.uk
Web: www.fulbright.org.uk

US-UK Fulbright Commission

Fulbright Alistair Cooke Award in Journalism

PROGRAM INFORMATION

Description: This award is named in honor of the great trans-Atlantic journalist and commentator Alistair Cooke, and is given to 1 scholar each year seeking a master's in journalism or in a specialist subject leading to a career in journalism (e.g. Middle Eastern Studies) at any accredited US university.

Levels of Study: Graduate

Field of Study: Area and Ethnic Studies, Communications and Journalism, Journalism, Photojournalism

Nationality: United Kingdom

AWARD INFORMATION

Award Type: Award, Grant, Scholarship

Average Amount: Up to $45,000

Number of Awards: 1

Award Coverage: Tuition, fees, living stipend, visa sponsorship, sickness and accident benefit coverage

ELIGIBILITY REQUIREMENTS

- Must be a UK citizen (resident anywhere)
- Must hold or expect to obtain a minimum 2:1 undergraduate degree or the equivalent prior to your anticipated enrollment with a US university

APPLICATION INFORMATION

Award Deadline: Oct 31

Instructions: Applications are made online; you will need to register with the online application site which can be accessed via the US-UK Fulbright website; you will be able to log in and out of your application account and will not be required to complete the application in 1 sitting

CONTACT

The US-UK Fulbright Commission
Fulbright Awards Programme
188 Kirtling Street
SW8 5BN London
United Kingdom
Email: programmes@fulbright.org.uk
Web: www.fulbright.org.uk

US-UK Fulbright Commission

Fulbright UK Postgraduate Student Awards

PROGRAM INFORMATION

Description: This award is offered to UK citizens for master's or PhD study in any discipline at any accredited US university (please note that there are separate awards for scholars specializing in journalism, film, or wishing to take an MBA at Harvard).

Levels of Study: Graduate

Field of Study: All

Nationality: United Kingdom

AWARD INFORMATION

Award Type: Award, Grant, Scholarship

Average Amount: Up to $45,000

Number of Awards: Up to 25

Award Coverage: Tuition, maintenance costs, health insurance, visa processing, participation in a number of Fulbright Scholar events

Award Duration: First postgraduate academic year

ELIGIBILITY REQUIREMENTS

- Must be a UK citizen (resident anywhere)
- Must hold or expect to obtain a minimum 2:1 undergraduate degree or the equivalent prior to your anticipated enrollment with a US university
- Preference will be given to those who do not have extensive, recent experience in the US (6 months or more)

APPLICATION INFORMATION

Award Deadline: Oct 31

Instructions: Applications are made online; you will need to register with the online application site which can be accessed via the US-UK Fulbright website; you will be able to log in and out of your application account and will not be required to complete the application in 1 sitting

CONTACT

The US-UK Fulbright Commission
Fulbright Awards Programme
188 Kirtling Street
SW8 5BN London
United Kingdom
Email: programmes@fulbright.org.uk
Web: www.fulbright.org.uk

US-UK Fulbright Commission

Fulbright Northern Ireland Public Sector Fellowships

PROGRAM INFORMATION

Description: In this Award category, approx 3 grants are offered to those working in the public sector in Northern Ireland at senior management level (equivalent to Grade 7 and above in the NICS) to pursue research and/or assess best practice affiliated with any US institution for a period of 3 to 5 months. Candidates from non-departmental government organizations across the whole public sector, covering the 3 main areas of health, education and local government, as well as the range of public sector arms-length bodies sponsored by government departments are encouraged to apply. Given the relatively short nature of the appointment, proposals should focus on research and assessing best practice rather than gaining a qualification for a period of 3-10 months.

Levels of Study: Professional

Field of Study: All

Nationality: Ireland, United Kingdom

AWARD INFORMATION

Award Type: Award, Fellowship, Grant, Scholarship

Average Amount: Varies

Number of Awards: Approx 3

Award Coverage: The award is for $5,000 per month paid in installments directly to the grantee, the first of which is typically given just prior to departure from the UK

Award Duration: 3-5 months

ELIGIBILITY REQUIREMENTS

- Must be a UK citizen (resident anywhere) or Irish citizen (resident in Northern Ireland)
- Must be a Northern Ireland Civil Servant at grade 7/A or above
- Must have the endorsement of employer/Permanent Secretary
- Preference will be given to those who do not have extensive, recent experience in the US (6 months or more)

APPLICATION INFORMATION

Award Deadline: Oct 31

Instructions: Applications are made online; you will need to register with the online application site which can be accessed via the US-UK Fulbright website; you will be able to log in and out of your application account and will not be required to complete the application in 1 sitting

CONTACT

The US-UK Fulbright Commission
Fulbright Awards Programme
188 Kirtling Street
SW8 5BN London
United Kingdom
Email: programmes@fulbright.org.uk
Web: www.fulbright.org.uk

US-UK Fulbright Commission

Fulbright Police Research Fellowships

PROGRAM INFORMATION

Description: The Fulbright Police Research Fellowships enable British police officers and civilian staff to conduct research, develop professional expertise, and gain experience in the US for periods of 3 to 5 months. In exchange for serving as host, fellows can be a resource for US institutions by offering to speak to students and faculty about policing in the UK. These fellowships are available to members of the Metropolitan Police Service and Scottish Police.

Levels of Study: Professional

Field of Study: All

Nationality: United Kingdom

AWARD INFORMATION

Award Type: Award, Fellowship, Grant

Average Amount: Up to $3680 per month

Number of Awards: Up to 3

Award Coverage: Living stipend, accident and sickness benefit coverage, visa processing, participation in a number of Fulbright Scholar events

Award Duration: 3-5 months

ELIGIBILITY REQUIREMENTS

- Must be a UK citizen (resident anywhere)
- Must be an active police officer or civilian staff (any rank)
- Preference will be given to those who do not have extensive, recent experience in the US (6 months or more)
- Female and ethnic minority staff are particularly encouraged to apply
- Must draw up a detailed project outline and provide evidence that a US institution will agree to act as host and supervisor
- Applications must be endorsed by the applicant's chief officer or head of human resources

APPLICATION INFORMATION

Award Deadline: Oct 31

Instructions: Applications are made online; you will need to register with the online application site which can be accessed via the US-UK Fulbright website; you will be able to log in and out of your application account and will not be required to complete the application in 1 sitting

CONTACT

The US-UK Fulbright Commission
Fulbright Awards Programme
188 Kirtling Street
SW8 5BN London
United Kingdom
Email: programmes@fulbright.org.uk
Web: www.fulbright.org.uk

Union for International Cancer Control UICC

UICC Yamagiwa-Yoshida Memorial International Cancer Study Grants

PROGRAM INFORMATION

Description: UICC Yamagiwa-Yoshida Memorial International Cancer Study Grants are funded with the objective of enabling cancer investigators from any country to carry out bilateral research projects abroad which take advantage of complementary materials or skills, including advanced training in experimental methods or special techniques.

Levels of Study: Post Doctorate, Professional

Field of Study: Health Professions, Medicine, Public Health

Nationality: Any Region

AWARD INFORMATION

Award Type: Grant

Average Amount: $10,000

Number of Awards: 14-16

Award Coverage: Living stipend, travel

Award Duration: 3 months

ELIGIBILITY REQUIREMENTS

- Must possess appropriate scientific or medical qualifications and a minimum of 2 years postdoctoral experience actively engaged in cancer research
- Research plan must be basic, translational or applied cancer research, prevention-oriented projects are especially encouraged
- Must be currently engaged in cancer research and/or clinical oncology practice
- Must demonstrate proficiency in English

APPLICATION INFORMATION

Award Deadline: Jan 15 and Jul 1

Instructions: Download or contact to request application materials

CONTACT

International Union Against Cancer/
Union Internationale Contre le Cancer
Fellowships Team
62 route de Frontenex
1207 Geneva
Switzerland
Tel: +41 (22) 809-18-11
Fax: +41 (22) 809-18-10
Email: fellows@uicc.org
Web: www.uicc.org

Union for International Cancer Control UICC

UICC International Fellowships for Beginning Investigators

PROGRAM INFORMATION

Description: This fellowship aims to foster a bi-directional flow of research knowledge, experience, expertise, and innovation between countries; to support the promotion of cancer control in developing countries through epidemiology and cancer control; to advance the academic career development of beginning cancer investigators through clinical, behavioral, or translational research projects.

Levels of Study: Doctorate, Post Doctorate, Professional

Field of Study: Health Professions, Medicine, Public Health

Nationality: Any Region

AWARD INFORMATION

Award Type: Fellowship

Average Amount: $50,000

Number of Awards: 6-8

Award Coverage: Living stipend, travel

Award Duration: 1 year

ELIGIBILITY REQUIREMENTS

- Must be a beginning investigator or clinician in the early stages of their independent investigator career and must possess a terminal, advanced degree with a desire to become an independent investigator
- Must be in the early phases of their career and no longer under research mentoring
- Must hold an academic university or hospital position with an explicit commitment to return to the home institute
- Must conduct the research at not-for-profit institutions

APPLICATION INFORMATION

Award Deadline: Nov

Instructions: Applicants must complete the online application in order to be considered

CONTACT

Union for International Cancer Control/
Union Internationale Contre le Cancer (UICC)
62 route de Frontenex
1207 Geneva
Switzerland
Tel: +41 (22) 809-18-11
Fax: +41 (22) 809-18-10
Email: fellows@uicc.org
Web: www.uicc.org/fellowships/beginning-investigators

US Institute of Peace

US Institute of Peace Grants

PROGRAM INFORMATION

Description: The US Institute of Peace offers financial support for research, education and training, and the dissemination of information on international peace and conflict resolution. Grants are awarded for support of projects. This program does not support degree work.

Levels of Study: Professional

Field of Study: Conflict Management

Nationality: Any Region

AWARD INFORMATION

Award Type: Grant
Average Amount: Varies
Number of Awards: Varies
Award Coverage: Project expenses
Award Duration: 1-2 years

ELIGIBILITY REQUIREMENTS

- It is preferred that individual grant recipients have an institutional affiliation

APPLICATION INFORMATION

Award Deadline: Oct
Instructions: Download or contact to request application materials

CONTACT

US Institute of Peace
2301 Constitution Avenue, NW
Washington, DC 20037
Tel: +1 (202) 457-1700
Fax: +1 (202) 429-6063
Email: fellows@usip.org
Web: www.usip.org/grants-fellowships/annual-grant-competition

US-India Educational Foundation

Fulbright-Nehru International Education Administrators Seminar

PROGRAM INFORMATION

Description: The Fulbright-Nehru International Education Administrators Seminar aims to provide Indian college and university administrators the opportunity to familiarize themselves with the US higher education system. Participants will gain a firsthand experience of a cross section of US institutions and meet with key university administrators and officials responsible for international programs and activities at their institutions. The 2-week visit will enable participants to learn about various facets of US higher education, including the types of institutions, accreditation, curriculum development, fund raising, student services and international education on US campuses, as well as share knowledge on Indian higher education. Topics addressed during visits and meetings at select campuses and organizations will also include research collaborations, faculty and student exchanges, and study abroad.
Nationality: India

AWARD INFORMATION

Award Type: Fellowship
Award Coverage: Round-trip economy class air travel from India to the US, travel within the US, lodging and a per-diem
Award Duration: 2 weeks

ELIGIBILITY REQUIREMENTS

- Applicants should be mid to senior-level college or university administrators (deans, department heads, directors of international centers/offices, foreign student advisors, or registrars etc.) working at Indian institutions
- Applicants should have substantial responsibility for enhancing the international dimension of their institutions and should wish to build capacity of their faculty and students through international collaborations and exchange and innovative curricular design
- Preferably be 55 years of age or under
- Have at least 2 years' experience in international education

APPLICATION INFORMATION

Instructions: For complete details, please visit USIEF's website: www.usief.org.in

CONTACT

US-India Educational Foundation (USIEF)
Indian Program
12, Hailey Road
New Delhi 110001
India
Tel: +91-11-4209-0909
Email: ip@usief.org.in
Web: www.usief.org.in

US-India Educational Foundation

Hubert H. Humphrey Fellowship Program

PROGRAM INFORMATION

Description: The Hubert H. Humphrey Fellowship Program, which is a Fulbright program, brings accomplished young and mid-career professionals from developing countries to the US for 10 months of non-degree graduate study and related practical professional experiences. The program is designed to meet the requirements of policy makers, planners, administrators, and managers in the government, public and private sectors, and non-governmental organizations, who have a public service commitment, demonstrated leadership potential, and commitment to their own country's development.
Nationality: India

AWARD INFORMATION

Award Type: Fellowship
Award Coverage: Tuition and fees, a monthly maintenance allowance, Accident and Sickness Program for Exchanges per US Government guidelines, a modest allowance for books and supplies, round-trip international air travel to the host institution, domestic travel to the Washington, DC workshop, allowances for professional activities such as field trips, professional visits, conferences
Award Duration: 10 months

ELIGIBILITY REQUIREMENTS

- Preferably have a master's degree or a professional degree of at least 4 years' duration
- At least 5 years of substantial professional experience in the respective field, and be eligible for leave
- Demonstrated leadership qualities
- Record of public service in the community
- Provide an undertaking to return to India on completion of the fellowship

APPLICATION INFORMATION

Instructions: For complete details, please visit USIEF's website: www.usief.org.in

CONTACT

US-India Educational Foundation (USIEF)
Indian Program
12, Hailey Road
New Delhi 110001
India
Tel: +91-11-4209-0909
Email: ip@usief.org.in
Web: www.usief.org.in

US-India Educational Foundation

Fulbright Foreign Language Teaching Assistant (FLTA) Program

PROGRAM INFORMATION

Description: The FLTA program is designed for young Indian teachers of English or training to become teachers of English, or young educators in a related field. Selected FLTAs from India will teach Bengali, Hindi or Urdu at selected U.S campuses during their 9 month non-degree grant.
Nationality: India

ELIGIBILITY REQUIREMENTS

- Should be an Indian citizen holding a valid Indian passport. Applicants must be residing in India throughout the application, nomination and selection process
- Fluency in English is mandatory; a score of no less than 213 (CBT), 79-80 (iBT) or 550 (PBT) on the TOEFL is required; TOEFL scores are not required at the time of application; candidates recommended by the selection committee will have to appear for the TOEFL
- Applicants should have at least a Master's degree and is a young teacher of English at the college level or training to become a teacher of English, or is a young educator in a related field
- Prior teaching experience is preferred in case of English language teachers or those training to become teachers of English, however, a candidate in a related field should have prior teaching experience

APPLICATION INFORMATION

Instructions: For complete details, please visit USIEF's website: www.usief.org.in

CONTACT

US-India Educational Foundation (USIEF)
Indian Program
12, Hailey Road
New Delhi 110001
India
Tel: +91-11-4209-0909
Email: ip@usief.org.in
Web: www.usief.org.in

US-India Educational Foundation

Fulbright Distinguished Awards in Teaching Program

PROGRAM INFORMATION

Description: The Fulbright Distinguished Awards in Teaching Program is designed for full-time teachers teaching any subject at any level (primary, middle or secondary) at a school in India; primary and secondary level media specialists/librarians, guidance counselors, curriculum specialists, special education coordinators, gifted and talented coordinators, and administrators who spend at least fifty percent of their time teaching or working directly with students.
Nationality: India

AWARD INFORMATION

Award Type: Fellowship
Award Duration: 1 semester

ELIGIBILITY REQUIREMENTS

- Be a citizen of India and reside in India at the time of application and be qualified to obtain/hold a valid Indian passport.
- Hold at least a bachelor's degree, a teacher training degree is preferred
- Demonstrate experience conducting and leading workshops or other professional development activities for the colleagues
- Demonstrate accomplishment in teaching or have previously received teaching awards or exemplary evaluations and good English language competence
- Teacher trainers are eligible to apply

APPLICATION INFORMATION

Instructions: For complete details, please visit USIEF's website: www.usief.org.in

CONTACT

US-India Educational Foundation (USIEF)
Indian Program
12, Hailey Road
New Delhi 110001
India
Tel: +91-11-4209-0909
Email: ip@usief.org.in
Web: www.usief.org.in

US-India Educational Foundation

Fulbright-Nehru Master's Fellowships

PROGRAM INFORMATION

Description: The Fulbright-Nehru Master's Fellowships are designed for outstanding Indians residing in India to pursue a master's degree program at selected US colleges and universities in the areas of Arts and Culture Management including Heritage Conservation and Museum Studies; Environmental Science/Studies; Higher Education Administration; Public Health; Urban and Regional Planning; and Women's Studies/Gender Studies. These fellowships are for highly motivated individuals who demonstrate leadership qualities, have completed the equivalent of a US bachelor's degree, have at least 3 years professional work experience, and are committed to return and contribute to their communities. The fellowships are for 1 to 2 years.

Nationality: India

AWARD INFORMATION

Award Type: Fellowship

Award Coverage: J-1 visa support; Round-trip economy class air travel from fellow's home city to the host institution in the US; Funding for tuition and fees, living and related costs; Accident and Sickness Program for Exchanges per US Government guidelines

Award Duration: 1 to 2 years

ELIGIBILITY REQUIREMENTS

- Should have completed an equivalent of a US bachelor's degree from a recognized Indian university with at least 55% marks
- Applicants should either possess a 4-year bachelor's degree or a completed master's degree, if the bachelor's degree is of less than 4 years' duration
- At least 3 years' full-time (paid or voluntary) professional work experience relevant to your proposed field of study
- Should experience in leadership and community service
- Should not have another degree from a US university or be enrolled in a US degree program

APPLICATION INFORMATION

Award Deadline: Jul 1, 2015

Instructions: For complete details, visit USIEF website: www.usief.org.in

CONTACT

US-India Educational Foundation (USIEF)
Indian Program
12, Hailey Road
New Delhi 110001
Tel: +91-11-4209-0909
Email: ip@usief.org.in
Web: www.usief.org.in

US-India Educational Foundation

Fulbright-Nehru Doctoral Research Fellowships

PROGRAM INFORMATION

Description: These are pre-doctoral level research fellowships, for 6 to 9 months, designed for Indian scholars who are registered for a PhD at an Indian institution. The fellows will be affiliated to 1 US host institution for their grant. USIEF strongly recommends all applicants to identify institutions with which they wish to be affiliated and to correspond, in advance, with potential host institutions.

Nationality: India

AWARD INFORMATION

Award Type: Fellowship

Award Coverage: Monthly stipend, Accident and Sickness Program for Exchanges per US Government guidelines, round-trip economy class air travel, applicable allowances and modest affiliation fees, if any

Award Duration: 6 - 9 months

ELIGIBILITY REQUIREMENTS

- You should have done adequate research in the relevant field, especially in the identification of resources in India and the US, you should be registered for your PhD at an Indian institution at least 1 year prior to the date of application
- This grant is intended for PhD students to conduct research essential to their dissertations/theses, therefore, your expected PhD thesis submission date should not be earlier than 3 months after your Fulbright-Nehru grant end date
- You should upload a 'writing sample' such as a copy of an article or paper published/presented or extracts from your M.Phil. thesis in your online application form
- If you are employed, please follow the instructions carefully regarding employer's endorsement. If applicable, please obtain the endorsement from the appropriate administrative authority on the FNDR Employer's Endorsement Form (available on the website), the employer must indicate that leave will be granted for the fellowship period

APPLICATION INFORMATION

Instructions: For complete details, please visit USIEF's website: www.usief.org.in

CONTACT

US-India Educational Foundation (USIEF)
Indian Program
12, Hailey Road
New Delhi 110001
India
Tel: +91-11-4209-0909
Email: ip@usief.org.in
Web: www.usief.org.in

US-India Educational Foundation

Fulbright-Nehru Postdoctoral Research Fellowships

PROGRAM INFORMATION

Description: The Postdoctoral Research Fellowships, for 8 to 24 months, are designed for Indian faculty and researchers residing in India, who have a PhD degree within the past 4 years. These Fellowships will provide opportunities to talented faculty and researchers to strengthen their research capacities. Postdoctoral fellows will have access to some of the finest resources in their areas of interest and will help build long-term collaborative relationships with US faculty and institutions.

Nationality: India

AWARD INFORMATION

Award Type: Fellowship

Award Duration: 8 - 24 months

ELIGIBILITY REQUIREMENTS

- You should have a PhD degree within the past 4 years. You must have obtained the PhD degrees in the last 4 years; you are required to upload your PhD degree certificate/provisional PhD degree certificate in your online application
- You must be published in reputed journals and demonstrate evidence of superior academic and professional achievement. Your recent publication has to be uploaded in your online application
- If you are employed, please follow the instructions carefully regarding employer's endorsement, if applicable, please obtain the endorsement from the appropriate administrative authority on the FNPostdoc Employer's Endorsement Form; the employer must indicate that leave will be granted for the fellowship period

APPLICATION INFORMATION

Instructions: For complete details, visit USIEF website: www.usief.org.in

CONTACT

US-India Educational Foundation (USIEF)
Indian Program
12, Hailey Road
New Delhi 110001
India
Tel: +91-11-4209-0909
Email: ip@usief.org.in
Web: www.usief.org.in

US-India Educational Foundation

Fulbright-Nehru Academic and Professional Excellence Fellowships

PROGRAM INFORMATION

Description: The Fulbright-Nehru Academic and Professional Excellence Fellowships aim to provide Indian faculty, researchers, and professionals residing in India the opportunity to teach, conduct research, or carry out a combination of lecturing and research at a US institution.

Nationality: India

AWARD INFORMATION

Award Type: Fellowship

Award Coverage: Round-trip economy class air travel, a monthly stipend, Accident and Sickness Program for Exchanges per US Government guidelines, a modest settling-in allowance, a professional allowance

Award Duration: 4 to 9 months

ELIGIBILITY REQUIREMENTS

- Faculty/researchers should have a PhD degree or equivalent published work with at least 5 years of relevant teaching/research experience
- Professionals outside academe should have a Master's degree or equivalent published work with recognized professional standing and at least 5 years relevant experience
- A recent significant publication (copy of paper/article) should be uploaded in your online application
- If you are employed, the employer must indicate that leave will be granted for the fellowship period; please obtain the endorsement from the appropriate administrative authority on the FNAPE Employer's Endorsement Form, you can download the Employer's Endorsement Form from the USIEF website

APPLICATION INFORMATION

Instructions: For complete details, please visit USIEF's website: www.usief.org.in

CONTACT

US-India Educational Foundation (USIEF)
Indian Program
12, Hailey Road
New Delhi 110001
India
Tel: +91-11-4209-0909
Email: ip@usief.org.in
Web: www.usief.org.in

US-India Educational Foundation

Fulbright-Nehru-CII Fellowships for Leadership in Management

PROGRAM INFORMATION

Description: The Fulbright-Nehru-CII Fellowships for Leadership in Management are awarded to Indian business managers, whose employers would be willing to bear 50% of the total cost of the fellowship, to attend a specially-designed general management program at the Tepper School of Business, Carnegie Mellon University, Pittsburgh, Pennsylvania for a period of 10 weeks.

Nationality: India

APPLICATION INFORMATION

Instructions: For more details, please visit USIEF website: www.usief.org.in

CONTACT

US-India Educational Foundation (USIEF)
Indian Program
12, Hailey Road
New Delhi 110001
India
Tel: +91-11-4209-0909
Email: ip@usief.org.in
Web: www.usief.org.in

US-Norway Fulbright Foundation

Norwegian Fulbright Student Program

PROGRAM INFORMATION

Description: Stipends are available for Norwegian students who will undertake a partial or complete master's or PhD degree in the US Stipends are available in all disciplines and can be used at any accredited American university. Stipends are for students planning a minimum of 1 academic year study in the US

Levels of Study: Graduate, Doctorate

Field of Study: All

Nationality: Norway

ELIGIBILITY REQUIREMENTS

- Must be a Norwegian citizen.
- Must not yet have started studies in the US
- Must have a bachelor degree by the time the grant commences
- Study must be at an accredited US university

APPLICATION INFORMATION

Award Deadline: Oct 1

Instructions: Please visit the Fulbright website: www.fulbright.no

CONTACT

US-Norway Fulbright Foundation
Arbinsgate 2
0275 Oslo
Norway
Tel: (+47) 22 01 40 10
Web: www.fulbright.no/en/grants/norwegian_citizens/norwegian_graduate_students/

US-Norway Fulbright Foundation

Norwegian Fulbright Scholar Program

PROGRAM INFORMATION

Description: The scholar program offers Norwegian citizens with a PhD or equivalent degree in any field the opportunity to do research and/or teach in the US for a period of 3 to 9 months.

Levels of Study: Post Doctorate, Professional

Nationality: Norway

AWARD INFORMATION

Award Type: Grant

Average Amount: 60,000 NOK

Number of Awards: Approx 20

Award Duration: 3-12 months

ELIGIBILITY REQUIREMENTS

- Must be a Norwegian citizen
- Must possess a PhD or other terminal degree
- Must have a minimum stay in the US of 3 months

APPLICATION INFORMATION

Award Deadline: Oct 1

Instructions: Please see www.fulbright.no for more information

CONTACT

US-Norway Fulbright Foundation
Arbinsgate 2
Oslo
0275 Oslo
Norway
Tel: (+47) 22 01 40 10
Web: www.fulbright.no/en/grants/norwegian_citizens/norwegian_scholars/

W. Eugene Smith Memorial Fund

W. Eugene Smith Grant in Humanistic Photography

PROGRAM INFORMATION

Description: The grant is intended to support a project that follows the tradition of Eugene Smith's companioned dedication to photojournalism exhibited during his 45-year career.

Levels of Study: Professional

Field of Study: Journalism, Photography, Photojournalism

Nationality: Any Region

AWARD INFORMATION

Award Type: Grant

Average Amount: $30,000-$35,000

Number of Awards: Varies

Award Coverage: Varies

ELIGIBILITY REQUIREMENTS

- Must demonstrate the merits of the intended project
- Must agree to provide set of 12 prints delivered to the Smith Fund within 18 months

APPLICATION INFORMATION

Award Deadline: Jun

Instructions: Download or contact to request application materials

CONTACT

International Center of Photography
W. Eugene Smith Memorial Fund
1114 Avenue of the Americas
New York, NY 10036
Web: www.smithfund.org/eugene-smith-grant

Wenner-Gren Foundation for Anthropological Research

Hunt Postdoctoral Fellowships

PROGRAM INFORMATION

Description: Richard Carley Hunt Postdoctoral Fellowships are available annually to scholars within 10 years of receipt of a postdoctorate degree. The award is to aid the write-up of research results for publication. Research must be of importance to anthropological topics and debates.

Levels of Study: Post Doctorate

Field of Study: Anthropology

Nationality: Any Region

AWARD INFORMATION

Award Type: Fellowship

Average Amount: Up to $40,000

Number of Awards: 8

Award Coverage: Living stipend to aid the write-up of research results for publication

Award Duration: 12 months

ELIGIBILITY REQUIREMENTS

- Must hold a PhD at the time of application
- Topics and research must make a contribution to the discipline of anthropology
- Must have received a PhD or equivalent within 10 years of the application deadline

APPLICATION INFORMATION

Award Deadline: May, Nov

Instructions: Visit the Foundation's website for further details and application materials

CONTACT

Wenner-Gren Foundation
470 Park Avenue
New York, NY 10016
Tel: +1 (212) 683-5000
Fax: +1 (212) 683-9151
Email: inquiries@wennergren.org
Web: www.wennergren.org/programs

Westminster Foundation for Democracy

Prospect Burma
Scholarship Programme

PROGRAM INFORMATION

Description: To further the peaceful development of education among young people who are citizens of Burma or who are by origin of Burmese descent or by reason of parental or family relationships, are connected with the country of Burma. Our aim is to develop and encourage the knowledge of the cultural and historical development of Burma.

Levels of Study: Undergraduate, Graduate, Doctorate

Field of Study: Agriculture and Related Sciences, Ecology, Economics, Education, Engineering, Human Rights

Nationality: Myanmar

AWARD INFORMATION

Award Type: Scholarship

Award Coverage: Tuition and fees, academic course materials, living expenses including accommodation, food

Award Duration: Academic year

ELIGIBILITY REQUIREMENTS

- Must be accepted to and/or enrolled in a first degree (undergraduate) course at a college or university
- Must be already studying, or accepted for, a master's degree course
- Must be a postgraduate student who has already started on a doctoral, or has a confirmed offer of a place to read for a doctoral

APPLICATION INFORMATION

Award Deadline: End of Mar

Instructions: Download application forms

CONTACT

Prospect Burma
Porters' Lodge
Rivermead Court
Ranelagh Gardens
SW6 3SF London
England
Tel: +44 (0) 20 7371 0887
Fax: +44 (0) 20 7371 0547
Email: information@prospectburma.org
Web: www.prospectburma.org

Whitworth University

Whitworth University Country-Specific Grants

PROGRAM INFORMATION

Description: Whitworth University offers special country-specific grants to qualifying undergraduate international students from a dozen countries. These need-based grants range in amount between $1,000 and $5,000 and may be combined with any scholarship for which a student is eligible. Please note that Whitworth does not offer scholarships and grants that cover the full cost of attendance.

Nationality: Armenia, Brazil, Ethiopia, Georgia, Ghana, India, Kazakhstan, Nigeria, Russia, South Africa, Turkey, Ukraine

ELIGIBILITY REQUIREMENTS

- Students must be residents of the qualifying countries
- Students must exhibit sufficient financial need to qualify

APPLICATION INFORMATION

Instructions: For more information please visit website

CONTACT

Whitworth University
International Admissions
300 W. Hawthorne Rd
Spokane, WA 99251
Tel: +1 (509) 777-4571
Fax: +1 (509) 777-3780
Email: mwhalen@whitworth.edu

Woodrow Wilson National Fellowship Foundation

Charlotte W. Newcombe Doctoral Dissertation Fellowships

PROGRAM INFORMATION

Description: Charlotte W. Newcombe Doctoral Dissertation Fellowships are designed to encourage original and significant study of ethical or religious values in all fields of the humanities and social sciences. In addition to topics in religious studies or in ethics (philosophical or religious), dissertations might consider the ethical implications of foreign policy, the values influencing political decisions, the moral codes of other cultures, and religious or ethical issues reflected in history, literature or art.

Levels of Study: Doctorate

Field of Study: Humanities, Philosophy and Religion, Religion/Theology

Nationality: Any Region

AWARD INFORMATION

Award Type: Fellowship

Average Amount: $25,000

Number of Awards: 21

Award Coverage: Tuition waiver, stipend for dissertation writing, dissertation titles sent to college publishers for possible publication at or near completion of the dissertation

Award Duration: Academic year

ELIGIBILITY REQUIREMENTS

- Must be enrolled in a doctoral program and have completed all pre-dissertation requirements in any field of study at a graduate school in the US
- Dissertations may be in any field and consider any period of time but should be concerned with religious or ethical questions of broad significance
- Must not accept other national awards which provide similar benefits
- Requires supporting paperwork: transcript from doctoral institution, 3 faculty recommendation letters, 1 of which must be from applicant's dissertation advisor, see site for full details

APPLICATION INFORMATION

Award Deadline: Nov 15

Instructions: Apply online

CONTACT

The Woodrow Wilson National Fellowship Foundation
Charlotte W. Newcombe Doctoral Dissertation Fellowships
PO Box 5281
Princeton, NJ 08543
Tel: +1 (609) 452-7007
Email: charlotte@woodrow.org
Web: www.woodrow.org/newcombe

World Bank

Robert S. McNamara Fellowship Program

PROGRAM INFORMATION

Description: The Robert S. McNamara Fellowships Program provides support to young researchers working in academic and research institutions from eligible countries preparing a doctoral thesis. Research grants cover residence costs for a 5 to 10 month period in a renowned university or research center. Fellows are expected to advance their research work mainly by using the facilities and resources provided by the host institution and by interacting with peers.

Levels of Study: Graduate, Doctorate

Field of Study: Agriculture and Related Sciences, Economics, Education, Environmental Policy, Environmental Studies, Health Professions, Health Studies, International Development, Natural Resources and Conservation

AWARD INFORMATION

Award Type: Fellowship

Average Amount: Varies

Number of Awards: Varies

Award Coverage: Research grants cover residence costs for a 5-10 month period in a renowned university or research center

Award Duration: 5-10 months

ELIGIBILITY REQUIREMENTS

- Only lecturers and researchers from eligible countries working on their doctoral thesis may apply for the fellowship
- Candidates should be under 45 years, have completed any course work or exams required for their doctoral program
- Must be a national and resident of a borrowing World Bank member country
- Must have completed and been awarded at least a master's degree, or equivalent, at the time of application
- Must be regularly registered in a development-related doctoral program in their home or another country
- Must have completed all coursework and exam requirements for their doctoral program

APPLICATION INFORMATION

Instructions: Applicants should download and fill-in the application forms, then submit their application packages including all the required documentation, visit our website for more information

CONTACT

The World Bank
Robert S. McNamara Fellowships Program
1818 H Street, NW - MSN J2-204
Washington, DC 20433
Tel: +1 (202) 473-6849
Fax: +1 (202) 522-4036
Email: rsm_fellowships@worldbank.org
Web: www.worldbank.org/wbi/scholarships

World Bank

Joint Japan/World Bank Graduate Scholarship Program

PROGRAM INFORMATION

Description: With support from the Government of Japan, the JJ/WBGS Program awards scholarships to individuals from World Bank member countries to undertake graduate studies at universities renowned for their development research and teaching. Scholars awarded scholarships receive their training and graduate degree from 1 of more than 150 universities in more than 30 countries.

Levels of Study: Graduate

Field of Study: All

Nationality: Any Region

AWARD INFORMATION

Award Type: Scholarship

Average Amount: $30,000

Number of Awards: Varies

Award Coverage: Tuition, living stipend, travel, health insurance

Award Duration: Academic year, renewable for second year

ELIGIBILITY REQUIREMENTS

- Must apply and be accepted to degree program at a recognized institution
- Must be between the ages of 25 and 40
- Must have at least 2 years of recent full-time professional work experience in the public sector
- Must hold a bachelor's degree or its equivalent in a development related field
- Must be citizen of any World Bank borrowing member country

APPLICATION INFORMATION

Award Deadline: Mar

Instructions: Apply online, download, or contact to request application materials, apply for admission to degree program directly through desired institution

CONTACT

World Bank Joint Japan/
World Bank Graduate Scholarship Program
1818 H Street, NW
MSN J2-204
Washington, DC 20433
Tel: +1 (202) 473-6849
Fax: +1 (202) 522-4036
Email: jjwbgsp@worldbank.org
Web: www.worldbank.org/wbi/scholarships

Zonta International

Zonta International Amelia Earhart Fellowship Program

PROGRAM INFORMATION

Description: The Zonta International Amelia Earhart Fellowships were established in 1938 in honor of Amelia Earhart, famed pilot and member of Zonta International. The awards are granted annually to women pursuing graduate degrees in aerospace-related sciences and aerospace-related engineering.

Levels of Study: Graduate, Doctorate

Field of Study: Aerospace

Nationality: Any Region

AWARD INFORMATION

Award Type: Fellowship

Average Amount: $10,000

Number of Awards: 35

Award Coverage: Tuition, fees, books, living expenses

Award Duration: Academic year

ELIGIBILITY REQUIREMENTS

- Must be registered in a full-time PhD program in a qualifying area of science or engineering closely related to advanced studies in aerospace-related science or aerospace-related engineering. A letter of acceptance or verification of enrollment is required
- Must demonstrate a superior academic record at a recognized university or college with accredited courses in aerospace-related studies as verified by transcripts and recommendations
- Must provide evidence of a well-defined research program in aerospace-related science or aerospace-related engineering as described in the application essay (in general scientific terms), the academic documents and publications
- Must clearly demonstrate the relationship of the research to aerospace and furnish verification of research program through at least 1 of the reference letters required with the application

APPLICATION INFORMATION

Award Deadline: Nov 15

Instructions: Download application materials from www.zonta.org

CONTACT

Zonta International
1211 West 22ns Street, Suite 900
Oak Brook, IL 60523
Tel: +1 (630) 928-1400
Fax: +1 (630) 928-1559
Email: Programs@zonta.org
Web: www.zonta.org

Funding Opportunities Provided by Foundations, Agencies, and Other Organizations:

For Study at a Specified Institution

American Jewish Archives
Marcus Center Fellowship Program

PROGRAM INFORMATION

Description: The Marcus Center's Fellowship Program provides recipients with month-long fellowships for research and writing at the Jacob Rader Marcus Center of the American Jewish Archives, located on the Cincinnati campus of the Hebrew Union College-Jewish Institute of Religion. Fellowship stipends will be sufficient to cover transportation and living expenses while in residence in Cincinnati.

Levels of Study: Doctorate, Post Doctorate

Field of Study: American Jewish History

Nationality: Any Region

Location of Study: Hebrew Union College
Cincinnati, OH

AWARD INFORMATION

Award Type: Fellowship

Average Amount: Varies

Number of Awards: 13

Award Coverage: Travel, living stipend

Award Duration: 1 month

ELIGIBILITY REQUIREMENTS

- Proposal must clearly demonstrate how the resources and holdings of the American Jewish Archives are vital to applicant's research

APPLICATION INFORMATION

Award Deadline: Feb

Instructions: Download the application materials on our website or contact the center to request them

CONTACT

The Jacob Rader Marcus Center of the American Jewish Archives
Director of the Fellowship Program
3101 Clifton Avenue
Cincinnati, OH 45220
Tel: +1 (513) 221-7444
Fax: +1 (513) 221-7812
Email: kproffitt@huc.edu
Web: americanjewisharchives.org/programs_fellowship.php#1

American Jewish Historical Society
Sid and Ruth Lapidus Fellowship

PROGRAM INFORMATION

Description: The Sid and Ruth Lapidus Fellowship supports 1 or more researchers wishing to use the collections of the American Jewish Historical Society. Preference is given to researchers interested in 17th and 18th century American Jewish history.

Levels of Study: Doctorate, Post Doctorate

Field of Study: American Jewish History

Nationality: Any Region

Location of Study: Brooklyn College, CUNY
Brooklyn, NY

AWARD INFORMATION

Award Type: Fellowship

Average Amount: $6,000

Number of Awards: Varies

Award Coverage: Varies

APPLICATION INFORMATION

Award Deadline: Apr 25

Instructions: Please see website for application information.

CONTACT

Brooklyn College, CUNY
School of Education
2900 Bedford Avenue
Brooklyn, NY 11210
Email: LapidusFellow@ajhs.org
Web: www.ajhs.org/scholarship/awards.cfm

American Political Science Association
Fulbright Congressional Fellowship Program

PROGRAM INFORMATION

Description: The American Political Science Association (APSA) Congressional Fellowship is a highly selective, nonpartisan program devoted to expanding public knowledge and awareness of the US Congress around the world. Fellows get firsthand experience serving on a congressional staff or committee for 10 months, gaining insight into the legislative process and the US political system in general.

Levels of Study: Professional

Field of Study: American Politics

Nationality: Germany

Location of Study: Washington, DC

AWARD INFORMATION

Award Type: Fellowship

Average Amount: $3,800 per month

Number of Awards: Varies

Award Coverage: Monthly stipend, roundtrip airfare, books

Award Duration: 10 months

ELIGIBILITY REQUIREMENTS

- Must have excellent written and spoken English skills
- Must have minimum of 3 years work experience

APPLICATION INFORMATION

Award Deadline: Dec

Instructions: Contact Fulbright office in home country to request application materials

CONTACT

Congressional Fellowship Program
American Political Science Association
1527 New Hampshire Avenue, NW
Washington, DC 20036-1206
Tel: +1 (202) 483-2512
Fax: +1 (202) 483-2657
Email: cfp@apsanet.org
Web: www.apsanet.org/section_165.cfm

American Turkish Society
Ahmet Ertegun Memorial Scholarship

PROGRAM INFORMATION

Description: Launched in 2007, this program supports students of Turkish descent pursuing undergraduate or graduate studies in music at The Juilliard School.

Levels of Study: Undergraduate, Graduate

Field of Study: Music

Nationality: Turkey

Location of Study: The Julliard School
New York, NY

ELIGIBILITY REQUIREMENTS

- Must be a student of Turkish descent

CONTACT

The American Turkish Society
Program & Administrative Coordinator
10018 New York NY
Tel: +1 (646) 434-4409
Email: diana.shin@americanturkishsociety.org
Web: www.americanturkishsociety.org/education.aspx

American Turkish Society
SVA Summer Studio Residency Scholarship

PROGRAM INFORMATION

Description: The American Turkish Society and the Moon and Stars Project offer a unique opportunity for an artist from Turkey to participate in the Summer Studio Residency Program at the School of Visual Arts in New York City. The resident artist has exclusive use of a small studio in SVA's Chelsea Building, receives individual critiques from SVA faculty, and attends weekly lectures. The program culminates in an open studio exhibition.

Levels of Study: Graduate

Field of Study: Arts and Culture

Nationality: Turkey

Location of Study: School of Visual Arts New York, NY

AWARD INFORMATION

Award Type: Scholarship

Average Amount: $7,000

Number of Awards: 1

ELIGIBILITY REQUIREMENTS

- Must be an emerging artist from Turkey

APPLICATION INFORMATION

Award Deadline: Rolling

Instructions: Please email for more information

CONTACT
The American Turkish Society
Program & Administrative Coordinator
54 W 40th St. Suite 818
New York, NY 10018
Tel: +1 (646) 434-4409
Email: diana.shin@americanturkishsociety.org
Web: www.maspny.org/summer-residency-program-at-sv/

American Turkish Society
The Arif Mardin Music Fellowship at Berklee College of Music

PROGRAM INFORMATION

Description: Launched in 2007 by The American Turkish Society in memory of Arif Mardin (1932-2006), world-renowned producer/arranger and Vice Chairman of the Society for many years, the Arif Mardin Music Fellowship aims to give promising musicians from Turkey a chance to study in the US. The program is conducted in partnership with Berklee College of Music in Boston, MA, where Mardin's successful music career began as the first recipient of the Quincy Jones Scholarship. The Fellowship covers the tuition, housing, and fees, as well as a stipend for the 6-week program.

Levels of Study: Undergraduate, Graduate, Doctorate

Field of Study: Music

Nationality: Any Region

Location of Study: Berklee College of Music Boston, MA

AWARD INFORMATION

Award Type: Fellowship

Average Amount: Approx $9,000

Award Coverage: Tuition, room and board, comprehensive fee, registration fee, along with a $500 stipend

Award Duration: 6 weeks

ELIGIBILITY REQUIREMENTS

- Must be of Turkish descent or nationality

APPLICATION INFORMATION

Award Deadline: Mar 1

Instructions: Recipients are selected by the Berklee College of Music through an application process each spring.

CONTACT
The American Turkish Society
Program & Administrative Coordinator
54 W 40th St. Suite 818
10018 New York NY
Tel: +1 (646) 434-4409
Email: diana.shin@americanturkishsociety.org
Web: www.berklee.edu/summer/5weeksummer/are-scholarships.php

Australian-American Fulbright Commission
Australian Fulbright Distinguished Chair in Agriculture and Life Sciences

PROGRAM INFORMATION

Description: The Distinguished Chair in Agriculture and Life Sciences at Kansas State University is for academics in any part of this broadly designated field. Scholars who want to work with their counterparts at K-State whose academic home is in the Colleges (Faculties) of Agriculture, Human Ecology and Veterinary Medicine are eligible as are those whose host is in a department such as Biology or Biochemistry. Academics whose host is outside these areas might also be eligible depending on the research project being proposed. For example, working on biofuels in an Engineering department, water issues in an engineering or geography department, or agricultural policy with a counterpart in the School of Leadership Studies or departments such as Politics and Economics could potentially be eligible.

Levels of Study: Doctorate, Professional

Field of Study: Agriculture and Related Sciences

Nationality: Australia

Location of Study: Kansas State University Manhattan, KS

AWARD INFORMATION

Award Type: Scholarship

Average Amount: Up to AUD $60,000

Number of Awards: 1

Award Coverage: Travel entitlement, stipend, accommodation, funds for public lecture tour, accident and health Insurance (ASPE)

Award Duration: maximum of 6 months

ELIGIBILITY REQUIREMENTS

- The Fulbright Distinguished Chair in Agriculture and Life Science is the Fulbright Distinguished Chair Scholarship for an exceptional Australian Scholar to carry out research at Kansas State University in the US
- Must be Australian citizens by birth or naturalization
- Applicants holding dual US/Australian citizenship, or Green Card holders residing abroad, are ineligible and will not be considered for a Fulbright Award
- Applicants are required to attend an interview via Skype or videoconferencing
- Applicants should be at Professorial level

APPLICATION INFORMATION

Award Deadline: 1 Aug

Instructions: For further information please refer to the Australian-American Fulbright Commission website www.fulbright.com.au

CONTACT
Australian-American Fulbright Commission
Senior Manager Scholarships
PO Box 9541
2600 Deakin ACT
Australia
Tel: +61 (02) 6260-4460
Fax: +61 (02) 6260-4461
Email: program@fulbright.com.au
Web: www.fulbright.com.au

Barra Foundation
Barra Foundation International Research Fellowships

PROGRAM INFORMATION

Description: The Library Company of Philadelphia and the Historical Society of Pennsylvania annually offer 2, 1-month fellowships to support research in residence in their collections by foreign national scholars of early American history and culture who currently live outside the US. The fellowships are funded by the Barra Foundation, Inc. Fellowships offered for advanced research in residence in our collections only. No employment or scholarships available.

Levels of Study: Doctorate, Post Doctorate, Professional

Field of Study: American History, American Jewish History, American Literature, American Politics, American Studies, Area and Ethnic Studies, Art History, Women's Studies

Nationality: Any Region

Location of Study: Library Company of Philadelphia/ Historical Society of Pennsylvania Philadelphia, PA

AWARD INFORMATION

Award Type: Fellowship

Average Amount: $2,500

Number of Awards: 2

Award Coverage: Living stipend, travel

Award Duration: 1 month

ELIGIBILITY REQUIREMENTS

- Must be engaged in research in US history before 1950 at the doctoral candidate level or higher
- Must be citizens and residents of any country except the US

APPLICATION INFORMATION

Award Deadline: Mar

Instructions: To apply, please visit our website to fill out a required electronic cover sheet, and submit a PDF containing a résumé and a 2-4 page description of the proposed research. 1 letter of recommendation should arrive under separate cover in PDF format as well. Please email materials to fellowships@librarycompany.org

CONTACT

Library Company of Philadelphia
Librarian
1314 Locust Street
Philadelphia, PA 19107
Tel: +1 (215) 546-3181
Fax: +1 (215) 546-5167
Email: jgreen@librarycompany.org
Web: www.librarycompany.org/fellowships/barra.htm

Center for Hellenic Studies

Fellowships in Ancient Greek Studies

PROGRAM INFORMATION

Description: The purpose of this fellowship program is to encourage and support research projects of the highest quality on various aspects of ancient Greek civilization.

Levels of Study: Post Doctorate

Field of Study: Classics, Greek Studies

Nationality: Any Region

Location of Study: Center for Hellenic Studies
Washington, DC

AWARD INFORMATION

Award Type: Fellowship

Average Amount: $17,000

Number of Awards: Varies

Award Coverage: Housing, living stipend, travel.

Award Duration: Academic semester

ELIGIBILITY REQUIREMENTS

- Must hold a postdoctorate degree.
- Must have professional competence in ancient Greek studies as documented by published work.

APPLICATION INFORMATION

Award Deadline: Oct

Instructions: For more information on how to apply, please visit the website.

CONTACT

Center for Hellenic Studies
3100 Whitehaven Street, NW
Washington, DC 20008
Tel: +1 (202) 745-4400
Email: fellowships@chs.harvard.edu
Web: www.chs.harvard.edu

Chu Scholarship

Hong Kong-Vincennes University Scholarship

PROGRAM INFORMATION

Description: Throughout the 1970s and 1980s, Dr. C.W. Chu provided scholarships for over 600 Chinese students to attend Vincennes University. Each student was extremely successful, beginning with transferring to a prestigious 4-year university in the USA and continuing with distinguished careers in engineering, education, investment banking, and industry. Dr. Chu's family, who still reside in Hong Kong, has recently reestablished the Chu Scholarship. This generous and honorable act has renewed a remarkable relationship between the Chu Family and Vincennes University. Some of the students who were sponsored by Dr. Chu have now joined other Hong Kong alumni to create a separate VU fund of their own. These funds will be used solely to provide additional financial assistance to future Hong Kong students attending Vincennes University.

Levels of Study: Undergraduate

Field of Study: All

Nationality: Hong Kong

Location of Study: Vincennes University
Vincennes, IN

AWARD INFORMATION

Award Type: Scholarship

Average Amount: Varies

Number of Awards: Varies

Award Coverage: Tuition, housing.

Award Duration: Varies

ELIGIBILITY REQUIREMENTS

- Must qualify for admission

APPLICATION INFORMATION

Instructions: Must submit a completed application form (1 form serves as both application for admission and application for scholarship) and a maximum 500-word essay that describes your academic interest and why you would like to study at VU. Applications are available to download online.

CONTACT

Institute of International Education/China - Hong Kong
General Commercial Building, Room 601
156-164 Des Voeux Road Central
Hong Kong
Tel: +1 (800) 742-9198
Email: iiehk@cuhk.edu.hk
Web: www.vinu.edu/content/international-student-cost

Council on Foreign Relations

Council on Foreign Relations Edward R. Murrow Fellowship

PROGRAM INFORMATION

Description: Each year, the Council offers a resident fellowship for a foreign correspondent or editor of international news for an English language medium. Named in honor of Edward R. Murrow and funded by the CBS Foundation, the fellowship gives the recipient a period of 9 months for sustained study and writing, free from the usual pressure of deadlines that characterize journalistic life.

Levels of Study: Professional

Field of Study: Journalism

Nationality: Any Region

Location of Study: Council on Foreign Relations
New York, NY

AWARD INFORMATION

Award Type: Fellowship

Average Amount: $65,000

Number of Awards: 1

Award Coverage: Varies

Award Duration: 9 months

ELIGIBILITY REQUIREMENTS

- Must have distinguished credentials in the field of journalism and have covered international news as a working journalist for print, broadcast, or online media widely available in the US.
- Must be authorized to work in the US and who will continue to be authorized for the duration of the fellowship.

APPLICATION INFORMATION

Award Deadline: Mar 1

Instructions: To receive an application for the Murrow Fellowship, a nomination letter must be submitted by a council member, current Murrow Fellow, the candidate's employer, or the candidate him or herself. Application materials will then be forwarded to eligible candidates.

CONTACT

Council on Foreign Relations
Membership & Fellowship Affairs
58 East 68th Street
New York, NY 10065
Tel: +1 (212) 434-9489
Fax: +1 (212) 434-9801
Email: fellowships@cfr.org
Web: www.cfr.org/about/fellowships/murrow.html

Deutsche Gesellschaft für Amerikastudien/American Antiquarian Society

Christoph Daniel Ebeling Fellowship

PROGRAM INFORMATION

Description: The Deutsche Gesellschaft für Amerikastudien (DGfA), in cooperation with the American Antiquarian Society (AAS), offers 1 fellowship to support research at AAS by doctoral and postdoctoral candidates in American Studies at German universities. The American Antiquarian Society's preeminent collections offer broad research opportunities in American history and culture through the year 1876.

Levels of Study: Doctorate, Post Doctorate

Field of Study: American Studies

Nationality: Germany

Location of Study: American Antiquarian Society
Worcester, MA

AWARD INFORMATION

Award Type: Fellowship

Average Amount: Up to €1,800

Number of Awards: 1

Award Coverage: Travel, housing

Award Duration: 1-2 months

ELIGIBILITY REQUIREMENTS

- Must be a postdoctoral candidate or have received a postdoctorate in American Studies at a German university

APPLICATION INFORMATION

Award Deadline: Feb

Instructions: Contact for more information and to request application materials

CONTACT

Institut für Anglistik und Amerikanistik
Philipps-Universität Marburg
Wilhelm-Röpke-Str. 6F
35032 Marburg
Germany
Email: birkle@dgfa.de
Web: dgfa.de/christoph-daniel-ebeling-fellowship-of-the-gaas-und-the-aas/

East-West Center

Obuchi Student Scholarships

PROGRAM INFORMATION

Description: Obuchi Student Scholarships support Okinawan students for master's or doctoral degree study at the University of Hawaii in fields of study that are beneficial to Okinawan development needs. Obuchi student participate in the residential, educational and leadership development programs at the East-West Center while pursuing a graduate degree at the University of Hawaii. Funded by the US government, Okinawa prefectural government and private contributions through the East-West Center. The program's mission is to help Okinawa develop and strengthen its human resources in order to take a proactive role in Asia Pacific intellectual, research, and business activities.

Levels of Study: Graduate

Field of Study: All

Nationality: Japan

Location of Study: East-West Center and the University of Hawaii
Honolulu, HI

AWARD INFORMATION

Award Type: Fellowship, Scholarship

Average Amount: Varies

Number of Awards: Up to 2 awards per year

Award Coverage: Tuition and fees at the University of Hawaii; housing in the East-West Center graduate residence hall; a monthly stipend to partially cover food and incidental expenses; allowance for books, materials and supplies; health insurance

Award Duration: Up to 2 years for master's or doctoral degree study

ELIGIBILITY REQUIREMENTS

- Must have already completed a bachelor's degree
- A minimum score of 550 TOEFL PBT/213 TOEFL CBT/ 79-80 TOEFL IBT, or 6.5 IELTS score
- This scholarship is designated for students from Okinawa; the Obuchi Student Scholarship invites applications from residents of Okinawa who have the intention of returning to Okinawa on completion of study, to contribute to the development needs of Okinawa
- Award recipients must meet the requirements for the Exchange Visitor (J-1 visa) program

APPLICATION INFORMATION

Award Deadline: Nov

Instructions: Download the application available from the website, or write to the Award Services office to request a copy to be mailed to you.

CONTACT

East-West Center
Award Services Office
John A. Burns Hall, Room 2066
1601 East - West Road
Honolulu, HI 96848-1601
Tel: +1 (808) 944-7735
Fax: +1 (808) 944-7730
Email: scholarships@eastwestcenter.org
Web: www.eastwestcenter.org/obuchi

East-West Center

US - Timor-Leste Scholarship Program (USTL)

PROGRAM INFORMATION

Description: The objective of the US - Timor-Leste Scholarship Program (USTL) is to identify and support the education of academically talented East Timorese who are expected to assume leadership roles in Timor-Leste in the future. The USTL scholarship provides the opportunity to pursue bachelor's (S1) degree study at a university in the US, in fields that are directly relevant to the needs of Timor-Leste. It will also enable the recipients to obtain a broader understanding of the US. The scholarship program will include a summer internship in Washington, D.C. as well as a 4 to 5 week community service project in Timor-Leste. USTL is administered by the East-West Center on behalf of the Bureau of Educational and Cultural Affairs (ECA) of the US Department of State.

Levels of Study: Undergraduate

Field of Study: Agriculture and Related Sciences, Business and Management, Communications and Journalism, Ecology, Economics, Education, Environmental Studies, International Relations, Natural Resources and Conservation, Political Science, Psychology

Nationality: East Timor

Location of Study: East-West Center
Honolulu, HI

AWARD INFORMATION

Award Type: Scholarship

Average Amount: Varies

Number of Awards: Up to 4 per year

Award Coverage: Tuition and fees, university residence hall room costs, monthly stipend for meals and incidental expenses, health insurance, settling in and book allowance, round-trip air transportation to all official activity sites

Award Duration: Up to 4 years

ELIGIBILITY REQUIREMENTS

- Must be citizens of Timor-Leste and must demonstrate a strong commitment to contribute to Timor-Leste's development.
- Must have graduated from secondary school in good academic standing. Applicants with no prior college/ university experience are eligible to apply
- Applicants who have completed some undergraduate (S1) study from an accredited tertiary institution are also invited to apply. Applicants must provide documented evidence of this course work for admissions and transfer credit consideration
- Preference will be given to applicants who have a strong academic record as evidenced by a grade point average of 2.5 or above on a 4.0 scale
- Must demonstrate English proficiency equivalent to a TOEFL score of at least 425 PBT, the Test of English Language Proficiency (TELP) will be administered in conjunction with the USET competition

APPLICATION INFORMATION

Award Deadline: Aug

Instructions: Applications are available at the US embassy in Dili, and also from the East-West Center's USTL representative in Dili, who can be contacted at: USTLscholarship@gmail.com. You may also visit our website to download application materials.

CONTACT

East-West Center
Award Services Office
1601 East West Road
Honolulu, HI 96848
Tel: +1 (808) 944-7735
Fax: +1 (808) 944-7730
Email: scholarships@eastwestcenter.org
Web: www.eastwestcenter.org/ustl

East-West Center

US-South Pacific Scholarship Program (USSP)

PROGRAM INFORMATION

Description: The US - South Pacific Scholarship Program (USSP) is a competitive, merit-based scholarship program that provides opportunities for academically talented individuals from South Pacific countries to pursue bachelor's or master's degree study at US institutions of higher education in fields that are directly relevant to development needs in the South Pacific Islands region. USSP is also intended to allow participants opportunities to obtain a broader understanding of the US. The USSP educational exchange experience includes participation in a variety of cultural activities, mentoring, host family and volunteer service programs.

Levels of Study: Undergraduate, Graduate

Field of Study: Agriculture and Related Sciences, Business and Management, Communications and Journalism, Computer Science, Economics, Education, Engineering, Environmental Policy, Environmental Studies, Information Technology, Journalism, Management, Mathematics, Political Science, Public Administration, Public Health, Science, Science Technologies, Women's Studies

Nationality: Cook Islands, Fiji, Kiribati, Nauru, Niue, Papua New Guinea, Samoa, Solomon Islands, Tonga, Tuvalu, Vanuatu

Location of Study: East-West Center
Honolulu, HI

AWARD INFORMATION

Award Type: Scholarship

Average Amount: Varies

Number of Awards: 4 awards per year

Award Coverage: Tuition and fees, university residence hall room costs, monthly stipend for meals and incidental expenses, health insurance, settling in and book allowance, round-trip air transportation

Award Duration: Varies

ELIGIBILITY REQUIREMENTS

- Bachelor's scholarship: Must have high school diploma at the time of application to apply for bachelor's degree study Individuals who have completed some undergraduate level courses but have not obtained the equivalent of a US 4-year bachelor's degree are also eligible
- Master's scholarship: Individuals who have completed at least a 3-year baccalaureate program may apply for a 1-year bridge program leading to master's degree study
- Must be from 1 of the sovereign Pacific Island nations, including the Cook Islands, Fiji, Kiribati, Nauru, Niue, Papua New Guinea, Samoa, Solomon Islands, Tonga, Tuvalu and Vanuatu
- Preference in the selection process is given to those who have not had recent extensive experience in the US or who have not had extensive opportunities for study at educational institutions outside the Pacific Islands region
- Must be able to meet the requirements of the Exchange Visitor (J-1 visa) program

APPLICATION INFORMATION

Award Deadline: Feb

Instructions: Download application materials or contact the Award Services office to request an application packet to be mailed to you

CONTACT

East-West Center
Award Services Office
1601 East West Road
Honolulu, HI 96848
Tel: +1 (808) 944-7735
Fax: +1 (808) 944-7730
Email: ussp@eastwestcenter.org
Web: www.eastwestcenter.org/ussp

East-West Center

East-West Center Graduate Degree Fellowship

PROGRAM INFORMATION

Description: The East-West Center Graduate Degree Fellowship provides master's and doctoral funding for graduate students with a commitment to the Asia Pacific region. Graduate degree fellows come from the US, Asia and the Pacific region to participate in residential, educational and leadership development programs at the East-West Center while pursuing graduate study at the University of Hawaii. Through East-West Center affiliation, awardees become part of an active social network of students and alumni committed to positive change. The East-West Center and the University of Hawaii offer premier resources for studies on Asia and the Pacific.

Levels of Study: Graduate, Doctorate

Field of Study: All

Nationality: Oceania, East Asia, Southeast Asia, Afghanistan, Bangladesh, Bhutan, India, Iran, Nepal, Pakistan, Republic of Maldives, Russia, Sri Lanka, US

Location of Study: East-West Center in partnership with the University of Hawaii
Honolulu, HI

AWARD INFORMATION

Award Type: Fellowship

Average Amount: Varies

Number of Awards: Varies

Award Coverage: Tuition and fees, housing, book allowance, health insurance coverage, stipend to partially cover food and incidental expenses.

Award Duration: Up to 2 years for Master's or Doctoral degree study

ELIGIBILITY REQUIREMENTS

- Must submit both the application for East-West Center Graduate Fellowship and the University of Hawaii Graduate Admissions Application to the East-West Center Award Services Office by Postmark deadline of Nov 3, 2014.
- The East-West Center invites applications from citizens of the US and countries in the Pacific and Asia, including Russia.
- A minimum TOEFL score of 550 PBT/213 CBT/79-80 IBT, or 6.5 IELTS score for international applicants or non-native speakers of English.
- Must meet the requirements for the Exchange Visitor (J-1 visa) program.

APPLICATION INFORMATION

Award Deadline: Nov

Instructions: Download application materials from the website or contact the Award Services office to request an application packet to be mailed to you.

CONTACT

East-West Center
Award Services Office
1601 East-West Road
John A. Burns Hall, Room 2066
Honolulu, HI 96848-1601
Tel: +1 (808) 944-7735
Fax: +1 (808) 944-7730
Email: scholarships@eastwestcenter.org
Web: www.eastwestcenter.org/gdf

East-West Center

East-West Center Affiliate Scholar Program

PROGRAM INFORMATION

Description: An opportunity for graduate students from universities around the world to have a short-term affiliation with the East-West Center while working on research for a thesis or dissertation related to the Asia Pacific region. Priority is given to students with research interests on the Asia Pacific region.

Levels of Study: Graduate, Doctorate

Field of Study: All

Nationality: Any Region

Location of Study: East-West Center
Honolulu, HI

AWARD INFORMATION

Award Type: Award

Average Amount: Varies

Number of Awards: Varies

Award Coverage: Discounted housing rate in East-West Center graduate residence halls, membership in the East-West Center Participants Association, participation in the Center's cultural and educational activities

Award Duration: 1-12 months

ELIGIBILITY REQUIREMENTS

- Must be a classified graduate student at the master's or doctoral level, with study plan for the study period in Honolulu
- Have funding, study plan, identified advisor for research or writing to be conducted in Honolulu

APPLICATION INFORMATION

Award Deadline: Rolling

Instructions: Application is available online at www.eastwestcenter.org/affiliatescholar

CONTACT

East-West Center
Education Program
1601 East-West Road
Honolulu, HI 96848
Email: affiliatescholar@eastwestcenter.org
Web: www.eastwestcenter.org/studentaffiliate

East-West Center

Asia Pacific Leadership Program (APLP)

PROGRAM INFORMATION

Description: The APLP is a 4.5 month residential program followed by a 4.5 month practicum in fieldwork, project development or employment. The objective of the APLP is to empower future leaders with the knowledge, skills, experiences, and supportive community needed to successfully navigate personal and regional change in the 21st century. The APLP equips participants to become agents of change in Asia and the Pacific through high-quality program content, an emphasis on applied experiential learning, and the development of an alumni network that spans the region. The core of the APLP curriculum focuses on 3 areas: interpreting emerging issues facing the Asia Pacific; developing personal leadership capacity; and advanced professional development with an emphasis on action.

Levels of Study: Graduate, Doctorate, Professional

Field of Study: Asian Studies, Business and Management, Governance/Civil Society, International Development, International Relations, Leadership, Management, Social Science

Nationality: Oceania, East Asia, Southeast Asia, Afghanistan, Bangladesh, Bhutan, India, Iran, Nepal, Pakistan, Republic of Maldives, Russia, Sri Lanka, US

Location of Study: East-West Center & University of Hawaii Honolulu, HI

AWARD INFORMATION

Award Type: Fellowship, Internship, Scholarship

Average Amount: Varies

Number of Awards: Varies

Award Coverage: Program events, workshops, course materials, health insurance for the residential component; scholarship assistance for program fees, housing, field study costs available

Award Duration: Up to 9 months

ELIGIBILITY REQUIREMENTS

- Must have a bachelor's degree from an accredited US institution or a recognized institution of higher learning outside the US
- Must have a minimum TOEFL score of 550 PBT/213 CBT/79-80 IBT; or 6.0 IELTS score for international applicants or non-native speakers of English
- Must have at least 3-5 years of professional work experience and either strong leadership experience or high leadership potential
- Non US participants are normally required to be on the East-West Center's Exchange Visitor (J-1) visa sponsorship
- Must be in residence for 4.5 months of the 9 month program

APPLICATION INFORMATION

Award Deadline: Dec

Instructions: For more information on how to apply, or to download application materials, please visit the website

CONTACT

East-West Center
Asia Pacific Leadership Program (APLP)
1601 East West Road
Honolulu, HI 96848-1601
Tel: +1 (808) 944-7744
Fax: +1 (808) 944-7070
Email: APLP@eastwestcenter.org
Web: www.eastwestcenter.org/aplp

East-West Center

Asian Development Bank-Japan Scholarship Program (ADBJSP)

PROGRAM INFORMATION

Description: This fellowship aims to provide an opportunity for well-qualified citizens of ADB's developing member countries to pursue postgraduate studies in economics, management, science and technology, and other development-related fields. Upon completion of their study programs, scholars are expected to contribute to the economic and social development of their home countries. The East-West Center administers the Asian Development Bank-Japan Scholarship Program in Honolulu which provides support for graduate studies in approved field of study at the University of Hawaii at Manoa and for participation in the educational, leadership development, and cultural activities at the East-West Center. In addition to the areas of study noted below, the ADBJSP scholarship is approved for the LL.M. (Law) degree.

Levels of Study: Graduate

Field of Study: Agriculture and Related Sciences, Architecture and Environmental Design, Business and Management, Economics, Environmental Studies, Geography, International Management, Law, Natural Resources and Conservation, Ocean and Resource Management, Oceanography, Public Administration, Sociology, Urban Planning

Nationality: South/Central Asia, Armenia, Azerbaijan, Cambodia, Cook Islands, East Timor, Fed. States of Micronesia, Fiji, Georgia, Indonesia, Kiribati, Laos, Malaysia, Marshall Islands, Mongolia, Myanmar, Nauru, Palau, Papua New Guinea, Philippines, Samoa, Solomon Islands, Thailand, Tonga, Tuvalu, Vanuatu, Vietnam

Location of Study: East-West Center in partnership with the University of Hawaii
Honolulu, HI

AWARD INFORMATION

Award Type: Scholarship

Average Amount: Varies

Number of Awards: Varies

Award Coverage: Tuition and fees, residence in an East-West Center graduate residence hall, monthly stipend for food and incidental expenses, allowance for books and study materials, health insurance, round trip airfare.

Award Duration: Up to 2 years

ELIGIBILITY REQUIREMENTS

- Must have completed a bachelor's degree to apply for master's degree funding, and completed a master's degree to apply for doctoral funding
- Must have 2 years work experience at the time of application
- GPA as specified by the University of Hawaii graduate department
- A minimum TOEFL score of 550 PBT/213 CBT/79-80 IBT, or 6.5 IELTS score
- Must be citizen of borrowing member country of the Asian Development Bank, visit www.adb.org/jsp for list of eligible countries and additional eligibility information

APPLICATION INFORMATION

Award Deadline: Nov

Instructions: Downloadable application available online, or write to request an application packet to be mailed to you

CONTACT

East-West Center
Education Program, ADB Scholarship Office
John A. Burns Hall, Room 2066
1601 East-West Road
Honolulu, HI 96848-1601
Tel: +1 (808) 944-7738
Fax: +1 (808) 944-7070
Email: adbjsp@eastwestcenter.org
Web: www.eastwestcenter.org/adb

Educational Testing Service

ETS Harold Gulliksen Psychometric Research Fellowship Program

PROGRAM INFORMATION

Description: Fellows study at their universities during the academic year and conduct a research project under the supervision of an academic mentor and in consultation with ETS research scientists or psychometricians. Applicants must be enrolled in a doctoral program, have completed all required coursework, and be working on a dissertation related to statistics, psychometrics, educational measurement, or quantitative methods.

Levels of Study: Doctorate

Field of Study: Cognitive Science, Education, Mathematics, Policy Research, Psychometric, Science Technologies, Statistics

Nationality: Any Region

Location of Study: Educational Testing Service Princeton, NJ

AWARD INFORMATION

Award Type: Fellowship

Average Amount: $27,000

Award Coverage: Stipend, partial tuition, fees, equipment; additional stipend and housing allowance if participating in summer internship program

Award Duration: Academic year

ELIGIBILITY REQUIREMENTS

- Must be enrolled in a doctoral program and have completed all coursework toward the degree
- Must be at the dissertation stage of their program and be working on a dissertation related to statistics, psychometrics, educational/psychological measurement, or quantitative methods
- Must demonstrate strong interest in the field of educational measurement and related disciplines
- Must have a record of superior academic achievement

APPLICATION INFORMATION

Award Deadline: Preliminary application: Dec; final application: Feb

Instructions: Applicants must receive a nomination from an academic advisor; all applications must be submitted electronically at the ETS website. Please see website for details about the 2-stage application process

CONTACT

Educational Testing Service
Research and Development Division
Rosedale Road, Mail Stop 19-T
Princeton, NJ 08541-0001
Tel: +1 (609) 734-5543
Fax: +1 (609) 734-5010
Email: internfellowships@ets.org
Web: www.ets.org/research/fellowships.html

Educational Testing Service

ETS Research Postdoctoral Fellowship Award

PROGRAM INFORMATION

Description: Selected fellows conduct independent research under the mentorship of ETS senior researchers in Princeton, NJ. The goals of the fellowship are to provide research opportunities to individuals who hold a doctorate in the fields indicated and to increase the number of women and under-represented minority professionals conducting research in educational measurement and related fields.

Levels of Study: Post Doctorate

Field of Study: Cognitive Science, Computer Science, Education, Literacy, Mathematics, Policy Research, Psychology, Psychometric, Statistics

Nationality: Any Region

Location of Study: Educational Testing Service Princeton, NJ

AWARD INFORMATION

Award Type: Fellowship

Average Amount: Varies

Number of Awards: Varies

Award Coverage: Living stipend, limited round-trip relocation expenses

Award Duration: 1 year, renewable for second year

ELIGIBILITY REQUIREMENTS

- Must hold a PhD or an EdD in a relevant discipline
- Must provide evidence of prior scholarly research
- Must submit an abstract. If invited, must write a 5-page proposal of research. If awarded a fellowship, the candidate will conduct this research at ETS in Princeton, NJ
- Must submit CV, graduate transcripts, scholarly publications and presentations, standardized letters of recommendation
- Fellowship renewed for a second year upon mutual consent

APPLICATION INFORMATION

Award Deadline: Jan 1 for preliminary application; Mar 1 for final application

Instructions: Applications must be submitted electronically at the ETS website; prior to applying, candidates should send a 1-page abstract of their research via e-mail to determine if the topic of research is relevant to ETS research, if approved, the applicant will be invited to submit a full fellowship application including a research proposal

CONTACT

Educational Testing Service
Research and Development Division
Rosedale Road, Mail Stop 19-T
Princeton, NJ 08541-0001
Tel: +1 (609) 734-1806
Fax: +1 (609) 734-5010
Email: internfellowships@ets.org
Web: www.ets.org/research/fellowships.html

Fulbright/Commission for Educational Exchange between the US, Belgium and Luxembourg

Harvard University Frank Boas Scholarship for Graduate Study

PROGRAM INFORMATION

Description: The Frank Boas Scholarship for Graduate Study is awarded each year to a candidate who has been admitted for graduate study at Harvard University. Candidates for graduate study or research may be in any field of study except business administration, and they must have completed a year of work-related experience by the time of departure for the US. Interested students must apply for consideration before entering the US and prior to the start of their Harvard programs.

Levels of Study: Graduate

Field of Study: All

Nationality: Belgium

Location of Study: Harvard University Cambridge, MA

AWARD INFORMATION

Award Type: Grant, Scholarship

Average Amount: Varies

Number of Awards: Varies

Award Coverage: All expenses for an academic year for a single student/scholar; in addition, the Boas Scholar receives a Fulbright travel grant, health insurance, visa sponsorship from the Commission for Educational Exchange

Award Duration: Academic year

ELIGIBILITY REQUIREMENTS

- Must be admitted for graduate study at Harvard
- Must be a citizen of Belgium
- Must have ambassadorial qualities, a proven level of academic excellence, outstanding records

APPLICATION INFORMATION

Award Deadline: Oct 31

Instructions: Interested candidates must download a preliminary application from the Commission's website and submit it to assess eligibility for the program; all eligible candidates will be sent the final application forms and supporting documents; applications must be submitted to the Commission for Educational Exchange in Brussels, which nominates a limited number of finalists each year to the Committee on General Scholarships; contact for more information

CONTACT

Commission for Educational Exchange between the US, Belgium and Luxembourg
Educational Adviser & Program Manager
The Royal Library Albert I, 3rd floor
Blvd. de L'Empereur 4, Keizerslaan
1000 Brussels
Belgium
Tel: +32 (2) 519-57-72
Fax: +32 (2) 519-57-73
Email: adviser@fulbright.be
Web: www.harvardboasscholars.org or www.fulbright.be

Fulbright/Commission for Educational Exchange between the US, Belgium and Luxembourg

Harvard University Frank Boas Scholarship in International Legal Studies

PROGRAM INFORMATION

Description: The Frank Boas Scholarship in International Legal Studies Study is awarded each year to a candidate who has been admitted for graduate study in law at Harvard University. Interested students must apply for consideration before entering the US and prior to the start of their Harvard programs.

Levels of Study: Graduate

Field of Study: Law

Nationality: Austria, Belgium, Denmark, Iceland, Netherlands, Norway, Portugal, Sweden

Location of Study: Harvard University
Cambridge, MA

AWARD INFORMATION

Award Type: Grant, Scholarship

Average Amount: Varies

Number of Awards: 1-2

Award Coverage: All or most expenses covered for a year of study at Harvard Law School (this does not include allowances for dependents)

Award Duration: Academic year

ELIGIBILITY REQUIREMENTS

- Must be citizens of Austria, Belgium, Denmark, Iceland, the Netherlands, Norway, Portugal, or Sweden and must be accepted for study at Harvard Law School
- Must have ambassadorial qualities, a proven level of academic and/or professional excellence, and outstanding records
- Must have a specific program of study based on the opportunities offered by Harvard Law School and must submit an application for admission directly to Harvard by Dec 1
- Must be proficient in English

APPLICATION INFORMATION

Award Deadline: Oct 31

Instructions: For more information, please visit our website; for application materials, interested candidates should contact the Fulbright Commission in their country of nationality

CONTACT

Commission for Educational Exchange between the US, Belgium and Luxembourg
Educational Adviser & Program Manager
The Royal Library Albert I, 3rd floor
Blvd. de L'Empereur 4, Keizerslaan
1000 Brussels
Belgium
Tel: +32 (2) 519-57-72
Email: adviser@fulbright.be
Web: www.fulbright.be

Fulbright/Iceland-US Educational Commission

Cobb Family Fellowship for Icelandic Graduate Students

PROGRAM INFORMATION

Description: Fellowship for first-year graduate students at University of Miami in Florida.

Levels of Study: Graduate

Field of Study: All

Nationality: Iceland

Location of Study: University of Miami
Coral Gables, FL

AWARD INFORMATION

Award Type: Fellowship

Average Amount: Varies

Number of Awards: 1

Award Coverage: Tuition, living stipend

Award Duration: Academic year

ELIGIBILITY REQUIREMENTS

- Must have or expect to have a bachelor's degree or equivalent by Jun of the award year

APPLICATION INFORMATION

Award Deadline: Oct

Instructions: Visit our website for more information.

CONTACT

Iceland-United State Education Commission
Laugavegur 59, 3rd floor
101 Reykjavik
Iceland
Tel: +354 552 0830
Email: adviser@fulbright.is
Web: www.fulbright.is

German Academic Exchange Service (DAAD)

DAAD John F. Kennedy Memorial Scholarship

PROGRAM INFORMATION

Description: Individual fellowship for postdoctoral research at the Minda de Gunzburg Center for European Studies at Harvard University.

Levels of Study: Post Doctorate

Field of Study: Business and Management, Economics, History, Law, Political Science, Public Law, Public Policy, Social Science

Nationality: Germany

Location of Study: Harvard University
Cambridge, MA

AWARD INFORMATION

Award Type: Fellowship

Average Amount: $60,000

Number of Awards: Approx 3

Award Coverage: Cost of living, office at the center, health insurance, round-trip airfare

Award Duration: 10 months

ELIGIBILITY REQUIREMENTS

- Must hold German citizenship
- Must have completed all requirements for the doctorate and be in possession of the degree at the time of application
- Must demonstrate proficiency in English

APPLICATION INFORMATION

Award Deadline: Dec

Instructions: Applications are submitted directly to DAAD in Bonn. For more information consult the program website

CONTACT

Deutscher Akademischer Austauschdienst (DAAD)
Referat 315
Kennedyallee 50
53175 Bonn
Germany
Tel: +49 (228) 882-0
Fax: +49 (228) 882-444
Email: skwara@daad.org
Web: www.daad.de

Getty Foundation

Getty Foundation Predoctoral and Postdoctoral Fellowships

PROGRAM INFORMATION

Description: Predoctoral and postdoctoral fellowships provide support for emerging scholars to complete work on projects related to the Getty Research Institute's annual theme. Recipients are in residence at the Getty Research Institute, where they pursue research to complete their dissertations or to expand them for publication.

Levels of Study: Doctorate, Post Doctorate

Field of Study: Arts and Culture, Humanities, Social Science

Nationality: Any Region

Location of Study: Getty Research Institute
Los Angeles, CA

AWARD INFORMATION

Award Type: Fellowship

Average Amount: $25,000-$30,000

Number of Awards: Up to 2

Award Coverage: Stipend, housing, health insurance, office space, travel to Los Angeles

Award Duration: Academic year

ELIGIBILITY REQUIREMENTS

- Predoctoral fellowship applicants must have advanced to candidacy and expect to complete their dissertations during the fellowship period
- Postdoctoral fellowship applicants must have received their degree no earlier than 2008

APPLICATION INFORMATION

Award Deadline: Nov

Instructions: Download or contact to request application materials

CONTACT

The Getty Foundation
Attn: Pre- and Postdoctoral Fellowships
1200 Getty Center Drive
Suite 800
Los Angeles, CA 90049
Tel: +1 (310) 440-7374
Fax: +1 (310) 440-7703
Email: researchgrants@getty.edu
Web: www.getty.edu/foundation/funding/residential/

H.J. Heinz Company Foundation

University of Pittsburgh Heinz Fellowship

PROGRAM INFORMATION

Description: The Heinz Fellowships are granted to individuals from developing countries who demonstrate potential as future leaders in the public, government, nonprofit, or private sectors. The goal is to improve, early in their careers, the fellows' capacity to contribute to the development of their country and to enhance their understanding of the US

Levels of Study: Graduate

Field of Study: Conflict Management, Government, Public Health

Nationality: Any Region

Location of Study: University of Pittsburgh
Pittsburgh, PA

AWARD INFORMATION

Award Type: Fellowship

Average Amount: Varies

Number of Awards: Varies

Award Coverage: Stipend, round-trip transportation, health insurance, professional activity fund

Award Duration: Academic year

ELIGIBILITY REQUIREMENTS

- Must have completed a university degree
- Must be proficient in speaking, reading, writing English
- Preference will be given to those applicants in the early stages of their careers
- The fellowship is intended for individuals in the practitioner/policy domains, it is not awarded for basic academic research, academic sabbaticals, or medical research or updating
- Must not be a citizen or permanent resident of the US

APPLICATION INFORMATION

Award Deadline: Mar

Instructions: For detailed application information, please visit the website.

CONTACT

University of Pittsburgh
University Center for International Studies
4400 Posvar Hall
Pittsburgh, PA 15260
Tel: +1 (412) 648-5085
Fax: +1 (412) 648-4672
Email: global@pitt.edu
Web: www.ucis.pitt.edu/global/heinz

Hellenic Harvard Foundation

Hellenic Harvard Foundation Graduate Scholarships

PROGRAM INFORMATION

Description: The Hellenic Harvard Foundation offers scholarships to graduate students with Greek citizenship who have been accepted for admissions to Harvard University.

Levels of Study: Graduate

Field of Study: All

Nationality: Greece

Location of Study: Harvard University
Cambridge, MA

AWARD INFORMATION

Award Type: Scholarship

Average Amount: Varies

Number of Awards: Varies

Award Coverage: Varies

Award Duration: Academic year

ELIGIBILITY REQUIREMENTS

- Must meet admissions requirements
- Must apply for consideration before entering the US and prior to the start of their Harvard programs
- Must return to Greece upon completion of their Harvard programs

APPLICATION INFORMATION

Instructions: Contact for further information and application instructions

CONTACT

Hellenic Harvard Foundation
7 Mourorizi Street
10674 Athens
Greece
Tel: +30 (1) 7211-047
Fax: +30 (1) 722-6313
Web: www.scholarship.harvard.edu/internationalinfo.html

International Foundation for Electoral Systems IFES

Charles and Kathleen Manatt Democracy Studies Fellowship

PROGRAM INFORMATION

Description: The Charles and Kathleen Manatt Fellowship, funded by former US Ambassador to the Dominican Republic and former Chair of IFES' Board of Directors, Charles Manatt, and his wife Kathleen, awards 1 $5,000 Manatt Fellowship ($2,000 upon the start of the fellowship, $2,000 midway through the fellowship, and $1,000 upon receipt of research paper) to bring outstanding graduate students from the American Midwest to Washington, D.C. to conduct research in democracy-building.

Levels of Study: Graduate

Field of Study: Government, International Relations, Political Science, Public Administration

Nationality: Any Region

Location of Study: International Foundation for Electoral Systems IFES
Washington, DC

AWARD INFORMATION

Award Type: Fellowship

Average Amount: $5,000

Number of Awards: 2

Award Coverage: Stipend

Award Duration: 8-10 weeks

ELIGIBILITY REQUIREMENTS

- US or international graduate students must be attending a university in the American Midwest (Illinois, Indiana, Iowa, Kansas, Michigan, Minnesota, Missouri, Nebraska, North Dakota, Ohio, Oklahoma, South Dakota, or Wisconsin)
- Must be graduate students working toward a degree in international relations, political science, public administration, or a related field
- PhD candidates should be pre-dissertation students only

APPLICATION INFORMATION

Award Deadline: Apr

Instructions: For more information on how to apply, please visit our website.

CONTACT

International Foundation for Electoral Systems IFES
1101 15th Street, NS 3rd Floor
Washington, DC 20005
Tel: +1 (202) 350-6733
Fax: +1 (202) 822-9744
Email: manattfellowship@ifes.org
Web: www.ifes.org/Research/Democracy-Fellowships.aspx

International House New York

International House NY Outreach Grants

PROGRAM INFORMATION

Description: Outreach Grants ranging from $500 to $3,500 will be awarded to qualified applicants applying to join the I. House community for the first time. Awards are based on demonstrated financial need and the applicants' interest in contributing to the I. House community through participation in its programs. Priority is given to applicants from countries, fields of study or backgrounds that are under-represented in the I. House community.

Levels of Study: Graduate, Doctorate

Field of Study: All

Nationality: Any Region

Location of Study: International House
New York, NY

AWARD INFORMATION

Award Type: Grant

Average Amount: $500-$3,500

Number of Awards: Varies

Award Coverage: Varies

Award Duration: Academic year, renewable for additional years

ELIGIBILITY REQUIREMENTS

- Must be admitted to full-time graduate or doctorate program in the New York City area
- Must be a resident member of the International House while receiving the award
- Only newly arriving residents are considered

APPLICATION INFORMATION

Award Deadline: Jun

Instructions: Download or contact to request application materials

CONTACT

International House
Director of Admissions
500 Riverside Drive
New York, NY
Tel: +1 (212) 316-8436
Fax: +1 (212) 316-1827
Email: admissions@ihouse-nyc.org
Web: www.ihouse-nyc.org

International Society for Optical Engineering (SPIE)

SPIE Optics and Photonics Education Scholarship

PROGRAM INFORMATION

Description: Scholarships are awarded to outstanding individuals based on their potential for long-range contribution to the field of optics and photonics, or related discipline.

Levels of Study: Undergraduate, Graduate, Doctorate

Field of Study: Engineering, Engineering-Related Technologies, Optics, Photonics, Physics

Nationality: Any Region

Location of Study: SPIE
Bellingham, WA

AWARD INFORMATION

Award Type: Scholarship

Average Amount: $2,000-$11,000

Number of Awards: Varies

Award Coverage: Varies

Award Duration: Academic year

ELIGIBILITY REQUIREMENTS

- Must be a student member of SPIE; non-members may submit an application for SPIE student membership with the completed scholarship application; dues payment must accompany the membership application to qualify
- Must be enrolled in an optics, photonics, or a related program at an accredited educational institution for the academic year in which the award will be used

APPLICATION INFORMATION

Award Deadline: Feb

Instructions: For detailed information on eligibility and the application form visit our website, spie.org/scholarships

CONTACT

SPIE Scholarship Committee
Attn: Education Services
PO Box 10
1000 20th Street
Bellingham, WA 98227-0010
Tel: +1 (360) 676-3290
Fax: +1 (360) 647-1445
Email: scholarships@spie.org
Web: www.spie.org/scholarships

John F. Kennedy Library Foundation

Kennedy Research Grant and Fellowship Program

PROGRAM INFORMATION

Description: Fellowships awarded to individuals to help defray costs of research on topics related to the Kennedy period or requiring use of the Kennedy Library. Preference is given to dissertation research by postdoctorate candidates working in newly opened or relatively unused collections, and to the work of recent postdoctorate recipients who are expanding or revising their dissertations for publication, but all proposals are welcome and will receive careful consideration.

Levels of Study: Graduate, Doctorate, Professional

Field of Study: All

Nationality: Any Region

Location of Study: Kennedy Library and Museum
Boston, MA

AWARD INFORMATION

Award Type: Fellowship, Grant

Average Amount: $200-$3,600

Number of Awards: Varies

Award Coverage: Travel, living expenses, research costs

ELIGIBILITY REQUIREMENTS

- Contact the program for further details and requirements
- Field of study must be related to holdings of the John F. Kennedy Library

APPLICATION INFORMATION

Award Deadline: Aug 15 or Nov 1

Instructions: To obtain information about the library's collections, each applicant should contact a member of the research room staff to explain the topic; download and mail application form along with 3-4 page proposal as well as additional required materials

CONTACT

John F. Kennedy Library
Grant and Fellowship Coordinator
Columbia Point
Boston, MA 02125
Tel: +1 (617) 514-1629
Fax: +1 (617) 514-1625
Email: kennedy.library@nara.gov
Web: www.jfklibrary.org/Research/Research-Grants-and-Fellowships.aspx

Karla Scherer Foundation

Karla Scherer Scholarship

PROGRAM INFORMATION

Description: The scholarship is available to women entering the Master of Arts in Humanities program at the University of Chicago.

Levels of Study: Graduate

Field of Study: Humanities

Nationality: Any Region

Location of Study: University of Chicago
Chicago, IL

AWARD INFORMATION

Award Type: Scholarship
Average Amount: Varies
Number of Awards: Varies
Award Coverage: Varies
Award Duration: Academic year

ELIGIBILITY REQUIREMENTS

- Must already be accepted into the Master of Arts Program at the University of Chicago
- Must hold a US visa for study
- Must be female

APPLICATION INFORMATION

Award Deadline: Mar
Instructions: Once admitted, candidates may write to the Foundation to request an application for scholarship aid

CONTACT

The University of Chicago, Classics 114
The Karla Scherer Center for the Study of American Culture
1010 East 59th Street
Chicago, IL 60637
Email: Scherer@lists.uchicago.edu
Web: www.karlascherer.org

Madame Marguerite Carriere Fellowship Fund

Madame Marguerite Carriere Harvard Fellowship

PROGRAM INFORMATION

Description: Every other year, the award is made to a newly admitted Harvard graduate student from France. The objective of the French student should be to study the US reaction to problems that concern both countries.
Levels of Study: Graduate
Field of Study: All
Nationality: France
Location of Study: Harvard University
Cambridge, MA

AWARD INFORMATION

Award Type: Scholarship
Average Amount: Varies
Number of Awards: Varies
Award Coverage: Tuition, fees
Award Duration: Academic year

ELIGIBILITY REQUIREMENTS

- Must meet admissions requirements
- Must be a Harvard graduate student for study in France or a French graduate student attending Harvard for study in the US

APPLICATION INFORMATION

Award Deadline: Dec, Jan; varies by department
Instructions: Applicants must be nominated by the financial aid office, see website for further information, do not apply directly

CONTACT

The Harvard University Committee on General Scholarships
14 Story Street, 3rd Floor
Cambridge, MA 02138
Tel: +1 (617) 496-9367
Fax: +1 (617) 496-4545
Email: cgs@fas.harvard.edu
Web: www.scholarships.harvard.edu/usstudents.html

National Endowment for Democracy NED

Reagan-Fascell Democracy Fellows Program

PROGRAM INFORMATION

Description: The Reagan-Fascell Democracy Fellows Program at the Washington, DC–based National Endowment for Democracy invites applications for fellowships. This federally-funded program enables democracy activists, practitioners, scholars, and journalists from around the world to deepen their understanding of democracy and enhance their ability to promote democratic change. This 5-month residential program allows fellows to conduct independent research and writing; and develop professional relationships within a global network of democracy advocates. The program is intended primarily to support practitioners, scholars, and journalists from developing and aspiring democracies; distinguished scholars from established democracies may also apply. Projects may focus on the political, social, economic, legal, and cultural aspects of democratic development and may include a range of methodologies and approaches. Awardees my not receive concurrent funding from the Endowment or its family of institutes during the fellowship period. A working knowledge of English is required.
Levels of Study: Professional
Field of Study: Conflict Management, Conflict Resolution, Governance/Civil Society, Government, Human Rights, International Development, International Education, International Law, International Relations, Journalism, Minority Rights, Peace Studies, Policy Research, Political Science, Social Justice, Social Science
Nationality: Any Region
Location of Study: National Endowment for Democracy (NED)
Washington, DC

AWARD INFORMATION

Award Type: Fellowship
Average Amount: Varies
Number of Awards: 16-20
Award Coverage: Monthly stipend, health insurance, round-trip travel, office space, research support
Award Duration: 5-10 months

APPLICATION INFORMATION

Award Deadline: Oct 15
Instructions: Applications will be accepted through our online application system at: fellowships.ned.org

CONTACT

National Endowment for Democracy
Fellowship Programs
1025 F Street NW
Suite 800
Washington, DC 20004
Tel: +1 (202) 378-9700
Fax: +1 (202) 378-9407
Email: fellowships@ned.org
Web: www.ned.org/fellowships/reagan-fascell-democracy-fellows-program

National Gallery of Art

National Gallery of Art Senior Fellowship Program

PROGRAM INFORMATION

Description: 1 Paul Mellon Fellowship and 4 to 6 Ailsa Mellon Bruce, Samuel H. Kress, and William C. Seitz Senior Fellowships will be awarded for the academic year, early fall to spring. The Paul Mellon and Ailsa Mellon Bruce Senior Fellowships are intended to support research in the history, theory, and criticism of the visual arts of any time period and geographical area. The Samuel H. Kress Senior Fellowships are intended primarily to support research on European art prior to the early nineteenth century. Applications are also solicited from scholars in other disciplines whose work examines artifacts or has implications for the analysis and criticism of physical form.
Levels of Study: Post Doctorate
Field of Study: Art History
Nationality: Any Region
Location of Study: Center for Advanced Study in the Visual Arts
Washington, DC

AWARD INFORMATION

Award Type: Fellowship
Average Amount: Up to $50,000
Number of Awards: Varies
Award Coverage: Half of current salary, up to $50,000; relocation costs
Award Duration: Academic year

ELIGIBILITY REQUIREMENTS

- Must have held the postdoctorate for 5 years or more or possess an equivalent record of professional accomplishment at the time of application

APPLICATION INFORMATION

Award Deadline: Oct
Instructions: Download application materials

CONTACT

National Gallery of Art
Center for Advanced Study in the Visual Arts
2000B South Club Drive
Landover, MD 20785
Tel: +1 (202) 842-6482
Fax: +1 (202) 789-3026
Email: casva@nga.gov
Web: www.nga.gov/content/ngaweb/research/casva/fellowships/senior-fellowships.html

National Humanities Center

National Humanities Center Fellowships

PROGRAM INFORMATION

Description: The National Humanities Center offers residential fellowships for advanced study in the humanities. Senior and younger scholars are eligible, though the latter should be engaged in research beyond the revision of a doctoral dissertation. In addition to scholars from all fields of the humanities, the Center accepts individuals from the natural and social sciences, the arts, the professions, and public life who are engaged in humanistic projects.

Levels of Study: Doctorate, Post Doctorate

Field of Study: Arts and Culture, Humanities, Natural Sciences, Social Science

Nationality: Any Region

Location of Study: National Humanities Center Research Triangle Park, NC

AWARD INFORMATION

Award Type: Fellowship

Average Amount: Varies

Number of Awards: 40

Award Coverage: Living stipend, travel

Award Duration: Academic year

ELIGIBILITY REQUIREMENTS

- Must hold PhD or have equivalent scholarly credentials
- Must demonstrate history of peer-reviewed publication

APPLICATION INFORMATION

Award Deadline: Oct 15

Instructions: Online application available via: nationalhumanitiescenter.org/fellowships/appltoc.htm

CONTACT

National Humanities Center
Fellowship Program
7 Alexander Drive, P.O. Box 12256
Research Triangle Park, NC 27709-2256
Tel: +1 (919) 549-0661
Fax: +1 (919) 990-8535
Email: nhc@nationalhumanitiescenter.org
Web: www.nationalhumanitiescenter.org

Omohundro Institute of Early American History Culture

Omohundro Institute-NEH Postdoctoral Fellowship

PROGRAM INFORMATION

Description: A 2-year postdoctoral fellowship in any area of early American studies circa 1450-1820, including related developments in the Caribbean, Latin America, Europe, and Africa—in short, any subject encompassing the Atlantic world in this period. A principal criterion for selection is that the candidate's dissertation or other manuscript have significant potential as a distinguished, book-length contribution to scholarship.

Levels of Study: Post Doctorate

Field of Study: History

Nationality: Any Region

Location of Study: Omohundro Institute of Early American History Culture, College of William and Mary Williamsburg, VA

AWARD INFORMATION

Award Type: Fellowship

Average Amount: $50,400 per year

Number of Awards: 1

Award Coverage: Health benefits, office space, research and computer facilities, funds for research and conference travel

Award Duration: 2 years

ELIGIBILITY REQUIREMENTS

- Must not have previously published or have under contract a scholarly monograph
- Must have met all requirements for the doctorate except conferral of the degree before commencing the fellowship. Those who have earned the PhD and begun careers are also encouraged to apply
- A substantial portion of the work must be submitted with the application
- Fellows teach 6 semester hours in the appropriate department at the College of William & Mary and hold concurrent appointment as assistant visiting professor

APPLICATION INFORMATION

Award Deadline: Oct

Instructions: Applications can be downloaded from our website.

CONTACT

Omohundro Institute of Early American History and Culture
Assistant to the Director
P.O. Box 8781
Williamsburg, VA 23187-8781
Tel: +1 (757) 221-1114
Fax: +1 (757) 221-1047
Email: IEAHC1@wm.edu
Web: oieahc.wm.edu/fellowship/postdoc/index.html

Smithsonian Astrophysical Observatory

Smithsonian Astrophysical Observatory Predoctoral Program

PROGRAM INFORMATION

Description: The Smithsonian Astrophysical Observatory (SAO) Predoctoral Program invites applications from current graduate students pursuing thesis research in astrophysics or related fields. The Harvard-Smithsonian Center for Astrophysics creates a rich environment for collaborations among future colleagues by bringing together over 300 SAO scientists across a broad spectrum of scientific endeavors in nearly all areas related to astronomy.

Levels of Study: Doctorate

Field of Study: Astronomy, Physics

Nationality: Any Region

Location of Study: Smithsonian Astrophysical Observatory Cambridge, MA

AWARD INFORMATION

Award Type: Fellowship

Average Amount: $33,204

Number of Awards: Varies

Award Coverage: Relocation, travel, research facilities, telescopes, work-stations, laboratory, library expenses

Award Duration: Academic year, renewable up to 3 years

ELIGIBILITY REQUIREMENTS

- Must be enrolled in a PhD program
- Must have completed preliminary coursework and examinations prior to the start of the SAO Predoctoral Program
- Must list the SAO scientist who has agreed to serve as a sponsor for each proposed research project, applicants must directly contact SAO scientists in their particular research areas
- Must gain approval of the Department Head of home university as their degrees will be granted by their home institutions

APPLICATION INFORMATION

Award Deadline: Rolling

Instructions: Apply online

CONTACT

Smithsonian Center for Astrophysics
Fellowship Program Coordinator
60 Garden Street
MS 67
Cambridge, MA 02138
Email: predoc@cfa.harvard.edu
Web: www.cfa.harvard.edu/opportunities/fellowships/predoc/overview.html

Smithsonian Center for Education and Museum Studies
Smithsonian Fellowships in Museum Practice

PROGRAM INFORMATION

Description: The Smithsonian's Fellowships in Museum Practice (FMP) program provides a means for addressing the information and learning needs of the museum profession. The program offers museum researchers, practitioners, and training providers a stimulating environment in which to examine an idea or practice, and to reflect on and share that information with colleagues. Fellowships are awarded in all subject areas of museum theory and operations. Preference is given to studies that address the new roles and challenges of the 21st century.

Levels of Study: Professional

Field of Study: Museum Studies

Nationality: Any Region

Location of Study: Smithsonian Center for Education and Museum Studies
Washington, DC

AWARD INFORMATION

Award Type: Fellowship

Average Amount: $3,500 per month

Number of Awards: Varies

Award Coverage: Living stipend, travel

Award Duration: Up to 6 months

ELIGIBILITY REQUIREMENTS

- The program is open to mid and senior-level museum personnel, experienced independent scholars, and museum studies training providers
- Must demonstrate fluency in written and spoken English

APPLICATION INFORMATION

Award Deadline: Feb

Instructions: Prospective applicants are encouraged to contact the Fellowships in Museum Practice program by email at least 1 month prior to the submission of a proposal for advice and guidance in developing a grant request; submit proposals by email or fax

CONTACT
Smithsonian Center for Education and Museum Studies
PO Box 37012
Arts and Industries Building, Room 2235
Washington, DC 20013-7012
Tel: +1 (202) 357-4061
Fax: +1 (202) 357-3346
Email: fmp@scems.si.edu
Web: museumstudies.si.edu/fmp.htm

The American Academy in Berlin
Berlin Prize 2015/16

PROGRAM INFORMATION

Description: The Academy welcomes applications from emerging and established scholars and from writers and professionals who wish to engage in independent study in Berlin. Approx 25 Berlin Prizes are conferred annually. Past recipients have included historians, economists, poets and novelists, journalists, legal scholars, anthropologists, musicologists, and public policy experts, among others. The Academy does not award fellowships in the natural sciences.

Levels of Study: Post Doctorate, Professional

Field of Study: Anthropology, Archaeology, Architecture and Environmental Design, Art History, Arts and Culture, Classics, Communications and Journalism, Creative Writing, Economics, Film, German-American Relations, History, Humanities, International Relations, Journalism, Law, Policy Research, Political Science, Public Health, Public Policy, Religion/Theology, Sociology, Theater, US Foreign Policy, Visual and Performing Arts, Women's Studies

Nationality: US

Location of Study: American Academy in Berlin
Berlin, Germany

AWARD INFORMATION

Award Type: Fellowship

Average Amount: $5,000 monthly stipend

Number of Awards: 25

Award Coverage: Round-trip airfare, partial board, a $5,000 monthly stipend, and accommodations

Award Duration: Academic semester or maximum of 1 year, shorter stays of 6 to 8 weeks possible

ELIGIBILITY REQUIREMENTS

- Fellowships are restricted to individuals based permanently in the US (US citizenship is not required)
- Must have completed a PhD at the time of application, applicants working in most other fields – such as journalism, filmmaking, or public policy – must have equivalent professional degrees
- Writers should have published at least 1 book at the time of application

APPLICATION INFORMATION

Award Deadline: Sep

Instructions: For further information and to apply online, please see www.americanacademy.de/home/fellows/applications

CONTACT
The American Academy in Berlin
Coordinator of Fellows Selection
Am Sandwerder 17–19
14109 Berlin
Germany
Tel: +49 (30) 804-83-107
Fax: +49 (30) 804-83-111
Email: jg@americanacademy.de
Web: www.americanacademy.de/home/fellows/applications

The Global Beca Foundation for San Mateo Colleges
Global Beca International Student Scholarship

PROGRAM INFORMATION

Description: The Global Beca Foundation supports and encourages qualifying international students to study in the US The Foundation's sole purpose is to attract and inspire talented international students to come to San Mateo Colleges. There are a limited number of 1-time scholarships for new international students ranging from $250 to $1,000 each, depending on availability of funds.

Levels of Study: Undergraduate

Field of Study: All

Nationality: Any Region

Location of Study: San Mateo Colleges
Redwood City, San Mateo, San Bruno, CA

AWARD INFORMATION

Award Type: Scholarship

Average Amount: $250 to $1,000

Number of Awards: Varies

Award Duration: 1 semester

APPLICATION INFORMATION

Instructions: Visit website for more information

CONTACT
San Mateo CCCD
Vice Chancellor, Educational Services and Planning
3401 CSM Drive
San Mateo, CA 94402
Tel: +1 (650) 358-6863
Fax: +1 (650) 574-6566
Email: luan@smccd.edu
Web: www.smccd.edu/international/english/about.php#scholarships

The International Youth Foundation
YouthActionNet Global Fellowship Program

PROGRAM INFORMATION

Description: YouthActionNet® invests in the power and promise of young social entrepreneurs around the globe. Launched in 2001 by the International Youth Foundation, YouthActionNet® strengthens, supports, and celebrates the role of young people in leading positive change in their communities. They support aspiring and accomplished young leaders by providing skill-building, advocacy, and networking opportunities.

Levels of Study: Professional

Field of Study: All

Nationality: Any Region

Location of Study: International Youth Foundation
Baltimore, MD

AWARD INFORMATION

Award Type: Fellowship

Number of Awards: 20

Award Coverage: All expenses paid for travel and accommodations to annual YouthActionNet leadership workshop

Award Duration: 1 year

ELIGIBILITY REQUIREMENTS

- Must be a founder of existing projects/organizations, or leading a project within an organization
- Applicants must have proficiency in English, applications must be submitted in English
- Open to all young people aged 18-29

APPLICATION INFORMATION

Award Deadline: Mar

Instructions: Visit our website for more information and to apply.

CONTACT

International Youth Foundation
32 South St
Suite 500
Baltimore, MD 21202
Tel: +1 (410) 951-1500
Fax: +1 (410) 347-1188
Email: yan@iyfnet.org
Web: www.youthactionnet.org

The Michelle Danner Acting Studio
Learn English Through Acting

PROGRAM INFORMATION

Description: Each class will fuse skill development with the practice of theatre and film performance and production, which may include: improvisation, grammar worksheets, focused discussion, reading samples, script analysis, in-class writing, pronunciation and articulation development, and watching/commenting on works of theatre and film. By making the learning environment safe and interactive, non-native students develop the comfort to let their guard down and subconsciously, welcome the new language with eagerness and enthusiasm.

Levels of Study: Professional

Field of Study: English as a Second Language, Fine Arts

Nationality: Any Region

Location of Study: The Michelle Danner Acting Studio Santa Monica, CA

ELIGIBILITY REQUIREMENTS

- Students must schedule a Skype interview with the Managing Director, Alexandra

APPLICATION INFORMATION

Instructions: Please e-mail m1visaatedgemar@gmail.com to receive an application and details on how to apply

CONTACT

The Michelle Danner Acting Studio
Managing Director
2437 Main Street
0405 Santa Monica CA
Tel: +1 (310) 392-0815
Fax: +1 (310) 399-2898
Email: info@michelledanner.com
Web: www.michelledanner.com/international-students/esl-for-actors/

The Michelle Danner Acting Studio
Acting Conservatory Los Angeles

PROGRAM INFORMATION

Description: We offer 6-12 month well-rounded actors' training intensives that include M1 Visa sponsorship. If you are interested in a short term stay, we offer 1-week to 3-month programs. These programs do not include the M1 Visa since it is a short-term stay.

Levels of Study: Undergraduate, Professional

Field of Study: Visual and Performing Arts

Nationality: Any Region

Location of Study: The Michelle Danner Los Angeles Acting Studio Santa Monica, CA

ELIGIBILITY REQUIREMENTS

- Students must schedule at Skype interview with our Managing Director, Alexandra

APPLICATION INFORMATION

Instructions: Please e-mail m1visaatedgemar@gmail.com to receive an application and details on how to apply

CONTACT

The Michelle Danner Los Angeles Acting Studio
Managing Director
2437 Main Street
Santa Monica, CA 90405
Tel: +1 (310) 392-0815
Fax: +1 (310) 399-2898
Email: m1visatedgemar@gmail.com
Web: www.michelledanner.com

US-UK Fulbright Commission
Fulbright British Friends of Harvard Business School MBA Awards

PROGRAM INFORMATION

Description: 3 to 5 awards for MBA study at Harvard Business School are offered. Applicants must gain acceptance to Harvard following the Nov or Jan admissions rounds before making an application to the Fulbright Commission. This award category is generously funded by the British Friends of Harvard Business School, a registered charity.

Levels of Study: Graduate

Field of Study: Master of Business Administration (MBA)

Nationality: United Kingdom

Location of Study: Harvard Business School Boston, MA

AWARD INFORMATION

Award Type: Award, Grant, Scholarship

Average Amount: $10,000-$50,000

Number of Awards: 3-5

Award Coverage: Contribution toward tuition fees at Harvard Business School, accident and sickness benefit coverage, visa processing, participation in a number of Fulbright Scholar events

Award Duration: First year of MBA study only

ELIGIBILITY REQUIREMENTS

- Must be a UK citizen (resident anywhere)
- Must hold or expect to obtain a minimum 2:1 undergraduate degree or the equivalent prior to your anticipated enrollment with a US university
- Preference will be given to those who do not have extensive, recent experience in the US (6 months or more)
- Preference will be given to those earning less than £40,000 per year

APPLICATION INFORMATION

Award Deadline: Apr

Instructions: Applications are made online but some supplemental forms will need to be mailed to the Fulbright Commission; you will need to register to the US-UK Fulbright Commission's website in order to make an application; you will be able to log in and out of your application account and will not be required to complete the application in 1 sitting

CONTACT

The US-UK Fulbright Commission
Fulbright Awards Programme
188 Kirtling Street
SW8 5BN London
United Kingdom
Email: programmes@fulbright.co.uk
Web: www.fulbright.co.uk

US-UK Fulbright Commission
Fulbright Robertson Visiting Professor in British History

PROGRAM INFORMATION

Description: This award offers a British historian the opportunity to teach British History and Western Civilization at Westminster College (Missouri), a small, selective liberal arts college. She/he will also undertake public speaking to non-academic audiences as well as participate in academic conferences in the US and Canada. The modest lecturing requirement will allow time for establishing a collaborative relationship with the Churchill Memorial and Library and for conducting personal research.

Levels of Study: Post Doctorate, Professional

Field of Study: History

Nationality: United Kingdom

Location of Study: Westminster College Fulton, MO

AWARD INFORMATION

Award Type: Award, Fellowship, Grant

Average Amount: $52,500

Number of Awards: 1

Award Coverage: $52,500 plus a significant travel budget that covers both economy round-trip travel for the scholar and up to 4 dependents (on a US airline); the scholar will also have the option of renting a reasonably priced house and car on campus

Award Duration: Up to 12 months

ELIGIBILITY REQUIREMENTS

- Must be a UK citizen (resident anywhere)
- Must hold or expect to receive a PhD in a relevant area before departure to the US
- Have at least 1 year's experience of lecturing to undergraduate students (the award is suitable for junior, mid-career, or senior scholars and is open to all areas of specialization in British history)
- Preference will be given to those who do not have extensive, recent experience in the US (6 months or more) and to those with knowledge of the American higher education system

APPLICATION INFORMATION

Award Deadline: Nov 15

Instructions: Applications are made online but some supplemental forms will need to be mailed to the Fulbright Commission; you will need to register to the US-UK Fulbright Commission's website in order to make an application; you will be able to log in and out of your application account and will not be required to complete the application in 1 sitting

CONTACT

The US-UK Fulbright Commission
Fulbright Awards Programme
188 Kirtling Street
WC1N 2JZ London
United Kingdom
Email: programmes@fulbright.co.uk
Web: www.fulbright.co.uk

US Institute of Peace

Jennings Randolph Peace Scholarship Dissertation Program

PROGRAM INFORMATION

Description: The Jennings Randolph (JR) Program for International Peace awards nonresidential Peace Scholar Dissertation Scholarships to students at US universities who are writing doctoral dissertations on topics related to peace, conflict, and international security.

Levels of Study: Doctorate

Field of Study: All

Nationality: Any Region

Location of Study: US Institute of Peace
Washington, DC

AWARD INFORMATION

Award Type: Fellowship

Average Amount: Approx $20,000

Number of Awards: Approx 10

Award Coverage: Completion of dissertation

Award Duration: 10 months

ELIGIBILITY REQUIREMENTS

- Must be enrolled in recognized doctoral programs (for example, PhD, SJD, EdD, ThD) in accredited universities in the US
- Proposals should be consistent with the Institute's mandate and present a research agenda with clear relevance to policy issues
- Must have completed all requirements for the degree except the dissertation by the commencement of the award

APPLICATION INFORMATION

Award Deadline: Dec

Instructions: For more information on how to apply, please visit the website

CONTACT

US Institute of Peace
Jennings Randolph Program for International Peace
2301 Constitution Avenue, NW
Washington, DC 20037
Tel: +1 (202) 457-1700
Fax: +1 (202) 429-6063
Email: jrprogram@usip.org
Web: www.usip.org/fellows/scholars.html

Whitworth University

Whitworth University International Student Scholarships

PROGRAM INFORMATION

Description: Whitworth University is offering partial academic scholarships ranging between $12,500 and $20,000 for qualified international students entering their first year. Whitworth does not offer scholarships that cover the cost of attendance. Students must have some financial resources.

Levels of Study: Undergraduate

Field of Study: All

Nationality: Any Region

Location of Study: Whitworth University
Spokane, WA

AWARD INFORMATION

Award Type: Scholarship, Tuition Reduction

Average Amount: $12,500 to $20,000

Number of Awards: Unlimited

Award Coverage: Partial tuition

Award Duration: Up to 4 years

ELIGIBILITY REQUIREMENTS

- Must be enrolled as a full-time, degree seeking student at Whitworth University
- Must be a first-year student
- Must have qualifying GPA and test scores (ACT, SAT, or GCE A Levels)

APPLICATION INFORMATION

Award Deadline: Mar 1

CONTACT

Whitworth University
International Admissions
300 W. Hawthorne Rd
Spokane, WA 99251
Tel: + 1 (509) 777-4571
Fax: + 1 (509) 777-3780
Email: mwhalen@whitworth.edu
Web: www.whitworth.edu

Whitworth University

International Transfer Student Scholarships

PROGRAM INFORMATION

Description: Whitworth University offers academic scholarships for qualifying undergraduate transfer students. Scholarships range between $6000 and $13000 per year. Whitworth does not offer scholarships that cover the full cost of attendance.

Levels of Study: Undergraduate

Field of Study: All

Nationality: Any Region

Location of Study: Whitworth University
Spokane, WA

AWARD INFORMATION

Award Type: Scholarship

Average Amount: Varies

Number of Awards: Unlimited

Award Duration: Up to 3 years

ELIGIBILITY REQUIREMENTS

- Must be enrolled as a full-time, degree-seeking student at Whitworth University
- Renewable up to 3 years as long as GPA and other requirements are met

APPLICATION INFORMATION

Award Deadline: Rolling

Instructions: For more information please visit website

CONTACT

Whitworth University
International Admissions
300 W. Hawthorne Rd
Spokane, WA 99251
Tel: +1 (509) 777-4571
Fax: +1 (509) 777-3780
Email: mwhalen@whitworth.edu
Web: www.whitworth.edu

Woodrow Wilson International Center for Scholars

Woodrow Wilson Residential Fellowships

PROGRAM INFORMATION

Description: Residential fellowships are awarded annually to individuals with outstanding project proposals in a broad range of the social sciences and humanities on national and/or international issues. Topics should intersect with questions of public policy or provide the historical and/or cultural framework to illuminate policy issues of contemporary importance.

Levels of Study: Post Doctorate, Professional

Field of Study: Government, Humanities, Public Policy, Social Science

Nationality: Any Region

Location of Study: Woodrow Wilson International Center for Scholars
Washington, DC

AWARD INFORMATION

Award Type: Fellowship

Average Amount: $26,200-$85,000

Number of Awards: Varies

Award Coverage: Living stipend, round-trip airfare, partial health insurance

Award Duration: Academic year

ELIGIBILITY REQUIREMENTS

- Academic candidates must have demonstrated their scholarly development by publications beyond their doctoral dissertations; for other applicants, an equivalent level of professional achievement is expected
- Must demonstrate proficiency in English
- Must not be working on a degree at the time of application (even if the degree is to be awarded prior to the proposed fellowship year)

APPLICATION INFORMATION

Award Deadline: Oct

Instructions: Download application materials

CONTACT

Woodrow Wilson Center
Scholar Selection and Services Office
1 Woodrow Wilson Plaza
1300 Pennsylvania Avenue, NW
Washington, DC 20004
Tel: +1 (202) 691-4170
Email: fellowships@wilsoncenter.org
Web: www.wilsoncenter.org/fellowships-grants

World Bank

World Bank Summer Internship Program

PROGRAM INFORMATION

Description: The purpose of the World Bank Internship Program is to provide graduate students with a chance to gain exposure to the work of the World Bank Group in the hopes that some will be interested in returning to the Bank for a career after completing their studies. Some interns research particular projects while others actually help design projects and occasionally participate in Bank missions.

Levels of Study: Graduate

Field of Study: All

Nationality: Any Region

Location of Study: World Bank
Washington, DC

AWARD INFORMATION

Award Type: Internship

Average Amount: Varies

Number of Awards: 150-200

Award Coverage: Hourly wage, travel

Award Duration: Summer

ELIGIBILITY REQUIREMENTS

- Must be currently enrolled in and have completed 1 year of a master's or doctorate program
- Must return to school in the fall following the summer internship
- Must be citizen of any World Bank borrowing member country

APPLICATION INFORMATION

Award Deadline: Jan

Instructions: Apply online: go.worldbank.org/7LMSGEJ6R0

CONTACT

Email: hrweb@worldbank.org

Web: go.worldbank.org/7LMSGEJ6R0

World Forest Institute

World Forest Institute International Fellowship Program

PROGRAM INFORMATION

Description: The WFI Fellowship brings professionals in natural resources to conduct a practical research project at the World Forestry Center. In addition to projects, Fellows participate in weekly field trips, interviews, and site visits to Northwest forestry organizations, research labs, universities, public and private timberlands, trade associations, mills, and corporations. The Fellowship is a unique opportunity to learn about sustainable forestry from the Pacific Northwest forestry sector, and to work with colleagues from around the world. Fellowships are open to any country, and there is a matching grant from the Harry A. Merlo Foundation.

Field of Study: Biology, Earth Science, Ecology, Environmental Policy, Environmental Studies, Natural Resources and Conservation, Natural Sciences

Nationality: Any Region

Location of Study: World Forest Institute
Portland, OR

AWARD INFORMATION

Award Type: Fellowship

Average Amount: Varies

Number of Awards: Varies

Award Coverage: Projects, interviews, site visits

Award Duration: 6-12 months

ELIGIBILITY REQUIREMENTS

- Must have a bachelor's degree or equivalent in the field of forestry, natural resources, or other related degree; alternatively, candidates with at least 4 years of forest-related work experience may apply
- Must have proficiency in English, both written and spoken
- Must have an initial research proposal on a topic relevant to forestry in the home country, the project should take advantage of forestry in the Pacific Northwest
- Must be self-motivated, able to work independently toward a clear research goal or output, and work with colleagues from diverse backgrounds
- Must obtain funding for the fellowship

APPLICATION INFORMATION

Award Deadline: Rolling

Instructions: Please read instructions on how to apply on our website here: wfi.worldforestry.org/index/international-fellowship/how-to-apply.html

CONTACT

World Forest Institute
WFI Director
4033 SW Canyon Rd
Portland, OR 97221
Email: swu@worldforestry.org
Web: wfi.worldforestry.org/index/international-fellowship.html

Funding Opportunities Provided by U.S. Colleges and Universities

Abilene Christian University
Cultures of ACU Scholarship

PROGRAM INFORMATION

Description: The Cultures of ACU Scholarship is a competitive scholarship that provides an award for students of any ethnicity who demonstrate diverse perspectives and experiences that will promote a culture of diversity at ACU.

Levels of Study: Undergraduate

Field of Study: All

Nationality: Any Region

Location of Study: Abilene Christian University Abilene, TX

AWARD INFORMATION

Award Type: Scholarship

Average Amount: $4,000

Number of Awards: 20

Award Coverage: Tuition

Award Duration: 8 semesters

ELIGIBILITY REQUIREMENTS

- Must apply for and be granted admission to ACU
- Must submit an essay
- Must graduate in the upper 50 percent of your senior class
- Must score 20 or above on the ACT (composite) or 960 or above on the SAT (math and verbal only) and/or transfer with a GPA of 2.5 or higher

APPLICATION INFORMATION

Award Deadline: Mar

Instructions: Complete and submit the online application

CONTACT

Abilene Christian University
Director of Multicultural and International Enrollment
ACU Box 29000
Abilene, TX 79699
Tel: +1 (325) 674-4917
Fax: +1 (325) 674- 2130
Email: international@admissions.acu.edu
Web: www.acu.edu

Abilene Christian University
ACU International Scholarship

PROGRAM INFORMATION

Description: Provides financial assistance to ACU students who are not US citizens or permanent residents.

Levels of Study: Undergraduate

Field of Study: All

Nationality: Any Region

Location of Study: Abilene Christian University Abilene, TX

AWARD INFORMATION

Award Type: Scholarship

Average Amount: $3,000 - full tuition

Award Coverage: Tuition

Award Duration: 8 semesters

ELIGIBILITY REQUIREMENTS

- Must apply for and be granted admission to ACU
- Must complete College Board's International Student Financial Aid Application.
- Must submit a resume and a letter of recommendation
- Must email all documents to international@admissions.acu.edu

APPLICATION INFORMATION

Award Deadline: Feb

Instructions: Apply for and be granted admission to ACU

CONTACT

Abilene Christian University
Director of Multicultural and International Enrollment
ACU Box 29000
Abilene, TX 79699
Tel: +1 (325) 674-4917
Fax: +1 (325) 674-2130
Email: international@admissions.acu.edu
Web: www.acu.edu

Abilene Christian University
Abilene Christian University Presidential Scholarship

PROGRAM INFORMATION

Description: The Presidential Scholarship is ACU's most prestigious scholarship. Students with an ACT of 27 or higher or an SAT of 1210 or higher have the opportunity to interview for this scholarship.

Levels of Study: Undergraduate

Field of Study: All

Nationality: Any Region

Location of Study: Abilene Christian University Abilene, TX

AWARD INFORMATION

Award Type: Scholarship

Average Amount: Up to full tuition

Award Coverage: Tuition

Award Duration: 8 semesters

ELIGIBILITY REQUIREMENTS

- Must have applied and been accepted for admission to ACU and submit all documents for the presidential scholarship
- Must have an ACT of 27 or higher or an SAT of 1210 or higher to interview for this scholarship

APPLICATION INFORMATION

Award Deadline: Mar

CONTACT

Abilene Christian University
Director of Multicultural and International Enrollment
ACU Box 29000
Abilene, TX 79699
Tel: +1 (325) 674-4917
Fax: +1 (325) 674-2130
Email: international@admissions.acu.edu
Web: www.acu.edu

Albion College
Albion College International Student Scholarship

PROGRAM INFORMATION

Description: Albion College considers all international candidates for academic merit scholarships. These are awarded based upon the strength of academic program and achievement, plus scores on the SAT or ACT, plus TOEFL and IELTS. Students are eligible for up to $20,000 per year.

Levels of Study: Undergraduate

Field of Study: All

Nationality: Any Region

Location of Study: Albion College Albion, MI

AWARD INFORMATION

Award Type: Scholarship

Average Amount: Up to $20,000

Number of Awards: Varies

Award Coverage: Tuition

Award Duration: 4 years

ELIGIBILITY REQUIREMENTS

- Must exceed the minimum criteria for admission on our website

APPLICATION INFORMATION

Award Deadline: Apr 1 for fall semester; Oct 1 for spring semester; Dec 1 for early action

CONTACT

Albion College
VP for Enrollment Management
611 E. Porter St.
c/o International Student Admission
Albion, MI 49224
Tel: +1 (517) 629-0497
Fax: +1 (517) 629-0569
Email: mrhyneer@albion.edu
Web: www.albion.edu/admission/internationalstudent

Alfred State University of New York

Alfred State Scholarships for International Students

PROGRAM INFORMATION

Description: Alfred State offers merit-based scholarships for students who apply to begin their studies in the Aug semester. There is no additional application necessary, and all qualified applicants will receive an award.

Levels of Study: Undergraduate

Field of Study: All

Nationality: Any Region

Location of Study: Alfred State University of New York Alfred, NY

AWARD INFORMATION

Award Type: Scholarship

Average Amount: Up to $7,000

Number of Awards: Varies

Award Coverage: Partial tuition

Award Duration: 2-4 years

ELIGIBILITY REQUIREMENTS

- Must apply to begin their studies at Alfred State in the Aug semester
- Must meet 2 of the following 4 criteria for the $7,000 award: (213 TOEFL/79-80 IBT/550 PBT), 3.25 college GPA (90 overall high school average may be substituted), 1200 (critical reading and math) combined SAT, and/or are a member of Phi Theta Kappa in good standing
- Must meet 2 of the following 3 criteria for the $3,000 award: (195 TOEFL/71 IBT/525 PBT), 3.0 college GPA (an 88 overall high school average may be substituted), 1100 (critical reading and math) SAT, and/or are a member of Phi Theta Kappa in good standing
- Must live on campus

APPLICATION INFORMATION

Award Deadline: Aug

Instructions: Must fill out a complete application for admission

CONTACT

SUNY Alfred State
Senior International Admissions Counselor
Admissions - International
10 Upper College Drive
Alfred, NY 14802
Tel: +1 (607) 587-4215
Fax: +1 (607) 587-4299
Email: admissions@alfredstate.edu
Web: www.alfredstate.edu/paying-for-college/international-student-scholarships

Alfred University

Alfred University Graduate Assistantships

PROGRAM INFORMATION

Description: Alfred University offers assistantships and fellowships coordinated by the appropriate academic departments.

Levels of Study: Graduate, Doctorate

Nationality: Any Region

Location of Study: Alfred University Alfred, NY

AWARD INFORMATION

Award Type: Associateship, Fellowship

Average Amount: Varies

Number of Awards: Varies

ELIGIBILITY REQUIREMENTS

- Requirements vary by department. Please consult website

APPLICATION INFORMATION

Instructions: See website for application information

CONTACT

Alfred University
Student Financial Aid Office
Alumni Hall
1 Saxon Drive
Alfred, NY 14802
Tel: +1 (800) 541-9229
Fax: +1 (607) 871-2252
Email: gradinquiry@alfred.edu
Web: www.alfred.edu/gradschool

Alma College

Alma College Scholarships

PROGRAM INFORMATION

Description: Alma College offers a private, rigorous liberal arts education, effective career development, solid preparation for graduate or professional study, productive internships, and personal growth through co-curricular activities. This scholarship provides partial tuition for undergraduate students of up to $12,000 and is renewable for 4 years.

Levels of Study: Undergraduate

Field of Study: All

Nationality: Any Region

Location of Study: Alma College Alma, MI

AWARD INFORMATION

Award Type: Scholarship

Average Amount: $12,000

Number of Awards: Varies

Award Coverage: Partial tuition

Award Duration: Renewable for 4 years

ELIGIBILITY REQUIREMENTS

- Must submit an official secondary school (high school) transcript translated into English along with a copy of official transcript in applicant's native language
- Must submit an official TOEFL score, or IELTS score, or SAT/ACT profile. Minimum: TOEFL 525 PBT/79 IBT; IELTS 6.5; SAT 1410; ACT 20; a student could also submit documentation of English language proficiency, such as completion of an approved ELS program
- Must submit a Secondary School Advisor Evaluation or a letter of recommendation from a teacher or associate who can speak of their qualifications for academic achievement
- Must submit a Declaration of Financial Support form with financial proof (i.e., bank statement) indicating the student has the financial ability to pay for an Alma College education for 4 years
- Students may submit a 300-500 word essay about how Alma College will help them achieve their personal and academic goals

APPLICATION INFORMATION

Award Deadline: Jun

Instructions: If you have any questions, please email foxal@alma.edu

CONTACT

Alma College
Senior Assistant Director of Admissions
614 W. Superior St.
Alma, MI 48801
Tel: +1 (800) 321-2562
Fax: +1 (989) 463-7057
Email: foxal@alma.edu
Web: www.alma.edu

American Honors at Community Colleges of Spokane

American Honors International Student Scholarship

PROGRAM INFORMATION

Description: If you are graduating high school with a competitive academic record, English language proficiency score, and you are accepted into the American Honors program, you'll be considered for a scholarship of up to $4,000.

Levels of Study: Undergraduate

Nationality: Any Region

Location of Study: Community Colleges of Spokane Spokane, WA

AWARD INFORMATION

Award Type: Scholarship

Average Amount: $4,000

Number of Awards: 20

Award Coverage: Tuition

Award Duration: Maximum of 2 years

ELIGIBILITY REQUIREMENTS

- Must have competitive academic record
- Must provide English language proficiency score
- Must submit scholarship essay
- Must be accepted into the American Honors program

APPLICATION INFORMATION

Instructions: Apply online via AmericanHonors.org

CONTACT

American Honors at Community Colleges of Spokane
International Admissions
Spokane, Washington 99224
Tel: +1 (509) 228-8022
Email: international@AmericanHonors.org
Web: www.AmericanHonors.org

American Honors at Mercer County Community College

American Honors International Student Scholarship

PROGRAM INFORMATION

Description: If you are graduating high school with a competitive academic record, English language proficiency score, and you are accepted into the American Honors program, you'll be considered for a scholarship of up to $4,000.

Levels of Study: Undergraduate

Nationality: Any Region

Location of Study: American Honors at Mercer County Community College
West Windsor, NJ

ELIGIBILITY REQUIREMENTS

- Must have competitive academic record
- Must provide English language proficiency score
- Must submit scholarship essay
- Must be accepted into the American Honors program

APPLICATION INFORMATION

Instructions: Apply online via AmericanHonors.org

CONTACT

American Honors at Mercer County Community College
1200 Old Trenton Road
West Windsor, New Jersey 08550, US
Tel: +1 (609) 770-6128
Email: international@AmericanHonors.org
Web: www.AmericanHonors.org

American Honors at Pierce College

American Honors International Student Scholarship

PROGRAM INFORMATION

Description: If you are graduating high school with a competitive academic record, English language proficiency score, and you are accepted into the American Honors program, you'll be considered for a scholarship of up to $4,000.

Levels of Study: Undergraduate

Nationality: Any Region

Location of Study: American Honors at Pierce College
Lakewood, WA

AWARD INFORMATION

Award Type: Scholarship

Average Amount: $4,000

Number of Awards: 20

Award Coverage: Tuition

Award Duration: Maximum of 2 years

ELIGIBILITY REQUIREMENTS

- Must have competitive academic record
- Must provide English language proficiency score
- Must submit scholarship essay
- Must be accepted into the American Honors program

APPLICATION INFORMATION

Instructions: Apply online via AmericanHonors.org

CONTACT

American Honors at Pierce College
9401 Farwest Drive SW
Spokane Lakewood Washington, US
Tel: +1 (253) 733-3442
Email: international@AmericanHonors.org
Web: www.AmericanHonors.org

American Institute for Contemporary German Studies/German Academic Exchange Service (DAAD)

AICGS/DAAD Fellowship Program

PROGRAM INFORMATION

Description: The program is designed to bring scholars and specialists working on Germany, Europe, and/or transatlantic relations to AICGS for research stays of 2 months each. Projects should be compatible with and supportive of the American Institute for Contemporary German Studies (AICGS) mission, which is to strengthen the German-American relationship in an evolving Europe and changing world.

Levels of Study: Graduate, Doctorate, Professional

Field of Study: Economics, German-American Relations, International Relations, Political Science

Nationality: Germany

Location of Study: American Institute for Contemporary German Studies
Washington, DC

AWARD INFORMATION

Award Type: Fellowship

Average Amount: Up to $4,725 per month

Number of Awards: Varies

Award Coverage: Stipend, roundtrip airfare, office space

Award Duration: 2 months

ELIGIBILITY REQUIREMENTS

- Must be eligible for J-1 Visa
- Must be a German or American citizen
- Applicants should have completed or currently be working on a PhD Only in exceptional cases will fellowships be awarded to applicants with an MA who are not PhD students

APPLICATION INFORMATION

Award Deadline: Aug, Feb

Instructions: Submit application materials by email or postal mail. Check AICGS website for deadline dates

CONTACT

American Institute for Contemporary German Studies
AICGS/DAAD Research Fellowship Program
1755 Massachusetts Avenue NW
Suite 700
Washington, DC 20036
Tel: +1 (202) 332-9312
Fax: +1 (202) 265-9531
Email: Fkwara@daad.org
Web: www.aicgs.org/fellows/opps/daad.aspx

American University

American University Merit Scholarships

PROGRAM INFORMATION

Description: American University (AU) is committed to providing academic quality and excellence, hands-on learning, and to creating an environment that welcomes students from around the world who wish to make a difference. AU offers a limited number of very competitive partial merit scholarships to academically qualified international freshman (first-year) students. (Talented international master's and doctoral students may qualify for Graduate Merit Awards or stipends through their departments. Applicants should check directly with departments for further information.)

Levels of Study: Undergraduate

Field of Study: All

Nationality: Any Region

Location of Study: American University
Washington, DC

AWARD INFORMATION

Award Type: Scholarship

Average Amount: $6,000-$27,000

Number of Awards: Varies

Award Coverage: Tuition

Award Duration: Up to 4 years

ELIGIBILITY REQUIREMENTS

- Must have outstanding academic credentials for 9-12 grades and proof of a rigorous secondary school curriculum
- Must submit the Common Application, essay, 2 letters of recommendation, and CV/resume
- Completed AU CFIS (Certification of Finances) form (see website), and bank letter, each showing a minimum of $57,039, and $65 application fee
- Undergraduate applicants must have official minimum scores on 1 of the following: TOEFL 90 IBT to be considered competitive with each sub-score 20 or higher; IELTS composite score of 6.5 with each sub-score 6.0 or higher; PTE 53

APPLICATION INFORMATION

Award Deadline: Jan 15

Instructions: Apply for admission online using the Common Application. Visit www.american.edu/admissions/international for details

CONTACT

American University
Director, International Admissions
4400 Massachusetts Ave., NW
Washington, DC 20016-8001
Tel: +1 (202) 885-6000
Fax: +1 (202) 885-6014
Email: intadm@american.edu
Web: www.american.edu/admissions/international

American University
International Legal Studies LLM Program (ILSP): Alumni Fund Scholarships

PROGRAM INFORMATION

Description: The ILSP Alumni Fund Scholarship offers 3-5 full tuition scholarships to newly admitted LLM students who display rigorous academic dedication to the advancement of issues in international law.

Levels of Study: Professional

Field of Study: International Law

Nationality: Any Region

Location of Study: American University Washington College of Law
Washington, DC

AWARD INFORMATION

Award Type: Scholarship

Average Amount: Full tuition

Number of Awards: 3-5

Award Coverage: Full tuition

Award Duration: Academic year

ELIGIBILITY REQUIREMENTS

- Must be a newly admitted LLM student starting in the fall semester (mid-Aug) who displays rigorous academic dedication to the advancement of issues in international law
- Must submit a complete LLM and scholarship application before Mar 1 to the ILSP program to be considered for the scholarships
- Must submit a complete LLM application before students can be considered for the scholarship

APPLICATION INFORMATION

Award Deadline: Mar 1 for fall semester

Instructions: Submit a resume and your essay responses to the Assistant Director of Admissions of the International Legal Studies Program; all submissions must be electronic via email

CONTACT

American University Washington College of Law
International Legal Studies Program
Tel: +1 (202) 274-4110
Email: llminfo@wcl.american.edu
Web: www.wcl.american.edu/ilsp/scholarly_competitions.cfm

Angelo State University
Carr Scholarship Program

PROGRAM INFORMATION

Description: ASU's Carr Scholarship Program honors dedication to learning by recognizing previous academic achievements. Awards are based on secondary school GPA and standardized test scores.

Levels of Study: Undergraduate

Field of Study: All

Nationality: Any Region

Location of Study: Angelo State University
San Angelo, TX

AWARD INFORMATION

Award Type: Scholarship, Tuition Reduction

Average Amount: $1,000 - $15,000

Number of Awards: Various

Award Coverage: Tuition and fees, room and board (scholarship award may not cover all the listed expenses)

Award Duration: Maximum of 4 years

ELIGIBILITY REQUIREMENTS

- Carr Distinguished: 32-36 composite ACT or 1400-1600 combined math and critical reading SAT/GPA 3.5-4.0
- Carr Excellence: 29-31 composite ACT or 1290-1390 combined math and critical reading SAT score/ GPA 3.5-4.0
- Carr Honors: 27-28 composite ACT or 1210-1280 combined math and critical reading SAT score/ GPA 3.5-4.0/acceptance into the ASU Honors Program
- Carr Fellow: 27-28 composite ACT or 1210-1280 combined math and critical reading SAT score/ GPA 3.5-4.0
- Carr Academic: 25-26 composite ACT or 1130-1200 combined math and critical reading SAT score/ GPA 3.0-4.0

APPLICATION INFORMATION

Award Deadline: Feb

Instructions: All students who apply for admission to ASU automatically apply for a Carr Scholarship.

CONTACT

Angelo State University
Office of Scholarship Programs
ASU Station #11048
San Angelo, TX 76909
Tel: +1 (325) 942-2777
Fax: +1 (325) 942-2666
Email: scholarships@angelo.edu
Web: www.angelo.edu/services/scholarship-programs/index.php

Angelo State University
Carr Graduate Scholarship

PROGRAM INFORMATION

Description: Carr Graduate Scholarships are the premier scholarship opportunity for graduate students to offset the cost of a graduate education at ASU. The university also offers Carr Doctor of Physical Therapy (DPT) scholarships for students entering the physical therapy program.

Levels of Study: Graduate, Doctorate

Field of Study: All

Nationality: Any Region

Location of Study: Angelo State University
San Angelo, TX

AWARD INFORMATION

Award Type: Scholarship, Tuition Reduction

Average Amount: Up to $3,000

Number of Awards: Varies

Award Coverage: Tuition and fees, room and board (scholarship may not cover all of the listed costs)

Award Duration: 3 years

ELIGIBILITY REQUIREMENTS

- Carr Graduate Fellow: 3.76-4.0 overall undergraduate GPA; Must be accepted for graduate admission at ASU
- Carr Graduate Academic: 3.51-3.75 overall undergraduate GPA; Must be accepted for graduate admission at ASU
- Carr Graduate Blue & Gold: 3.4-3.5 overall undergraduate GPA; Must be accepted for graduate admission at ASU

APPLICATION INFORMATION

Award Deadline: Feb

Instructions: There is no formal scholarship application

CONTACT

Angelo State University
Office of Scholarship Programs
ASU Station #11048
San Angelo, TX 76909
Tel: +1 (325) 942-2777
Fax: +1 (325) 942-2666
Email: scholarships@angelo.edu
Web: www.angelo.edu/services/scholarship-programs/carr_grad_scholarship.php

Angelo State University
Carr Transfer Scholarship

PROGRAM INFORMATION

Description: ASU's Carr Scholarship Program honors dedication to learning by recognizing previous academic achievements. Awards are based on GPA on transfer work and the number of credit hours transferring to ASU.

Levels of Study: Undergraduate

Field of Study: All

Nationality: Any Region

Location of Study: Angelo State University
San Angelo, TX

AWARD INFORMATION

Award Type: Scholarship, Tuition Reduction

Average Amount: $1,000-$4,000

Number of Awards: Varies

Award Coverage: Scholarship will cover tuition, fees, room and board, (Scholarship award may not cover all the listed costs)

Award Duration: 2 years

ELIGIBILITY REQUIREMENTS

- Carr Transfer Fellow: Students with a 3.75-4.0 GPA on all transferable coursework and at least 60 transferable credit hours or an associate's degree are eligible; must be recognized as an "All-Texas Academic Team" member at the most recent college attended or submit a letter of recommendation from community college president
- Carr Transfer Academic: Students with a 3.75-4.0 GPA on all transferable coursework and at least 30 transferable credit hours are eligible
- Carr Transfer Blue & Gold: Students with a 3.25-4.0 GPA on all transferable coursework and at least 18 transferable credit hours are eligible
- Carr Transfer: Students with a 3.0-3.24 GPA on all transferable coursework and at least 30 transferable credit hours are eligible

APPLICATION INFORMATION

Award Deadline: Feb

Instructions: Students must be accepted for admission to ASU to be considered for this scholarship

CONTACT

Angelo State University
Office of Scholarship Programs
ASU Station #11048
San Angelo, TX 76909
Tel: +1 (325) 942-2777
Fax: +1 (325) 942-2666
Email: scholarships@angelo.edu
Web: www.angelo.edu/services/scholarship-programs/scholarships.php

Armstrong Atlantic State University

Armstrong International Out-of-State Tuition Waiver

PROGRAM INFORMATION

Description: Academically competitive waiver that reduces tuition rate for first-time Armstrong students, including freshmen and transfers.

Levels of Study: Undergraduate

Field of Study: All

Nationality: Any Region

Location of Study: Armstrong Atlantic State University Savannah, GA

AWARD INFORMATION

Award Type: Tuition Reduction

Average Amount: Varies

Number of Awards: Varies

Award Duration: Up to 4 years

ELIGIBILITY REQUIREMENTS

- Must be enrolled full time
- Freshmen must have a minimum 2.5 overall GPA on a 4.0 scale at end of the semester directly prior to the requested academic year
- Transfers (30+ hours) must have a 3.0 on a 4.0 scale at end of the semester directly prior to the requested academic year
- Must be a non-US citizen and be "in legal status" with the US Citizenship and Immigration Services (USCIS) to be considered for this waiver, proof of current status is required
- Must not have previously earned the equivalent of a bachelor's degree

APPLICATION INFORMATION

Award Deadline: Jul

Instructions: Must submit an original essay covering the current waiver topic: "Why do you believe you should be awarded an International tuition waiver?" For more information, please download the application form

CONTACT

Armstrong Atlantic State University
Office of the Registrar
11935 Abercorn Street
Savannah, GA 31419
Tel: +1 (912) 344-2576
Fax: +1 (912) 344-3470
Web: www.armstrong.edu

Auburn University

Auburn University Graduate Assistantships

PROGRAM INFORMATION

Description: Auburn University offers graduate assistantships for degree-seeking students.

Levels of Study: Graduate

Field of Study: All

Nationality: Any Region

Location of Study: Auburn University Auburn, AL

AWARD INFORMATION

Award Type: Fellowship

Average Amount: Varies

Number of Awards: Varies

Award Coverage: Stipend, tuition

Award Duration: Maximum of 12 months

ELIGIBILITY REQUIREMENTS

- Must be admitted to a graduate degree program at Auburn University

APPLICATION INFORMATION

Award Deadline: Varies

Instructions: For further information, contact the academic department of interest

CONTACT

Auburn University
Graduate School
Hargis Hall
Auburn, AL 36849
Tel: +1 (334) 844-4700
Fax: +1 (334) 844-4348
Email: gradadm@auburn.edu
Web: www.grad.auburn.edu

Auburn University

Auburn University Undergraduate Scholarships

PROGRAM INFORMATION

Description: Auburn University offers scholarships for incoming freshmen.

Levels of Study: Undergraduate

Field of Study: All

Nationality: Any Region

Location of Study: Auburn University Auburn, AL

AWARD INFORMATION

Award Type: Scholarship

Average Amount: Varies

Number of Awards: Varies

Award Coverage: Tuition

Award Duration: Maximum of 4 years

ELIGIBILITY REQUIREMENTS

- Must be accepted to Auburn University by the Dec prior to student's first fall semester
- Must have at least 1 of the following: a GPA of 3.5 or above, an SAT score of 1300 or above, an ACT score of 30 or above
- Must have a TOEFL score of 213 CBT/80 IBT/550 PBT or above if student is a non-native speaker of English

APPLICATION INFORMATION

Award Deadline: Dec

Instructions: Visit our website for more information

CONTACT

Auburn University
Assoc. Director, International Student Life
322 Foy Union
Auburn, AL 36849
Tel: +1 (334) 844-2353
Fax: +1 (334) 844-4415
Email: orgenny@auburn.edu
Web: www.auburn.edu/international2

Augana College

Augana College International Merit Scholarship

PROGRAM INFORMATION

Description: Augana College offers the International Merit Scholarships to qualified undergraduate international students. Awards are based upon the overall academic strength of each applicant, and are renewable each year. Financial assistance is awarded only after a student has been officially accepted into Augana, having provided the college all official documentation as requested (such as official transcripts in English, official TOEFL score, and Certification of Finance Form)

Levels of Study: Undergraduate

Field of Study: All

Nationality: Any Region

Location of Study: Augana College Rock Island, IL

AWARD INFORMATION

Award Type: Scholarship

Average Amount: $14,000-$17,000

Number of Awards: Varies

Award Coverage: Tuition

Award Duration: Academic year, renewable for up to 4 years

ELIGIBILITY REQUIREMENTS

- Must apply and be accepted to Augana College
- Must arrange for official copies of all final transcript/grade reports from each institution attended. Transcripts must be in English
- The successful scholarship applicant will have arranged for an official TOEFL score to be sent directly to Augana (minimum 550 PBT/213 CBT/80 IBT)
- Must attach Certification of Finance Form with bank statement indicating financial responsibility for at least 2/3s of the educational expenses for each year of enrollment
- Must submit 2 letters of recommendation from teachers or school officials

APPLICATION INFORMATION

Award Deadline: Mar

Instructions: For more information, please visit the website

CONTACT

Augana College
Coordinator of International Recruitment
639 38th Street
Rock Island, IL 61201-2296
Tel: +1 (309) 794-7540
Fax: +1 (309) 794-8797
Email: kellypulford@Augana.edu
Web: www.Augana.edu/x578.xml

Baldwin-Wallace College

Baldwin-Wallace College Scholarships and Awards

PROGRAM INFORMATION

Description: Baldwin-Wallace College, a 4-year private liberal arts college offering over 50 majors, including a conservatory of music, provides a comprehensive program of scholarships and awards that recognize academic achievement, outstanding leadership, extracurricular involvement, and service. The student's completed B-W admission application is the only document needed in determining scholarship and award qualifications. We celebrate our close location to and connections with Cleveland, Ohio, through our professional internships, research opportunities, and social activities.

Levels of Study: Undergraduate, Graduate

Field of Study: Biology, Business and Management, Engineering 3-2, Management, Master of Business Administration (MBA), Medicine, Music, Psychology

Nationality: Any Region

Location of Study: Baldwin-Wallace College Berea, OH

AWARD INFORMATION

Award Type: Scholarship

Average Amount: Varies

Number of Awards: Varies

Award Coverage: Varies

Award Duration: 4 years

ELIGIBILITY REQUIREMENTS

- Must have a minimum TOEFL score of 62 IBT
- Must have a minimum IELTS score of 5.5

APPLICATION INFORMATION

Award Deadline: Feb

Instructions: Visit our website for more information

CONTACT

Baldwin-Wallace College
275 Eastland Road
Berea, OH 44017
Tel: +1 (440) 826-2222
Email: admission@bw.edu
Web: www.bw.edu/admission

Ball State University

Rinker Center for International Programs

PROGRAM INFORMATION

Description: Ball State University (BSU) is a doctoral institution located in Muncie, Indiana, a Midwestern city of 80,000 1 hour northeast of Indianapolis. BSU is 1 of the hidden gems of public education in the US The campus is home to 18,000 students from more than 80 countries. Ball State offers a comprehensive range of academic programs with more than 170 major and minor areas. Applications can be filed online or by mail. The TOEFL or IELTS is required for all non-native English speakers. Admission for international students is conducted on a rolling basis.

Levels of Study: Undergraduate, Graduate, Doctorate

Field of Study: All

Nationality: Any Region

Location of Study: Ball State University Muncie, IN

AWARD INFORMATION

Award Type: Associateship, Award, Fellowship, Scholarship

Average Amount: Varies

Number of Awards: Varies

Award Coverage: Undergraduate awards: partial tuition; graduate awards: full tuition, stipends

Award Duration: 1 semester, renewable

ELIGIBILITY REQUIREMENTS

- Awards for undergraduates are limited to academically exceptional students, typically 3.5-4.0 GPA (on a 4.0 scale) or better
- Graduate assistantships' requirements will vary dramatically by department

APPLICATION INFORMATION

Award Deadline: Feb

Instructions: Visit the website for application and instructions

CONTACT

Ball State University
Center for International Programs, SC-102
2000 W. University Ave
Muncie, IN 47306
Tel: +1 (765) 285-5422
Fax: +1 (765) 285-3710
Email: intadmit@bsu.edu
Web: www.bsu.edu/internationaladmit

Bard College

Bard College International Student Scholarship Program

PROGRAM INFORMATION

Description: All international students demonstrating financial need are eligible for partial funding of their tuition from Bard College. Aid is given in the form of grants, loans and campus employment. All international students are expected to pay some portion of their expenses to attend Bard College. International students are chosen on the basis of their excellent academics and suitability for our programs and curriculum.

Levels of Study: Undergraduate, Graduate, Professional

Field of Study: All

Nationality: Any Region

Location of Study: Bard College Annandale-on-Hudson, NY

AWARD INFORMATION

Award Type: Grant, Scholarship, Tuition Reduction

Average Amount: $5,000-$26,500

Number of Awards: Varies

Award Coverage: Partial to full tuition

Award Duration: Maximum of 4 years

ELIGIBILITY REQUIREMENTS

- Must have completed high school and fulfill our academic requirements for admission
- Must have excellent written and spoken English
- Minimum TOEFL 600 PBT/250 CBT/100 IBT. IELTS band 7 is required

APPLICATION INFORMATION

Award Deadline: Jan

Instructions: Applicants may use the Common Application online, all international students must submit the International Student Declaration of Finances and those seeking financial aid must submit the Foreign Student Financial Aid Application; international students are not eligible for Early Action application.

CONTACT

Bard College
Coordinator of International Applications
PO Box 5000
Annandale-on-Hudson, NY 12504
Tel: +1 (845) 758-7472
Fax: +1 (845) 758-5208
Email: admission@bard.edu
Web: www.bard.edu/admission/finances/financial_aid/international/index.shtml

Bay Path University

Bay Path University Undergraduate International Scholarships

PROGRAM INFORMATION

Description: Bay Path University offers undergraduate programs for women in over 30 majors. We offer partial scholarships for international students up to $15,000 for first year and transfer students.

Levels of Study: Undergraduate

Field of Study: All

Nationality: Any Region

Location of Study: Bay Path University Longmeadow, MA

AWARD INFORMATION

Award Type: Scholarship

Average Amount: Up to $15,000

Number of Awards: Varies

Award Duration: Up to 4 years

ELIGIBILITY REQUIREMENTS

- Must demonstrate academic merit
- Must meet minimum English requirement for admission
- Must be admitted into an undergraduate degree program at Bay Path University

APPLICATION INFORMATION

Award Deadline: Rolling

CONTACT

Bay Path University
Coordinator of International Admissions
588 Longmeadow Street
Longmeadow, MA 01106
Tel: +1 (413) 565-1331
Fax: +1 (413) 565-1105
Email: international@baypath.edu
Web: www.baypath.edu

Bemidji State University

Bemidji State University In-State Tuition

PROGRAM INFORMATION

Description: Bemidji State University offers resident tuition rates to all international students.

Levels of Study: Undergraduate, Graduate

Field of Study: All

Nationality: Any Region

Location of Study: Bemidji State University Bemidji, MN

AWARD INFORMATION

Award Type: Tuition Reduction

Average Amount: Varies

Number of Awards: Varies

Award Coverage: Tuition

Award Duration: Varies

ELIGIBILITY REQUIREMENTS

- Must maintain F-1 or J-1 non-immigrant status

APPLICATION INFORMATION

Instructions: Visit our website to access information and online application forms

CONTACT

Bemidji State University
103 Deputy Hall
1500 Birchmont Drive NE
Bemidji, MN 56601-2699
Tel: +1 (218) 755-4096
Fax: +1 (218) 755-2074
Email: international@bemidjistate.edu
Web: www.bemidjistate.edu/students/international

Berea College

Berea College Full Scholarship for International Students

PROGRAM INFORMATION

Description: Berea College offers every admitted international student a full-tuition scholarship for all 4 years of attendance, as well as full funding during the first year for room and board through scholarship and on-campus work.

Levels of Study: Undergraduate

Field of Study: All

Nationality: Any Region

Location of Study: Berea College Berea, KY

AWARD INFORMATION

Award Type: Scholarship

Average Amount: Approx $28,000

Number of Awards: Approx 25

Award Coverage: Tuition, room and board

Award Duration: 4 years

ELIGIBILITY REQUIREMENTS

- Must submit complete International Application for Admission
- Must enroll at Berea College as a full-time, degree-seeking student

APPLICATION INFORMATION

Award Deadline: Feb

Instructions: Applications can be downloaded on our website, contact the Berea College Office of Admissions for more information

CONTACT

Berea College
209 Chestnut Street
Berea, KY 40403
Tel: +1 (859) 985-3500
Fax: +1 (859) 985-3512
Email: admissions@berea.edu
Web: www.berea.edu/prospectivestudents/international/default.asp

Berkeley College

Berkeley College International Student Scholarship

PROGRAM INFORMATION

Description: Upon applying to Berkeley College, International Student Scholarship applications are reviewed by admissions office for students who pursue a full-time degree program. Selection is based on merit and financial need.

Levels of Study: Undergraduate

Field of Study: Accounting, Business and Management, Fashion Marketing & Management, Information Technology, International Management, Law, Management, Marketing

Nationality: Any Region

Location of Study: Berkeley College New York, NY

AWARD INFORMATION

Award Type: Scholarship

Average Amount: Varies

Number of Awards: Varies

Award Coverage: Partial tuition (10-25 %)

Award Duration: Academic year, renewable

ELIGIBILITY REQUIREMENTS

- Must have a minimum GPA of 2.5 on a 4.0 scale
- Must have minimum TOEFL score of 61 IBT
- Students will continue to receive the scholarship throughout their study as long as they study full time and maintain a 3.0 GPA

APPLICATION INFORMATION

Instructions: Visit our website for more information

CONTACT

Berkeley College
Associate Vice President, International Student Services
International Division
12 East 41 St., 14th FL
New York, NY 10017
Tel: +1 (212) 687-3730
Fax: +1 (212) 986-7827
Email: international@berkeleycollege.edu
Web: www.berkeleycollege.edu

Birmingham-Southern College

Birmingham-Southern College International Partnership Scholarship

PROGRAM INFORMATION

Description: Birmingham-Southern College offers merit-based scholarships and need-based aid to all qualifying international students admitted to a degree-seeking program. Applicants to the college are considered for scholarship and aid eligibility upon successful application for admission. No additional application is necessary. Birmingham-Southern College offers a welcoming, rigorous, and supportive environment for students from around the world to reach their potential and succeed.

Levels of Study: Undergraduate

Field of Study: All

Nationality: Any Region

Location of Study: Birmingham-Southern College Birmingham, AL

AWARD INFORMATION

Award Type: Scholarship

Average Amount: Approx $17,000 per year

Award Coverage: Tuition

Award Duration: up to 4 years

ELIGIBILITY REQUIREMENTS

- Successful application for admission to Birmingham-Southern College

APPLICATION INFORMATION

Instructions: Please visit the Birmingham-Southern College website for complete application instructions

CONTACT

Birmingham-Southern College
Assistant Director of International Admission
900 Arkadelphia Road
Birmingham, Alabama 35254
Tel: +1 (205) 226-4684
Fax: +1 (205) 226-3074
Email: jmcginni@bsc.edu
Web: www.bsc.edu

Bisk Education

Bisk Foundation Teacher Education Scholarship - University of Scranton Online

PROGRAM INFORMATION

Description: The University of Scranton, in partnership with University Alliance, is proud to announce the availability of Bisk Foundation Teacher Education Scholarships for students who are enrolling in 1 of the 2 online Master of Science in Education programs. The University of Scranton's Master of Science in Education degrees are designed for working teachers committed to gaining the skills needed to teach in today's ever-evolving classrooms. Bisk Foundation Teacher Education Scholarships support the ongoing career and professional development of teachers who have already made a difference in the lives of others.

Levels of Study: Graduate

Field of Study: Education

Nationality: Any Region

AWARD INFORMATION

Award Type: Award, Scholarship

Average Amount: $4,533

Number of Awards: 2

Award Coverage: Tuition

Award Duration: 2 years

ELIGIBILITY REQUIREMENTS

- Must be a first-time applicant to the University of Scranton's online Master of Science in Education degree programs

APPLICATION INFORMATION

Instructions: Applicants must submit a written essay of no more than 750 words demonstrating how they have made a difference in the lives of others; applicants should include all teaching-related awards and recognitions, including attainment of National Board Certification, if applicable; applicants must submit a written recommendation of no more than 500 words from the principals of the school where they are currently teaching

CONTACT

Bisk Education
9417 Princess Palm Avenue
Tampa, FL 33619
Tel: +1 (800) 605-5346
Fax: +1 (800) 345-8273
Web: www.uscranton.com/graduate-scholarships-teachers/

Bisk Education

Bisk Foundation Teacher Education Scholarship - Dominican University Online

PROGRAM INFORMATION

Description: Dominican University, in partnership with University Alliance, is proud to announce the Bisk Foundation Teacher Education Scholarships for students who are enrolling in 1 of the 3 online Master of Arts in Education programs. Dominican's MA Ed degrees are designed for working teachers committed to gaining the skills needed to teach in today's classroom. Bisk Foundation Teacher Education Scholarships support the ongoing career and professional development of teachers who have already made a difference in the lives of others.

Levels of Study: Graduate

Field of Study: Education

Nationality: Any Region

AWARD INFORMATION

Award Type: Award, Scholarship

Average Amount: $1,395

Number of Awards: 2

Award Coverage: Tuition

ELIGIBILITY REQUIREMENTS

- Must be a first-time applicant of Dominican University's online MA in Education degree programs

APPLICATION INFORMATION

Instructions: Applicants must submit a written explanation demonstrating how they have made a difference in the lives of others; applicants should include all teaching-related awards and recognitions, including attainment of National Board Certification, if applicable; the essay should be no more than 750 words in length. Applicants must submit a written recommendation of no more than 500 words from the principals of the school where they are currently teaching, on school or district letterhead

CONTACT

Bisk Education
9417 Princess Palm Avenue
Tampa, FL 33619
Tel: +1 (800) 441-5408
Fax: +1 (800) 576-8509
Web: www.dominicanu.com/graduate-scholarships-teachers/

Boise State University

International Student Tuition Waiver

PROGRAM INFORMATION

Description: This is a prestigious tuition assistance program for outstanding international students who show academic achievement and a commitment to being a successful international student at Boise State University.

Levels of Study: Undergraduate

Field of Study: All

Nationality: Any Region

Location of Study: Boise State University Boise, ID

AWARD INFORMATION

Award Type: Tuition Reduction

Average Amount: $12,600 per year

Number of Awards: Approx 8 awards

Award Coverage: Out-of-state tuition waiver worth approximately $12,600 per year; student is still responsible for in-state tuition fees (approximately $7,000 per year), and living expenses

Award Duration: Renewable up to 4 years

ELIGIBILITY REQUIREMENTS

- Equivalent 3.0 GPA or higher
- Must complete admissions and scholarship application
- The participant must also include an official transcripts and English proficiency test scores by the scholarship application deadline
- Open to all majors with the exception of Nursing, Pre-Nursing, Radiology, and Pre-Radiology

APPLICATION INFORMATION

Award Deadline: Mar

Instructions: The International Student Scholarship application can be found on the International Admissions Office website: admissions.boisestate.edu/international

CONTACT

Boise State University
International Admissions Counselor
1910 University Drive
Boise, Idaho 83625-1320
Tel: +1 (208) 426-1757
Email: interntl@boisestate.edu
Web: admissions.boisestate.edu/international

Boise State University

GEM Scholarship

PROGRAM INFORMATION

Description: Awarded to our top academic applicants, Gem Scholarships waive the entire full time nonresident portion of tuition for out-of-state students. There is no separate application process. For priority consideration, complete and submit all admission materials by Dec 15th for fall entrance priority consideration. Applications completed between Dec 16 and Feb 15 will be considered if scholarship resources remain available.

Levels of Study: Undergraduate

Field of Study: All

Nationality: Any Region

Location of Study: Boise State University Boise, ID

AWARD INFORMATION

Award Type: Tuition Reduction

Average Amount: $12,600

Number of Awards: Varies

Award Coverage: Nonresidential portion of tuition

Award Duration: Renewable up to 4 years

ELIGIBILITY REQUIREMENTS

- Must be accepted as a degree-seeking student with an eligible undergraduate program
- Must have a GPA of at least 3.0
- Must be a new freshmen or transfer applicant
- All majors are eligible with the exception of Nursing, Pre-Nursing, Radiology, and Pre-Radiology. See the scholarship website for a current list of eligible majors
- Scholarships are available for students starting in the fall semester only

APPLICATION INFORMATION

Award Deadline: Dec 15 for priority

Instructions: No separate scholarship application is required, just submit a complete admissions application

CONTACT

Boise State University
International Admissions Coordinator
1910 University Drive
Boise, Idaho 83725-1320
Tel: +1 (208) 426-1757
Email: interntl@boisestate.edu
Web: www.admissions.boisestate.edu/international

Boston College

MBA Program

PROGRAM INFORMATION

Description: The Full-Time MBA is a 2-year program for students who plan to take a break from their careers while completing their degree. In the first year, students progress through the program as a cohort of approximately 100 students, developing close ties with their classmates and building a strong sense of community. The second year focuses on electives and opportunities for academic-year internships.

Levels of Study: Graduate

Field of Study: Accounting, Finance, Master of Business Administration (MBA)

Nationality: Any Region

Location of Study: Boston College Chestnut Hill, MA

AWARD INFORMATION

Award Type: Scholarship

Average Amount: $27,000

Number of Awards: Varies

Award Coverage: Tuition remission and graduate assistantship

Award Duration: 2 years

APPLICATION INFORMATION

Award Deadline: Mar 15

Instructions: No application necessary. Admitted candidates automatically considered for merit-based scholarship

CONTACT

Boston College
Director, Graduate Enrollment
140 Commonwealth Avenue
Fulton Hall 315, Boston College
02467 Chestnut Hill MA, US
Tel: +1 (617) 552-3920
Fax: +1 (617) 552-8078
Email: bcmba@bc.edu
Web: bc.edu/mba

Boston University School of Education

Boston University School of Education Scholarships and Fellowships

PROGRAM INFORMATION

Description: Our graduate school offers degrees in over 20 areas within the field of education. Examples of popular programs are teaching, counseling, administration and leadership. The school offers a number of different scholarships and fellowships.

Levels of Study: Graduate, Doctorate, Professional

Field of Study: Education

Nationality: Any Region

Location of Study: Boston University Boston, MA

AWARD INFORMATION

Award Type: Award, Fellowship

Award Duration: Varies

ELIGIBILITY REQUIREMENTS

- Requirements vary by award program

APPLICATION INFORMATION

Award Deadline: Varies

Instructions: See a full list of scholarships and fellowships at the website: www.bu.edu/sed/admissions/graduate-students/financial-assistance/

CONTACT

Boston University School of Education
SED Office of Graduate Financial Assistance
Room 115, 2 Silber Way
Boston, MA 02215
Tel: +1 (617) 353-4238
Fax: +1 (617) 353-8937
Email: sedaid@bu.edu
Web: www.bu.edu/sed/

Brandeis University
Brandeis International Business School Awards

PROGRAM INFORMATION

Description: The Brandeis International Business School offers both generous merit and need-based financial aid. Our major merit-based scholarship programs make awards to nearly one-third of incoming students. Every applicant - whether from the US or from another country - is automatically considered for merit-based scholarships, and every student who completes the Statement of Financial Resources in our application is also considered for need-based awards. Financial aid awards are communicated to the student at the time he or she is admitted.

Levels of Study: Graduate, Doctorate, Professional

Field of Study: Business and Management, Economics

Nationality: Any Region

Location of Study: Brandeis University Waltham, MA

AWARD INFORMATION

Award Type: Fellowship, Loan, Scholarship

Average Amount: $22,000

Number of Awards: 90

Award Coverage: Covers tuition for master's level. Covers all costs for PhD students

Award Duration: 2 years for Master's degrees, 5 years for PhD

ELIGIBILITY REQUIREMENTS

- Merit and need based scholarship awards are determined at time of admission to business program, applicants should indicate when asked on their application that they are interested in being considered for scholarship, open to all applicants from any country for PhD., MBA and MA programs

APPLICATION INFORMATION

Award Deadline: Nov-Apr for Master's degrees; PhD deadline is Jan 15th

Instructions: Please submit online application for admission and scholarship at: www.Brandeis.edu/global

CONTACT

Brandeis International Business School
Associate Dean
415 South street
032
Waltham, MA 02453-2728
USA
Tel: +1 (781) 736-4829
Fax: +1 (781) 736-2263
Email: HChase@Brandeis.edu
Web: www.Brandeis.edu/global

Brandeis University
Brandeis International Business School Scholarship

PROGRAM INFORMATION

Description: The Brandeis International Business School is a pioneering professional school dedicated to teaching and research in global finance, management and economic policy. This learning experience transforms the way our graduates view the world, and helps them develop skills and insights to chart its future. Generous scholarship awards are available for PhD, MBA and MA programs based on merit and need.

Levels of Study: Graduate, Doctorate

Field of Study: Business and Management, Economics

Nationality: Any Region

Location of Study: Brandeis University Waltham, MA

AWARD INFORMATION

Award Type: Fellowship, Loan, Scholarship, Tuition Reduction

Number of Awards: 90-100

Award Coverage: Average award is $22,000.00 per year for 2 year Master's degree program, PhD program is fully-funded plus living stipend for 5 years

Award Duration: 2 years

ELIGIBILITY REQUIREMENTS

- Must complete online application for Admission and be accepted to program choice; merit and need based scholarships are available; PhD candidates must submit application for admission and scholarship by Jan 15th; scholarships decisions for all other programs are made on rolling basis Nov through Jun Scholarships are available to student from all countries

APPLICATION INFORMATION

Instructions: Complete online application for admission available at: www.Brandeis.edu/global

CONTACT

Brandeis International Business School
Associate Dean
415 South street
Waltham, Massachusetts 02453
Tel: +1 (781) 736-2252
Fax: +1 (781) 736-2263
Email: admission@lemberg.Brandeis.edu
Web: www.Brandeis.edu/global

Brandeis University
The Wien International Scholarship Program

PROGRAM INFORMATION

Description: The Wien International Scholarship Program is a need-based scholarship that meets the full demonstrated financial need of high achieving international applicants. Each Wien Scholar also receives 1 round-trip air ticket each year between the US and the student's home country. Wien Scholarships are awarded to exceptionally accomplished international applicants who demonstrate strong academic achievement as well as significant extracurricular or community involvement.

Levels of Study: Undergraduate

Nationality: Any Region

Location of Study: Brandeis University Waltham, MA

AWARD INFORMATION

Award Type: Grant, Loan, Scholarship

Average Amount: Full or partial need-based tuition

Number of Awards: Varies

Award Coverage: Tuition, round-trip airfare

ELIGIBILITY REQUIREMENTS

- Must present evidence of outstanding academic and personal achievement

APPLICATION INFORMATION

Instructions: Visit the website at www.brandeis.edu/admissions/financial/scholarships.html for more information

CONTACT

Brandeis University
Development and Alumni Relations
P.O. Box 549110 - MS 124
Waltham, MA 02454
Tel: +1 (800) 333-1948
Email: sfs@brandeis.edu
Web: www.brandeis.edu/sfs/scholarships/meritscholsintlexp.html

Brandeis University
Sylvia and Joseph Slifka Israeli Coexistence Scholarship

PROGRAM INFORMATION

Description: The Sylvia and Joseph Slifka Israeli Coexistence Scholarship is a full scholarship awarded to 2 Israeli citizens: 1 Arab and 1 Jewish. The scholarship provides resources for tuition, on-campus room and board, and a round-trip flight each year between Israel and the US Applicants must be Israeli citizens, demonstrate strong academic achievement and English proficiency, and have been involved significantly in coexistence efforts. Slifka scholars are chosen on the basis of their academic achievements and their ability to make a contribution to student life through their leadership skills and interaction with other students. The scholarship is open to Israeli Jews and Israeli Arabs, who are committed to, and will work to foster, greater tolerance and understanding between Arab and Jewish Israelis.

Levels of Study: Undergraduate

Nationality: Israel

Location of Study: Brandeis University Waltham, MA

AWARD INFORMATION

Award Type: Scholarship

Average Amount: Varies

Number of Awards: 2 per year

Award Coverage: Tuition, on-campus room and board, round-trip flight

ELIGIBILITY REQUIREMENTS

- Must be an Israeli citizen
- Must demonstrate strong academic achievement and English proficiency
- Must have been involved significantly in coexistence efforts

APPLICATION INFORMATION

Instructions: Applicants interested in the Slifka Scholarship should submit standard application materials as well as a description of their coexistence efforts.

CONTACT

Brandeis University
Office of Admissions
415 South Street
Waltham, MA 02454
Tel: +1 (800) 622-0622
Email: sendinfo@brandeis.edu
Web: www.brandeis.edu/admissions/international/scholarships.html

Brandeis University
Malkin Endowed Scholarship

PROGRAM INFORMATION

Description: The Malkin Scholarship is provided by the Malkin Israeli Scholar Endowment Fund. This fund was created to foster greater tolerance and understanding in both Israel and the US. Candidates must be Israeli citizens and must present evidence of serious involvement in coexistence efforts.

Levels of Study: Undergraduate

Field of Study: All

Nationality: Israel

Location of Study: Brandeis University Waltham, MA

AWARD INFORMATION

Award Type: Scholarship

Number of Awards: 2, every other year

Award Coverage: Tuition, on-campus room and board, round-trip airfare

Award Duration: 2 years

ELIGIBILITY REQUIREMENTS

- Must be an Israeli citizen
- Must present evidence of serious involvement in coexistence efforts

APPLICATION INFORMATION

Award Deadline: Varies

Instructions: Visit website for more information

CONTACT

Brandeis University
Office of Admissions
415 South Street
Waltham, MA 02454
Tel: +1 (800) 622-0622
Email: sendinfo@brandeis.edu
Web: www.brandeis.edu/sfs/scholarships/meritscholsintlexp.html

Brandeis University Graduate School of Arts and Sciences
Brandeis University Master of Arts in Classical Studies, Ancient Greek and Roman Studies

PROGRAM INFORMATION

Description: Generous scholarships available for the MA in Classical Studies program that investigates aspects of life in ancient Greece and Rome through such lenses as classical archaeology, ancient history, or anthropology. This program is good preparation for PhD study. Fieldwork includes excavations in Italy and Greece, research in Brandeis' Classical Artifact Research Collection, or summer study on the Bay of Naples.

Levels of Study: Graduate

Field of Study: Anthropology, Archaeology, Architecture and Environmental Design, Arts and Culture, Greek Studies, History

Nationality: Any Region

Location of Study: Brandeis University Greater Boston/Waltham, MA

AWARD INFORMATION

Award Type: Scholarship, Tuition Reduction

Average Amount: $9,500

Award Coverage: Tuition

APPLICATION INFORMATION

Instructions: Please visit www.brandeis.edu/gsas/programs/greek_roman.html for application instructions

CONTACT

Brandeis University
Graduate School of Arts and Sciences
450 South Street
Waltham, MA 02454
Tel: +1 (781) 736-3410
Fax: +1 (781) 736-3412
Email: gradschool@brandeis.edu
Web: www.brandeis.edu/gsas/programs/greek_roman.html

Brandeis University Graduate School of Arts and Sciences
Brandeis University Master's and PhD Merit Scholarships

PROGRAM INFORMATION

Description: Brandeis University offers merit scholarships for 18 PhD and over 40 master's programs. Just outside of the city of Boston, Brandeis University is an exciting, multifaceted research university that attracts students from around the world.

Levels of Study: Graduate, Doctorate

Field of Study: All

Nationality: Any Region

Location of Study: Brandeis University Greater Boston/Waltham, MA

AWARD INFORMATION

Award Type: Award, Fellowship, Grant, Scholarship, Tuition Reduction

Average Amount: Varies depending on program

Award Coverage: Master's: partial tuition scholarship; Doctorate: tuition waiver, health insurance support, and a monthly living stipend

ELIGIBILITY REQUIREMENTS

- Varies depending on the program, please see individual departments for details

APPLICATION INFORMATION

Instructions: Please visit our website for departmental instructions

CONTACT

Brandeis University
Graduate School of Arts and Sciences
415 South Street
Waltham, MA 02454
Tel: +1 (781) 736-3410
Fax: +1 (781) 736-3412
Email: gradschool@brandeis.edu
Web: www.brandeis.edu/gsas

Brandeis University Graduate School of Arts and Sciences
Brandeis University Master of Arts in Computational Linguistics

PROGRAM INFORMATION

Description: Computational Linguistics appeals to students with a desire to develop cutting-edge, practical tools that can benefit society, such as speech recognition, automated text analysis, information retrieval, machine translation, and computer security. Brandeis University's 2 year Master of Arts in Computational Linguistics is perfect for students who wish to delve into the study of language/linguistics with its foundation in technology and computer science.

Levels of Study: Graduate

Field of Study: Computer Science, Linguistics

Nationality: Any Region

Location of Study: Brandeis University Greater Boston/Waltham, MA

AWARD INFORMATION

Award Type: Award, Scholarship, Tuition Reduction

Average Amount: $19,000

Award Coverage: Partial tuition scholarship

APPLICATION INFORMATION

Instructions: Please visit www.brandeis.edu/gsas/programs/comp_ling.html for application instructions

CONTACT

Brandeis University
Graduate School of Arts and Sciences
415 South Street
Waltham, MA 02454
Tel: +1 (781) 736-3410
Fax: +1 (781) 736-3412
Email: gradschool@brandeis.edu
Web: www.brandeis.edu/gsas/programs/comp_ling.html

Brandeis University Graduate School of Arts and Sciences

Brandeis University Master of Arts in Global Studies

PROGRAM INFORMATION

Description: Generous scholarships available for Brandeis' Master of Arts in Global Studies, offering advanced study of processes of globalization, including globally shared issues such as health care, the environment, human rights, and communications. Highlights: dynamic, interdisciplinary 1-year program providing a broad perspective on global institutions, critical issues, and complexities of globalization; receive intensive training in research, analysis, and writing, plus a solid foundation in theories and issues of globalization; excellent preparation for further graduate study; develop skills and expertise that are valuable in the public or private sectors in a range of professions impacted by globalization, such as nonprofits, NGOs, and service agencies; located just outside of Boston.

Levels of Study: Graduate

Nationality: Any Region

Location of Study: Brandeis University Greater Boston/Waltham, MA

AWARD INFORMATION

Award Type: Scholarship, Tuition Reduction

Average Amount: $19,000

Award Coverage: Tuition

APPLICATION INFORMATION

Instructions: Please visit www.brandeis.edu/gsas/programs/global_studies.html for application instructions

CONTACT

Brandeis University
Graduate School of Arts and Sciences
415 South Street
Waltham, MA 02454
Tel: +1 (781) 736-3410
Fax: +1 (781) 736-3412
Email: gradschool@brandeis.edu
Web: www.brandeis.edu/gsas/programs/global_studies.html

Broward College

Broward College International Student Merit Scholarship

PROGRAM INFORMATION

Description: Broward College (BC) offers a "Merit Scholarship" for students currently attending the college.

Levels of Study: Undergraduate

Field of Study: All

Nationality: Any Region

Location of Study: Broward College Fort Lauderdale, FL

AWARD INFORMATION

Award Type: Scholarship

Average Amount: $500.00 - $1,000.00

Number of Awards: Varies

Award Coverage: Tuition

Award Duration: For the duration of studies

ELIGIBILITY REQUIREMENTS

- Must have an immigration status of F-1 or M-1
- Must have successfully completed 24 credits at Broward College, credits received for EAP (English for Academic Purposes) classes will be counted
- Must be in good academic standing
- Must have an overall minimum 3.0 (3.0/4.0) GPA (Grade Point Average)
- Must be enrolled full time

APPLICATION INFORMATION

Award Deadline: Aug 1 for fall semester; Dec 1 for winter term

Instructions: For scholarship application and minimum requirements, please visit our website

CONTACT

Broward College
International Education
225 E Las Olas Blvd
31/302
Fort Lauderdale, Florida 33301
Tel: +1 (954) 201-7705
Fax: +1 (954) 201-7708
Email: rcarvalh@broward.edu
Web: www.broward.edu/international/students

Bryant University

Bryant University International Scholarships

PROGRAM INFORMATION

Description: Throughout its 150-year history, Bryant University has earned a distinguished reputation for innovative academic programs and technology that are marketplace-driven and highly attuned to the emerging needs of industry and society. Bryant's close-knit, student-centered community of scholars delivers challenging academic programs that integrate business and the arts and sciences, with an emphasis on real-world application and a global perspective.

Levels of Study: Undergraduate, Graduate

Field of Study: Accounting, American Studies, Biology, Biotechnology, Business and Management, Business Law, Communications and Journalism, Computer and Information Sciences, Creative Writing, Economics, Environmental Studies, Film, Finance, Fine Arts, Foreign Languages, French, History, Information Technology, Journalism, Law, Liberal/General Studies, Literature, Management, Marketing, Master of Arts in Teaching, Master of Business Administration (MBA), Mathematics, Multi/Interdisciplinary Studies, Philosophy and Religion, Political Science, Sociology, Spanish, Statistics, Tax Law, Visual and Performing Arts, Women's Studies

Nationality: Any Region

Location of Study: Bryant University Smithfield, RI

AWARD INFORMATION

Award Type: Scholarship

Average Amount: $5,000 - $30,000

Number of Awards: Open

Award Coverage: Tuition

Award Duration: Renewable up to 4 years as long as specific GPA requirements are met

ELIGIBILITY REQUIREMENTS

- Submit Common Application or Universal College Application, with Bryant University supplement.
- Mail secondary-school transcripts
- Test scores TOEFL (minimum: 80) or IELTS (minimum: 6.5). *Some applicants may be eligible for a waiver
- Certification of Finances
- Please contact Office of International Admission with any questions: +1 (401) 232-6107

APPLICATION INFORMATION

Award Deadline: Feb

Instructions: International students are automatically reviewed for scholarship consideration once a completed admission application is received

CONTACT

Bryant University
Sr. Associate Director for International Admission
1150 Douglas Pike
Smithfield, RI 02917
Tel: +1 (401) 232-6100
Fax: +1 (401) 232-6741
Email: jeriksen@bryant.edu
Web: success.bryant.edu

Bryn Mawr College

Bryn Mawr College Financial Aid

PROGRAM INFORMATION

Description: Bryn Mawr is a liberal arts and science college for women. The College has need-based financial aid available for outstanding young women who meet the academic standards, but cannot afford the cost of attendance.

Levels of Study: Undergraduate

Field of Study: All

Nationality: Any Region

Location of Study: Bryn Mawr College Bryn Mawr, PA

AWARD INFORMATION

Award Type: Award, Grant, Loan, Scholarship

Average Amount: Varies

Number of Awards: Varies

Award Coverage: Varies

Award Duration: 4 years

ELIGIBILITY REQUIREMENTS

- The undergraduate college is for women only
- Bryn Mawr will only consider applicants with strong academic profiles
- Minimum TOEFL IBT score for consideration is 100

APPLICATION INFORMATION

Award Deadline: Jan (for Regular Decision applicants)

Instructions: A student must indicate her intent to apply for financial aid on the Common Application at the time she applies for admission; she must also submit a completed financial aid application by the stated deadline

CONTACT

Bryn Mawr College
Associate Director of Admissions
101 N. Merion Ave
Gateway Admission Building
Bryn Mawr, PA 19010
Tel: +1 (610) 526-5152
Fax: +1 (610) 526-7471
Email: jrussell@brynmawr.edu
Web: www.brynmawr.edu/admissions

BUCKNELL UNIVERSITY

Bucknell University Undergraduate & Graduate Financial Aid

PROGRAM INFORMATION

Description: Bucknell offers significant resources to support international students who are a) admitted to Bucknell, and b) demonstrate financial aid need through the application process. Bucknell financial aid for international students is, however, extremely limited. In each class we consider all applicants for financial assistance, but only a very small number of highly qualified international applicants are ultimately chosen to receive financial assistance

Levels of Study: Undergraduate, Graduate

Field of Study: All

Nationality: Any Region

Location of Study: Bucknell University
Lewisburg, PA

AWARD INFORMATION

Award Type: Award, Scholarship, Tuition Reduction

Average Amount: Varies

Number of Awards: Varies

Award Coverage: Tuition, housing, living expenses, depending on amount

Award Duration: Entire duration of degree program

ELIGIBILITY REQUIREMENTS

- Students need to apply using the Common Application + TOEFL scores + SAT scores. SAT reporting code: 2050
- Students seeking need-based aid must submit a Bucknell International Student Financial Aid Application
- Canadian citizens are also required to complete the CSS PROFILE

APPLICATION INFORMATION

Award Deadline: Nov 15, Jan 15

Instructions: Please visit the website to learn more about the application. www.bucknell.edu/x17084.xml

CONTACT

Bucknell University
Office of Admissions
1 Dent Drive
Lewisburg, Pennsylvania 17837
Tel: +1 (570) 577-3000
Fax: +1 (570) 577-3538
Email: admissions@bucknell.edu
Web: www.bucknell.edu/admissions/international-admissions/paying-for-bucknell.html

Buena Vista University

Buena Vista University International Student Scholarships

PROGRAM INFORMATION

Description: This is a grant program for international students enrolled in the undergraduate program at Buena Vista University. Award typically range from $9,000 to $18,000 per year and are based on academic credentials at the time of admission. Awards are renewable for up to 4 years based on academic performance.

Levels of Study: Undergraduate

Field of Study: All

Nationality: Any Region

Location of Study: Buena Vista University
Storm Lake, IA

AWARD INFORMATION

Award Type: Grant

Average Amount: Varies

Number of Awards: Varies

Award Coverage: Tuition

Award Duration: Up to 4 years

ELIGIBILITY REQUIREMENTS

- Financial assistance is based on academic credentials at the time of acceptance, no additional application is necessary
- Must have the equivalent of a 2.0 grade point average (4.0 scale)

APPLICATION INFORMATION

Instructions: For more information on how to apply, please visit the website

CONTACT

Buena Vista University
Director of Admissions
610 West Fourth Street
Storm Lake, IA 50588
Tel: +1 (712) 749-2235
Fax: +1 (712) 749-2035
Email: admissions@bvu.edu
Web: www.bvu.edu/international

Butler University

Butler University Merit & Talent Scholarships

PROGRAM INFORMATION

Description: Butler University offers Freshman Academic Scholarships, Athletic Grants-in-Aid, and Jordan College of Fine Arts Audition Awards.

Field of Study: All

Nationality: Any Region

Location of Study: Butler University
Indianapolis, IN

ELIGIBILITY REQUIREMENTS

- Freshman Academic Scholarships: Awards are based on the student's academic record—SAT or ACT scores, class rank, high school curriculum, and extracurricular involvement at the time of admission
- Athletic Grants-in-Aid (Athletic Scholarship): Athletic ability as determined by the coach. Awards are made in 13 NCAA Division I athletic programs

APPLICATION INFORMATION

Award Deadline: Varies

Instructions: For more information, visit www.go.butler.edu/international

CONTACT

Butler University
Associate Director
4600 Sunset Ave.
Indianapolis, IN 46208
Tel: +1 (317) 940-8100
Fax: +1 (317) 940-8150
Email: intadmission@butler.edu
Web: www.butler.edu/financial-aid

Butte Community College

Butte Community College International Fee Waiver Scholarship

PROGRAM INFORMATION

Description: Each semester our international students are encouraged to apply for our international student fee waiver scholarship, which waives a portion of the non-resident fees for a semester that the student completes. It may only be received once and is competitive. We award this to nearly 10 percent of our international students each semester.

Levels of Study: Undergraduate

Field of Study: All

Nationality: Any Region

Location of Study: Butte College
Chico, CA

AWARD INFORMATION

Award Type: Tuition Reduction

Average Amount: $1,000

Number of Awards: Varies

Award Coverage: Partial tuition

Award Duration: 1 semester

ELIGIBILITY REQUIREMENTS

- Student must be registered in 12 units to apply. Not available prior to admission and class registration

APPLICATION INFORMATION

Award Deadline: Oct 15 for fall semester; Mar 15 for spring semester

Instructions: See website for detailed information

CONTACT

Butte College International Admissions
International Admissions Coordinator
3536 Butte Campus Drive
Oroville, CA 95965-8399
Tel: +1 (530) 895-2991
Email: woodra@butte.edu
Web: www.butte.edu/international

California Institute of Integral Studies

California Institute of Integral Studies Opportunity Scholarship

PROGRAM INFORMATION

Description: All newly admitted students are considered for the CIIS Opportunity Scholarship. There is no separate application for this scholarship. Awards are determined primarily on financial need.

Levels of Study: Undergraduate, Graduate, Doctorate

Field of Study: All, American Politics, Anthropology, Area and Ethnic Studies, Arts and Culture, Asian Studies, Behavioral Sciences, Creative Writing, Dance, Film, Fine Arts, Health Studies, Human Rights, Leadership, Liberal/General Studies, Multi/Interdisciplinary Studies, Peace Studies, Philosophy and Religion, Psychology, Religion/Theology, Social Justice, Social Movements, Social Science, Theater, Visual and Performing Arts, Women's Studies

Nationality: Any Region

Location of Study: California Institute of Integral Studies (CIIS) San Francisco, CA

AWARD INFORMATION

Award Type: Scholarship

Average Amount: $1,000-$4,000

Award Coverage: The average scholarship award is $2,500 per year for 2 years (fall and spring semesters only) for masters and doctoral levels; Clinical Psychology students receive $4,000/year for 2 years (fall and spring semester only); Bachelor's degree students receive an average of $1,000 per year, applied over 3 semesters; the scholarship is applied as a tuition discount for the first 2 years of study. Students are responsible for the additional tuition fees and living expenses

Award Duration: Maximum of 2 years

ELIGIBILITY REQUIREMENTS

- All newly admitted F-1 visa holders will receive a scholarship

APPLICATION INFORMATION

Instructions: Visit our website at www.ciis.edu/international for more information

CONTACT

California Institute of Integral Studies
International Student Advisor
1453 Mission St.
4th Floor
San Francisco, CA 94103
Tel: +1 (415) 575-6157
Fax: + 1 (415) 575-1268
Email: international@ciis.edu
Web: www.ciis.edu/international

California State University San Marcos

CSU-San Marcos Limited Tuition Waiver

PROGRAM INFORMATION

Description: This tuition waver is open only to students already studying at CSUSM. A limited number of partial waivers of non-resident tuition are available on a competitive basis to CSUSM international students who have completed at least 1 year of studies at CSUSM. This program is not open to newly-admitted CSUSM undergraduate International students.

Levels of Study: Undergraduate, Graduate

Field of Study: All

Nationality: Any Region

Location of Study: California State University - San Marcos San Marcos, CA

AWARD INFORMATION

Award Type: Tuition Reduction

Average Amount: Varies

Number of Awards: 15

Award Coverage: Non-resident portion of tuition

Award Duration: Academic year, renewable for additional years

ELIGIBILITY REQUIREMENTS

- Must already be studying at CSU San Marcos
- Undergraduate eligibility limited to students enrolled at California State University for at least 1 year; graduate applicants are eligible when they apply
- Must demonstrate excellent academic performance in grades at CSU San Marcos

APPLICATION INFORMATION

Award Deadline: Mar

Instructions: Visit our website for more information

CONTACT

California State University San Marcos
Associate Director
Office of Global Education
333 South Twin Oaks Valley Road
San Marcos, CA 92096
Tel: +1 (760) 750-8821
Fax: +1 (760) 750-3284
Email: dmcmarti@csusm.edu
Web: www.csusm.edu/global

California State University, Los Angeles

CSU-LA International Graduate Student Tuition Waiver Program

PROGRAM INFORMATION

Description: The International Graduate Student Tuition Waiver provides tuition waivers for selected international graduate students, for up to 24 units per academic year. The actual support enables an international student to waive the non-resident portion of their fees for a maximum of 12 units for the fall, winter, and/or spring quarters.

Levels of Study: Graduate

Field of Study: All

Nationality: Any Region

Location of Study: California State University - Los Angeles Los Angeles, CA

AWARD INFORMATION

Award Type: Tuition Reduction

Average Amount: Varies

Number of Awards: Varies

Award Coverage: Non-resident portion of tuition

Award Duration: Academic year, renewable for second year

ELIGIBILITY REQUIREMENTS

- Please view the application package for requirements

APPLICATION INFORMATION

Award Deadline: Apr

Instructions: Applicants must include a completed application form, including a written statement describing the student's goals/objectives and their need for financial assistance; 2 letters of recommendation from department chairs, faculty members who have taught or advised the student; unofficial copies of transcripts from colleges and universities attended by the student.

CONTACT

California State University, Los Angeles
Office of Graduate Studies & Research
5151 State University Drive
Los Angeles, CA 90032
Tel: +1 (323) 343-3820
Fax: +1 (323) 343-5653
Email: amuchli@calstatela.edu
Web: www.calstatela.edu/academic/aa/gsr/cal_la/students/studentInternational.html

Calvin College

Calvin College International Awards

PROGRAM INFORMATION

Levels of Study: Undergraduate

Field of Study: All

Nationality: Any Region

Location of Study: Calvin College Grand Rapids, MI

AWARD INFORMATION

Award Type: Grant, Scholarship
Average Amount: Up to $17,000
Award Duration: Maximum of 4 years

ELIGIBILITY REQUIREMENTS

- Must have completed Declaration of Finances form by Apr 1
- Financial documents from all sources must be received and approved
- Must possess strong grades and coursework and good performance on the SAT, ACT, or relevant national exams
- All admitted students are given work options on campus and grants are given based on need, not on academic performance

APPLICATION INFORMATION

Award Deadline: Jun 1
Instructions: All application materials are online at our website

CONTACT

Calvin College
Associate Director of International Admissions
3201 Burton St SE
Grand Rapids, MI 49546
Tel: +1 (616) 526-6106
Fax: +1 (616) 526-6777
Email: intladm@calvin.edu
Web: www.calvin.edu/international

Capital University

Capital University International Scholarships

PROGRAM INFORMATION

Description: Generous, merit-based tuition scholarships for international students with strong academic records who are pursuing a bachelor's degree. Most scholarships are partial, but renewable for a total of 4 years. Scholarships are available for any major of study that Capital offers. Capital's Conservatory of Music offers performance awards. International students must submit an audition CD or DVD by the audition deadlines. Scholarships are only for Capital international students pursuing a bachelor's degree.
Levels of Study: Undergraduate
Field of Study: All
Nationality: Any Region
Location of Study: Capital University
Columbus, OH

AWARD INFORMATION

Award Type: Scholarship
Average Amount: 30-40% of tuition
Number of Awards: 12
Award Coverage: Partial tuition
Award Duration: Maximum of 4 years

ELIGIBILITY REQUIREMENTS

- Must submit completed international undergraduate application
- Must submit a completed scholarship application with essays
- Must meet undergraduate TOEFL requirement
- Must submit strong secondary grade point average or test scores

APPLICATION INFORMATION

Award Deadline: Rolling
Instructions: Complete the undergraduate international application form and the international student scholarship application, submit all required supporting documents; visit us online for more information

CONTACT

Capital University
Office of International Education
1 College and Main
Columbus, OH 43209-2394
Tel: +1 (614) 236-7102
Fax: +1 (614) 236-6171
Email: international@capital.edu
Web: www.capital.edu/international-scholarships/

Cardozo School of Law

Cardozo LLM Scholarship for Dispute Resolution and Advocacy

PROGRAM INFORMATION

Description: The Cardozo LLM Scholarship for Dispute Resolution and Advocacy is a grant of $30,000 awarded each term to 1 outstanding candidate to pursue a full-time LLM degree in Dispute Resolution and Advocacy. This scholarship will take the form of a partial reduction of tuition, 1-half to be credited toward tuition for the first semester of study, and the other half to be credited toward tuition in the second semester of study. Recipients are chosen on the basis of their intellect, academic credentials, demonstrated academic promise, and achievement in the field of dispute resolution and advocacy.
Levels of Study: Professional
Field of Study: Law
Nationality: Any Region
Location of Study: Benjamin N. Cardozo School of Law
New York, NY

AWARD INFORMATION

Award Type: Scholarship, Tuition Reduction
Average Amount: $30,000
Number of Awards: 1
Award Duration: Maximum of 2 semesters

ELIGIBILITY REQUIREMENTS

- Must complete the LLM application.
- Must submit 2 supplementary essays for candidates of the Cardozo LLM Scholarship for Dispute Resolution and Advocacy

APPLICATION INFORMATION

Award Deadline: Dec (spring admission); Apr (fall admission)
Instructions: Please see website for instructions: www.cardozo.yu.edu/admissions/llm-admissions/tuition-and-scholarships

CONTACT

Benjamin N. Cardozo School of Law
55 Fifth Avenue
New York City, NY 10003
Tel: +1 (212) 790-0392
Email: clfinaid@yu.edu
Web: www.cardozo.yu.edu

Carnegie Mellon University, Information Networking Institute

Carnegie Mellon University Executive Women's Forum Fellowship

PROGRAM INFORMATION

Description: The Information Networking Institute (INI) and Carnegie Mellon CyLab have partnered with the Executive Women's Forum (EWF), sponsored by Alta Associates, to offer a full scholarship to an incoming INI Master of Science in Information Security Technology and Management (MSISTM) or Master of Science in Information Networking (MSIN) student. Alta Associates is a premier executive recruitment firm specializing in information security, IT audit, risk management, and privacy. This scholarship was first offered in fall 2007 to support a student from a historically underrepresented population (including women) in the area of information networking and security. Awardees, known as EWF Fellows, receive a full scholarship and are mentored by an EWF participant who is a woman at a senior level in the information security field.
Levels of Study: Graduate
Field of Study: Computer Science, Engineering, Information Technology
Nationality: Any Region
Location of Study: Carnegie Mellon University, Information Networking Institute
Pittsburgh, PA

AWARD INFORMATION

Award Type: Fellowship
Average Amount: Approx $71,400
Number of Awards: 1
Award Coverage: Full tuition
Award Duration: 16 months (4 semesters)

ELIGIBILITY REQUIREMENTS

- Must meet all criteria for admission to the INI MSISTM or MSIN program
- Must be a female student
- Must have an accumulated GPA of at least 3.25 prior to entering Carnegie Mellon and maintain a minimum 3.25 GPA while at the INI
- Must have no outstanding employment contract or obligation while attending Carnegie Mellon
- Must show exemplary promise and potential and demonstrate exceptional leadership skills

APPLICATION INFORMATION

Award Deadline: Feb 1
Instructions: Female students admitted to the MSIN and MSISTM programs will be considered for this award at the time of admission reviews on the basis of their application for admission; students should also indicate an interest in being considered for this award in their Statement of Purpose for admission

CONTACT

Carnegie Mellon, Information Networking Institute
Director of Admissions
4616 Henry St.
Pittsburgh, PA 15213
Tel: +1 (412) 268-9598
Fax: +1 (412) 268-7196
Email: ini@cmu.edu
Web: www.ini.cmu.edu

Carnegie Mellon University, Information Networking Institute

Carnegie Mellon University Tuition Scholarships

PROGRAM INFORMATION

Description: All students admitted to the INI graduate programs in information security, information networking, mobility, and software management who request financial assistance are considered for partial tuition scholarships. Award amounts vary and are based on a combination of need and merit as well as the availability of resources at the INI.

Levels of Study: Graduate

Field of Study: Computer Science, Engineering, Information Technology

Nationality: Any Region

Location of Study: Carnegie Mellon University, Information Networking Institute
Pittsburgh, PA

AWARD INFORMATION

Award Type: Scholarship

Average Amount: $10,000-$35,000

Number of Awards: Unlimited

Award Coverage: Partial tuition

Award Duration: 4 semesters

ELIGIBILITY REQUIREMENTS

- Must have an admission offer to 1 of the INI's graduate programs: MS in Information Security, Technology & Management (MSISTM), MS in Information Networking (MSIN), MS in Information Technology-Mobility (MSIT-MOB), MS in Information Technology-Software
- Must remain in good academic standing, defined as maintaining a GPA of at least 3.0 in core courses and all courses taken, excluding the project, and having no administrative violations on your record
- Award amounts vary and are based on need and merit as well as program needs and available resources

APPLICATION INFORMATION

Award Deadline: Feb

Instructions: Students who have been offered admission to the INI, and have indicated they would like to be considered for assistance in their admission application, will be considered for tuition scholarships on the basis of their admission application, no separate application is required

CONTACT

Carnegie Mellon, Information Networking Institute
Director of Admissions
4616 Henry St
Pittsburgh, PA 15213
Tel: +1 (412) 268-9598
Fax: +1 (412) 268-7196
Email: ini@cmu.edu
Web: www.ini.cmu.edu

Carroll College-Montana

Carroll College Academic Merit Awards

PROGRAM INFORMATION

Description: All prospective first year and transfer students who have applied and been admitted to Carroll are automatically considered for the following guaranteed minimum scholarships and awards based on official secondary school transcripts and SAT/ACT scores for first year students. Students with 24 post-secondary credits are automatically considered for our transfer student scholarships.

Levels of Study: Undergraduate

Field of Study: All

Nationality: Any Region

Location of Study: Carroll College
Helena, MT

AWARD INFORMATION

Award Type: Tuition Reduction

Average Amount: $12,500

Number of Awards: 90 percent of students receive merit awards

Award Coverage: Tuition

Award Duration: Maximum of 4 years

ELIGIBILITY REQUIREMENTS

- Must provide official SAT/ACT scores
- Must have a minimum GPA of 2.8
- Must maintain satisfactory academic progress for automatic renewal
- Must be enrolled at Carroll College full time (12 or more credits)
- Must have graduated from high school, or completed less than 1 full year of college

APPLICATION INFORMATION

Award Deadline: Scholarship priority deadline is Feb 15

Instructions: Students are automatically considered for a scholarship with the submission of a complete application package, including SAT or ACT, which can be found on our website

CONTACT

Carroll College
Director of International Programs
1601 N Benton Avenue
Helena, MT 56625-0002
Tel: +1 (406) 447-5406
Fax: +1 (406) 447-5461
Email: intl@carroll.edu
Web: www.carroll.edu

Central College

Central College International Student Scholarship

PROGRAM INFORMATION

Description: Founded in 1853, Central College is a private, residential, liberal arts college and offers the bachelor's degree in 39 majors as well as advising in pre-professional programs. Located 40 miles east of Des Moines, in the scenic, small town of Pella, Central College is among the top 10 comprehensive colleges for a bachelor's degree in the Midwest, according to US News & World Report. With a national reputation for international education, an average of 200 students also study at one of Central's 8 overseas campuses each semester. In a safe and friendly environment, dedicated professors encourage the nearly 1,600 students to develop varied interests in pursuit of advanced study and careers.

Levels of Study: Undergraduate

Field of Study: All

Nationality: Any Region

Location of Study: Central College
Pella, IA

AWARD INFORMATION

Award Type: Tuition Reduction

Average Amount: $8,000-$12,000

Number of Awards: Varies

Award Coverage: Partial tuition

Award Duration: Maximum of 8 semesters

ELIGIBILITY REQUIREMENTS

- All international students applying to Central College are evaluated for financial aid at the time of their admission
- No special application for the scholarship is required
- The decision is based primarily upon high school grade transcripts (or college for transfer students), test scores (TOEFL, IELTS, STEP, SAT/ACT, A-levels, etc), personal essay

APPLICATION INFORMATION

Award Deadline: Nov, Apr

Instructions: Visit the website for more information.

CONTACT

Central College
Director of Admission
Campus Box 5100
812 University Street
Pella, IA 50219
Tel: +1 (641) 628-7637
Fax: +1 (641) 628-5983
Email: freiburgerc@central.edu
Web: www.central.edu/admission/international

Central Michigan University

Central Michigan University President's Award

PROGRAM INFORMATION

Description: Awards are automatically given to applicants that are admitted to a CMU undergraduate degree program and meet minimum award requirements. The award allows for international students to pay Michigan-resident tuition rates for the duration of the degree program.

Levels of Study: Undergraduate

Field of Study: All

Nationality: Any Region

Location of Study: Central Michigan University Mount Pleasant, MI

AWARD INFORMATION

Award Type: Tuition Reduction

Average Amount: $10,000

Number of Awards: Varies

Award Coverage: Tuition

Award Duration: Academic year, renewable for additional years

ELIGIBILITY REQUIREMENTS

- Must be admitted to an undergraduate degree program
- Must have undergraduate grade point average of 3.3 on a 4.0 scale
- Must have minimum SAT I score of 1,000 or minimum ACT score of 22
- Must have a minimum TOEFL score of 550 PBT/213 CBT/79 IBT

APPLICATION INFORMATION

Award Deadline: Rolling

Instructions: Apply for admission online or contact to request application materials

CONTACT

Bovee University Center 106
Office of International Education
Central Michigan University
Mount Pleasant, MI 48859
Tel: +1 (989) 774-4308
Fax: +1 (989) 774-3690
Email: intlapp@cmich.edu
Web: www.oia.cmich.edu

Central Washington University

Central Washington University International Student Scholarship

PROGRAM INFORMATION

Description: Central Washington University is pleased to offer incoming undergraduate international students a scholarship of $3,000-$6,000 per year.

Levels of Study: Undergraduate, Graduate

Field of Study: All

Nationality: Any Region

Location of Study: Central Washington University, WA

AWARD INFORMATION

Award Type: Tuition Reduction

Average Amount: $5,000

Number of Awards: Approximately 30 per quarter

Award Coverage: Tuition only

Award Duration: First academic year, renewable each year

ELIGIBILITY REQUIREMENTS

- Student must possess a GPA of at least 3.0
- Student is not an exchange student, not sponsored by their government or receiving any other kind of waiver from CWU
- Graduate students receiving an assistantship do not qualify

APPLICATION INFORMATION

Instructions: E-mail with scholarship application will be sent out after student is accepted to CWU. Qualified students will be notified via email of scholarship award within 2-3 weeks after the scholarship deadline

CONTACT

Central Washington University
International Office
400 E. University Way
Ellensburg, WA 98926
Email: CassS@cwu.edu
Web: www.cwu.edu/admissions/international-scholarship

Centralia College

Centralia College International Programs

PROGRAM INFORMATION

Description: International students will find more than 50 academic degrees and transfer programs and many 1-year technical certificates from which to choose their field of study. With no TOEFL requirement needed for Intensive English Program admission, a 61 IBT score for admission to college-level programs, and an easy transfer process to 4-year universities, Centralia College is an excellent bargain for international students wishing to earn their first 2 years of a bachelor's degree in smaller classes taught by acclaimed faculty. The International Programs staff provides advising support in academic, immigration, career, and personal matters. An active International Club provides many opportunities for students to be involved in activities on- and off-campus. International housing and host families are also available.

Levels of Study: Undergraduate

Field of Study: All

Nationality: Any Region

Location of Study: Centralia College Centralia, WA

AWARD INFORMATION

Award Type: Scholarship, Study Abroad

Average Amount: Varies

Number of Awards: 3 per year

Award Coverage: Tuition

Award Duration: Quarter

ELIGIBILITY REQUIREMENTS

- Must have full-time status as a student
- Must have a 3.0 grade point average
- Must demonstrate commitment to the International Network (club)
- Must submit letters of recommendation

APPLICATION INFORMATION

Award Deadline: Awarded after student's first quarter

Instructions: Students can apply for this scholarship only after arriving on campus

CONTACT

Centralia College
International Programs
600 Centralia College Boulevard
Centralia, WA 98531-4099
Tel: +1 (360) 736 9391, ext. 625
Fax: +1 (360) 330 7503
Email: bcacchione@centralia.edu
Web: www.centralia.edu/international

Chadron State College

Chadron State College Non-resident Scholars Program

PROGRAM INFORMATION

Description: The Non-resident Scholars Program is a scholarship equal to 1 half of the out-of-state tuition and is available to all new undergraduate and graduate international applicants who enroll in campus-based courses and who have submitted documentation supporting qualifying criteria.

Levels of Study: Undergraduate, Graduate

Field of Study: All

Nationality: Any Region

Location of Study: Chadron State College Chadron, NE

AWARD INFORMATION

Award Type: Tuition Reduction

Average Amount: Varies

Award Coverage: Tuition reduction

Award Duration: Academic year

ELIGIBILITY REQUIREMENTS

- Entering freshmen must meet at least 1 of the following criteria: ranking in upper 1 half of graduating high school class; minimum of a 3.25 (on a 4.0 scale) overall high school grade point average (GPA); minimum composite ACT score of 22 or SAT score of 1530
- Undergraduate transfer students must have a cumulative GPA of 3.0 or above (on a 4.0 scale) for all previous work attempted at all colleges attended prior to their enrollment at Chadron State College
- Must have TOEFL scores of 600 PBT/100 CBT, or an IELTS score of 7 or better
- Graduate students must have a minimum cumulative GPA of 3.5 for all previous work attempted at all colleges attended prior to their enrollment at Chadron State College

APPLICATION INFORMATION

Instructions: Award will automatically be awarded during in-processing and receipt of official transcripts and test scores

CONTACT

Chadron State College
Extended Campus Programs
1000 Main Street
Chadron, NE 69337
Tel: +1 (308) 432-6496
Fax: +1 (308) 432-6473
Email: cousin@csc.edu
Web: www.csc.edu/extended/international/financial.csc

Chadron State College

Chadron State College International Student Tuition Waiver Program

PROGRAM INFORMATION

Description: In addition to the financial benefits of the non-resident scholars program, automatically granted to all qualifying international students, selected new international undergraduate degree-seeking applicants may also qualify for an additional tuition waiver equal to 50 percent of the on-campus residential tuition rate.

Levels of Study: Undergraduate

Nationality: Any Region

Location of Study: Chadron State College Chadron, NE

AWARD INFORMATION

Award Type: Scholarship

Average Amount: Varies

Number of Awards: 40 awards (based on availability)

Award Coverage: Tuition reduction

Award Duration: Up to 4 years

ELIGIBILITY REQUIREMENTS

- Must be a new or transfer applicant and complete and submit International Student Tuition Waiver
- Must be undergraduate degree-seeking status
- Must have TOEFL scores of 600 PBT/100 CBT, or an IELTS score of 7 or better
- Must meet GPA and English proficiency criteria of the Non-resident Scholars Program
- Must commit to living in CSC residence halls or apartments and meet all other CSC residency requirements for housing

APPLICATION INFORMATION

Award Deadline: Jun

Instructions: Complete and submit International Student Application

CONTACT

Chadron State College
Extended Campus Programs
1000 Main Street
Crites Hall #229
Chadron, NE 69337
Tel: +1 (308) 432 6496
Fax: +1 (308) 432 6473
Email: ccousin@csc.edu
Web: www.csc.edu/extended/international/waiver.csc

Chaminade University of Honolulu

Chaminade University of Honolulu Undergraduate Program Scholarship

PROGRAM INFORMATION

Description: Chaminade University of Honolulu is a small, Catholic, comprehensive university sponsored by the Province of the United States of America of the Society of Mary (Marianists). It is located on a hillside in suburban Honolulu, 2 miles from Waikiki beach. Chaminade currently offers 3 bachelor's degrees in 22 undergraduate majors, 5 graduate degree programs, and several professional certificate programs.

Levels of Study: Undergraduate

Field of Study: All

Nationality: Any Region

Location of Study: Chaminade University of Honolulu Honolulu, HI

AWARD INFORMATION

Award Type: Award, Scholarship, Tuition Reduction

Average Amount: $5,000 - $5,500

Number of Awards: 40

Award Coverage: 26.5% of tuition

Award Duration: Until degree completion

ELIGIBILITY REQUIREMENTS

- Must achieve a minimum TOEFL score of 550 PBT
- Must have a minimum secondary school GPA of 3.0 out of 4.0 scale
- Must be enrolled full-time in a degree program

APPLICATION INFORMATION

Award Deadline: Mar 1

Instructions: For more information on how to apply, please visit the website

CONTACT

Chaminade University of Honolulu
Dean of Enrollment Management
3140 Waialae Avenue
Honolulu, HI 96816
Tel: +1 (808) 739-4619
Fax: +1 (808) 739-4647
Email: jbouey@chaminade.edu
Web: www.chaminade.edu/admissions/ug/index.php

Charles Babbage Institute, University of Minnesota

Adelle and Erwin Tomash Fellowship

PROGRAM INFORMATION

Description: The Adelle and Erwin Tomash Fellowship will be awarded to a graduate student for research in the history of computing. The fellowship may be held at the recipient's home academic institution, the Charles Babbage Institute at the University of Minnesota, or any other location where there are appropriate research facilities.

Levels of Study: Doctorate

Field of Study: Computer Science

Nationality: Any Region

AWARD INFORMATION

Award Type: Fellowship

Average Amount: $14,000

Number of Awards: 1

Award Coverage: Stipend, tuition, fees, travel

Award Duration: Academic year

ELIGIBILITY REQUIREMENTS

- Must have completed all requirements for the doctoral degree except the dissertation

APPLICATION INFORMATION

Award Deadline: Jan

Instructions: Submit application materials by postal mail

CONTACT

Center for the History of Information Processing
Charles Babbage Institute, Associate Director
211 Anderson Library, 222 21st Ave. South
University of Minnesota
Minneapolis, MN 55455
Tel: +1 (612) 624-5050
Email: yostx003@tc.umn.edu
Web: www.cbi.umn.edu/research/tfellowship.html

Chatham University

Chatham University Undergraduate Merit Scholarships

PROGRAM INFORMATION

Description: Chatham University offers several merit-based scholarships including: Presidential Merit Scholarships; International Student Merit Scholarship; Leadership Scholarship; Visual Arts Scholarship; and Interior Architecture Scholarship.

Levels of Study: Undergraduate

Field of Study: Accounting, Architecture and Environmental Design, Art History, Biochemistry, Biology, Business and Management, Chemistry, Economics, Environmental Studies, Health Studies, History, Intensive English, Management, Master of Business Administration (MBA), Multi/Interdisciplinary Studies, Music, Photography, Physics, Political Science, Psychology, Social Service

Nationality: Any Region

Location of Study: Chatham University Pittsburgh, PA

AWARD INFORMATION

Award Type: Scholarship

Average Amount: $10,000

Number of Awards: Varies

Award Coverage: Tuition

Award Duration: Maximum of 4 years

ELIGIBILITY REQUIREMENTS

- International Student Merit Scholarship is based on academic performance and awards $6,000-$12,000, which is renewable annually based on GPA of 2.0 or higher and full-time enrollment
- Leadership Scholarship is for students that display outstanding leadership qualities, awards $1,000-$3,000, which is renewable annually based on GPA of 2.0 or higher and full-time enrollment
- Visual Arts Scholarship is based on completed visual arts scholarship application; students must submit portfolio or work on CD (JPEG format), DVD, mini DV, via URL or as a printed image; $2,000 scholarship renewable annually based on GPA of 2.0 or higher
- Interior Architecture Scholarships are for students that plan to major in interior architecture at Chatham University, based on completed interior architecture scholarship application; students must submit portfolio (art or interiors work) or essay; $2,000 scholarship renewable annually based on GPA of 2.0 or higher
- The Presidential Scholarship is an annually renewable scholarship that covers full tuition, room, board and fees for each academic year, for a total of 4 years (or 120 credits) of study at Chatham University; students must submit the Chatham Scholars and Scholarship Application. Renewable for up to 4 years must maintain a minimum 3.0 GPA and full-time enrollment

APPLICATION INFORMATION

Award Deadline: Rolling

Instructions: For most merit scholarships, students do not need to complete a separate application; applications are automatically considered when they submit complete application for undergraduate admission

CONTACT

Chatham University
International Admissions
Berry Hall
Woodland Road
Pittsburgh, PA 15232
Tel: +1 (412) 365-1100
Fax: +1 (412) 365-1609
Email: internationaladm@Chatham.edu
Web: www.chatham.edu

Chatham University

Chatham University Graduate Programs Assistantships and Fellowships

PROGRAM INFORMATION

Description: Graduate Teaching Fellowships and Assistantships are available to qualified full-time graduate students. These are awarded in the form of tuition remission and can save a student 30% or more off the price of tuition, depending on the number of credits taken per term.

Levels of Study: Graduate, Doctorate, Professional

Field of Study: Accounting, Biology, Business and Management, Chemistry, Creative Writing, Environmental Policy, Environmental Studies, Film, Health Professions, Master of Business Administration (MBA), Multi/Interdisciplinary Studies, Psychology

Nationality: Any Region

Location of Study: Chatham University Pittsburgh, PA

AWARD INFORMATION

Award Type: Fellowship, Tuition Reduction

Average Amount: 30% or more off tuition

Number of Awards: Varies

Award Coverage: Partial tuition

Award Duration: Maximum of 2 years

APPLICATION INFORMATION

Award Deadline: Mar

Instructions: Complete application online at www.chatham.edu/admission/forms/assistantship_app.cfm

CONTACT

Chatham University
Admissions
Berry Hall
Woodland Road
Pittsburgh, Pennsylvania 15232
Tel: +1 (412) 365-1100
Fax: +1 (412) 365-1609
Email: gradadmissions@chatham.edu
Web: www.chatham.edu

Chestnut Hill College

Chestnut Hill College Academic International Student Scholarships

PROGRAM INFORMATION

Description: Chestnut Hill College offers generous merit awards and scholarship opportunities.

Levels of Study: Undergraduate

Field of Study: All

Nationality: Any Region

Location of Study: Chestnut Hill College Philadelphia, PA

AWARD INFORMATION

Award Type: Award, Tuition Reduction

Average Amount: $12,500

Number of Awards: 100

Award Coverage: Tuition

Award Duration: Maximum of 4 years

ELIGIBILITY REQUIREMENTS

- Must have high academic regard

APPLICATION INFORMATION

Award Deadline: Jul 1 for fall semester; Dec 1 for spring semester

Instructions: Complete the application online. Send WES evaluated transcripts, letters of recommendation, personal statement, and letters of financial support

CONTACT

Chestnut Hill College
Director of International Student Services
9601 Germantown Avenue
Philadelphia, PA 19118
Tel: +1 (215) 242-7989
Fax: +1 (215) 753-3705
Email: brownt2@chc.edu
Web: www.chc.edu

City University of Seattle

New International Student Scholarship

PROGRAM INFORMATION

Description: International bachelor's and master's degree students applying to the City University of Seattle are eligible to apply for this scholarship.

Levels of Study: Undergraduate, Graduate

Field of Study: All

Nationality: Any Region

Location of Study: City University of Seattle Seattle, WA

AWARD INFORMATION

Award Type: Scholarship, Tuition Reduction

Average Amount: $3,000

Number of Awards: 20

Award Coverage: Tuition

Award Duration: First 3 quarters of full-time enrollment

ELIGIBILITY REQUIREMENTS

- Must be a new international student (F-1 visa category) applying to City University of Seattle
- Application must be submitted from outside of the US
- Applicant must be admitted to City University of Seattle for a bachelor's or master's degree program
- Applicant must be able to demonstrate involvement in the community and satisfactory academic progress

APPLICATION INFORMATION

Award Deadline: Sep, Dec, Mar, Jun

Instructions: Submit application form, essay, and community involvement statement

CONTACT

City University of Seattle
Student Financial Aid Office
521 Wall Street, Suite 100
Seattle, WA 98121
Tel: 1(206) 239.4533
Fax: +1 (206) 239.4544
Email: finaid@cityu.edu
Web: www.cityu.edu/admissions-financialaid/scholarships/international.aspx

Clackamas Community College

Clackamas Community College Program for Intensive English

PROGRAM INFORMATION

Description: The Program for Intensive English (PIE) at Clackamas Community College in Oregon City, Oregon, has 6 levels of reading/writing, 5 levels of grammar, and 4 levels of conversation, as well as electives including intercultural communication, vocabulary building, idioms and conversation, pronunciation, spelling, and business English. Clackamas is located in a small, safe city about 20 minutes from Portland, Oregon, and is less than 2 hours away by car from the Cascade Mountains and the Pacific Ocean. Students enrolling full time in PIE are eligible to receive a scholarship of $721.50, which pays for 1 3-hour per week class during fall, winter, or spring terms. This offer applies for each term (except for the summer term) that they are full-time PIE students. Clackamas has conditional admission; students who complete the PIE program may enter a college academic program without a TOEFL score.

Levels of Study: Undergraduate

Field of Study: English as a Second Language, Intensive English

Nationality: Any Region

Location of Study: Clackamas Community College Oregon City, OR

AWARD INFORMATION

Award Type: Scholarship, Tuition Reduction

Average Amount: $721.50

Number of Awards: 1 per student per term, excluding summer

Award Coverage: Tuition

Award Duration: Duration of full-time enrollment

ELIGIBILITY REQUIREMENTS

- Must be enrolled as a full-time student in the Program for Intensive English (PIE) at Clackamas Community College

APPLICATION INFORMATION

Award Deadline: Rolling

Instructions: For more information on how to apply, please visit the website

CONTACT

Clackamas Community College
19600 Molalla Avenue
Oregon City, OR 97045
Tel: +1 (503) 594-6100
Fax: +1 (503) 655-8925
Email: admissions@clackamas.edu
Web: depts.clackamas.edu/intl

Clark University

Clark University Undergraduate Awards

PROGRAM INFORMATION

Description: Awards are offered to international applicants based on merit as well as demonstrated financial need. Awards are competitive and do not always meet full need.

Levels of Study: Undergraduate

Field of Study: All

Nationality: Any Region

Location of Study: Clark University Worcester, MA

AWARD INFORMATION

Award Type: Award

Average Amount: $24,005

Number of Awards: Unlimited

Award Coverage: $10,000-$35,000 for general awards. The LEEP scholarship covers tuition, room and board

Award Duration: 4 years

ELIGIBILITY REQUIREMENTS

- Must file CSS Profile with Common Application to be considered for general awards
- LEEP scholarship has separate essay requirement included on application supplement

APPLICATION INFORMATION

Award Deadline: Jan 15

Instructions: File CSS Profile, together with Common application, by admission deadline

CONTACT

Clark University
Admissions
950 Main Street
Worcester, MA 01610
Tel: +1 (508) 793-7431
Fax: +1 (508) 793-8839
Email: intadmissions@clarku.edu
Web: www.clarku.edu

Clark University

Clark University Graduate Awards

PROGRAM INFORMATION

Description: Awards are offered to international applicants based on merit. All applicants admitted to a degree program are automatically considered for an award, there is no separate application. For PhD candidates, assistantships are also available.

Levels of Study: Graduate, Doctorate

Field of Study: Accounting, American History, American Jewish History, American Politics, Biochemistry, Biology, Business and Management, Chemistry, Computer and Information Sciences, Computer Science, Economics, Education, Environmental Policy, Environmental Policy, Curatorial Studies, Master of Arts in Teaching, Environmental Studies, Finance, Geography, History, Information Technology, International Development, Management, Marketing, Master of Arts in Teaching, Master of Business Administration (MBA), Molecular Biology, Public Administration

Nationality: Any Region

Location of Study: Clark University Worcester, MA

AWARD INFORMATION

Award Type: Award, Fellowship, Scholarship, Student Exchange

Number of Awards: Unlimited

Award Coverage: Tuition for master's degree, tuition and assistantship for PhD

Award Duration: Entire length of program

APPLICATION INFORMATION

Instructions: Apply to degree program by deadline

CONTACT

Clark University
Director of Graduate Student Recruitment
950 Main Street
Worcester, Massachusetts 01610, US
Tel: +1 (508) 793-7373
Email: gradadmissions@clarku.edu
Web: www.clarku.edu/graduate

Clemson University

International Graduate Student Funding

PROGRAM INFORMATION

Description: Clemson is growing selected graduate programs and building new research and economic development centers to support a knowledge-based economy, focusing on advanced materials, automotive and transportation technology, biotechnology and environmental sustainability. IIE, LASPAU, and AMIDEAST scholars may qualify for in-state tuition rates.

Levels of Study: Graduate

Field of Study: All

Nationality: Any Region

Location of Study: Clemson University Clemson, SC

AWARD INFORMATION

Award Type: Tuition Reduction

ELIGIBILITY REQUIREMENTS

- IIE, LASPAU, AMIDEAST scholars may qualify for in-state tuition rates

APPLICATION INFORMATION

Instructions: Contact Graduate Admissions Office

CONTACT

Clemson University
International Graduate Admissions Coordinator
Graduate Admissions
E-209 Martin Hall
Clemson, SC 29634-5713
Tel: +1 (864) 656-3195
Fax: +1 (864) 656-4723
Email: grdapp@clemson.edu
Web: grad.clemson.edu

Coe College
Coe College Music Scholarship

PROGRAM INFORMATION

Description: Coe College offers talent-based scholarships for students who are interested in continuing their music training. Scholarships are available for full-time degree-seeking students admitted to Coe College.

Levels of Study: Undergraduate

Field of Study: All

Nationality: Any Region

Location of Study: Coe College
Cedar Rapids, IA

AWARD INFORMATION

Award Type: Scholarship

Average Amount: $2,000

Number of Awards: Varies

Award Duration: Maximum of 4 years

ELIGIBILITY REQUIREMENTS

- Student must be admitted to Coe College as a full-time degree-seeking student
- Student must participate in 1 music ensemble to maintain scholarship

APPLICATION INFORMATION

Award Deadline: Jan

Instructions: Visit www.coe.edu/admission/international for more information or contact the Office of Admission at admission@coe.edu

CONTACT

Coe College
Associate Director of Admission for Operations and International Recruitment
1220 1st Ave NE
Cedar Rapids, Iowa 52402
Tel: +1 (319) 399-8500
Fax: +1 (319) 399-8816
Email: cpaasch@coe.edu
Web: www.coe.edu/admission/international

Coe College
Coe College International Scholarship Program

PROGRAM INFORMATION

Description: Our International Scholarship Program is designed to assist international students with their full-time undergraduate studies at Coe College. We are able to offer up to 70 percent tuition to strong academic students.

Levels of Study: Undergraduate

Field of Study: All

Nationality: Any Region

Location of Study: Coe College
Cedar Rapids, IA

AWARD INFORMATION

Award Type: Scholarship

Average Amount: $22,000

Number of Awards: Varies

Award Coverage: Up to 70% of tuition

Award Duration: Maximum of 4 years

ELIGIBILITY REQUIREMENTS

- Must be a full-time degree-seeking student who has been admitted to the college
- Must complete the international application for admission, as well as the required financial documentation
- Must submit a translated secondary school transcript, 1 recommendation letter, TOEFL/IELTS/STEP AIKEN (if English is not first language), SAT/ACT score reports

APPLICATION INFORMATION

Award Deadline: Mar

Instructions: For additional information visit: www.coe.edu/admission/international or contact via email: cpaasch@coe.edu

CONTACT

Coe College
Associate Director of Admission for Operations and International Recruitment
1220 First Avenue NE
Cedar Rapids, IA 52402
Tel: +1 (319) 399-8500
Fax: +1 (319) 399-8816
Email: cpaasch@coe.edu
Web: www.coe.edu/admission/international

Colburn School
Colburn Conservatory of Music

PROGRAM INFORMATION

Description: The Conservatory provides full financial scholarships, including tuition, room and board for all students. Programs include the Bachelor of Music degree, Performance Diploma, Professional Studies Certificate, Artist Diploma, and the Master of Music degree. All students must have completed secondary-level education prior to beginning study in the Conservatory.

Levels of Study: Undergraduate, Graduate

Field of Study: Music

Nationality: Any Region

Location of Study: The Colburn School
Los Angeles, CA

AWARD INFORMATION

Award Type: Grant, Scholarship

Average Amount: $50,000

Number of Awards: All enrolled students

Award Coverage: All students enrolled in the Conservatory receive a full scholarship for tuition and full grants for on-campus housing and board (food); need-based financial aid is available for support of other costs such as health insurance, comprehensive fee, textbooks, audition travel

Award Duration: All years of study, automatically renewed

ELIGIBILITY REQUIREMENTS

- Extraordinarily high performance level on an orchestral instrument or piano, as demonstrated in an in-person audition
- Satisfactory academic achievement, as documented in school transcript
- TOEFL BM: 79 IBT/PD: 65 IBT/AD: 65 IBT/PSC: 65 IBT/MM: 86 IBT

APPLICATION INFORMATION

Award Deadline: Dec

Instructions: Submit application and all supplemental materials, including TOEFL score and prescreening recording by Dec 1

CONTACT

The Colburn School
Conservatory of Music
200 South Grand Avenue
Los Angeles, California 90012
Tel: +1 (213) 621-4534
Fax: +1 (213) 625-0371
Email: admissions@colburnschool.edu
Web: www.colburnschool.edu

College of Saint Benedict/ Saint John's University - Minnesota
College of Saint Benedict/Saint John's University - Minnesota Undergraduate Academic Scholarships

PROGRAM INFORMATION

Description: The College of Saint Benedict and Saint John's University–Minnesota award academic scholarships to qualified international students. Students are also eligible for on-campus student employment. Full-time on-campus employment is available during the summer months of May, Jun, Jul and Aug

Levels of Study: Undergraduate

Field of Study: All

Nationality: Any Region

Location of Study: College of Saint Benedict/Saint John's University, MN

AWARD INFORMATION

Award Type: Scholarship

Average Amount: $9,000-$21,500

Number of Awards: Approx 110

Award Coverage: Tuition, room and board

Award Duration: Maximum 4 years

ELIGIBILITY REQUIREMENTS

- Must submit a minimum TOEFL score of 70 iBT (523 PBT), SAT 1500, and 3.5 GPA (on 4.0 scale)
- An essay is required along with the completion of the college's Common Application
- Must also submit College Board Application for Financial Aid and Certification for Finances form

APPLICATION INFORMATION

Award Deadline: Rolling

Instructions: Applications for admission can be found on our website, student is automatically considered for the scholarship by applying for admission, no additional scholarship application is needed

CONTACT

College of Saint Benedict/Saint John's University—Minnesota
Director of International Admission
International Admission Office, Quad #118
56321 Collegeville MN
Tel: +1 (320) 363-2196
Fax: +1 (320) 363-2750
Email: admissions@csbsju.edu
Web: www.csbsju.edu

College of Saint Elizabeth

College of Saint Elizabeth International Scholarships

PROGRAM INFORMATION

Description: Each fall semester, the Women's College awards 2 full scholarships covering tuition, room, and board. Those women selected for these highly competitive scholarships must prove that they can cover all remaining costs including transportation, books, insurance, and personal expenses.

Levels of Study: Undergraduate

Field of Study: All

Nationality: Any Region

Location of Study: College of Saint Elizabeth Morristown, NJ

AWARD INFORMATION

Award Type: Scholarship

Average Amount: Varies

Number of Awards: 2

Award Coverage: Tuition, room, board

Award Duration: Academic year, renewable for additional years

ELIGIBILITY REQUIREMENTS

- Must be first-year student pursuing full-time study
- Must submit TOEFL and SAT scores
- Only those with a minimum combined SAT of 1150 are encouraged to apply
- Must maintain a minimum GPA of 3.0

APPLICATION INFORMATION

Award Deadline: Mar for fall semester; Nov for spring semester

Instructions: Apply for admission online or contact to request application materials

CONTACT

College of Saint Elizabeth
Coordinator of International Admissions
2 Convent Road
Morristown, NJ 07960
Tel: +1 (973) 290-4000
Fax: +1 (973) 290-4710
Email: apply@cse.edu
Web: www.cse.edu/admissions/financial-aid/types-of-scholarships.dot

College of Staten Island of the City University of New York

CSI Scholarship Program

PROGRAM INFORMATION

Description: The scholarship program at CSI recognizes academic excellence and college or community service. In addition to scholarships offered directly by the College, the CSI Foundation and departments and associations of the College, memorial scholarships have been endowed through the generosity of many individuals and organizations who value higher education.

Levels of Study: Undergraduate

Field of Study: All

Nationality: Any Region

Location of Study: College of Staten Island of the City University of New York Staten Island, NY

AWARD INFORMATION

Award Type: Scholarship

Average Amount: Varies

Number of Awards: Varies

Award Coverage: Varies

Award Duration: Varies

ELIGIBILITY REQUIREMENTS

- All students must complete the application and provide all supporting documentation
- Transfer students must: Transfer a minimum of 28 credits from previous college(s) and pass the 3 CUNY assessment tests in reading, writing, mathematics
- Must maintain a minimum cumulative transfer GPA of 3.25 (with some exceptions)
- Incoming first year students with a 90 percent high school average or higher are encouraged to apply

APPLICATION INFORMATION

Award Deadline: Feb

Instructions: Visit www.csi.cuny.edu/career/scholarships.html#3 to download application materials from the Career and Scholarship Center

CONTACT

College of Staten Island of the City University of New York
Office of Recruitment and Admissions
2800 Victory Blvd., 2A-103
Staten Island, NY 10314
Tel: +1 (718) 982-2246
Fax: +1 (718) 982-2500
Email: international@csi.cuny.edu
Web: www.csi.cuny.edu/career/scholarships.html

College of William and Mary

College of William and Mary Jack Wolf Scholarship

PROGRAM INFORMATION

Description: Administered by the Reves Center for International Studies, the Jack Wolf Scholarship is awarded to an international undergraduate student who has distinguished him/herself in academics.

Levels of Study: Undergraduate

Location of Study: College of William and Mary Williamsburg, VA

AWARD INFORMATION

Award Type: Scholarship

Average Amount: 3,500

Number of Awards: 1

ELIGIBILITY REQUIREMENTS

- Must have standing as rising degree-seeking sophomore, junior, or senior at the College of William & Mary
- Must have valid F-1 or J-1 non-Immigrant status
- Must have exemplary academic achievement as evidenced by a minimum GPA of 3.4
- Open to all majors, including students who have not yet declared a major

APPLICATION INFORMATION

Award Deadline: Mar

Instructions: Application instructions are communicated to all eligible William & Mary students

CONTACT

College of William & Mary
Reves Center for International Studies
P.O. Box 8795
Williamsburg, VA 23187
Tel: +1 (757) 221-3590
Fax: +1 (757) 221-3597
Email: globe@wm.edu
Web: www.wm.edu/revescenter

College of William and Mary

Clark-Campbell Scholarship

PROGRAM INFORMATION

Description: Administered by the Reves Center for International Studies, the scholarship is awarded to an international undergraduate student who has distinguished him/herself in academics and service to the W&M community.

Levels of Study: Undergraduate

Nationality: Any Region

Location of Study: College of William and Mary Williamsburg, VA

AWARD INFORMATION

Award Type: Scholarship

Average Amount: $3,000

Number of Awards: 1

Award Coverage: Tuition and fees

ELIGIBILITY REQUIREMENTS

- Must have standing as a rising degree-seeking sophomore, junior, or senior at the College of William & Mary
- Must have valid F-1 or J-1 non-immigrant status
- Must have solid academic achievement evidenced by a minimum GPA of 3.0
- Must demonstrate service to the William & Mary community
- Open to all majors, including students who have not yet declared a major

APPLICATION INFORMATION

Award Deadline: Nov

Instructions: Application instructions will be communicated to all eligible William & Mary students

CONTACT

College of William & Mary
Reves Center for International Studies
P.O. Box 8795
Williamsburg, VA 23187
Tel: +1 (757) 221-3590
Fax: +1 (757) 221-3597
Email: ywong@wm.edu
Web: www.wm.edu/offices/revescenter/issp/scholarships/index.php

College of William and Mary
Jack Wolf Scholarship

PROGRAM INFORMATION

Description: Administered by the Reves Center for International Studies, the Jack Wolf Scholarship is awarded to an international undergraduate student who has distinguished him/herself in academics, leadership, and service to the William & Mary community.

Levels of Study: Undergraduate

Nationality: Any Region

Location of Study: College of William & Mary Williamsburg, VA

AWARD INFORMATION

Award Type: Scholarship

Average Amount: $3,500

Number of Awards: 1

Award Coverage: Tuition and fees

ELIGIBILITY REQUIREMENTS

- Must have standing as a rising degree-seeking sophomore, junior, or senior at the College of William & Mary
- Must have valid F-1 or J-1 non-immigrant status
- Must have exemplary academic achievement evidenced by a minimum GPA of 3.4
- Must demonstrate service to the William & Mary community
- Open to all majors, including students who have not yet declared a major

APPLICATION INFORMATION

Award Deadline: Mar

Instructions: Application instructions are communicated to all eligible William & Mary students

CONTACT

College of William and Mary
Reves Center for International Studies
P.O. Box 8795
Williamsburg, VA 23187-8795
Tel: +1 (757) 221-2590
Fax: +1 (757) 221-3597
Email: ywong@wm.edu
Web: www.wm.edu/offices/revescenter/issp/scholarships/index.php

Colorado Heights University
International Business Degrees

PROGRAM INFORMATION

Description: Students in BA and MBA level curriculum contribute to the international business discussion and are provided with career services for internships in the Denver, Colorado area business community. Low tuition rate can be supported with merit scholarships for those who qualify and payment plans are available.

Levels of Study: Undergraduate, Graduate

Field of Study: Business and Management, Intensive English

Location of Study: Colorado Heights University Denver, CO

AWARD INFORMATION

Award Type: Scholarship

Average Amount: Varies

Number of Awards: Varies

Award Duration: Renewable each semester

APPLICATION INFORMATION

Instructions: Fill out electronic application on www.chu.edu or contact the admissions staff at admissions@chu.edu to apply

CONTACT

Colorado Heights University
3001 S. Federal Boulevard
Denver, Colorado 80236
Tel: 303.937.4225
Fax: 303.937.4224
Email: admissions@chu.edu
Web: www.chu.edu

Columbia College of Missouri
Columbia College of Missouri Scholarship

PROGRAM INFORMATION

Description: Attend our Scholarship Day to compete for 1 of 10 prestigious awards, including the Columbia College Scholarship.

Levels of Study: Undergraduate

Field of Study: All

Nationality: Any Region

Location of Study: Columbia College Columbia, MO

AWARD INFORMATION

Award Type: Scholarship

Average Amount: Varies

Number of Awards: 10

Award Coverage: Full tuition, room and board

Award Duration: Renewable each year of undergraduate study

ELIGIBILITY REQUIREMENTS

- Must have a minimum 3.5 cumulative GPA and 26 ACT or SAT equivalent
- Must demonstrate school/community leadership
- Must attend our Scholarship Day

APPLICATION INFORMATION

Award Deadline: Nov

Instructions: Visit our website for more information

CONTACT

Columbia College
International Admissions
1001 Rogers St.
Columbia, MO 65216
Tel: +1 (573) 875-7155
Fax: +1 (573) 875-7235
Email: lcburetta@ccis.edu
Web: www.ccis.edu/offices/financialaid/scholarshipfinder/InternationalStudents.asp

Columbia College of Missouri
Columbia College of Missouri International Excellence Award

PROGRAM INFORMATION

Description: New freshman international students are eligible for the International Excellence Award.

Levels of Study: Undergraduate

Field of Study: All

Nationality: Any Region

Location of Study: Columbia College Columbia, MO

AWARD INFORMATION

Award Type: Scholarship

Average Amount: Half tuition

Number of Awards: Varies

Award Coverage: Tuition

Award Duration: Renewable each year of undergraduate study

ELIGIBILITY REQUIREMENTS

- Must be new freshman international students
- Must have a minimum TOEFL score of 560 PBT/220 CBT/79 IBT, or a minimum IELTS band score of 6.0 with no individual band score below 6.0, or 28 ACT or SAT equivalent and a 3.0 secondary school cumulative grade point average on a 4.0 scale

APPLICATION INFORMATION

Instructions: Visit our website for more information

CONTACT

Columbia College
International Admissions
1001 Rogers St.
Columbia, MO 65216
Tel: +1 (573) 875-7155
Fax: +1 (573) 875-7235
Email: lcburetta@ccis.edu
Web: www.ccis.edu/offices/financialaid/scholarshipfinder/InternationalStudents.asp

Columbia College of Missouri

Columbia College of Missouri International Award

PROGRAM INFORMATION

Description: New freshman international students are eligible for the International Award at Columbia College.

Levels of Study: Undergraduate

Field of Study: All

Nationality: Any Region

Location of Study: Columbia College
Columbia, MO

AWARD INFORMATION

Award Type: Scholarship

Average Amount: $1,000

Number of Awards: Varies

Award Coverage: Tuition

Award Duration: Renewable each year of undergraduate study

ELIGIBILITY REQUIREMENTS

- Must be new freshman international students.
- Must have a minimum TOEFL score of 530 PBT/197 CBT/71 IBT.
- Must have a minimum IELTS overall band score of 5.5, or 22 ACT, or 1030 SAT.
- Must have a minimum GPA of 3.0 from secondary school on a 4.0 scale.
- Must enroll in ESL courses and earn 24 hours in their first year at Columbia College.

APPLICATION INFORMATION

Instructions: Visit our website for more information

CONTACT

Columbia College
International Admissions
1001 Rogers St.
Columbia, MO 65216
Tel: +1 (573) 875-7155
Fax: +1 (573) 875-7235
Email: lcburetta@ccis.edu
Web: www.ccis.edu/offices/financialaid/scholarshipfinder/InternationalStudents.asp

Columbia College of Missouri

Columbia College of Missouri ESL Tuition Grant

PROGRAM INFORMATION

Description: Available to new, full-time English as second language students enrolled in ESOL courses.

Levels of Study: Undergraduate

Field of Study: English as a Second Language

Nationality: Any Region

Location of Study: Columbia College
Columbia, MO

AWARD INFORMATION

Award Type: Grant

Average Amount: $1,000 per semester

Number of Awards: Varies

Award Coverage: Tuition

Award Duration: Maximum of 1 year

ELIGIBILITY REQUIREMENTS

- Must be enrolled in ESOL 100, ESOL 101, ESOL 102, ESOL 103, ESOL 104 or ESOL 105

APPLICATION INFORMATION

Award Deadline: Varies

Instructions: Visit our website for more information

CONTACT

Columbia College
International Admissions
1001 Rogers St.
Columbia, MO 65216
Tel: +1 (573) 875-7155
Fax: +1 (573) 875-7235
Email: lcburetta@ccis.edu
Web: www.ccis.edu/offices/financialaid/scholarshipfinder/InternationalStudents.asp

Columbia College of Missouri

Columbia College of Missouri Canadian Tuition Grant

PROGRAM INFORMATION

Description: Available to Canadian students who enroll full-time at Columbia College in order to offset the imbalance in exchange rate.

Levels of Study: Undergraduate

Field of Study: All

Nationality: Canada

Location of Study: Columbia College
Columbia, MO

AWARD INFORMATION

Award Type: Grant

Average Amount: $3,000

Number of Awards: Unlimited

Award Coverage: Tuition

Award Duration: Renewable each year of undergraduate study

ELIGIBILITY REQUIREMENTS

- Must be a Canadian student who is enrolled full time at Columbia College

APPLICATION INFORMATION

Instructions: Visit our website for more information

CONTACT

Columbia College
International Admissions
1001 Rogers St.
Columbia, MO 65216
Tel: +1 (573) 875-7155
Fax: +1 (573) 875-7235
Email: lcburetta@ccis.edu
Web: www.ccis.edu/offices/financialaid/scholarshipfinder/InternationalStudents.asp

Columbia College of Missouri

Columbia College of Missouri Capstone Scholarship

PROGRAM INFORMATION

Description: Several scholarships are available to international students who attend traditional day classes at Columbia College.

Levels of Study: Undergraduate

Field of Study: All

Nationality: Any Region

Location of Study: Columbia College
Columbia, MO

AWARD INFORMATION

Award Type: Award, Grant, Scholarship

Average Amount: 60 percent off tuition

Number of Awards: Varies

Award Coverage: Tuition

Award Duration: 4 years

ELIGIBILITY REQUIREMENTS

- Must have a minimum of 28 ACT or SAT equivalent and either 3.75 cumulative GPA or GED equivalent

APPLICATION INFORMATION

Instructions: Visit our website for more information

CONTACT

Columbia College
Coordinator of International Admissions
1001 Rogers St.
Columbia, MO 65216
Tel: +1 (573) 875-7155
Fax: +1 (573) 875-7235
Email: lcburetta@ccis.edu
Web: www.ccis.edu/offices/financialaid/scholarshipfinder/InternationalStudents.asp

Columbia University

Society of Fellows in the Humanities

PROGRAM INFORMATION

Description: Founded in 1976, with the financial support of the Andrew W. Mellon Foundation, the Society of Fellows in the Humanities at Columbia University ranks as 1 of the first and most prestigious of postdoctoral fellowship programs. Over the years, it has supported the research of over 160 fellows in a variety of humanistic disciplines—from literature, art history, and music, to anthropology, history, philosophy, and political theory—whose scholarship has garnered numerous book prizes, grants, awards, and other forms of professional recognition and acclaim.

Levels of Study: Post Doctorate

Field of Study: Humanities

Nationality: Any Region

Location of Study: Columbia University
New York, NY

AWARD INFORMATION

Award Type: Fellowship

Average Amount: Up to $65,000

Number of Awards: Varies

Award Coverage: Stipend, research expenses.

Award Duration: Maximum of 3 years

ELIGIBILITY REQUIREMENTS

- Must have received a PhD in the last 4 years

APPLICATION INFORMATION

Award Deadline: Oct

Instructions: For application instructions, please visit our website

CONTACT

Columbia University
2960 Broadway
New York, NY 10027
Tel: +1 (212) 854-8443
Fax: +1 (212) 662-7289
Email: sof-fellows@columbia.edu
Web: www.columbia.edu/cu/societyoffellows

Columbia University, School of International and Public Affairs SIPA

SIPA Fellowships and Scholarships

PROGRAM INFORMATION

Description: These funds, which do not have to be repaid, are provided to students by SIPA. Fellowships are direct support with no additional obligation beyond maintaining good academic standing. Assistantships are support linked to a position as a teaching assistant, research assistant or program assistant within SIPA. Statistics discussed below are for fellowships in the 2-year full-time masters programs.

Levels of Study: Graduate

Field of Study: International Relations, Public Affairs

Nationality: Any Region

Location of Study: Columbia University, School of International and Public Affairs
New York, NY

AWARD INFORMATION

Award Type: Fellowship, Scholarship

Average Amount: $5,000-$ 21,000

Number of Awards: Varies

Award Coverage: tuition, fees, expenses

Award Duration: 1-2 academic years

APPLICATION INFORMATION

Instructions: Contact or visit our website for more information

CONTACT

Columbia University, School of International and Public Affairs
Office of Admissions and Financial Aid
Room 408, MC 3325
New York, NY 10027
Tel: +1 (212) 854-6216
Fax: +1 (212) 854-3010
Email: sipa_admission@columbia.edu
Web: www.new.sipa.columbia.edu/sipagiving/recognizing-donors/endowed-fellowships

Columbia University, Teachers College

Columbia University Teachers College Scholarships

PROGRAM INFORMATION

Description: Teachers College is more than its name implies—it is an urban, independent, thoroughly diverse, and multicultural, comprehensive graduate and professional school of education. Since its inception in 1887, Teachers College has also been a leading institution concerned with extending educational opportunity and improving the quality of education in and out of the classroom and across the lifespan. With more than 120 top-ranked graduate degree programs from which to choose, Teachers College offers students an unmatched array of areas of study. Students can concentrate in areas including education and educational leadership, clinical and counseling psychology, social and behavioral sciences, the arts and humanities, health and health promotion, international and comparative education, policy, and technology.

Levels of Study: Graduate, Doctorate

Field of Study: Cognitive Science, Conflict Management, Education, Health Studies, International Education, Linguistics, Peace Studies, Psychology

Nationality: Any Region

Location of Study: Teachers College, Columbia University
New York, NY

AWARD INFORMATION

Award Type: Fellowship, Scholarship

Average Amount: Varies

Number of Awards: Varies

Award Coverage: Partial tuition-only scholarships, endowed fellowships, assistantships

Award Duration: Academic year

ELIGIBILITY REQUIREMENTS

- Application to degree program by early deadline (Dec 15 for PhD; Jan 2 for EdD; Jan 15 for master's)
- Scholarships, fellowships, and assistantships awarded by academic departments
- All awards are merit-based

APPLICATION INFORMATION

Award Deadline: Dec 15-Jan 15, depending on degree

Instructions: Apply by early deadline for degree program; all eligible applicants are considered by the academic departments, visit our website for more information

CONTACT

Columbia University, Teachers College
525 West 120th St.
New York, NY 10027
Tel: +1 (212) 678-3714
Fax: +1 (212) 678-4089
Email: FinancialAid@tc.columbia.edu
Web: www.tc.columbia.edu

Concordia College

Concordia College King Olav V Scholarships

PROGRAM INFORMATION

Description: Concordia College was founded by Norwegian immigrants, and we seek to maintain ties with Norway in many ways. Kong Olav V visited Concordia's campus, and with the permission of the Norwegian Royal family we are pleased to provide these scholarships to students who are citizens of Norway.

Levels of Study: Undergraduate

Field of Study: All

Nationality: Norway

Location of Study: Concordia College
Moorhead, MN

AWARD INFORMATION

Award Type: Scholarship

Average Amount: $13,000

Number of Awards: Varies - every Norwegian citizen can receive.

Award Coverage: This award plus Lånekassen assistance covers all costs

Award Duration: Unlimited

ELIGIBILITY REQUIREMENTS

- Must meet all requirements for admission
- Must be a citizen of Norway
- Scholarships are available only to students enrolled at Concordia College

APPLICATION INFORMATION

Award Deadline: Jul

Instructions: Indicate Norway as country of citizenship on application, no financial aid application is required for students from Norway

CONTACT

Concordia College
Director of International Student Recruiting and Support
901 8th Street
Moorhead, MN 56562
Tel: +1 (218) 299-3004
Fax: +1 (218) 299-4720
Email: buegel@cord.edu
Web: www.concordiacollege.edu

Concordia College

Concordia College International Student Scholarships

PROGRAM INFORMATION

Description: Concordia offers a high quality education at a reasonable cost. We are a national leader for our school type in international education. We prize the contributions international students make on campus, and we provide international student scholarships, based on academic ability and family need, to qualified international students.

Levels of Study: Undergraduate

Field of Study: All

Nationality: Any Region

Location of Study: Concordia College
Moorhead, MN

AWARD INFORMATION

Award Type: Scholarship

Average Amount: Average $15,000, Maximum up to $25,000

Number of Awards: Approx 100

Award Coverage: Partial tuition

Award Duration: Varies

ELIGIBILITY REQUIREMENTS

- Must meet all requirements for admission, award amount is based on academic ability and family need
- Scholarships are available only to students enrolled at Concordia College

APPLICATION INFORMATION

Award Deadline: Jun

Instructions: Please complete International Student Financial Aid and Certification form as part of the application, visit our website for more application information

CONTACT

Concordia College
Director of International Student Recruiting and Support
901 8th Street S
Moorhead, MN 56562
Tel: +1 (218) 299-3004
Fax: +1 (218) 299-4720
Email: buegel@cord.edu
Web: www.concordiacollege.edu

Concordia College

Concordia College
Performance Scholarships

PROGRAM INFORMATION

Description: Concordia College offers performance scholarships to talented enrolled students in music, theatre performance or production, visual arts, and speech and debate. Scholarships are $2,500 per year and based entirely on the talent of the student without regard to citizenship or financial ability. Information is available on our website.

Levels of Study: Undergraduate

Field of Study: Arts and Culture, Music, Speech and Debate, Theater, Visual and Performing Arts

Nationality: Any Region

Location of Study: Concordia College
Moorhead, MN

AWARD INFORMATION

Award Type: Scholarship

Average Amount: $2,500 per year

Number of Awards: Varies

Award Coverage: Partial tuition

Award Duration: Commensurate with enrollment

ELIGIBILITY REQUIREMENTS

- Must be an academically above average incoming freshman student with demonstrated English proficiency
- Must be enrolled at Concordia College

APPLICATION INFORMATION

Award Deadline: Dec

Instructions: For more information on how to apply, please visit the website www.concordiacollege.edu/admission-aid/apply/international-students/costs-financial-aid/

CONTACT

Concordia College
Director of International Student Recruiting and Support
901 8th Street
Moorhead, MN 56562
Tel: +1 (218) 299-3004
Fax: +1 (218) 299-4720
Email: admissions@cord.edu
Web: www.concordiacollege.edu

Concordia University

Concordia University International
Student Scholarships

PROGRAM INFORMATION

Description: Undergraduate scholarships from $2,000-$14,000 are available, depending on the student's overall grade point average and test scores.

Levels of Study: Undergraduate, Graduate

Field of Study: All

Nationality: Any Region

Location of Study: Concordia University
Portland, OR

AWARD INFORMATION

Award Type: Scholarship

Average Amount: $2,000-$6,000

Number of Awards: Unlimited

Award Coverage: Tuition

Award Duration: Maximum of 4 years

ELIGIBILITY REQUIREMENTS

- TOEFL 71 IBT/ELS Level 112/IELTS 6.0 for undergraduate. 80 IBT/6.5 IELTS for graduate
- Must complete admission process
- Location of study must be on campus
- Other merit awards are based on SAT/ACT and GPA

APPLICATION INFORMATION

Award Deadline: No deadline

Instructions: Students submit online application and supporting documents official transcripts, including language proficiency test results, financial guarantee documents, health documents, 2 letters of recommendation

CONTACT

Concordia University
Director of International Admission
2811 NE Holman Street
Portland, OR 97211
Tel: +1 (503) 493-6548
Fax: +1 (971) 322-8722
Email: vgroves@cu-portland.edu
Web: www.cu-portland.edu/international

Connecticut College

Connecticut College
Need-Based Financial Aid

PROGRAM INFORMATION

Description: Financial aid at Connecticut College provides access to a quality educational experience for students who could not otherwise afford the full cost of tuition. As a highly selective institution, all of our students bring special talents and abilities that enhance the quality of our community. While some colleges and universities offer financial assistance to students based on their academic, athletic, musical, or artistic abilities, Connecticut College determines a student's eligibility for financial aid based on a detailed assessment of the income, assets, and special circumstances presented by his or her family. It is not our intent to reward student's performance through the distribution of financial aid. Rather it is our desire to open the doors of the college to highly qualified students from all economic backgrounds.

Levels of Study: Undergraduate

Field of Study: All

Nationality: Any Region

Location of Study: Connecticut College
New London, CT

AWARD INFORMATION

Award Type: Grant

Average Amount: Up to the full comprehensive fees

Number of Awards: 15-20

Award Coverage: Tuition, room, board, books & supplies, travel, health insurance, miscellaneous expenses.

Award Duration: Maximum of 4 years

ELIGIBILITY REQUIREMENTS

- Must submit the Common Application with essay and Connecticut College Supplement to the Common Application
- Results of the SAT Reasoning Test, 2 SAT Subject Tests or ACT are optional
- Must submit TOEFL or equivalent test if English is not your first language
- Must submit official secondary school transcript and Common Application International Supplement to the Secondary School Report
- Must submit school administrator recommendation and 2 teacher recommendations

APPLICATION INFORMATION

Award Deadline: Feb

Instructions: The Common Application and Connecticut College Supplement may be found at the Common Application website

CONTACT

Connecticut College
Associate Director of Admission & Coordinator of International Admission
270 Mohegan Avenue
New London, CT 06320
Tel: +1 (860) 439-2058
Fax: +1 (860) 439-2159
Email: finaid@conncoll.edu
Web: www.conncoll.edu

Cornell College

Cornell College Merit and Fine Arts Scholarships

PROGRAM INFORMATION

Description: Cornell awards academic merit scholarships to a select group of incoming students who have demonstrated records of academic success and scholarly potential. Select fine arts scholarships are also available for students interested in pursuing art, music, or theater.

Levels of Study: Undergraduate

Field of Study: All

Nationality: Any Region

Location of Study: Cornell College
Mount Vernon, IA

AWARD INFORMATION

Award Type: Scholarship

Average Amount: Varies

Number of Awards: Varies

APPLICATION INFORMATION

Award Deadline: Feb

Instructions: For more information on how to apply, including eligibility requirements, please visit the website

CONTACT

Cornell College
International Student Recruitment Coordinator
600 First Street SW
Mount Vernon, IA 52314-1098
Tel: +1 (319) 895-4159
Email: mschofer@cornellcollege.edu
Web: www.cornellcollege.edu

Cornell University

Cornell University Graduate Fellowships

PROGRAM INFORMATION

Description: Cornell University lives up to its motto of "any person, any study" by providing a rich and diverse learning community for students, faculty, and researchers. The Cornell graduate school promotes academic diversity by encouraging interdisciplinary study in its over 90 different fields of study. Although they confer 15 different advanced research and professional degrees, Cornell graduate school programs are bound by a common philosophy of academic freedom and flexibility. Faculty, grouped by common academic interest, often have cross-disciplinary ties and are available for student mentorship opportunities.

Levels of Study: Graduate

Field of Study: All

Nationality: Any Region

Location of Study: Cornell University
Ithaca, NY

AWARD INFORMATION

Award Type: Fellowship

Average Amount: Varies

Number of Awards: Varies

Award Coverage: Tuition, a 9-month stipend, and Cornell student health insurance

Award Duration: Varies

APPLICATION INFORMATION

Award Deadline: Varies

Instructions: Fellowships are awarded through the fields on the basis of ability and promise of achievement; see the Cornell University Graduate School Financial Aid Office website listed above

CONTACT

Cornell University
Graduate Admissions
143 Caldwell Hall
Ithaca, NY 14853-2602
Tel: +1 (607) 255-5820
Fax: +1 (607) 255-1816
Email: gfao@cornell.edu
Web: www.gradschool.cornell.edu

Creighton University

Matteo Ricci, S.J. Scholarship Program

PROGRAM INFORMATION

Description: The program is named in honor of Father Matteo Ricci, S.J., the founder of the first Christian missions in China in the sixteenth century.

Field of Study: All

Nationality: Any Region

Location of Study: Creighton University
Omaha, NE

AWARD INFORMATION

Award Type: Scholarship

Average Amount: $10,000

Number of Awards: No limit

Award Coverage: Up to 50 percent of tuition

Award Duration: Maximum of 4 years

ELIGIBILITY REQUIREMENTS

- International freshman and transfer applicants will be considered for Ricci Awards if they submit a completed application prior to Mar 1

APPLICATION INFORMATION

Award Deadline: Mar

Instructions: Ricci applicants must submit a completed application for admission to be considered for scholarships

CONTACT

Creighton University
International Admissions
2500 California Plaza
Omaha, NE 68178
Tel: +1 (402) 280-2523
Fax: +1 (402) 280-2685
Email: admissionsinternational@creighton.edu
Web: admissions.creighton.edu/international-students

Creighton University

Creighton University World Scholar Award

PROGRAM INFORMATION

Description: The World Scholar Award is reserved for 5 outstanding international freshman applicants to Creighton University. In addition to a sterling academic record, strong service, and leadership skills are required.

Field of Study: All

Location of Study: Creighton University
Omaha, NE

ELIGIBILITY REQUIREMENTS

- Must be an international freshman applicant and have completed an application for admission
- Interview and additional essay required for World Scholar consideration

APPLICATION INFORMATION

Award Deadline: Jan

Instructions: Candidates should submit a completed application for admission no later than Jan 15, qualified applicants will be notified of World Scholar Award eligibility

CONTACT

Creighton University
International Admissions
2500 California Plaza
Omaha, NE 68178
Tel: +1 (402) 280-2523
Fax: +1 (402) 280-2685
Email: admissionsinternational@creighton.edu
Web: admissions.creighton.edu/international-students

Daemen College

Daemen College Scholarships

PROGRAM INFORMATION

Description: Both undergraduate and graduate students who complete the entire application process will have an opportunity to receive a scholarship based on academic performance.

Levels of Study: Undergraduate, Graduate, Doctorate

Field of Study: All

Nationality: Any Region

Location of Study: Daemen College
Buffalo, NY

AWARD INFORMATION

Award Type: Scholarship

Average Amount: $1000-$8000

Number of Awards: Based on scholarship - a portion is applied each semester

Award Coverage: Partial tuition

Award Duration: 4 years for undergraduate, approx 2 years for graduate

ELIGIBILITY REQUIREMENTS

- Scholarships are based on leadership, academic performance, and TOEFL or IELTS or SAT score

APPLICATION INFORMATION

Award Deadline: Rolling

Instructions: For more information, please visit www.daemen.edu/admissions

CONTACT

Daemen College
Vice President Enrollment
4380 Main St
Amherst, NY 14226
Tel: +1 (716) 839-8484
Fax: +1 (716) 839-8229
Email: pbrown@daemen.edu
Web: www.daemen.edu/admissions/international

Darton College

Darton State College International Student Fellowship

PROGRAM INFORMATION

Description: The fellowship waives the cost of out-of-state tuition for eligible students.

Levels of Study: Undergraduate

Field of Study: All

Nationality: Any Region

Location of Study: Darton State College Albany, GA

AWARD INFORMATION

Award Type: Tuition Reduction

Average Amount: Over $7,000 per year

Number of Awards: Approx 35

Award Coverage: Tuition

Award Duration: Renewable every semester as long as academic/volunteer requirements are met, must renew annually

ELIGIBILITY REQUIREMENTS

- Must meet admissions requirements
- Must have outstanding potential as evidenced by high school academic record, test scores, personal essay, and letters of recommendation
- Must have clear understanding of academic goals and academic abilities
- Must be willing to assist the college with campus and community activities that promote multicultural understanding

APPLICATION INFORMATION

Award Deadline: Apr, Jul, Nov

Instructions: Download application for International Student Fellowship and submit with application for admission; for more information on how to apply, please visit the website

CONTACT

Darton State College
International Student Services
2400 Gillionville Road
Albany, GA 31707
Tel: +1 (229) 317-6924
Fax: +1 (229) 317-6614 Attn: Int'l Student Coordinator
Email: darton_international@darton.edu
Web: www.darton.edu/international

Davidson College

Davidson College International Student Aid

PROGRAM INFORMATION

Description: Davidson is a highly selective independent liberal arts college. Since its founding by Presbyterians in 1837, the college has graduated 23 Rhodes Scholars and is consistently recognized as 1 of the leading liberal arts colleges in the nation. A limited number of students who are nationals of countries other than the US receive financial assistance each year. These funds vary in amount and are based on a combination of need and merit.

Levels of Study: Undergraduate

Field of Study: All

Nationality: Any Region

Location of Study: Davidson College Davidson, NC

AWARD INFORMATION

Award Type: Grant, Scholarship

Average Amount: Varies

Number of Awards: Varies

Award Coverage: Varies

Award Duration: Maximum of 4 years

ELIGIBILITY REQUIREMENTS

- Must apply for financial aid at the time of admission and be admitted to Davidson College

APPLICATION INFORMATION

Award Deadline: May

Instructions: For more detailed information, please visit our website

CONTACT

Davidson College
Box 7156
Davidson, NC 28035-7156
Tel: +1 (704) 894-2232
Email: admission@davidson.edu
Web: www.davidson.edu

Denison University

Denison University International Student Grant

PROGRAM INFORMATION

Description: Denison offers partial tuition merit scholarships to academically talented international students.

Levels of Study: Undergraduate

Field of Study: All

Nationality: Any Region

Location of Study: Denison University Granville, OH

AWARD INFORMATION

Award Type: Grant

Average Amount: $15,000-$45,000

Number of Awards: Varies

Award Coverage: Partial - full tuition

Award Duration: 4 years

ELIGIBILITY REQUIREMENTS

- Must have an excellent academic record

APPLICATION INFORMATION

Award Deadline: Jan 15

CONTACT

Denison University
Director of International Admissions
100 West College Street, Box 740
Granville, Ohio 43023 USA
Granville, OH 43023-0740
Tel: +1 (740) 587-6789
Fax: +1 (740) 587-6352
Email: leavell@denison.edu
Web: www.denison.edu

DePaul University

DePaul University Doctoral Scholarship in Computer Science for a Syrian Student

PROGRAM INFORMATION

Description: DePaul University offers a full scholarship (tuition waiver and graduate assistantship) to a Syrian doctoral student in computer science, software engineering, or related fields. The scholarship does NOT cover housing and other living expenses.

Levels of Study: Doctorate

Field of Study: Computer and Information Sciences

Nationality: Syria

Location of Study: DePaul University Chicago, IL

AWARD INFORMATION

Award Type: Fellowship, Tuition Reduction

Average Amount: $15,000

Number of Awards: 1

Award Coverage: Full tuition waiver, graduate assistantship. The award does not cover housing or other living expenses

Award Duration: Maximum of 4 years

ELIGIBILITY REQUIREMENTS

- Visit our website at www.cdm.depaul.edu/Prospective%20Students/Pages/PhD.aspx for more information

APPLICATION INFORMATION

Award Deadline: Open

Instructions: If interested, please contact Dr. Besana by phone or email (see below).

CONTACT

DePaul University
Associate Vice President for academic affairs
1 East Jackson
Chicago, IL 60611
Tel: +1 (312) 362-5554
Email: gbesana@depaul.edu
Web: www.cdm.depaul.edu/Prospective%20Students/Pages/PhD.aspx

Dowling College

Dowling College Academic Scholarships

PROGRAM INFORMATION

Description: Academic performance scholarships available based on SAT test scores.

Levels of Study: Undergraduate

Field of Study: All

Nationality: Any Region

Location of Study: Dowling College Oakdale, NY

AWARD INFORMATION

Award Type: Grant, Scholarship

Average Amount: Up to $13,500

Number of Awards: Varies

Award Coverage: Tuition

Award Duration: Academic year, renewable if GPA criteria met

ELIGIBILITY REQUIREMENTS

- Must send official SAT score report, and all application documents

APPLICATION INFORMATION

Award Deadline: Rolling admissions but preference by Apr 1

Instructions: Please see the website for application information

CONTACT

Dowling College
Director, Admissions
150 Idle Hour Blvd.
Oakdale, NY 11769
Tel: +1 (631) 244-5097
Fax: +1 (631) 244-1164
Email: International@Dowling.edu
Web: www.dowling.edu

Drexel University School of Law

Drexel University School of Law Scholarships

PROGRAM INFORMATION

Description: Distinguish yourself from the competition with Drexel Law's LLM program in American Legal Practice. Our approach offers LLM students an opportunity to learn from unusually talented faculty with a unique commitment to teaching the distinct skills of American legal practice. Drexel Law stands apart from other law schools by offering small classes and personalized education in a close and supportive community. The program gives LLM students an opportunity to gain firsthand legal experience by working side by side with American lawyers. Our Co-op Externship allows highly qualified LLM students to earn credit by working in corporate offices, law firms, government agencies and courts.

Levels of Study: Graduate, Doctorate, Post Doctorate

Field of Study: Law

Nationality: Any Region

Location of Study: Drexel University School of Law Philadelphia, PA

AWARD INFORMATION

Award Type: Scholarship

Award Coverage: Drexel Law offers exceptional applicants merit and country-based scholarships, for more information, contact leslie.a.friedman@drexel.edu

ELIGIBILITY REQUIREMENTS

- Drexel Law offers exceptional applicants merit and country-based scholarships
- For further details, please contact leslie.a.friedman@drexel.edu

CONTACT

Drexel University School of Law
Director, Dean's Office
3320 Market Street
Philadelphia, PA 19104
Tel: +1 (215) 571-4729
Fax: +1 (215) 571-4763
Email: leslie.a.friedman@drexel.edu
Web: www.drexel.edu/law

Dumbarton Oaks

Dumbarton Oaks Fellowships

PROGRAM INFORMATION

Description: Dumbarton Oaks research library and museum offers residential fellowships in 3 areas of study: Byzantine studies (including related aspects of late Roman, early Christian, Western medieval, Slavic, and Near Eastern studies), Pre-Columbian studies (of Mexico, Central America, and Andean South America), and garden and landscape studies.

Levels of Study: Graduate

Field of Study: Classics

Nationality: Any Region

AWARD INFORMATION

Award Type: Fellowship

Average Amount: Varies

Number of Awards: Varies

Award Coverage: Stipend, living expenses, housing

Award Duration: Academic year

ELIGIBILITY REQUIREMENTS

- Junior Fellowship: must be a degree candidate who at the time of application has fulfilled all preliminary requirements for a PhD or appropriate final degree and will be working on a dissertation or final project at Dumbarton Oaks
- Fellowships: must be scholars who hold a doctorate or appropriate final degree or have established themselves in their field and wish to pursue their own research
- Summer Fellowships: Summer Fellowships are for Byzantine, Pre-Columbian, or Garden and Landscape scholars on any level of advancement beyond the first year of graduate (post-baccalaureate) study
- Must be able to communicate satisfactorily in English

APPLICATION INFORMATION

Award Deadline: Nov

Instructions: Please see website for application information

CONTACT

Dumbarton Oaks
1703 32nd St, NW
Washington, DC 20007
Tel: +1 (202) 339-6401
Email: DumbartonOaks@doaks.org
Web: www.doaks.org

D'Youville College

International Academic Freshman Scholarships

PROGRAM INFORMATION

Description: All first-time, undergraduate international students are eligible to receive our merit scholarships. These are based on high school GPA and SAT scores (math and critical reading).

Levels of Study: Undergraduate

Field of Study: All

Nationality: Any Region

Location of Study: D'Youville College Buffalo, NY

AWARD INFORMATION

Award Type: Scholarship

Average Amount: Varies

Number of Awards: Unlimited

Award Duration: Maximum of 5 years

ELIGIBILITY REQUIREMENTS

- SAT or ACT scores are required for scholarship consideration

APPLICATION INFORMATION

Award Deadline: Rolling

Instructions: No separate application required, all students are automatically considered upon application to the college. Apply to 1 of our over 45 programs of study: www.dyc.edu/apply

CONTACT

D'Youville College
International Admissions Counselor
320 Porter Avenue
Buffalo, New York 14201
Tel: +1 (716) 829-8355
Fax: +1 (716) 829-7691
Email: intadmissions@dyc.edu
Web: www.dyc.edu/financial_aid/scholarships/undergraduate.aspx

D'Youville College

D'Youville College Honors Scholarship

PROGRAM INFORMATION

Description: The D'Youville College Honors Scholarship comes with 50% off tuition and 25% off room and board. This is non-competitive and renewable for up to 5 years depending on undergraduate program of study.

Levels of Study: Undergraduate

Field of Study: All

Nationality: Any Region

Location of Study: D'Youville College Buffalo, NY

AWARD INFORMATION

Award Type: Scholarship

Average Amount: $14,246

Number of Awards: Unlimited

Award Coverage: 50% off tuition and 25% off room and board

Award Duration: Maximum of 5 years

ELIGIBILITY REQUIREMENTS

- 88/100 (3.0/4.0) secondary school average for last 3 years
- 1100 SAT (math & critical reading) or 24 ACT composite

APPLICATION INFORMATION

Award Deadline: Rolling

Instructions: Students are automatically reviewed for scholarship upon acceptance into a program of study

CONTACT

D'Youville College
International Admissions
320 Porter Avenue
Buffalo, New York 14201
Tel: +1 (716) 829-8355
Fax: +1 (716) 829-7691
Email: moranb@dyc.edu
Web: www.dyc.edu/financial_aid/scholarships/undergraduate.aspx

East Tennessee State University

International Students Academic Merit Scholarship

PROGRAM INFORMATION

Description: This scholarship covers 50 percent of the total of in-state and out-of-state tuition for new international students.

Levels of Study: Undergraduate, Graduate, Doctorate

Field of Study: All

Nationality: Any Region

Location of Study: East Tennessee State University Johnson City, TN

AWARD INFORMATION

Award Type: Scholarship

Average Amount: Varies

Number of Awards: Up to 100

Award Coverage: 50 percent of in and out-of-state tuition and maintenance fees. Approx $11,669 per year for undergraduates; $10,871 per year for graduates

Award Duration: 8 semesters for undergraduates; 5 semesters for master's degree students; 8 semesters for doctoral students

ELIGIBILITY REQUIREMENTS

- Must submit an admissions application with application fee before applying for the scholarship
- Must have or plan to have an F-1 or J-1 student visa
- Must have a demonstrated record of academic achievement
- Must be admitted to East Tennessee State University as a full-time, degree-seeking student

APPLICATION INFORMATION

Award Deadline: Jul 1 for fall semester; Oct 1 for spring semester

Instructions: The application is available online at www.etsu.edu/iss; applicants must be admitted to the university before applications can be reviewed, to learn how to apply for admission, contact our International Admissions Counselor at shupej@etsu.edu

CONTACT

East Tennessee State University
International Admissions Counselor
ETSU Office of Admissions 1276 Gilbreath drive
Burgin Dossett Hall room 106, P.O. Box 70731
Johnson City, TN 37614
Tel: +1 (423) 439-4808
Email: shupej@etsu.edu
Web: www.etsu.edu/iss

Eastern Michigan University

Eastern Michigan University National Scholars Program

PROGRAM INFORMATION

Description: The National Scholars Program (NSP) Scholarship Award pays the difference between in-state and out-of-state tuition ($15,000 per year). Open to incoming freshman and transfer students with a 3.0 GPA. You must be admitted as a nonresident for tuition purposes. Transfer students must have completed 30 transferable credits prior to admission for eligibility. National Scholars Program: $7,000 a year. This scholarship is for a first master's degree program, and is only awarded to non-resident students. Graduate students must have at least a 3.6 undergraduate GPA and cannot have previously earned Master's degree. The graduate award is renewable for up to 2 years or for a maximum of 32 credit hours. EMU Success Scholarship: $3,100 a year. This grant is awarded for your first Master's degree program, and is only awarded upon admission to EMU to non-resident students.

Levels of Study: Undergraduate, Graduate

Field of Study: All

Nationality: Any Region

Location of Study: Eastern Michigan University Ypsilanti, MI

AWARD INFORMATION

Award Type: Scholarship, Tuition Reduction

Average Amount: Varies

Award Coverage: Award goes toward tuition

Award Duration: 2 years

ELIGIBILITY REQUIREMENTS

- Undergraduate students must have a 3.0 GPA
- Graduate students must have a 3.6 or 3.2 GPA

APPLICATION INFORMATION

Award Deadline: May

Instructions: Awarded upon admissions to Eastern Michigan University

CONTACT

Eastern Michigan University
Coordinator, International Recruiting
401 Pierce Hall
Office of Admissions
48197 Ypsilanti Michigan
Tel: +1 (734) 487-0205
Fax: +1 (734) 487-6559
Email: international.admissions@emich.edu
Web: www.emich.edu

Eastern Michigan University

Eastern Michigan University Graduate International Student Scholarship

PROGRAM INFORMATION

Description: Several options are available to help international graduate students finance their graduate studies at Eastern Michigan University, including the National Scholars Program Scholarship and the EMU Student Success Scholarship, as well as other forms of assistance from the EMU Graduate School.

Levels of Study: Graduate

Field of Study: All

Nationality: Any Region

Location of Study: Eastern Michigan University Ypsilanti, MI

AWARD INFORMATION

Award Type: Scholarship

Average Amount: Varies

Number of Awards: Varies

Award Coverage: Tuition

Award Duration: Varies

ELIGIBILITY REQUIREMENTS

- International graduate students who completed their undergraduate degree with a 3.6 or higher cumulative grade point average on a 4.0 scale are eligible to receive an award of $6,600 per academic year for up to 2 years
- International graduate students who completed their undergraduate degree with a 3.2-3.59 GPA on a 4.0 scale are eligible to receive an award of $3,100 per academic year
- Must be admitted as a non-resident for tuition purposes before May 1

APPLICATION INFORMATION

Award Deadline: May

Instructions: Visit our website for more information

CONTACT

Eastern Michigan University
Assistant Director, International Admissions
401 Pierce Hall Office of Admissions
Ypsilanti, MI 48197
Tel: +1 (734) 487-0205
Fax: +1 (734) 487-6559
Email: international.admissions@emich.edu
Web: www.emich.edu/graduate/admissions/financialassistance/international_scholarships.php

Eastern Michigan University

Eastern Michigan University International Student Scholarship

PROGRAM INFORMATION

Description: To attract talented students from around the country and world, Eastern Michigan University presents the International Student Scholarship. This scholarship is for new international students who have demonstrated academic excellence and plan to pursue their education at Eastern Michigan University.

Levels of Study: Undergraduate

Field of Study: All

Nationality: Any Region

Location of Study: Eastern Michigan University Ypsilanti, MI

AWARD INFORMATION

Award Type: Scholarship

Average Amount: $12,000

Number of Awards: Varies

Award Coverage: Tuition, housing, travel expenses

Award Duration: Up to 4 years

APPLICATION INFORMATION

Award Deadline: May

Instructions: Visit our website for more information

CONTACT

Eastern Michigan University
Assistant Director, International Admissions
401 Pierce Hall Office of Admissions
Ypsilanti, MI 48197
Tel: +1 (734) 487-0205
Fax: +1 (734) 487-6559
Email: international.admissions@emich.edu
Web: www.emich.edu/ois/

Eastern Washington University

Eastern Washington University New International Student Scholarship

PROGRAM INFORMATION

Description: Partial tuition scholarships are available for new international students.

Levels of Study: Undergraduate

Field of Study: All

Nationality: Any Region

Location of Study: Eastern Washington University Cheney, WA

AWARD INFORMATION

Award Type: Scholarship

Average Amount: Varies

Number of Awards: Varies

Award Coverage: Partial tuition

Award Duration: Academic year

ELIGIBILITY REQUIREMENTS

- Must have F-1 visa status while enrolled at EWU
- Must have minimum grade point average of 3.0 on 4.0 scale
- Students applying to study in the English Language Institute, exchange programs, master's preparation programs, or off-campus programs are not eligible

APPLICATION INFORMATION

Award Deadline: Jul, Nov, Feb

Instructions: Download or contact to request application materials

CONTACT

Eastern Washington University
International Education Office
127 Showalter Hall
Cheney, WA 99004
Tel: +1 (509) 359-2331
Fax: +1 (509) 359-7869
Email: global@ewu.edu
Web: www.ewu.edu/Admissions/Financial-Aid/Waivers/FA_International_Waivers.xml

Elizabethtown College

Elizabethtown College International Student Scholarship

PROGRAM INFORMATION

Description: Financial assistance is available to international students who study at Elizabethtown College.

Levels of Study: Undergraduate

Field of Study: All

Nationality: Any Region

Location of Study: Elizabethtown College Elizabethtown, PA

AWARD INFORMATION

Award Type: Scholarship

Average Amount: Varies

Award Coverage: Tuition, room and board

Award Duration: Maximum of 4 years

ELIGIBILITY REQUIREMENTS

- The College assists international students who wish to study as 4 year degree candidates or those who will be attending Elizabethtown College as 1-year non-degree candidates
- Must complete an application for admission, certified financial documents, transcripts, letters of recommendation, test scores, an essay
- Must meet minimum English requirement. Student must submit TOEFL, IELTS, SAT, ACT, or other English language test

APPLICATION INFORMATION

Instructions: For more information on how to apply, please visit the website.

CONTACT

Elizabethtown College
Coordinator of International Recruitment
One Alpha Drive
Elizabethtown, PA 17022
Tel: +1 (717) 361-1191
Fax: +1 (717) 361-1365
Email: deiblerl@etown.edu
Web: www.etown.edu/admissions/international-students/international-scholarships.aspx

Elmhurst College

Elmhurst College Nyako Foreign Student Endowed Scholarship

PROGRAM INFORMATION

Description: A scholarship awarded to an international student of sophomore standing or above, who is maintaining a 3.0 GPA and majoring in mathematics or science.

Levels of Study: Undergraduate

Field of Study: Mathematics, Science

Nationality: Any Region

Location of Study: Elmhurst College
Elmhurst, IL

AWARD INFORMATION

Award Type: Scholarship

Average Amount: $500-$1,000

Number of Awards: 1-2

Award Coverage: Tuition

Award Duration: Academic year

ELIGIBILITY REQUIREMENTS

- Must have a 3.0 GPA (on a 4.0 scale)
- Must be majoring in mathematics or science
- Must be of sophomore standing or above

APPLICATION INFORMATION

Instructions: Current international students who are majoring in science or mathematics will be notified of eligibility and provided with application instructions

CONTACT

Elmhurst College
International Student Coordinator
Center for Professional Excellence
190 Prospect Avenue
Elmhurst, IL 60126
Tel: +1 (630) 617-3296
Fax: +1 (630) 617-3464
Web: www.elmhurst.edu

Embry-Riddle Aeronautical University

Embry-Riddle Aeronautical University International Scholarships

PROGRAM INFORMATION

Description: Embry-Riddle Aeronautical University offers more than 30 bachelor's and master's degree programs in the colleges of Arts and Sciences, Aviation, Business, and Engineering, including degrees such as MBA, meteorology, air traffic management, software engineering, global security, physics, communication, and computer science. US News and World Report ranks Embry-Riddle as #1 in aerospace engineering. Embry-Riddle educates more than 32,000 students at residential campuses in Daytona Beach, Florida, and in Prescott, Arizona, through the worldwide campus at more than 130 centers worldwide, and through distance learning. The University offers scholarships and graduate assistantships to international students.

Levels of Study: Undergraduate, Graduate

Field of Study: Aviation/Aerospace, Business and Management, Computer Science, Engineering, Engineering-Related Technologies, Science, Transportation and Material Moving

Nationality: Any Region

Location of Study: Embry-Riddle Aeronautical University
Daytona Beach, FL

AWARD INFORMATION

Award Type: Scholarship

Average Amount: $1,000-$10,000

Number of Awards: Unlimited

Award Coverage: Tuition

Award Duration: Bachelor's: 4 years; master's: 2-3 years

ELIGIBILITY REQUIREMENTS

- Must submit the SAT or ACT for scholarship consideration, a separate application for scholarships is not necessary
- Admission and scholarship decisions are made on a rolling basis, applicants are encouraged to apply up to a year in advance
- Students with strong academic credentials and high scores on standardized tests SAT, ACT, GMAT, GRE and who apply early typically receive larger scholarships than those who wait to apply near the deadline

APPLICATION INFORMATION

Award Deadline: Jun 1

Instructions: Visit the website and complete the online form for prospective students or write directly to the listed contact to request an international application booklet, which includes the scholarship application

CONTACT

Embry-Riddle Aeronautical University
Director of International & Graduate Admissions
600 S. Clyde Morris Blvd.
Daytona Beach, FL 32114
Tel: +1 (386) 226-7178
Fax: +1 (386) 226-7070
Email: goonanj@erau.edu
Web: www.erau.edu

Emory University

Emory University
Robert W. Woodruff Fellowship

PROGRAM INFORMATION

Description: MBA Woodruff Fellowship is awarded to those who fit the description of "the highest caliber students." These annual fellowships are Emory University's most prestigious awards and support exceptional candidates in the full-time 2-year MBA program.

Levels of Study: Graduate

Field of Study: All

Nationality: Any Region

Location of Study: Goizueta Business School - Emory University
Atlanta, GA

AWARD INFORMATION

Award Type: Scholarship

Average Amount: Full tuition and $10,000 stipend

Number of Awards: 4

Award Coverage: Full tuition, fees

Award Duration: Length of MBA program

ELIGIBILITY REQUIREMENTS

- Must possess high academic excellence as well as demonstrated commitment to the university's core values

APPLICATION INFORMATION

Award Deadline: Jan

Instructions: Must apply by Feb 1 deadline; no additional scholarship application is required

CONTACT

Goizueta Business School - Emory University
1300 Clifton Road, Suite W288
Atlanta, GA 30322
Tel: +1 (404) 727-6311
Fax: +1 (404) 727-4612
Email: admissions@bus.emory.edu
Web: www.goizueta.emory.edu

Emory University

Emory University School of Law Woodruff Fellowships

PROGRAM INFORMATION

Description: Emory Law School awards up to 5 Robert W. Woodruff Fellowships in law each year to men and women of exceptional character, scholastic abilities, and leadership qualities.

Levels of Study: Graduate, Professional

Field of Study: Law

Nationality: Any Region

Location of Study: Emory Law School
Atlanta, GA

AWARD INFORMATION

Award Type: Fellowship

Average Amount: Full tuition and $3,000 stipend

Number of Awards: Up to 5

Award Coverage: Tuition, fees

Award Duration: Renewable for each year of law school

ELIGIBILITY REQUIREMENTS

- Must submit a complete application for admission to the Office of Admission
- LLM students are not eligible for the Woodruff Fellows Program

APPLICATION INFORMATION

Award Deadline: Jan

Instructions: A nomination letter should be submitted from an academic dean, a pre-law advisor, professor, or another appropriate official from your undergraduate or graduate institution; if you have been out of school for more than 2 years and are employed, you may seek a nomination letter from your current employer

CONTACT

Emory University School of Law
Office of Admission
1301 Clifton Road
Atlanta, GA 30322
Tel: +1 (404) 727-6802
Fax: +1 (404) 727-2477
Email: admission@law.emory.edu
Web: www.law.emory.edu/admission/admission-tuition.html

Emory University
Emory University School of Law Merit-Based Scholarships

PROGRAM INFORMATION

Description: All students who are accepted to Emory University School of Law are automatically considered for merit-based scholarships.

Levels of Study: Graduate, Professional

Field of Study: Law

Nationality: Any Region

Location of Study: Emory University School of Law
Atlanta, GA

AWARD INFORMATION

Award Type: Scholarship

Average Amount: Varies

Number of Awards: Varies

Award Coverage: Tuition

Award Duration: Renewable each year of law school

ELIGIBILITY REQUIREMENTS

- Must first be accepted to Emory University School of Law in order to be considered for scholarships
- LLM students are not eligible for scholarship funding

APPLICATION INFORMATION

Instructions: All applicants subsequently admitted to the School of Law are eligible for merit-based funding, a separate application form is not required

CONTACT

Emory University School of Law
Office of Admission
1301 Clifton Road
Atlanta, GA 30322
Tel: +1 (404) 727-6802
Fax: +1 (404) 727-2477
Email: admission@law.emory.edu
Web: www.law.emory.edu/admission/admission-tuition.html

Emory University
Emory University Theology Scholarships

PROGRAM INFORMATION

Description: Graduate theology students who are not citizens of the US may be eligible for scholarships covering up to full tuition.

Levels of Study: Graduate, Professional

Field of Study: Religion/Theology

Nationality: Any Region

Location of Study: Candler School of Theology, Emory University
Atlanta, GA

AWARD INFORMATION

Award Type: Scholarship

Average Amount: Varies

Number of Awards: Varies

Award Coverage: Tuition

Award Duration: Varies

APPLICATION INFORMATION

Award Deadline: Jan 15

Instructions: For more information on how to apply, please visit the Candler website. For scholarship details go to: www.candler.emory.edu/admissions/financial-aid/index.cfm

CONTACT

Emory Candler School of Theology
1531 Dickey Drive
Suite 301
Atlanta, GA 30322
Tel: +1 (404) 727-6326
Fax: +1 (404) 727-2915
Email: candleradmissions@emory.edu
Web: www.candler.emory.edu

Emporia State University
Emporia State University Tuition Reduction

PROGRAM INFORMATION

Description: Students who have demonstrated academic competencies, been successfully admitted into an academic program at ESU are eligible for tuition reduction awards.

Levels of Study: Undergraduate, Graduate

Field of Study: All

Nationality: Any Region

Location of Study: Emporia State University
Emporia, KS

AWARD INFORMATION

Award Type: Tuition Reduction

Average Amount: $4,000-$5,000 per semester depending on level of study

Number of Awards: Approx 5 per country, per semester

Award Coverage: Up to 60 percent off of out-of-state tuition costs

Award Duration: Degree completion

ELIGIBILITY REQUIREMENTS

- Students advised by EducationUSA must have their adviser put them forward as a candidate by submitting a completed form
- Applicants must have a minimum GPA of 2.5 on a 4.0 scale (varies by program)
- Students should submit an English Proficiency Score (TOEFL or IELTS)

APPLICATION INFORMATION

Award Deadline: May 1 for fall, Oct 1 for spring

Instructions: Since there are a limited number of waivers we encourage you to submit your application and adviser/scholarship forms as soon as possible; visit www.emporia.edu/oie to get started

CONTACT

Emporia State University
1200 Commercial
ESU Box 4041
Emporia, KS 66801
Tel: +1 (620) 341-5374
Fax: +1 (620) 341-5918
Email: oisa@emporia.edu
Web: www.emporia.edu/oie

Emporia State University
Emporia State University Scholarship Program for Syrian Students

PROGRAM INFORMATION

Description: Emporia State University offers 20 partial tuition waivers to qualified Syrian students. The tuition waiver program targets undergraduate and graduate students who successfully receive an admission offer from Emporia State University, in any of its academic programs.

Levels of Study: Undergraduate, Graduate

Field of Study: All

Nationality: Syria

Location of Study: Emporia State University
Emporia, KS

AWARD INFORMATION

Award Type: Tuition Reduction

Average Amount: Approx $4,000 per semester

Number of Awards: 20 per year

Award Coverage: Admitted undergraduate students will receive a tuition discount of about 60 percent and graduate students will receive a tuition discount of approximately 50 percent, based on the out-of-state tuition

Award Duration: Maximum 5 years for undergraduate students, 6 semesters for graduate students

ELIGIBILITY REQUIREMENTS

- Students must be successfully admitted for studies at Emporia State University

APPLICATION INFORMATION

Award Deadline: Varies

Instructions: Contact the school's Office of International Education

CONTACT

Emporia State University
Office of International Education
1 Kellogg Circle
MU 40
Emporia, KS
Tel: +1 (620) 341-5374
Fax: +1 (620) 341-5918
Email: sverhuls@emporia.edu
Web: www.emporia.edu/oie

Emporia State University

Emporia State University Diversity Scholarship

PROGRAM INFORMATION

Description: The scholarship is designed to financially assist academically strong students from underrepresented student populations at ESU.

Levels of Study: Undergraduate, Graduate

Field of Study: All

Nationality: Africa, Europe, Latin America, Oceania, South/Central Asia, Southeast Asia, Bahrain, Bermuda, Canada, Hong Kong, Iran, Iraq, Israel, Jordan, Korea, Dem. People's Rep., Kuwait, Lebanon, Macao, Mongolia, Oman, Palestinian Authority, Qatar, Syria, Taiwan, United Arab Emirates, Yemen

Location of Study: Emporia State University Emporia, KS

AWARD INFORMATION

Award Type: Scholarship

Average Amount: $8,000

Number of Awards: 5 per country

Award Coverage: Tuition

Award Duration: Length of Degree

ELIGIBILITY REQUIREMENTS

- Admission to Emporia State University
- Must submit letters of nomination

APPLICATION INFORMATION

Award Deadline: Rolling

Instructions: Contact the office of international education for more information

CONTACT

Emporia State University
International Education
1 Kellogg Circle
MU 40
Emporia, KS 66801
Tel: +1 (620) 341-5374
Fax: +1 (620) 341-5918
Email: oisa@emporia.edu
Web: www.emporia.edu/oie

Emporia State University

Emporia State University Academic Merit Scholarship

PROGRAM INFORMATION

Description: Undergraduates will automatically receive academic scholarships if they are admitted with a "B" average (3.0+ GPA) or better and a Critical Reading + Math score of 980 or better and/or an ACT score of 21 or better. Students must meet both the grade and test score requirements to be eligible.

Levels of Study: Undergraduate

Field of Study: All

Nationality: Any Region

Location of Study: Emporia State University Emporia, KS

AWARD INFORMATION

Award Type: Scholarship

Average Amount: $2,300

Number of Awards: Unlimited

Award Coverage: Partial tuition, other

Award Duration: Maximum of 4 years

ELIGIBILITY REQUIREMENTS

- Submit SAT or ACT scores
- Be admitted and maintain a GPA of 3.0 or better throughout your degree seeking studies

APPLICATION INFORMATION

Award Deadline: Rolling

Instructions: Submit all application materials including your SAT or ACT score to International Education

CONTACT

Emporia State University
Director of International Recruitment
1 Kellogg Circle
Box 4041
Emporia, KS 66801
Tel: +1 (620) 341-5374
Fax: +1 (620) 341-5918
Email: oisa@emporia.edu
Web: www.emporia.edu/oie/Scholarships/

Erikson Institute

Erikson Institute Doctoral Fellowships

PROGRAM INFORMATION

Description: Doctoral fellowships are awarded to newly admitted PhD students and provide partial to full tuition scholarships, depending on availability of funding each year. The fellowships typically include a research or teaching assistantship.

Levels of Study: Doctorate

Nationality: Any Region

Location of Study: Erikson Institute Chicago, IL

AWARD INFORMATION

Award Type: Fellowship

Number of Awards: 1-2

Award Coverage: Full or partial tuition

Award Duration: Varies

ELIGIBILITY REQUIREMENTS

- Must be admitted to the PhD program in child development
- Must have outstanding academic credentials

APPLICATION INFORMATION

Instructions: Visit the website for more information

CONTACT

Erikson Institute
Office of Admission
451 N. LaSalle Street
Chicago, IL 60654
Tel: +1 (312) 755-2250
Email: admission@erikson.edu
Web: www.erikson.edu/graduate-school/admission/international-student/

Erikson Institute

Erikson Institute Harris Master's Fellowships and Scholarships

PROGRAM INFORMATION

Description: Harris leadership fellowships provide full tuition scholarships for up to 38 credits in Erikson's core master's degree programs. The fellowships are awarded to newly admitted master's degree students who exhibit the highest level of potential for leadership in the fields of child development and early childhood education.

Levels of Study: Graduate

Field of Study: Education

Nationality: Any Region

Location of Study: Erikson Institute Chicago, IL

AWARD INFORMATION

Award Type: Fellowship, Scholarship

Average Amount: Varies

Number of Awards: Varies

Award Coverage: Full or partial tuition

Award Duration: Maximum of 3 years

ELIGIBILITY REQUIREMENTS

- Must be admitted to 1 of Erikson's master's degree programs
- Must have outstanding academic credentials
- Must have a minimum of 1 year of experience working with children and their families in a supervised setting

APPLICATION INFORMATION

Award Deadline: Mar

Instructions: For more information on how to apply, please visit the website

CONTACT

Erikson Institute
Financial Aid Office
451 N. LaSalle Street
Chicago, IL 60654-4510
Tel: +1 (312) 755-2250
Fax: +1 (312) 755-0928
Email: admission@erikson.edu
Web: www.erikson.edu/default/admissions/financialaid/scholarships.aspx

Fairleigh Dickinson University
Colonel Fairleigh S. Dickinson Scholarship

PROGRAM INFORMATION

Description: Academic scholarships based on academic merit as demonstrated by secondary school grade point average and SAT/ACT scores.

Levels of Study: Undergraduate

Field of Study: All

Nationality: Any Region

Location of Study: Fairleigh Dickinson University Teaneck and Madison, NJ

AWARD INFORMATION

Award Type: Scholarship

Average Amount: $11,000-$25,000

Number of Awards: Unlimited

Award Coverage: Partial tuition

Award Duration: Academic year, available for 4 years as long as academic requirements are met

ELIGIBILITY REQUIREMENTS

- Must submit secondary school transcripts and/or national exam results
- The recommended academic criteria for consideration are 1050 SAT on a 1600 scale (23 ACT) and a 3.0 GPA
- Must maintain a minimum 3.0 cumulative grade point average

APPLICATION INFORMATION

Award Deadline: Jul 1 (for fall term); Dec 1 (for spring term)

Instructions: 1-Complete online application: https://www.applyweb.com/apply/fdu/index_i.html 2-Mail all required documents to the address below; list of required documents can be found on the undergraduate applicant checklist here: view.fdu.edu/default.aspx?id=6400

CONTACT

Fairleigh Dickinson University
Office of International Admissions
1000 River Road
T-KB1-01
Teaneck, NJ 07666
Tel: +1 (201) 692-2205
Fax: +1 (201) 692-2560
Email: global@fdu.edu
Web: www.fdu.edu

Fairleigh Dickinson University
Fairleigh Dickinson University International Scholarship

PROGRAM INFORMATION

Description: Academic scholarships based on academic merit and demonstrated financial need. Scholarships are renewable for each of the 4 years of a bachelor's degree and for 2 to 3 years of a master's degree program.

Levels of Study: Undergraduate, Graduate

Field of Study: All

Nationality: Any Region

Location of Study: Fairleigh Dickinson University Teaneck and Madison, NJ

AWARD INFORMATION

Award Type: Scholarship

Average Amount: Undergraduate: $1,000-$15,000; graduate: $1,000-$10,000

Number of Awards: Unlimited

Award Coverage: Partial tuition

Award Duration: Academic year, renewable until all academic requirements are met

ELIGIBILITY REQUIREMENTS

- Must submit a completed international scholarship application along with the FDU application and all other admission documents

APPLICATION INFORMATION

Award Deadline: Jul 1 for fall semester; Dec 1 for spring semester

Instructions: Scholarships are awarded once student is admitted to FDU and has submitted an FDU International Scholarship Application; 1-complete online application: https://www.applyweb.com/apply/fdu/index_i.html 2-mail all required documents to the address below; list of required documents can be found on the undergraduate applicant checklist here: view.fdu.edu/default.aspx?id=6400

CONTACT

Fairleigh Dickinson University
1000 River Road
T-KB1-01
Teaneck, NJ 07666
Tel: +1 (201) 692-2205
Fax: +1 (201) 692-2560
Email: global@fdu.edu
Web: www.fdu.edu

Fairleigh Dickinson University
Fairleigh Dickinson University Global Housing Grant

PROGRAM INFORMATION

Description: First-time undergraduate students living in the residence halls at the Metropolitan Campus will be considered for an annual $3,000 Global Housing Grant. These grants are awarded on the basis of academic merit, financial need and extracurricular involvement. Housing grants are renewable for up to 2 years.

Levels of Study: Undergraduate

Field of Study: All

Nationality: Any Region

Location of Study: Fairleigh Dickinson University Teaneck, NJ

AWARD INFORMATION

Award Type: Grant

Average Amount: $3,000

Number of Awards: 30

Award Coverage: Partial room and board fees

Award Duration: Up to 2 years

ELIGIBILITY REQUIREMENTS

- Must be a first time freshman student who will reside on campus at the Metropolitan campus only
- Must submit the International Scholarship application along with all other required application documents

APPLICATION INFORMATION

Award Deadline: Jul 1 for fall semester; Dec 1 for spring semester

Instructions: Since there are a limited number of Global Housing Grants available, we encourage you to apply as early as possible; 1-complete online application: https://www.applyweb.com/apply/fdu/index_i.html 2-mail all required documents to the address below; list of required documents can be found on the undergraduate applicant checklist here: view.fdu.edu/default.aspx?id=6400

CONTACT

Fairleigh Dickinson University
Office of International Admissions
1000 River Road
T-KB1-01
Teaneck, NJ 07666
Tel: +1 (201) 692-2205
Fax: +1 (201) 692-2560
Email: global@fdu.edu
Web: www.fdu.edu

Fairleigh Dickinson University
Fairleigh Dickinson University Undergraduate Scholarships for Syrian Students

PROGRAM INFORMATION

Description: FDU offers 1 scholarship of $25,000 applicable towards tuition expenses at the University and $10,000 applicable towards on-campus housing costs.

Levels of Study: Undergraduate

Field of Study: Accounting, Biochemistry, Biology, Business and Management, Chemistry, Computer Science, Creative Writing, Economics, Engineering, Engineering-Related Technologies, Film, Finance, Fine Arts, French, History, Information Technology, Management, Mathematics, Nursing, Political Science, Psychology, Science, Spanish

Nationality: Syria

Location of Study: Fairleigh Dickinson University Teaneck or Madison, NJ

AWARD INFORMATION

Award Type: Scholarship

Average Amount: $35,000

Number of Awards: 1

Award Coverage: $25,000 for tuition, $10,000 for housing only if living on campus

Award Duration: renewable 4years with 3.0 GPA

ELIGIBILITY REQUIREMENTS

- Fill out the International Application for Admission (www.fdu.edu/global)
- Must submit official transcripts from secondary and post-secondary studies and 2 letters of recommendation from teachers/faculty
- Must have TOEFL score above 79 IBT or IELTS overall band score above 6.0
- Original financial support documentation from sponsor (original bank statement and affidavit of financial support) showing sufficient financial sponsorship to cover the balance cost of study at FDU
- Statement of academic purpose, brief resume and copy of passport information page

APPLICATION INFORMATION

Award Deadline: Mar 31

Instructions: Contact the office of International Admissions for details

CONTACT

Fairleigh Dickinson University
Associate Director of International Admissions
1000 River Road, T-KB1-01
Office of International Admissions
Teaneck, NJ 07666
Tel: +1-201-692-2205
Fax: +1-201-692-2560
Email: global@fdu.edu
Web: www.fdu.edu/global

Felician College

Felician College Undergraduate Scholarships for Syrian Students

PROGRAM INFORMATION

Description: Felician College is pleased to offer scholarship awards to Syrian undergraduate students.

Levels of Study: Undergraduate

Field of Study: All

Nationality: Syria

Location of Study: Felician College Rutherford, NJ

AWARD INFORMATION

Award Type: Scholarship

Average Amount: At least partial tuition ($10,000)

Number of Awards: Varies

Award Coverage: Partial tuition scholarships will cover from $4500 up to $15,000 per year, tuition for 2013 is $28,360., fees are approximately $1600 per year, but may vary depending on course, medical insurance is $900 per year, housing and meal plan is $11,650 per year, any personal expenses and books

Award Duration: Maximum 4 years

ELIGIBILITY REQUIREMENTS

- Complete the undergraduate application form, which can be found online at apply.felician.edu/apply/secure/adm_login.asp
- English Language: If TOEFL has been taken, please submit a copy of the exam, however, as we understand there is a lack of testing centers available, we may be able to make exceptions, as we do offer our own ESL program; if you are currently in a country that offers TOEFL or IELTS, a score must be submitted; a Skype interview may be required to help gauge English language capability; minimum TOEFL is 61 or 500 PBT, we also accept a 5.5 on the IELTS
- Student must submit all transcripts from high school and any university work; transcripts need to be translated into English; student must have equivalent of 3.0 GPA on a 4.0 scale to be eligible for the scholarship
- Submit a personal essay
- If submitting university work, please try to also submit course syllabi to be considered for transfer credit, must be in English

APPLICATION INFORMATION

Award Deadline: Apr

Instructions: Please submit all necessary documents by no later than Apr 1 to be considered for a scholarship, if admitted and awarded a scholarship, a confirmation of enrollment must be submitted by May 15

CONTACT

Felician College
Director of International Enrollment Services
223 Montross Ave.
Rutherford, NJ 07070
Tel: +1 (201) 559-6196
Fax: +1 (201) 355-1121
Email: oip@felician.edu
Web: www.felician.edu

Felician College

Felician College International Scholarship

PROGRAM INFORMATION

Description: Felician College is proud to offer highly competitive International Merit-Based Scholarships to international undergraduate applicants.

Levels of Study: Undergraduate

Field of Study: All

Nationality: Any Region

Location of Study: Felician College Rutherford, NJ

AWARD INFORMATION

Award Type: Scholarship

Average Amount: $10,000

Number of Awards: Approx 80% of applicants

Award Coverage: Tuition

Award Duration: 4 years

ELIGIBILITY REQUIREMENTS

- Students must have at least equivalent to a 3.0 GPA (on a 4.0 scale)
- Students must score a 900 or above on the SAT Critical Reading and Math to qualify for the scholarship

APPLICATION INFORMATION

Award Deadline: Jul

Instructions: Students considered for scholarship upon admission to the college

CONTACT

Felician College
Director of International Enrollment Services
223 Montross Ave.
Rutherford, NJ 07070
Tel: +1 (201) 559-3518
Email: oip@felician.edu
Web: www.felician.edu

Felician College

Felician College International Award

PROGRAM INFORMATION

Description: Merit-Based International Award offered to international student applicants applying without SATs.

Levels of Study: Undergraduate

Field of Study: All

Nationality: Any Region

Location of Study: Felician College Rutherford, NJ

AWARD INFORMATION

Award Type: Award

Average Amount: $5,000-$10,000

Number of Awards: Approx 80% of applicants

Award Coverage: Tuition

Award Duration: 4 years

ELIGIBILITY REQUIREMENTS

- Students will automatically be considered for International Award upon admission to the college, awards are based on holistic review of the application

APPLICATION INFORMATION

Award Deadline: Jul

Instructions: Students are automatically considered for scholarship upon admission to the college

CONTACT

Felician College
Director of International Enrollment Services
223 Montross Ave.
Rutherford, NJ 07070
Tel: +1 (201) 559-3518
Email: oip@felician.edu
Web: www.felician.edu

Felician College

Felician College International Transfer Scholarships

PROGRAM INFORMATION

Description: International students with more than 12 earned university credits will be considered for our International Transfer Scholarships. Scholarships range from $4500 up to $15,000 per year. Students who are members of Phi Theta Kappa will be awarded an additional $3500.

Levels of Study: Undergraduate

Field of Study: All

Nationality: Any Region

Location of Study: Felician College Rutherford, NJ

ELIGIBILITY REQUIREMENTS

- Students must have a GPA equivalent to a 2.5-4.0 to be considered for scholarship

APPLICATION INFORMATION

Award Deadline: Jul

Instructions: Students are automatically considered for scholarship upon admission to the college. Please visit www.felician.edu/oip to find out more about applying to Felician as an international student.

CONTACT

Felician College
Director of International Enrollment Services
223 Montross Ave.
Rutherford, NJ 07070
Tel: +1 (201) 559-3518
Email: oip@felician.edu
Web: www.felician.edu

Ferris State University

Ferris State University WNF Scholarship Program

PROGRAM INFORMATION

Description: Scholarships based on merit for first time international students or transfer students wishing to attend an undergraduate program at Ferris State University.

Levels of Study: Undergraduate

Field of Study: All

Nationality: Any Region

Location of Study: Ferris State University Big Rapids, MI

AWARD INFORMATION

Award Type: Scholarship

Average Amount: $5,000

Number of Awards: 20 awards per semester

Award Coverage: Tuition, housing

Award Duration: Up to 4 years or undergraduate degree completion

ELIGIBILITY REQUIREMENTS

- Must have a GPA of 3.0 or better
- Must submit 1 of the following test scores: SAT 980 English/Math; TOEFL 65 IBT; or IELTS 6.0
- Transfer students: GPA of 3.3 or better and 24 credits complete at an institution of higher education (no English test required)

APPLICATION INFORMATION

Award Deadline: Apr

Instructions: Automatic review upon applying to Ferris State University

CONTACT

Ferris State University
International Recruitment Manager
1301 S. State Street, IRC 134
Big Rapids, MI 49307
Tel: +1 (231) 591-5444
Fax: +1 (231) 591-2423
Email: tartaril@ferris.edu
Web: www.ferris.edu/international

Florida Atlantic University

Florida Atlantic University International Student Scholarships

PROGRAM INFORMATION

Description: Depan International Freshman Student Scholarship Awards of $2,000 per year for first-time-in-college freshmen entering FAU on a student or scholar visa. Depan International Transfer Student Scholarship Awards are for a student transferring to FAU on a student or scholar visa, and include a nonresident tuition fee waiver after completion of at least 1 year of study at another institution.

Levels of Study: Undergraduate

Field of Study: All

Nationality: Any Region

Location of Study: Florida Atlantic University Boca Raton, FL

AWARD INFORMATION

Award Type: Scholarship

Average Amount: $2,000 per academic year

Number of Awards: Varies

Award Coverage: Varies

Award Duration: Varies

ELIGIBILITY REQUIREMENTS

- Must demonstrate outstanding academic achievement, English proficiency, evidence of community service or activity
- Must have a 3.0 minimum GPA
- Must renew
- Eligible for international freshman and transfer students

APPLICATION INFORMATION

Award Deadline: Mar 1

Instructions: Visit our website for more information.

CONTACT

Florida Atlantic University
Office of Admissions
777 Glades Road - SU 80
Boca Raton, FL 33431-0991
Tel: +1 (561) 297-3040
Email: Admissions@fau.edu
Web: wise.fau.edu/admissions/Scholarship-Intl.php

Florida Institute of Technology

Florida Institute of Technology Undergraduate International Student Scholarships

PROGRAM INFORMATION

Description: Scholarships are awarded to students with strong secondary school grades. Scholarships may be available to qualified students regardless of country of citizenship.

Levels of Study: Undergraduate

Field of Study: All

Nationality: Any Region

Location of Study: Florida Institute of Technology Melbourne, FL

AWARD INFORMATION

Award Type: Grant

Average Amount: $8,000-$18,000

Number of Awards: Varies

Award Coverage: Tuition

Award Duration: 4 years

ELIGIBILITY REQUIREMENTS

- These scholarships are only awarded to students with no prior community college or university course work
- Must submit official transcripts

APPLICATION INFORMATION

Award Deadline: Feb

Instructions: Apply for admission, the award process is automatic, please visit www.fit.edu to apply

CONTACT

Florida Institute of Technology
Office of Undergraduate Admissions
150 W. University Blvd.
Melbourne, FL 32901
Tel: +1 (321) 674-8030
Fax: +1 (321) 674-8004
Email: admission@fit.edu
Web: www.fit.edu/ugrad/international/financial_assistance.php

Fordham University

Fordham University Dean's Scholarships

PROGRAM INFORMATION

Description: Fordham University offers merit scholarships to qualified first-year fall semester undergraduate applicants.

Levels of Study: Undergraduate

Field of Study: All

Nationality: Any Region

Location of Study: Fordham University New York, NY

AWARD INFORMATION

Award Type: Scholarship

Average Amount: $10,000

Number of Awards: Varies

Award Coverage: Partial tuition

Award Duration: Up to 4 years

ELIGIBILITY REQUIREMENTS

- Minimum high school GPA of 3.7
- Must submit a minimum SAT score of 1400 (combined critical reading and math)
- Must be ranked in top 10 percent of high school class
- Must have approval of the admission committee
- Transfer applicants are not eligible

APPLICATION INFORMATION

Award Deadline: Jan 1

Instructions: Submit completed admission application (with required transcripts, test scores, recommendations, etc.) to Undergraduate Admission Office, visit our website for more information

CONTACT

Fordham University
Director of Enrollment Group International Initiatives
Duane Library
441 East Fordham Road
10458-9993 Bronx NY
Tel: +1 (718) 817-5204
Fax: +1 (718) 817-2424
Email: intadmission@fordham.edu
Web: www.fordham.edu/intl

Fordham University

Fordham University Graduate School of Religion and Religious Education

PROGRAM INFORMATION

Description: The Graduate School of Religion and Religious Education (GRE) located at Fordham University's beautiful Rose Hill campus was 1 of the first graduate, higher education institutions in the world to offer comprehensive programs in religious education, pastoral counseling, and spiritual direction in response to the call for renewal of the Second Vatican Council. Since 1968, men and women from around the world have joined our community of learning, and are now serving as leaders in the church worldwide.

Levels of Study: Graduate, Professional

Field of Study: Religion/Theology

Nationality: Any Region

Location of Study: Graduate School of Religion and Religious Education
New York, NY

AWARD INFORMATION

Award Type: Grant

Average Amount: 45 percent of tuition cost

Number of Awards: Varies

Award Coverage: Tuition

ELIGIBILITY REQUIREMENTS

- International students must be enrolled in a 36-credit master's program at Fordham University's Graduate School of Religion and Religious Education
- Must complete the International Student Scholarship Form
- Must attach a copy of your Certificate of Eligibility Application & Affidavit of Support

APPLICATION INFORMATION

Award Deadline: May 1 for fall semester; Dec 1 for spring semester

Instructions: Visit our website for more information on how to apply

CONTACT

Fordham University
Graduate School of Religion and Religious Education
441 East Fordham Road
Bronx, NY 10458
Tel: +1 (718) 817-4801
Fax: +1 (718) 817-3352
Email: gre@fordham.edu
Web: www.fordham.edu/gre

Fort Hays State University

Fort Hays State University Master of Business Administration Scholarship for Indian Students

PROGRAM INFORMATION

Description: The Master of Business Administration program is available in accounting, finance, health care management, sports management, information assurance, international business, leadership studies, management information systems, marketing, and tourism and hospitality management.

Levels of Study: Graduate

Nationality: India

Location of Study: Fort Hays State University
Hays, KS

AWARD INFORMATION

Award Type: Scholarship

Average Amount: $2,000

Number of Awards: 5 per year

Award Coverage: Tuition, room, board

Award Duration: 2 years

ELIGIBILITY REQUIREMENTS

- Must be from the Indian subcontinent with India citizenship status and desire to study at Fort Hays State University at the master's level (post-graduate) in the US on an F-1 visa
- Scholarships will be competitive with preference being given to first- and second-class students with the highest final marks Students agree to provide email addresses from professors who can validate the academic quality of the applicant; students with UK-system 3-year diplomas will be considered equivalent to US 4-year degrees for admission purposes
- Must have completed their studies and present their university diploma in addition to all mark sheets for admission and scholarship consideration

APPLICATION INFORMATION

Award Deadline: Jun

Instructions: All applicants must submit an online application for admission to the FHSU Graduate School with a nonrefundable $50 application fee in addition to this scholarship application; scholarship students must maintain a minimum of 3.0 program GPA in order to retain the scholarship

CONTACT

Fort Hays State University
Dean, Graduate School
600 Park Street
Hays, KS 67601
Tel: +1 (785) 628-4236
Fax: +1 (785) 628-4479
Email: tcrowley@fhsu.edu
Web: www.fhsu.edu/academic/internationalization/Scholarship-Application—-Students-from-India/

Fort Hays State University

Fort Hays State University Master of Professional Studies Scholarship for Indian Students

PROGRAM INFORMATION

Description: The Master of Professional Studies degree is a multidisciplinary master's degree designed to meet emerging workforce development needs. It is designed to develop advanced professional skill sets in various subject areas not currently represented at FHSU by Master of Science (MS) credentials. A salient feature of the degree program is the flexibility for the student to combine a major subject area with 1 or more cognate areas designed to enhance professional workforce skills desired by employers in industry, government, healthcare, and information technology careers.

Levels of Study: Graduate

Nationality: India

Location of Study: Fort Hays State University
Hays, KS

AWARD INFORMATION

Award Type: Scholarship

Average Amount: $2,000

Number of Awards: 5 awards per year

Award Coverage: Tuition, room, board

Award Duration: 2 years

ELIGIBILITY REQUIREMENTS

- Must be from the Indian subcontinent with India citizenship status and desire to study at Fort Hays State University at the master's level (post-graduate) in the US on an F-1 visa
- Scholarships will be competitive with preference being given to first- and second-class students with the highest final marks. Students agree to provide email addresses from professors who can validate the academic quality of the applicant; students with UK-system 3-year diplomas will be considered equivalent to US 4-year degrees for admission purposes
- Must have completed their studies and present their university diploma in addition to all mark sheets for admission and scholarship consideration

APPLICATION INFORMATION

Award Deadline: Jun

Instructions: All applicants must submit an online application for admission to the FHSU Graduate School with a nonrefundable $50 application fee in addition to this scholarship application; scholarship students must maintain a minimum of 3.0 program GPA in order to retain the scholarship

CONTACT

Fort Hays State University
Dean, Graduate School
600 Park Street
Hays, KS 67601
Tel: +1 (785) 628-4236
Fax: +1 (785) 628-4479
Email: tcrowley@fhsu.edu
Web: www.fhsu.edu/academic/internationalization/Scholarship-Application—-Students-from-India/

Frostburg State University

Frostburg State University Harold R. Rowe International Scholarship

PROGRAM INFORMATION

Description: Funding for F-1 and J-1 visa students, both graduate and undergraduate, designed to supplement costs. Students may apply prior to attending FSU and again after a semester or year.

Levels of Study: Undergraduate, Graduate

Field of Study: All

Nationality: Any Region

Location of Study: Frostburg State University Frostburg, MD

AWARD INFORMATION

Award Type: Scholarship

Average Amount: $1,000-$3,000

Number of Awards: 5-8

Award Coverage: Tuition, housing, personal expenses

Award Duration: Academic semester

ELIGIBILITY REQUIREMENTS

- Must be attending or about to attend FSU as a full time F-1 or J-1 undergraduate or graduate student
- Must have an overall GPA of at least 2.5
- Must demonstrate some financial need (essay and references required)
- Must either have been accepted to FSU for the next semester or have been attending FSU for 1 full year (F-1) or 1 semester (J-1) when the award is granted

APPLICATION INFORMATION

Award Deadline: Jul for fall semester; Oct for spring semester; Mar for summer semester

Instructions: Rowe application forms may be downloaded from the website

CONTACT

Frostburg State University
101 Braddock Rd.
Frostburg, MD 21532
Tel: +1 (301) 687-4714
Fax: +1 (301) 687-1069
Email: FSUinternational@frostburg.edu
Web: www.frostburg.edu/admin/cie/ishome/financing/rowe/

Frostburg State University

Frostburg State University International Student Scholarship

PROGRAM INFORMATION

Description: For undergraduate students with exceptional academic potential, holding F-1 or J-1 visas, and attending Frostburg State University as full time students.

Levels of Study: Undergraduate

Field of Study: All

Nationality: Any Region

Location of Study: Frostburg State University Frostburg, MD

AWARD INFORMATION

Award Type: Scholarship

Average Amount: $5,000 or $10,000 available

Number of Awards: Varies based on availability

Award Coverage: Tuition, fees

Award Duration: Maximum of 4 years

ELIGIBILITY REQUIREMENTS

- Must present a strong academic record. For a $5,000 scholarship it requires minimum of 3.2 high school grade point average and 1600 SAT (critical reading + mathematics + writing)
- Must present a strong academic record. For a $10,000 scholarship it requires minimum of 3.5 high school grade point average and 1720 SAT (critical reading + mathematics + writing)
- Must maintain a minimum GPA of 3.0 (on a 4.0 scale) to renew scholarship.
- Must be enrolled as a full-time undergraduate student

APPLICATION INFORMATION

Award Deadline: Jul 1

Instructions: Students are automatically considered with completion of application for admission, visit our website for more information

CONTACT

Frostburg State University
Center for International Education
101 Braddock Road
Frostburg, MD 21532
Tel: +1 (301) 687-4714
Fax: +1 (301) 687-1069
Email: FSUinternational@frostburg.edu
Web: www.frostburg.edu/admin/cie

Frostburg State University

Frostburg State University International Graduate Fellowship

PROGRAM INFORMATION

Description: International Graduate Fellowships support full-time graduate study through a combination of a graduate assistantship and a scholarship.

Levels of Study: Graduate

Field of Study: Biology, Computer and Information Sciences, Education, Master of Arts in Teaching, Psychology

Nationality: Any Region

Location of Study: Frostburg State University Frostburg, MD

AWARD INFORMATION

Award Type: Associateship, Grant, Tuition Reduction

Average Amount: Approx $23,000

Number of Awards: 6

Award Coverage: Tuition for 30 credits, health insurance, stipend

Award Duration: Maximum of 3 years

ELIGIBILITY REQUIREMENTS

- Must be admitted to a graduate degree program in good standing

APPLICATION INFORMATION

Award Deadline: Mar 15

Instructions: Application instructions are provided upon initiating a new application to a graduate program

CONTACT

Frostburg State University
Office of Graduate Services
101 Braddock Road
Frostburg, MD 21532
Tel: +1 (301) 687-7053
Fax: +1 (301) 687-4597
Email: vmmazer@frostburg.edu
Web: www.frostburg.edu/grad

Fundacion de ANTEL (FANTEL) Educational Consortium

FANTEL Scholarships for Higher Education

PROGRAM INFORMATION

Description: Scholarships for promising Salvadorans providing opportunities for academic or professional development at the national and international level. Scholarships promote professional specialization for contributions to El Salvador's advancement.

Levels of Study: Graduate, Doctorate

Field of Study: Economics, International Development, Social Service

Nationality: El Salvador

AWARD INFORMATION

Award Type: Grant

Average Amount: Varies

Number of Awards: Varies

Award Coverage: Varies

ELIGIBILITY REQUIREMENTS

- Academic Excellence Grants: Excellent academic record and demonstration of financial need for higher education or specialization
- President Grants: For graduate studies in El Salvador or abroad, to recognize students with the highest grades each year in the Aptitude and Learning Exam (PAES), and outstanding students from the Mathematics Talent Program
- Grants to Salvadoran Talent: 3 annual grants for students and professionals with academic potential to strengthen specialization in El Salvador

APPLICATION INFORMATION

Instructions: For more information visit our website or contact us

CONTACT

LASPAU: Academic and Professional Programs for the America
25 Mount Auburn Street, Suite 300
Cambridge, MA 02138-6095
Tel: +1 (617) 495-0369
Email: sandhya_klein@harvard.edu
Web: www.laspau.harvard.edu/current-programs/fantel-scholarships-higher-education

Gannon University
Gannon University Awards

PROGRAM INFORMATION

Description: Gannon University is a private, co-educational Catholic, comprehensive university in Erie, Pennsylvania, offering associate's, bachelor's, master's degrees, certificates, and doctoral degrees.

Levels of Study: Undergraduate, Graduate

Field of Study: All

Nationality: Any Region

Location of Study: Gannon University
Erie, PA

AWARD INFORMATION

Award Type: Award

Average Amount: Varies

Award Coverage: Tuition

Award Duration: 4 years

ELIGIBILITY REQUIREMENTS

- Must complete the undergraduate application.
- Must be admitted into a program of study

APPLICATION INFORMATION

Instructions: Please visit our website for further information

CONTACT

Gannon University
Associate Director, Office of International Admissions
109 University Square
16541 Erie PA
Tel: +1 (814) 871-5577
Fax: +1 (814) 871-4679
Email: hajec002@gannon.edu
Web: www.gannon.edu/admiss/intl/default.asp

Georgetown Law, Georgetown University
Georgetown Law
Graduate Fellowships

PROGRAM INFORMATION

Description: Georgetown Law provides the opportunity for legal students and professionals to deepen their understanding of both domestic and international law in a dynamic environment. Located within close proximity to Capitol Hill in Washington, DC, Georgetown offers its students unparalleled access to the US branches of government, agencies, media outlets, and NGOs. The school offers numerous fellowships in the areas of taxation, employee benefits law, and law teaching in addition to clinical program fellowships. Georgetown Law also awards 5 international scholarships for foreign-educated lawyers to apply to the LLM program.

Levels of Study: Professional

Field of Study: Law

Nationality: Any Region

Location of Study: Georgetown University
Washington, DC

AWARD INFORMATION

Award Type: Fellowship

Average Amount: Varies

Number of Awards: Varies

Award Coverage: Varies

APPLICATION INFORMATION

Award Deadline: Feb 1

Instructions: For more information on how to apply, please visit the website

CONTACT

Georgetown University
Georgetown University Law Center
600 New Jersey Ave, NW
Washington, DC 20001
Tel: +1 (202) 662-9020
Fax: +1 (202) 662-9439
Web: www.law.georgetown.edu

Georgetown University Center for Contemporary Arab Studies
Georgetown University Master of Arts in Arab Studies

PROGRAM INFORMATION

Description: The Master of Arts in Arab Studies program (MAAS) was established in 1978 to rigorously train researchers, practitioners, and activists about the language, history, culture, society, politics, and economics of the contemporary Arab world. Students design a program of study that prepares them for a wide variety of careers, including those in government, development, business and finance, teaching, higher education, human rights, journalism, public relations, and cultural affairs. The program's demanding Arabic language requirement is a distinctive feature regularly cited by students and alumni alike as a major draw and strength.

Levels of Study: Graduate

Field of Study: Political Science

Nationality: Middle East, North Africa

Location of Study: Georgetown University - Center for Contemporary Arab Studies
Washington DC

AWARD INFORMATION

Award Type: Scholarship

Average Amount: $50,000

Number of Awards: 1

Award Coverage: The scholarship includes full tuition, fees, living stipend

Award Duration: Maximum of 2 years

ELIGIBILITY REQUIREMENTS

- Applicant must apply to the MA in Arab Studies program at Georgetown University
- Be a resident of a country in the MENA region
- Plan to concentrate their studies in politics or development
- Express an interest in working in the MENA region following graduation
- As part of the stipend agreement, the scholarship recipient will serve as a research assistant in the Center for Contemporary Arab Studies

APPLICATION INFORMATION

Award Deadline: Jan 15

Instructions: To be considered for the scholarship, please send a statement of intent addressing the eligibility requirements to the Academic Program Coordinator of the MA in Arab Studies program at maas@georgetown.edu

CONTACT

Georgetown University -
Center for Contemporary Arab Studies
Academic Coordinator
ICC 241
37th and O Street, N.W.
20057 Washington DC District of Columbia
Tel: 2026878957
Fax: 2026877001
Email: kmh79@georgetown.edu
Web: ccas.georgetown.edu/

Georgetown University, Edmund A. Walsh School of Foreign Service
Georgetown University Master of Science in Foreign Service (MSFS)

PROGRAM INFORMATION

Description: MSFS is a 2-year, full time master's degree program in the Edmund A. Walsh School of Foreign Service at Georgetown University. We offer a highly personalized setting that prepares students for leadership and service in international affairs in the non-profit, public, and private sectors. In addition to our core curriculum in international relations, trade, finance, history, and statistical and analytical tools, students can choose a concentration in Global Politics and Security, International Development, Global Business and Finance, or a self-designed/regional concentration. Students enter the program with a variety of professional experiences in fields such as journalism, law, government, development, the armed forces, consulting, and teaching, to name a few. Between 30 and 40% of our students are non-US citizens, and we hope that, with this scholarship, we can foster diversity and valuable international perspectives at MSFS.

Levels of Study: Graduate

Nationality: Africa

Location of Study: Georgetown University, Edmund A. Walsh School of Foreign Service
Washington, DC

AWARD INFORMATION

Award Type: Scholarship

Average Amount: $43,200

Number of Awards: 1

Award Coverage: Tuition only

Award Duration: 2 years

ELIGIBILITY REQUIREMENTS

- A completed undergraduate degree from an accredited university and a strong academic record
- 1 set of standardized test scores: TOEFL/IELTS or GRE/GMAT (for more information on which test applicants need to take, visit msfs.georgetown.edu/admissions/faq#standardized)
- Completion of a course in microeconomics and a course in macroeconomics, or ability to complete both courses before the beginning of the MSFS program in fall 2015
- Professional work experience, ideally in a field related to their future professional goals, students have an average of 4 years of work experience prior to joining MSFS
- For complete information on required application items, please visit msfs.georgetown.edu/admissions/howtoapply/

APPLICATION INFORMATION

Award Deadline: Awards are given at the time of admission; the deadline to apply for admission is Jan 15

Instructions: For complete information on required application items, please visit msfs.georgetown.edu/admissions/howtoapply/

CONTACT

Georgetown University
Director of Admissions, MSFS
37th & O Streets, NW, ICC 7th Floor
Washington, DC 20057, US
Tel: 2026875763
Fax: 2026875116
Email: msfsinfo@georgetown.edu
Web: msfs.georgetown.edu

Georgetown University, International Initiatives

Georgetown-CSC Fellowships

PROGRAM INFORMATION

Description: Georgetown University and China Scholarship Council (CSC) established the CSC-Georgetown Fellowship Program in May 2006 to support graduate and postgraduate education programs for students from People's Republic of China. Under the agreement, Georgetown and CSC will jointly support 30 1-year postdoctoral fellows for studies at Georgetown in fields of mutual interest such as physical, life, and health sciences; public policy; applied social sciences; and international affairs. Fellows will receive a stipend and travel support, as well as access to academic facilities at Georgetown, selective auditing of graduate classes, and space in which to work and conduct research.

Levels of Study: Post Doctorate

Field of Study: All

Nationality: China

Location of Study: Georgetown University Washington, DC

AWARD INFORMATION

Award Type: Fellowship

Average Amount: Varies

Number of Awards: 30

Award Coverage: Stipend, medical insurance, round-trip travel expenses between China and Washington, DC, access to academic facilities at Georgetown, selective auditing of graduate classes, space to work and conduct research

Award Duration: 1 - 2 years

ELIGIBILITY REQUIREMENTS

- Must have Chinese citizenship
- Must have completed a PhD within the past 5 years and be currently employed at a university or research institute in China
- Must possess high-level English language skills
- Must present a compelling and explicit statement of interest in Georgetown research and teaching projects

APPLICATION INFORMATION

Award Deadline: Mar

Instructions: Application form completed online, letter of recommendation, statement of research project, evidence of proficiency in English (e.g., TOEFL score or interview)

CONTACT

Georgetown University
3700 O ST, NW
Washington, DC 20057
Email: cscfellowship@georgetown.edu
Web: china.georgetown.edu/csc/

Georgia College & State University

Georgia College & State University International Graduate Assistantship

PROGRAM INFORMATION

Description: Assistantship waives out-of-state graduate tuition in exchange for 10 hours of work per week.

Field of Study: All

Nationality: Any Region

Location of Study: Georgia College & State University Milledgeville, GA

AWARD INFORMATION

Award Type: Tuition Reduction

Average Amount: $13,000/yr.

Number of Awards: 15

Award Coverage: Out-of-State tuition waiver

Award Duration: 2-3 yrs.

ELIGIBILITY REQUIREMENTS

- Application for an International Graduate Assistantship (found inside application for admission at www.gcsu.edu/international).
- 2 letters of recommendation
- Personal Statement

APPLICATION INFORMATION

Award Deadline: Apr

Instructions: The application for the International Graduate Assistantship (IGA) is found inside of the international graduate application for admission at www.gcsu.edu/international

CONTACT

Georgia College & State University
International Admissions
CBX 049
Milledgeville, GA 31061
Tel: 478-445-4789
Fax: 478-445-2623
Email: intladm@gcsu.edu
Web: www.gcsu.edu/international

Georgia College & State University

Georgia College & State University International Student Scholarship

PROGRAM INFORMATION

Description: Undergraduate international students are encouraged to apply for this scholarship, which may come in the form of a full or half out-of-state tuition waiver for the duration of undergraduate study at GCSU.

Levels of Study: Undergraduate

Field of Study: All

Nationality: Any Region

Location of Study: Georgia College & State University Milledgeville, GA

AWARD INFORMATION

Award Type: Scholarship, Tuition Reduction

Average Amount: Varies

Number of Awards: 20

Award Coverage: Tuition

Award Duration: Maximum of 4 years

ELIGIBILITY REQUIREMENTS

- Must meet minimum GPA requirement
- Applicant must prove that he/she would greatly contribute to the process of internationalization on campus, minimum commitment to internationalization activities is required

APPLICATION INFORMATION

Award Deadline: Apr, Sep

Instructions: Please download an application found in the undergraduate international student application at the website (www.gcsu.edu/international)

CONTACT

Georgia College & State University
International Education Center
Campus Box 49
Milledgeville, GA 31061
Tel: +1 (478) 445-4789
Fax: +1 (478) 445-2623
Email: intladm@gcsu.edu
Web: www.gcsu.edu/international

Georgia Southern University

Georgia Southern University International Student Diversity Scholarships

PROGRAM INFORMATION

Description: Offers academic and need-based scholarships for international students.

Levels of Study: Undergraduate, Graduate

Field of Study: All

Nationality: Any Region

Location of Study: Georgia Southern University Statesboro, GA

AWARD INFORMATION

Award Type: Scholarship, Tuition Reduction
Average Amount: $12,000
Number of Awards: Varies
Award Coverage: Partial Tuition
Award Duration: Varies

ELIGIBILITY REQUIREMENTS

- Must meet minimum SAT and/or TOEFL requirements for admission
- Must demonstrate good academic standing, financial need, commitment to the university and community

APPLICATION INFORMATION

Award Deadline: Feb
Instructions: Visit our website for more information on how to apply

CONTACT

Georgia Southern University
International Admissions
P.O. Box 8024
Statesboro, GA 30460
Tel: +1 (912) 478-5836
Email: intladmissions@georgiasouthern.edu
Web: admissions.georgiasouthern.edu/requirements/international/

Glendale Community College (California)

Glendale Community College Bhupesh Parikh Scholarship Program

PROGRAM INFORMATION

Description: The Bhupesh Parikh Scholarship Program is designed for new International visa students (specifically, citizens from India and Sri Lanka) enrolling at Glendale Community College for the first time. This is a partial tuition scholarship of $1,000 for the academic year and renewable for the second year of study.
Levels of Study: Undergraduate
Field of Study: All
Nationality: India, Sri Lanka
Location of Study: Glendale Community College Glendale, CA

AWARD INFORMATION

Award Type: Award, Grant, Scholarship, Tuition Reduction
Average Amount: $1,000
Number of Awards: 20
Award Coverage: Tuition reduction
Award Duration: 2 years

ELIGIBILITY REQUIREMENTS

- Must complete International Application forms and supporting documents
- Must have above-average English level proficiency/ TOEFL score or IELTS band score, or high national examination results
- Must have bank statement certification and Sponsorship Form
- Must have diploma/certificate of secondary school or high school completion; national examination results
- At least 1-page personal statement/essay

APPLICATION INFORMATION

Award Deadline: Jul fall semester; Dec spring semester
Instructions: Please see website for application instructions

CONTACT

Glendale Community College (California)
International Student Program
1500 North Verdugo Road
Glendale, CA 91208-2894
Tel: +1 (818) 240-1000, ext. 5439/5887
Fax: +1 (818) 240-1345
Email: gcciso@glendale.edu
Web: www.glendale.edu/international

Golden Gate University School of Law

LLM in US Legal Studies; International Law; Environmental Law; Intellectual Property, Taxation, and an SJD Program for International Law

PROGRAM INFORMATION

Description: Students can choose among 5 LLM programs so they can focus on the area of study that most interests them. We also can prepare students to take a bar exam in California, NY, or Washington, DC.
Levels of Study: Graduate, Doctorate
Field of Study: Law
Nationality: Any Region
Location of Study: Golden Gate University School of Law San Francisco, CA

AWARD INFORMATION

Award Type: Scholarship, Tuition Reduction
Average Amount: $3,000-$12,000
Number of Awards: Varies
Award Coverage: Partial tuition
Award Duration: Maximum of 2 years

ELIGIBILITY REQUIREMENTS

- Applicant must have a good academic record
- TOEFL of 92 or above
- Must submit an impressive personal statement

APPLICATION INFORMATION

Award Deadline: Jul 1 for fall semester; Nov 1 for spring semester
Instructions: Apply through LSAC website, lsac.org, or print out an application from www.ggu.edu/media/law/documents/law-admissions/2013-04-23-GGU-SOL-LLM-Application.pdf

CONTACT

Golden Gate University School of Law
Director, LLM Programs
536 Mission St.
San Francisco, CA 94105
Tel: +1 (415) 442-6629
Fax: +1 (415) 442-6609
Email: lburton@ggu.edu
Web: www.ggu.edu

Gonzaga University

Gonzaga University Scholarships

PROGRAM INFORMATION

Description: Gonzaga University is a private, Jesuit University located in Spokane, Washington. Established in 1887, the university has over 75 fields of study.
Levels of Study: Undergraduate, Graduate, Doctorate
Field of Study: All
Nationality: Any Region
Location of Study: Gonzaga University Spokane, WA

AWARD INFORMATION

Award Type: Scholarship
Average Amount: $3,500 - $16,000
Award Coverage: Tuition
Award Duration: 2 years for transfer, 4 years for freshmen, 1 year for international graduate students

ELIGIBILITY REQUIREMENTS

- Merit Scholarships: all students who complete the application for admission are automatically considered for 1 of several merit-based scholarships
- Gonzaga Entrepreneurial Scholarship: academically outstanding with an understanding of, and passion for, entrepreneurship and a record of service and extracurricular involvement; minimum unweighted GPA of 3.5; minimum test scores of 1250 SAT (combined Critical Reading and Math) OR 28 ACT
- Ignatial Leadership Scholarship: ILS is a leadership scholarship that rewards and helps to develop the Ignatian style of servant leadership; criteria for nomination and self-nomination: student must be in the top of his/her high school class in academic performance

APPLICATION INFORMATION

Award Deadline: Feb 1; Nov 15
Instructions: All students are automatically considered for the merit-based scholarship at the time of application submission, all other scholarships must be applied for (see website). Email the financial aid office for more information

CONTACT

Gonzaga University
Director, International Admissions and Student Services
502 East Boone Avenue, AD 41
99258 Spokane WA
Email: isss@gonzaga.edu
Web: www.gonzaga.edu/BeAGlobalZag

Grand Canyon University

Grand Canyon University Awards

PROGRAM INFORMATION

Levels of Study: Undergraduate, Graduate
Field of Study: All
Nationality: Any Region
Location of Study: Grand Canyon University Phoenix, AZ

AWARD INFORMATION

Award Type: Grant, Scholarship
Average Amount: Undergraduate: $7,000; graduate $1,000
Award Coverage: Tuition, housing
Award Duration: Length of program as long as sufficient GPA is maintained

ELIGIBILITY REQUIREMENTS

- Must maintain sufficient GPA

APPLICATION INFORMATION

Instructions: Contact us for the application

CONTACT

Grand Canyon University
International Student Coordinator
3300 W Camelback Rd
Phoenix, AZ 85017
Tel: +1 (602) 639-6351
Fax: +1 (602) 589-2445
Email: Deborah.Parris@gcu.edu
Web: www.gcu.edu

Grand Valley State University

Grand Valley State University International Merit Award

PROGRAM INFORMATION

Description: Every year, Grand Valley awards International Merit Scholarships to incoming international students who have demonstrated an outstanding academic achievement record.

Levels of Study: Undergraduate, Graduate

Field of Study: All

Nationality: Any Region

Location of Study: Grand Valley State University Allendale, MI

AWARD INFORMATION

Award Type: Scholarship

Average Amount: $5,000

Number of Awards: 25

Award Coverage: Partial tuition scholarship

Award Duration: Maximum of 4 years

ELIGIBILITY REQUIREMENTS

- Must apply before May 1 and must be new degree-seeking students at Grand Valley State University, and be citizens of a country outside the US
- Must write a 1-2 page personal statement on the following topic: "What will I do to bring cultural and international perspectives to Grand Valley that will enhance the learning environment for the entire GVSU community?"
- Must have a minimum TOEFL score of 80 IBT or IELTS score of 6.5 for undergraduates and graduates

APPLICATION INFORMATION

Award Deadline: May

Instructions: All students that submit a complete application file prior to May 1 will be considered for this scholarship, for information on starting the application process, please go to this link: secure.gvsu.edu/admissions/international/apply-for-admission-23.htm

CONTACT

Grand Valley State University
Associate Director of Admissions
1 Campus Drive
Allendale, MI 49544
Tel: +1 (616) 331-2025
Fax: +1 (616) 331-2000
Email: global@gvsu.edu
Web: secure.gvsu.edu/admissions/international/international-student-scholarships-13.htm#merit

Green River Community College

Green River Community College International Student Scholarships

PROGRAM INFORMATION

Description: Green River Community College, near Seattle, Washington, is now offering scholarships for new and continuing international students. Both tuition scholarships and work grants are available in amounts ranging from $250-$5,000 per student.

Levels of Study: Undergraduate

Field of Study: All

Nationality: Any Region

Location of Study: Green River Community College Auburn, WA

AWARD INFORMATION

Award Type: Grant, Scholarship

Average Amount: $300-$5,000

Number of Awards: Varies

Award Coverage: Tuition, work grants

Award Duration: Quarter and academic year

ELIGIBILITY REQUIREMENTS

- Must be granted admission to the college
- A separate scholarship application must be completed and submitted to be considered for awards

APPLICATION INFORMATION

Award Deadline: Varies

Instructions: For more information on the type of scholarships and work grants available, as well as a link to the PDF application, please visit the website

CONTACT

Green River Community College
Dean International Programs
12401 SE 320th Street
Auburn, WA 98092-3699
Tel: +1 (253) 288-3300
Fax: +1 (253) 333-4940
Email: international@greenriver.edu
Web: www.greenriver.edu/international

Grinnell College

Grinnell College Grants and Scholarships for International Students

PROGRAM INFORMATION

Description: Each year, Grinnell offers grants, merit scholarships, loans, and work study to international students. The majority of students receive grants to meet their need, though students who demonstrate exceptional academic and leadership abilities may be considered for merit scholarships, regardless of their need.

Levels of Study: Undergraduate

Field of Study: All

Nationality: Any Region

Location of Study: Grinnell College Grinnell, IA

AWARD INFORMATION

Award Type: Scholarship

Average Amount: Varies

Number of Awards: Varies

Award Coverage: Tuition, room, board, allowances for books, travel, miscellaneous expense

Award Duration: Academic year, renewable for additional years of study

ELIGIBILITY REQUIREMENTS

- Students applying for need-based financial aid must submit the CSS Profile by their admission application deadline

APPLICATION INFORMATION

Award Deadline: Jan 15

Instructions: For more information on how to apply, please visit the website

CONTACT

Grinnell College
Office of Admission
John Chrystal Center
1103 Park St. 2nd Floor
Grinnell, IA 50112
Tel: +1 (641) 269-3600
Fax: +1 (641) 269-4800
Email: intladmission@grinell.edu
Web: www.grinnell.edu

Hamilton College

Hamilton College Financial Aid for International Students

PROGRAM INFORMATION

Description: Hamilton College, a liberal arts college with an emphasis on individualized instruction and independent research, is a national leader in teaching effective writing and persuasive speaking.

Levels of Study: Undergraduate

Field of Study: Liberal/General Studies

Nationality: Any Region

Location of Study: Hamilton College Clinton, NY

AWARD INFORMATION

Award Type: Grant

Average Amount: Varies

Number of Awards: Approx half of all students are on financial aid

Award Coverage: Tuition, room and board, student activity fees

Award Duration: 4 years

ELIGIBILITY REQUIREMENTS

- Acceptance to Hamilton College

APPLICATION INFORMATION

Award Deadline: Feb

Instructions: Please complete an admission application at the website, students should complete the International Student Financial Aid Application and the Certification of Finances; international students who are US citizens need to complete the FAFSA, the C.S.S. Profile, and the Hamilton College Financial Aid Application; to download the required financial aid forms, please visit the website

CONTACT

Hamilton College
198 College Hill Road
Clinton, NY 13323
Tel: +1 (315) 859-4421
Fax: +1 (315) 859-4457
Email: admission@hamilton.edu
Web: www.hamilton.edu

Hamline University

Hamline University International Undergraduate Student Scholarships

PROGRAM INFORMATION

Description: Founded in 1854, Hamline University was the first university in Minnesota. Hamline is a high-quality, nationally ranked university with more than 5,500 students in its undergraduate, graduate, and law school programs. Hamline brings together a wide and diverse group of students from more than 56 countries around the world. In addition to scholarships, students have the opportunity to earn up to $2,500 per year by securing a job on campus.

Levels of Study: Undergraduate, Graduate, Doctorate, Professional

Field of Study: All

Nationality: Any Region

Location of Study: Hamline University
St. Paul, MN

AWARD INFORMATION

Award Type: Award, Scholarship

Average Amount: Up to $20,000

Number of Awards: Varies

Award Coverage: Tuition only, scholarships are the equivalent of up to 65 percent tuition discount

Award Duration: Academic year, renewable for up to 4 years

ELIGIBILITY REQUIREMENTS

- The scholarships and the on-campus work awards are determined by the admission committee based on academic performance (transcripts), English proficiency test score (TOEFL, IELTS), recommendation letters, and personal essay
- No additional application is necessary, all international students applying to Hamline for admission are reviewed for eligibility at the time of application

APPLICATION INFORMATION

Award Deadline: Rolling

Instructions: Apply online using the Common Application: www.commonapp.org/CommonApp/default.aspx

CONTACT

Hamline University
Assistant Director of Admissions
1536 Hewitt Avenue
St. Paul, MN 55104
Tel: +1 (651) 523-2207
Fax: +1 (651) 523-2458
Email: i-contact@hamline.edu
Web: www.hamline.edu

Harvard University

Harvard Kennedy School
International Student Fellowships

PROGRAM INFORMATION

Description: The Kennedy School and outside foundations offer a number of full and partial fellowships/scholarships for students from specific geographic regions. The selection processes for these fellowships are highly competitive.

Levels of Study: Graduate, Doctorate, Professional

Field of Study: International Development, Public Administration, Public Policy, Social Service, Urban Planning

Nationality: Africa, Middle East, Afghanistan, Albania, Armenia, Azerbaijan, Barbados, Bosnia & Herzegovina, Bulgaria, Chile, China, Croatia, Czech Republic, Denmark, France, Georgia, Germany, Greece, Hong Kong, Hungary, India, Indonesia, Italy, Kazakhstan, Kyrgyzstan, Macedonia, Moldova, Montenegro, Norway, Philippines, Poland, Romania, Serbia, Slovakia, Slovenia, Taiwan, Tajikistan, Turkmenistan, Uzbekistan

Location of Study: Harvard University
Cambridge, MA

AWARD INFORMATION

Award Type: Scholarship

Average Amount: Varies

Number of Awards: Varies

Award Coverage: Varies

Award Duration: Academic year

ELIGIBILITY REQUIREMENTS

- Must have academic distinction at the undergraduate level, evidence of leadership, public service involvement and commitment, 1 or more years of full-time work experience
- Must have minimum TOEFL score of 600 PBT/250 CBT/100 IBT for those applicants whose native language is not English
- Must submit GRE or GMAT scores
- Candidates should hold an undergraduate degree recognized by their native state and an academic and/or professional background in 1 of the following fields: social sciences, public policy and/or administration, the nonprofit sector, law, economics, business

APPLICATION INFORMATION

Award Deadline: Feb or earlier

Instructions: Apply online for admission and international student financial aid; separate criteria and applications may be applicable, please see website for further information on specific scholarships and fellowships

CONTACT

John F. Kennedy School of Government
International Student Financial Services Office
79 John F. Kennedy Street
Cambridge, MA 02138
Tel: +1 (617) 495-1152
Email: financial_aid@hks.harvard.edu
Web: www.hks.harvard.edu/degrees/sfs/prospective-students/fellowships-scholarships/intl

Harvard University/ Ecole Normale Superieure

Harvard–Ecole Normale Superieure Exchange Program

PROGRAM INFORMATION

Description: This is an exchange program between Harvard University and the Ecole Normale Superieure in Paris. Students from France attending the Ecole Normale Superieure may apply to study at Harvard University for 1 academic year.

Levels of Study: Undergraduate

Field of Study: All

Nationality: France

Location of Study: Harvard University
Cambridge, MA

AWARD INFORMATION

Award Type: Student Exchange

Average Amount: Varies

Number of Awards: Varies

Award Coverage: Varies

Award Duration: Academic year

ELIGIBILITY REQUIREMENTS

- Contact the program for further details and requirements

APPLICATION INFORMATION

Instructions: Contact for application instructions

CONTACT

Ecole Normale Superieure
Directrice des Relations Internationales
45, rue d'Ulm
75230 Paris
France
Tel: +33 (01) 44-32-31-36
Email: isabelle.de.vendeuvre@ens.fr
Web: www.scholarship.harvard.edu/internationalinfo.html

Harvard University Center for International Development

Sustainability Science Fellowship

PROGRAM INFORMATION

Description: The competition is open to students and professionals engaged in research or practice in sustainability science to facilitate the design, implementation, and evaluation of effective interventions that promote sustainable development.

Levels of Study: Doctorate, Post Doctorate, Professional

Field of Study: Agriculture and Related Sciences, Environmental Studies, International Development, Natural Resources and Conservation, Public Administration, Public Health, Science, Urban Planning

Nationality: Any Region

Location of Study: Cambridge, MA

AWARD INFORMATION

Award Type: Fellowship

Average Amount: $28,000-$55,000

Number of Awards: 15-20

Award Coverage: Stipend, office space and supplies, personal computers, telecommunications, project workshop expenses, access to Harvard University libraries and other facilities, limited support for field research expenses

Award Duration: 3-12 months

ELIGIBILITY REQUIREMENTS

- Professional applicants must be in governmental, non-governmental, private organizations, or academia with at least 5 years of professional experience doing work involved in linking science and practice for sustainable development
- Post-doctoral applicants must have completed their PhD between 2006 and Jul 2012
- Doctoral applicants must have completed coursework and passed oral and/or written exams by Jul 2012

APPLICATION INFORMATION

Award Deadline: Jan 15

Instructions: Applicants should describe how their work would contribute to "sustainability science," the emerging field of use-inspired research seeking understanding of the interactions between human and environmental systems as well as the application of such knowledge to sustainability challenges relating to advancing development of agriculture, habitation, energy and materials, health and water while conserving the earth's life support systems.

CONTACT

Harvard University
Kennedy School of Government
79 John F. Kennedy St.
Cambridge, MA 02138
Tel: +1 (617) 496-0739
Fax: +1 (617) 496-8753
Email: sustsci_grants@hks.harvard.edu
Web: www.hks.harvard.edu/centers/mrcbg/programs/sustsci/grants-fellowships/fellows

Hawaii Pacific University

Hawai'i Pacific University Transfer Merit Scholarships

PROGRAM INFORMATION

Description: Full-time, degree seeking, undergraduate transfer applicants are considered for academic merit scholarships up to $7,000 per academic year (fall and spring only) at the time of admission based on academic abilities. Academic merit scholarships are applied towards tuition. To determine your academic merit scholarship eligibility, please complete an application for undergraduate admission.

Levels of Study: Undergraduate

Field of Study: All

Nationality: Any Region

Location of Study: Hawai'i Pacific University Honolulu, HI

AWARD INFORMATION

Award Type: Scholarship, Tuition Reduction

Average Amount: Varies

Number of Awards: Varies

Award Coverage: $3,000 - $7,000 per academic year

Award Duration: Renewable for up to 3 years

ELIGIBILITY REQUIREMENTS

- Full-time, degree seeking, undergraduate transfer applicants
- Must submit the Undergraduate Application
- Must be in good academic standing to be eligible for renewal

APPLICATION INFORMATION

Instructions: Please see website for application information

CONTACT

Hawai'i Pacific University
International Scholarship Committee
1164 Bishop Street
Suite 200
96813 Honolulu HI
Tel: +1 (808) 544-0238
Fax: +1 (808) 543-8065
Email: international@hpu.edu
Web: www.hpu.edu/international

Hawaii Pacific University

Allen and Nobuko Zecha Scholarship

PROGRAM INFORMATION

Description: This scholarship is awarded to incoming international freshman/high school graduates.

Levels of Study: Undergraduate

Nationality: Any Region

Location of Study: Hawai'i Pacific University Honolulu, HI

AWARD INFORMATION

Award Type: Scholarship

Average Amount: Up to $1,500

Number of Awards: 1 scholarship per academic year, per recipient

ELIGIBILITY REQUIREMENTS

- Must have a high school cumulative grade point average (GPA) of 3.75 and scoring in the top 10 percent on the SAT, ACT, or international equivalent tests; or in the top 3 percent of graduating class
- Must major in 1 of the following: marine biology; oceanography; pre-medical studies; 3-2 engineering

APPLICATION INFORMATION

Award Deadline: Mar

Instructions: Please visit www.hpu.edu/scholarships for application information

CONTACT

Hawai'i Pacific University
International Scholarship Committee
Suite 1100
Honolulu, HI 96813-2882
Tel: +1 (808) 543-8088
Fax: +1 (808) 543-8065
Email: international@hpu.edu
Web: www.hpu.edu/international

Hawaii Pacific University

Hawai'i Pacific University Graduate Scholarship

PROGRAM INFORMATION

Description: Hawai'i Pacific University offers several types of graduate scholarships to new, full-time, degree-seeking students. US citizens, permanent residents and international students who have a demonstrated financial need may apply. Applications will be reviewed based on: applicant's financial need; previous academic record; professional work experience and achievements; and community involvement and services. The amount of the award will be determined by the Scholarship Committee.

Levels of Study: Graduate

Nationality: Any Region

Location of Study: Hawai'i Pacific University Honolulu, HI

AWARD INFORMATION

Award Type: Scholarship

Average Amount: Varies

Number of Awards: Varies

Award Coverage: Dean's Scholarship: $4,000 per year; Graduate Kokua Scholarship: $2,000 per year; Trustee's Scholarship: $6,000 per year

Award Duration: Maximum of 2 years

ELIGIBILITY REQUIREMENTS

- Must apply for either the fall or spring semesters
- Must apply and be admitted to a master's program (applicants applying to the 12-month MBA, executive MBA, organizational change online or business administration online programs, or the business administration military flextrack program are not eligible to apply)
- Must plan to enroll as a full-time student (minimum 9 credit hours per fall and spring semesters)
- Must maintain a 3.0 GPA

APPLICATION INFORMATION

Award Deadline: Fall semester: Apr 15; spring semester: Oct 15

Instructions: Complete and submit a Graduate Application for Admission with all supporting documents; complete and submit the scholarship application form, along with the essay; submit a resume/CV (optional)

CONTACT

Hawai'i Pacific University
International Scholarship Committee
1164 Bishop St. Suite 200
96813 Honolulu HI
Tel: +1 (808) 544-0238
Fax: +1 (808) 543-8065
Email: international@hpu.edu
Web: www.hpu.edu/scholarships

Hawaii Pacific University

Hawai'i Pacific University Merit Scholarships

PROGRAM INFORMATION

Description: Hawai'i Pacific University (HPU) is a private, nonprofit university with a diverse student population. HPU is 1 of the most culturally diverse universities in America with students from all 50 US states and more than 80 countries. Founded in 1965, HPU prides itself on maintaining strong academic programs, small class sizes, individual attention to students, and a diverse faculty and student population. HPU is recognized as a "Best in the West" college by Princeton Review and a "Best Buy" by Barron's business magazine. Eligible full-time degree-seeking students are encouraged to apply for a partial tuition waiver.

Levels of Study: Undergraduate

Field of Study: All

Nationality: Any Region

Location of Study: Hawaii Pacific University Honolulu, HI

AWARD INFORMATION

Award Type: Scholarship, Tuition Reduction

Average Amount: Varies

Number of Awards: Varies

Award Coverage: $3,000-$12,500 per academic year

Award Duration: Maximum of 4 years

ELIGIBILITY REQUIREMENTS

- Applicant must be a full-time, degree seeking, undergraduate freshmen

APPLICATION INFORMATION

Instructions: Please see website for application information

CONTACT

Hawai'i Pacific University
International Scholarship Committee
1164 Bishop Street
Suite 200
96813 Honolulu HI
Tel: +1 (808) 544-0238
Fax: +1 (808) 543-8065
Email: international@hpu.edu
Web: www.hpu.edu/financialaid/Scholarships/ScholarshipsforInternationalStudents.html

Hendrix College

Hays Memorial Scholarship

PROGRAM INFORMATION

Description: The Hays Memorial Scholarship Program seeks students with outstanding potential for intellectual vitality and academic success, whose records of achievement – both in and out of the classroom – predict leadership and initiative to enhance life at Hendrix and in the world beyond. The Hays Scholarship provides full tuition, room, board, and mandatory fees for 4 years of study at Hendrix. Hays Scholars are also eligible to apply for special grants to support summer research and travel during their college years. Students who wish to compete for the Hays Scholarship must:

Levels of Study: Undergraduate

Field of Study: All

Nationality: Any Region

Location of Study: Hendrix College Conway, AR

AWARD INFORMATION

Award Type: Scholarship

Average Amount: $28,000

Number of Awards: 4

Award Coverage: Full tuition and fees, room and board

Award Duration: Academic year, renewable for additional years of study

ELIGIBILITY REQUIREMENTS

- Must have a minimum SAT score of 1410 or ACT score of 32
- Must have minimum grade point average of 3.6 on 4.0 scale
- Must have a record of extracurricular activities

APPLICATION INFORMATION

Award Deadline: Feb

Instructions: Apply for admission online. Download scholarship application, finalists will be interviewed on campus or via telephone

CONTACT

Hendrix College
Office of Admission
1600 Washington Avenue
Conway, AR
Tel: +1 (800) 277-9017
Fax: +1 (501) 450-3843
Email: adm@hendrix.edu
Web: www.hendrix.edu

Hendrix College

Hendrix College Odyssey Honors and Distinction Awards

PROGRAM INFORMATION

Description: Odyssey Awards recognize a candidate's extracurricular accomplishments and activities that contribute to his/her personal growth. Awards are made in 1 of 6 categories: Artistic Creativity, Global Awareness, Leadership Development, Service to the World, Undergraduate Research, and Special Projects.

Levels of Study: Undergraduate

Field of Study: All

Nationality: Any Region

Location of Study: Hendrix College Conway, AR

AWARD INFORMATION

Award Type: Scholarship

Average Amount: $1,000-$6,000

Number of Awards: Unlimited

Award Coverage: Partial tuition

Award Duration: Academic year, renewable for additional years

ELIGIBILITY REQUIREMENTS

- Must meet admissions requirements

APPLICATION INFORMATION

Award Deadline: Mar

Instructions: Apply for admission online

CONTACT

Hendrix College
Office of Admission
1600 Washington Avenue
Conway, AR
Tel: +1 (800) 277-9017
Fax: +1 (501) 450-3843
Email: adm@hendrix.edu
Web: www.hendrix.edu

Hesston College

Hesston College International Scholarship

PROGRAM INFORMATION

Description: Hesston College is a private 2-year residential school located in Hesston, Kansas. The college, which was founded in 1909, offers partial scholarships. International students are encouraged to apply. The scholarships are valid only for study at Hesston College.

Levels of Study: Undergraduate

Field of Study: All

Nationality: Any Region

Location of Study: Hesston College Hesston, KS

AWARD INFORMATION

Award Type: Grant, Scholarship

Average Amount: $6,000-$16,000

Number of Awards: 50

Award Coverage: Partial tuition

Award Duration: Maximum of 2 years

ELIGIBILITY REQUIREMENTS

- Must have graduated high school or plan to graduate within the coming 12 months
- Must have average to above-average secondary school grades

APPLICATION INFORMATION

Award Deadline: Rolling

Instructions: For more information, email the listed contact

CONTACT
Hesston College
Director of International Admissions
P.O. Box 3000
325 South College Drive
Hesston, KS 67062
Tel: +1 (620) 327-8133
Fax: +1 (620) 327-8246
Email: daveo@hesston.edu
Web: www.hesston.edu

Hillsdale College

Hillsdale College International Student Scholarship

PROGRAM INFORMATION

Description: All successful applicants to Hillsdale College are automatically considered for a number of merit-based scholarships. Candidates for admission from other countries follow the customary entrance procedures, except they are also responsible for submitting all transcripts with English translation from their international preparatory schools or universities at the time of application. Students whose first language is not English must demonstrate proficiency by submitting the results of the TOEFL or an equivalent test.

Levels of Study: Undergraduate

Field of Study: All

Nationality: Any Region

Location of Study: Hillsdale College
Hillsdale, MI

AWARD INFORMATION

Award Type: Scholarship, Tuition Reduction

Average Amount: Varies

Award Duration: Academic year

APPLICATION INFORMATION

Instructions: Must apply under Hillsdale's general admissions procedure, visit our website for more information

CONTACT
Hillsdale College
Office of Admissions
33 East College Street
Hillsdale, MI 49242
Tel: +1 (517) 607-2327
Email: admissions@hillsdale.edu
Web: www.hillsdale.edu

Hiram College

Hiram College Global Scholarship

PROGRAM INFORMATION

Description: International applicants are eligible to compete for merit-based Global Scholarships at Hiram College.

Levels of Study: Undergraduate

Field of Study: All

Nationality: Any Region

Location of Study: Hiram College
Hiram, OH

AWARD INFORMATION

Award Type: Scholarship

Average Amount: $18,000

Number of Awards: Multiple

Award Coverage: Partial tuition

Award Duration: Maximum of 4 years

ELIGIBILITY REQUIREMENTS

- Students must have a grade point average (GPA) of a 2.5 out of 4.0 to be considered for the scholarship
- International students are not required to submit an SAT report to qualify for this scholarship
- For students 23 years of age or older who elect to live off-campus and commute to Hiram, the maximum Global Scholarship is $16,000 per year

APPLICATION INFORMATION

Award Deadline: Jul (fall), Dec (spring)

Instructions: International students will be automatically considered for a Global Scholarship upon admission to the College, no separate application is required, detailed application guidelines are on the Hiram College website: www.hiram.edu/international

CONTACT
Hiram College
Director, International Admission
Office of Admission-6832 Hinsdale St.
PO Box 96
Hiram, OH 44234
Tel: +1 (330) 569-5175
Fax: +1 (330) 569-5944
Email: interal@hiram.edu
Web: www.hiram.edu/international

Hiram College

Hiram College Transfer Global Scholarship

PROGRAM INFORMATION

Description: International students with 12 or more transfer credits and a GPA of 2.5-4.0 will be considered.

Levels of Study: Undergraduate

Field of Study: All

Nationality: Any Region

Location of Study: Hiram College
Hiram, OH

AWARD INFORMATION

Award Type: Scholarship

Average Amount: $16,000

Number of Awards: Multiple

Award Coverage: Partial Tuition

Award Duration: Maximum 3 years

ELIGIBILITY REQUIREMENTS

- Students must have a grade point average (GPA) of a 2.5 out of 4.0 to be considered for the scholarship
- International students are not required to submit an SAT report to qualify for this scholarship
- For students 23 years of age or older who elect to live off-campus and commute to Hiram, the maximum Transfer Global Scholarship is $16,000 per year

APPLICATION INFORMATION

Award Deadline: Jul (fall), Dec (spring)

Instructions: International students will be automatically considered for a Global Scholarship upon admission to the College, no separate application is required, detailed application guidelines are on the Hiram College website: www.hiram.edu/international

CONTACT
Hiram College
Director, International Admission
Office of Admission-6832 Hinsdale St.
PO Box 96
Hiram, Ohio 44234, US
Tel: 3305695175
Fax: 3305695944
Email: interal@hiram.edu
Web: www.hiram.edu/international

Hofstra University School of Law

Master of Laws (LLM) in American Legal Studies Merit Scholarship

PROGRAM INFORMATION

Description: The LLM concentration in American Legal Studies is designed for foreign law graduates who seek general training in US law and practice. This degree is particularly valuable to those who seek to become a licensed lawyer in the US and is also recommended for those who plan to work in international law firms and corporations with US clientele, or in government service. Hofstra offers courses taught by faculty expert on every aspect of the American legal system, from trial and appellate advocacy, to transactional work and alternative dispute resolution, to international civil litigation in US courts. Candidates for the American Legal Studies LLM may select courses from the almost 200 courses offered at the Law School each year, with very few exceptions. An academic advisor will recommend the most relevant courses to those students who are interested in applying to take the New York State bar examination.

Levels of Study: Graduate

Field of Study: Law

Nationality: Any Region

Location of Study: Hofstra University School of Law
Hempstead, NY

AWARD INFORMATION

Award Type: Scholarship

Average Amount: Varies

Number of Awards: Varies

Award Coverage: Tuition and fees

Award Duration: 1 year

ELIGIBILITY REQUIREMENTS

- Apply and be accepted into the LLM in American Legal Studies Program
- Complete the scholarship application and submit any additional supporting documentation

APPLICATION INFORMATION

Award Deadline: Rolling

Instructions: To pursue a scholarship at Hofstra University School of Law, simply apply for our Master of Laws (LLM) in American Legal Studies; once accepted, students can apply for scholarship aid, scholarships are awarded based on the strength of an applicant's background

CONTACT

Hofstra University School of Law
Assistant Dean for Global Initiatives & Multicultural Affairs
121 Hofstra University, Suite 307
Hempstead, NY 11549
Tel: +1 (516) 463-0417
Email: Jeffrey.Dodge@hofstra.edu
Web: law.hofstra.edu/LLM

Hope College

Hope College International Scholarship Program

PROGRAM INFORMATION

Description: Academic Tuition Scholarships are given based on academic record and involvement in service and leadership activities. Awards are for 4 years and range from $3,000 to $15,000. Students are encouraged to apply by Dec and award notifications are made in Mar. The application for admission serves as the application for scholarship consideration. No separate application is necessary.

Levels of Study: Undergraduate

Field of Study: All

Nationality: Any Region

Location of Study: Hope College
Holland, MI

AWARD INFORMATION

Award Type: Tuition Reduction

Average Amount: $3,000-$15,000

Number of Awards: Unlimited

Award Coverage: Tuition

Award Duration: Up to 4 years

ELIGIBILITY REQUIREMENTS

- Must complete application for admission which includes academic record, essays responses, TOEFL, and Declaration of Finances

APPLICATION INFORMATION

Award Deadline: Jan

Instructions: For more information on how to apply, please visit the website.

CONTACT

Hope College
Admissions
69 East 10th Street
Holland, MI 49423
Tel: +1 (616) 395-7850
Fax: +1 (616) 395-7130
Email: admissions@hope.edu
Web: www.hope.edu/admissions/apply/international-students/costs-and-international-scholarships

Hope College

Hope College Fried Fund

PROGRAM INFORMATION

Description: This fund was created by and in honor of Dr. Paul Fried, long-time director of international education at Hope College. Dr. Fried served as a professor of history prior to becoming director of international education, and developed the first overseas study program offered in America, which continues to be the longest running program, the Vienna Summer Program.

Field of Study: All

Nationality: Austria, Germany

Location of Study: Hope College
Holland, MI

AWARD INFORMATION

Award Type: Tuition Reduction

Average Amount: Varies

Number of Awards: 1-2

Award Coverage: Tuition

Award Duration: Maximum 4 years

ELIGIBILITY REQUIREMENTS

- Must be a degree-seeking applicant for admission to Hope College.
- Must have citizenship from Germany or Austria.

APPLICATION INFORMATION

Award Deadline: Dec

Instructions: Complete application for admission by visiting our website.

CONTACT

Hope College
Admissions
69 East 10th Street
Holland, MI 49423
Tel: +1 (616) 395-7850 or +1 (800) 968-7850
Fax: +1 (616) 395-7130
Email: admissions@hope.edu
Web: www.hope.edu

Husson University

Husson University Emergency Support for Syrian Students

PROGRAM INFORMATION

Description: Global Perspectives Scholarship: Husson University sponsors 2 full scholarships annually for international students whose access to education has become dangerous, restricted, or terminated due to social or political events.

Levels of Study: Undergraduate, Graduate

Nationality: Syria

Location of Study: Husson University
Bangor, ME

AWARD INFORMATION

Award Type: Scholarship

Average Amount: $25,000

Number of Awards: 2

Award Coverage: Scholarship includes: application fee, tuition, room (standard), meals, undergraduate and orientation fees; not covered: books, insurance, personal supplies, added fees for graduate programs, air fare

Award Duration: Undergraduate: 4 years; Master's: 2 years

ELIGIBILITY REQUIREMENTS

- Must be a Syrian Student
- Must complete the application process as outlined on the International Students page of the Husson website (www.husson.edu)
- Students must meet admission requirements for the specific major desired, including requisite courses, admission test scores, essays, recommendations, Skype interview
- For SEVIS reporting, students must submit an affidavit of support guaranteeing $1,000 in personal funds

APPLICATION INFORMATION

Award Deadline: Mar 15; Oct 1

Instructions: Applicants should send an electronic copy of their application materials to Colleen Grover, Director of International Initiatives at groverc@husson.edu; the subject line of the email should read: GLOBAL PERSPECTIVES SCHOLARSHIP APPLICATION

CONTACT

Husson University
Director of International Initiatives
1 College Circle
Bangor, Maine 04401
Tel: +1 (207) 404-5640
Email: groverc@husson.edu
Web: www.husson.edu

Idaho State University

Idaho State University Non-Resident Tuition Waiver Scholarships

PROGRAM INFORMATION

Description: Non-resident tuition waivers available to undergraduate and graduate students in many areas of study. Student pays only in-state portion of tuition if awarded a waiver.

Levels of Study: Undergraduate, Graduate, Doctorate

Nationality: Any Region

Location of Study: Idaho State University
Pocatello, ID

AWARD INFORMATION

Award Type: Tuition Reduction

Average Amount: $12,000

Number of Awards: Approx 100

Award Coverage: Non-resident portion of tuition

Award Duration: Academic year, renewable for additional years

ELIGIBILITY REQUIREMENTS

- Must have a minimum cumulative GPA equivalent to 3.0 for undergraduate awards
- Must have a minimum posted TOEFL or IELTS requirement or equivalent
- Must meet required deadlines and GPA for consideration. May (fall entry) & Nov (spring entry)

APPLICATION INFORMATION

Award Deadline: May; Nov

Instructions: Undergraduate students must complete admission application for consideration of NRTW by required deadlines These are competitive. Graduate students must fill out a special NRTW application through the Graduate Program: www.isu.edu/graduate/finsupp.shtml#non_resident_tuition_waivers

CONTACT

Idaho State University
ISU Scholarship Office
921 S 8th Ave
Stop 83209-8391
Pocatello, ID 83209-8391
Tel: +1 (208) 282-3315
Fax: +1 (208) 282-5717
Email: scholar@isu.edu
Web: www.isu.edu/scholar/international.shtml

Illinois Institute of Technology

Dimiter Etimov Scholarship for Bulgarian Students

PROGRAM INFORMATION

Description: The Dimiter Etimov Scholarships are for graduate and undergraduate students who are Bulgarian citizens and intend to return to Bulgaria after their studies.

Levels of Study: Undergraduate, Graduate, Doctorate

Field of Study: All

Nationality: Bulgaria

Location of Study: Illinois Institute of Technology Chicago, IL

AWARD INFORMATION

Award Type: Fellowship, Scholarship

Average Amount: Varies

Number of Awards: 1 per semester

Award Coverage: Tuition, living expenses

Award Duration: Duration of studies

ELIGIBILITY REQUIREMENTS

- Must be admitted to an IIT degree program
- Must be a graduate of a Bulgarian high school
- Must be a Bulgarian citizen
- Must intend to return to Bulgaria after studies and practical training
- Must be nominated by a professor/teacher at your home university

APPLICATION INFORMATION

Award Deadline: Feb 1

Instructions: Write a brief essay explaining how studying in the US at IIT will move you toward your career goals in Bulgaria

CONTACT

Illinois Institute of Technology
Tel: +1 (312) 567-7219
Fax: +1 (312) 567-3982
Email: nikolov@iit.edu
Web: www.iit.edu/departments/oia

Illinois Institute of Technology

Illinois Institute of Technology International Scholarship

PROGRAM INFORMATION

Description: Illinois Institute of Technology offers renewable scholarships for degree-seeking undergraduate students.

Levels of Study: Undergraduate

Field of Study: All

Nationality: Any Region

Location of Study: Illinois Institute of Technology Chicago, IL

AWARD INFORMATION

Award Type: Scholarship

Average Amount: Varies

Number of Awards: 50

Award Coverage: 30 percent of tuition and on-campus room and board

Award Duration: Until completion of bachelor's degree

ELIGIBILITY REQUIREMENTS

- Must be a new, full-time bachelor's-degree-seeking freshman or transfer student
- Freshmen: completion of high school in top 25 percent of class; Transfer: completion of high school plus at least 30 credit hours
- Must have a TOEFL equivalent to 550 PBT (waived if SAT verbal is 550 or higher)
- Grades must average at least 3.0 GPA on a 4.0 scale (or equivalent)
- See website for additional requirements

APPLICATION INFORMATION

Award Deadline: Rolling

Instructions: All admitted students are automatically considered for this scholarship

CONTACT

Illinois Institute of Technology
10 West 33rd St. - PH 101
Chicago, IL 60616
Tel: +1 (312) 567-3965
Fax: +1 (312) 567-6939
Email: admission@iit.edu
Web: www.iit.edu/undergrad_admission

Illinois State University

Illinois State University Betty Plummer Senior Scholarship

PROGRAM INFORMATION

Description: The Betty Plummer Award is offered in the spring semester for a graduating international senior student. Grades, accomplishments, international activities, and goals are all considered for this competitive award. This award is in honor of Betty Plummer, who was the international student advisor at Illinois State University for 16 years.

Levels of Study: Undergraduate

Field of Study: All

Nationality: Any Region

Location of Study: Illinois State University Normal, IL

AWARD INFORMATION

Award Type: Scholarship

Average Amount: Varies

Number of Awards: 1

Award Coverage: Varies

ELIGIBILITY REQUIREMENTS

- Must be a graduating international senior from Illinois State University
- Must be in good academic standing and have demonstrated outstanding service to university and community
- Must have a cumulative GPA of 3.0 and show involvement in international activities at ISU as well as examples of leadership

APPLICATION INFORMATION

Award Deadline: Mar

Instructions: Please visit website for more information

CONTACT

Illinois State University
Campus Box 6120
308 Fell Hall
Normal, IL 61790-6120
Tel: +1 (309) 438-5276
Fax: +1 (309) 438-3987
Email: oisp@ilstu.edu
Web: www.internationalstudies.ilstu.edu

Illinois State University

Illinois State University Graduate Assistantships

PROGRAM INFORMATION

Description: Graduate assistantships at Illinois State University are part-time, on-campus jobs with payment in the form of a full tuition waiver as well as a small monthly stipend.

Levels of Study: Graduate

Field of Study: All

Nationality: Any Region

Location of Study: Illinois State University Normal, IL

AWARD INFORMATION

Award Type: Award
Average Amount: Varies
Award Coverage: Tuition and small monthly stipend
Award Duration: Renewable each semester

ELIGIBILITY REQUIREMENTS

- Must be admitted to a graduate program or be admitted as a degree student in a graduate academic program or have a minimum of 120 undergraduate hours if in an integrated degree program
- Must be enrolled full time (9 hours per semester) during the contract period (with the exception of summer-only contracts) and maintain good academic standing

APPLICATION INFORMATION

Instructions: Download application materials and register online to apply for assistantships

CONTACT

Illinois State University
Campus Box 6120
308 Fell Hall
Normal, IL 61790-6120
Tel: +1 (309) 438-2583
Fax: +1 (309) 438-7912
Email: rrcarac@IllinoisState.edu
Web: www.grad.ilstu.edu/financial/assistantships.shtml

Illinois State University

Illinois State University International House Merit Award

PROGRAM INFORMATION

Description: The I-House Merit Award is a scholarship for undergraduate international students who are residents of International House, and been deeply involved in international activities at Illinois State University.
Levels of Study: Undergraduate
Field of Study: All
Nationality: Any Region
Location of Study: Illinois State University Normal, IL

AWARD INFORMATION

Award Type: Scholarship
Number of Awards: 1-2 per semester

ELIGIBILITY REQUIREMENTS

- Must be a current international undergraduate student and resident of International House at Illinois State University
- Must be in good academic standing
- Must demonstrate participation in international activities at Illinois State University

APPLICATION INFORMATION

Award Deadline: Oct
Instructions: Complete application and supporting documents

CONTACT

Illinois State University
Campus Box 6120, 308 Fell Hall
Normal, IL 61790-6120
Tel: +1 (309) 438-5276
Fax: +1 (309) 438-3987
Email: oisp@ilstu.edu
Web: www.internationalstudies.ilstu.edu

Illinois State University

Illinois State University Lucy Jen Huang Hickrod Award

PROGRAM INFORMATION

Description: This award is given every other year to a Chinese graduate student who shows academic excellence and outstanding community service.
Levels of Study: Graduate, Doctorate
Field of Study: All
Nationality: China, Hong Kong, Taiwan
Location of Study: Illinois State University Normal, IL

AWARD INFORMATION

Award Type: Scholarship
Average Amount: Varies
Number of Awards: 1 every other year
Award Coverage: Varies

ELIGIBILITY REQUIREMENTS

- Must be a Chinese graduate student at Illinois State University
- Must be in good academic standing

APPLICATION INFORMATION

Award Deadline: Feb
Instructions: Visit the website for application form and more information

CONTACT

Illinois State University
Campus Box 6120
Normal, IL 61790-6120
Web: www.internationalstudies.illinoisstate.edu/students/money/financial_aid.shtml

Illinois State University

Illinois State University Support for Syrian Students

PROGRAM INFORMATION

Description: Illinois State University offers 5 tuition waiver scholarships for Syrian students.
Levels of Study: Undergraduate, Graduate
Nationality: Syria
Location of Study: Illinois State University Normal, IL

AWARD INFORMATION

Award Type: Tuition Reduction
Average Amount: Varies
Number of Awards: Varies
Award Coverage: Not Applicable
Award Duration: Varies

ELIGIBILITY REQUIREMENTS

- Verification of English Language Proficiency (eg, Toefl 550 paper/213 computer/79 iBT) and GRE score for graduate students
- Proof of funding

APPLICATION INFORMATION

Award Deadline: Not applicable

CONTACT

International Studies and Programs
308 Fell Hall Campus Box 6120
Normal, IL 61790-61204
Tel: +1 (309) 438-5276
Fax: +1 (309) 438-3987
Email: oisp@illinoisstate.edu
Web: www.internationalstudies.illinoisstate.edu

Indiana Tech

Indiana Tech Merit Scholarships

PROGRAM INFORMATION

Description: Indiana Tech offers undergraduate international students the opportunity to receive up to $13,000/year in merit scholarships.
Levels of Study: Undergraduate
Field of Study: Accounting, Business and Management, Communications and Journalism, Computer and Information Sciences, Computer Science, Education, Engineering, Fashion Marketing & Management, Human Resource Development, Information Technology, Management, Marketing, Psychology
Nationality: Any Region
Location of Study: Indiana Tech Fort Wayne, IN

AWARD INFORMATION

Award Type: Scholarship
Average Amount: $9,000
Number of Awards: Varies
Award Coverage: Partial tuition
Award Duration: 4 years

ELIGIBILITY REQUIREMENTS

- Student must be accepted to Indiana Tech before an official scholarship is offered

CONTACT
Indiana Tech
Assistant Director of International Student Admissions & Orientation
1600 East Washington Blvd
Fort Wayne, Indiana 46803
Tel: +1 (260) 422-5561
Fax: +1 (260) 422-7696
Email: InternationalAdmissions@IndianaTech.edu
Web: www.admissions.indianatech.edu/apply/international/

Indiana University Bloomington

IU Bloomington International Student Awards, Assistantships and Fellowships

PROGRAM INFORMATION

Description: Indiana University Bloomington is the flagship campus of the Indiana University system. IUB's campus is located in the rolling hills of southern Indiana. IUB is 1 of America's great teaching and research universities. IUB offers fellowships and assistantships to undergraduate and graduate international students. International graduate students are eligible for various amounts of funding on a competitive basis, depending on the graduate department.

Levels of Study: Undergraduate, Graduate, Doctorate, Professional

Field of Study: Business and Management, Computer and Information Sciences, Education, Foreign Languages, Law, Life Sciences, Music, Public Affairs

Nationality: Any Region

Location of Study: Indiana University Bloomington
Bloomington, IN

AWARD INFORMATION

Award Type: Award, Fellowship, Scholarship, Tuition Reduction

Average Amount: Varies

Number of Awards: Varies

Award Coverage: Awards range from a 1-time disbursement to a monthly stipend, and may cover as much as tuition remission plus a stipend

Award Duration: Minimum of 1 semester, renewable for additional semesters

ELIGIBILITY REQUIREMENTS

- Must be admitted to and enrolling in Indiana University Bloomington

APPLICATION INFORMATION

Award Deadline: Nov 1 for undergraduate awards; Dec 1 for graduate awards (Nov 15 for business programs)

Instructions: All international students who submit a completed application packet by the specified deadlines will be automatically considered for funding, applications are available to download online at the website

CONTACT
Indiana University Bloomington
Office of International Services
400 East 7th Street
Bloomington, IN 47405
Tel: +1 (812) 855-9086
Fax: +1 (812) 856-5378
Email: newtoiu@iu.edu
Web: www.ois.iu.edu/financial-aid/scholarships/index.shtml

Indiana University Purdue University Indianapolis

IUPUI Valedictorian & Salutatorian Scholarships

PROGRAM INFORMATION

Description: Students who are ranked first or second in their class in secondary school may qualify for this scholarship. Recipients of this scholarship who also meet the requirements for the Chancellor's Non-Resident Scholarship will receive an additional $4,000 each of the 4 years of this award.

Levels of Study: Undergraduate

Field of Study: All

Nationality: Any Region

Location of Study: Indiana University-Purdue University Indianapolis
Indianapolis, IN

AWARD INFORMATION

Award Type: Scholarship

Average Amount: $10,000-$14,000 renewable

Number of Awards: Unlimited

Award Coverage: Partial tuition, fees, books, living expenses

Award Duration: Maximum of 4 years

ELIGIBILITY REQUIREMENTS

- Must have secondary school rank of first or second in graduating class
- Must maintain a 3.0 GPA on a 4.0 scale

APPLICATION INFORMATION

Award Deadline: Mar 1

Instructions: No separate application is required; admission application must be received by Mar 1 for fall and Oct 1 for spring

CONTACT
Indiana University Purdue University Indianapolis
International Admissions - Undergraduate
902 West New York Street, Room ES2126
Indianapolis, IN 46202-5197
Tel: +1 (317) 274-7000
Fax: +1 (317) 278-2213
Email: iapply@iupui.edu
Web: www.iapply.iupui.edu/scholarships/

Indiana University Purdue University Indianapolis

IUPUI Chancellor's Non-Resident Scholarship

PROGRAM INFORMATION

Description: High school students who have achieved a cumulative GPA of 3.75 or higher on a 4.0 scale, and have SAT scores of 1250 (total represents Critical Reading and Math scores only) or an ACT composite score of 28 may be eligible for this scholarship. Chancellor's Scholars are automatically admitted to the IUPUI Honors College. To be considered for renewal, students must attend full time, be an active participant in the Honors College, and maintain a 3.3 GPA.

Levels of Study: Undergraduate

Field of Study: All

Nationality: Any Region

Location of Study: Indiana University-Purdue University Indianapolis
Indianapolis, IN

AWARD INFORMATION

Award Type: Scholarship

Average Amount: $12,000 renewable

Number of Awards: Varies

Award Coverage: $12,000 per year for tuition, books, housing expenses

Award Duration: Maximum of 4 years

ELIGIBILITY REQUIREMENTS

- Must have a minimum GPA of 3.75 (on a 4.0 scale)
- Must have a minimum 1250 SAT I (Critical Reading and Math scores only) or 28 on ACT is required
- Must maintain a 3.3 GPA for renewal

APPLICATION INFORMATION

Award Deadline: Dec

Instructions: A separate application for this scholarship is not required, but students must submit a complete application for fall admission by Dec 1

CONTACT
Indiana University-Purdue University Indianapolis
International Admissions - Undergraduate
902 West New York Street, ES2126
Indianapolis, IN 46202-5197
Tel: +1 (317) 274-7000
Fax: +1 (317) 278-3292
Email: iapply@iupui.edu
Web: www.iapply.iupui.edu/scholarships

Indiana University Purdue University Indianapolis

IUPUI Plater International Scholars Program

PROGRAM INFORMATION

Description: This highly competitive program is available to exceptional incoming freshmen who are committed to combining academic excellence with global citizenship.

Levels of Study: Undergraduate

Field of Study: All

Nationality: Any Region

Location of Study: Indiana University-Purdue University Indianapolis
Indianapolis, IN

AWARD INFORMATION

Award Type: Scholarship

Average Amount: $64,000 over 4 years

Number of Awards: 7

Award Coverage: $16,000 per year of study, $2,500 toward 1 study abroad experience, $2,500 housing stipend for living in IUPUI International House during the freshman year

Award Duration: Maximum of 4 years

ELIGIBILITY REQUIREMENTS

- Must submit excellent SAT or ACT examination results and TOEFL results of non-native English speakers
- Must have a minimum cumulative GPA of 3.75 on a 4.0 scale or higher in secondary school
- Students residing outside Indiana must be interviewed by phone
- Must be a freshman student

APPLICATION INFORMATION

Award Deadline: Nov 15

Instructions: For more information on how to apply, please visit the website

CONTACT

Indiana University-Purdue University Indianapolis
Assistant Director: Scholarship Coordinator
IUPUI Honors College UL 0124D
IUPUI University Library 755 West Michigan Street
Indianapolis, IN 46202
Tel: +1 (317) 274-2660
Email: honors@iupui.edu
Web: www.honorscollege.iupui.edu/scholarships/plater/

Indiana University Purdue University Indianapolis

IUPUI Bepko Scholars & Fellows Program

PROGRAM INFORMATION

Description: This highly competitive program requires extensive civic engagement experience in addition to outstanding performance in a rigorous college preparatory curriculum, excellent SAT or ACT scores, and early admission and scholarship application. It provides academic, financial, and professional support for the top 1 to 2 international freshmen each year. Bepko Scholar support extends through 4 years of undergraduate and up to 4 years of graduate study at IUPUI. To be eligible students must be beginning freshmen.

Levels of Study: Undergraduate, Graduate

Field of Study: All

Nationality: Any Region

Location of Study: Indiana University-Purdue University Indianapolis
Indianapolis, IN

AWARD INFORMATION

Award Type: Grant, Scholarship, Tuition Reduction

Average Amount: Approx $80,000 over 8 years

Number of Awards: Up to 2

Award Coverage: In-state tuition rate, fees, books for 4 years, on-campus housing for 2 years, $2,500 study abroad stipend, $5,000 per year for up to 4 years of graduate study at IUPUI

Award Duration: Up to 8 years

ELIGIBILITY REQUIREMENTS

- Must have excellent SAT or ACT scores
- Must have excellent academic grades and be in the top 10 percent of graduating class
- Must demonstrate extensive community service experience
- Must submit 3 letters of recommendation

APPLICATION INFORMATION

Award Deadline: Nov

Instructions: Application is available online or by request

CONTACT

Indiana University Purdue University Indianapolis
Assistant Director/Scholarship Coordinator, IUPUI Honors College
IUPUI UL 0124
755 West Michigan Street
Indianapolis, IN 46202-5164
Tel: +1 (317) 274-2660
Fax: +1 (317) 274-2365
Email: honors@iupui.edu
Web: www.honorscollege.iupui.edu/scholarships/bepko

Indiana University Purdue University Indianapolis

IUPUI Merit and Competitive Scholarships

PROGRAM INFORMATION

Description: IUPUI offers a wide range of merit scholarships. International student applicants are automatically considered for merit scholarships when they apply for admission. Scholarships are based on academic standings reflected in a completed application for both incoming freshman and transfer students. Awards range from $5,000 to $12,000 per year. The Plater International Scholars Program is a competitive scholarship of $64,000 ($16,000 x 4 years) and other benefits. Recipients must demonstrate academic excellence with global citizenship along with an outstanding academic performance.

Levels of Study: Undergraduate

Field of Study: All

Nationality: Any Region

Location of Study: Indiana University-Purdue University Indianapolis
Indianapolis, IN

AWARD INFORMATION

Award Type: Scholarship

Average Amount: $10,000-$64,000

Number of Awards: Varies

Award Duration: Maximum of 2 or 4 years

ELIGIBILITY REQUIREMENTS

- All scholarships require full-time enrollment (12 credit hours or more per semester) in the fall and spring semesters

APPLICATION INFORMATION

Instructions: Visit www.iapply.iupui.edu/scholarships for information for merit and competitive scholarships and www.iupui.edu/~scentral/search.html for information on major-specific scholarships

CONTACT

Indiana University-Purdue University Indianapolis
International Admissions - Undergraduate
902 West New York Street, Room ES2126
Indianapolis, IN 46202-5197
Tel: +1 (317) 274-7000
Fax: +1 (317) 278-2213
Email: iapply@iupui.edu
Web: www.iapply.iupui.edu/scholarships

Indiana University Purdue University Indianapolis
IUPUI Service Award

PROGRAM INFORMATION

Description: This merit-based scholarship is for strong students who have applied for admission by Mar 1 for fall semester, or by Oct 1 for spring semester.
Levels of Study: Undergraduate
Field of Study: All
Nationality: Any Region
Location of Study: Indiana University-Purdue University Indianapolis
Indianapolis, IN

AWARD INFORMATION

Award Type: Scholarship
Average Amount: $7,000 renewable
Number of Awards: Unlimited
Award Coverage: Partial tuition, books, housing expenses
Award Duration: Up to 4 years

ELIGIBILITY REQUIREMENTS

- Must have a high school GPA 3.0 (on a 4.0 scale)
- Must score 1050 or higher on the SAT (Critical Reading and Math only; international students from non-English speaking countries must have a minimum SAT Math score of 530) or ACT Score of 23
- Applicants for spring semester enrollment may be considered for this scholarship, but the first award will begin the following fall semester
- Must maintain a 2.75 to be considered for renewal

APPLICATION INFORMATION

Award Deadline: Mar 1 for fall semester; Oct 1 for spring semester
Instructions: A separate application for this scholarship is not required but students must submit a complete application for admission by Mar 1 for fall or Oct 1 for spring

CONTACT
Indiana University Purdue University Indianapolis
International Admissions - Undergraduate
902 West New York Street, Room ES2126
Indianapolis, IN 46202-5197
Tel: +1 (317) 274-7000
Fax: +1 (317) 278-3292
Email: iapply@iupui.edu
Web: www.iapply.iupui.edu/scholarships

Indiana University Purdue University Indianapolis
IUPUI International Ambassador Award

PROGRAM INFORMATION

Levels of Study: Undergraduate
Field of Study: All
Nationality: Any Region
Location of Study: Indiana University-Purdue University Indianapolis
Indianapolis, IN

AWARD INFORMATION

Award Type: Scholarship
Average Amount: $7,000
Number of Awards: Unlimited
Award Coverage: Partial tuition, fees, books, housing
Award Duration: Maximum of 4 years

ELIGIBILITY REQUIREMENTS

- Must have a 3.0 GPA at time of application
- Must be fully-qualified admitted beginning freshmen by May 1
- Must have a minimum TOEFL 80 IBT, or a minimum SAT critical reading score of 450, ACT score of 19, or an IELTS score of 6.0.
- Must maintain a 2.75 GPA (on a 4.0 scale) for renewal
- Must volunteer annually for 15 hours of service at IUPUI events that have an international theme

APPLICATION INFORMATION

Award Deadline: Mar 1
Instructions: Submit complete application for admission no later than May 1, though preferably Mar 1, no other application is required, visit www.iapply.iupui.edu/scholarships for information on merit and competitive scholarships

CONTACT
Indiana University-Purdue University Indianapolis
International Admissions - Undergraduate
902 West New York Street, Room ES2126
Indianapolis, IN 46202-5197
Tel: +1 (317) 274-7000
Fax: +1 (317) 278-2213
Email: iapply@iupui.edu
Web: www.iapply.iupui.edu/scholarships

Indiana University School of Law - Indianapolis
IUPUI Master of Laws (LLM) Program

PROGRAM INFORMATION

Description: Scholarship opportunities are available for outstanding international students who apply to the Master of Laws (LLM) Program.
Levels of Study: Graduate, Doctorate
Field of Study: Law
Nationality: Any Region
Location of Study: Indiana University School of Law - Indianapolis
Indianapolis, IN

AWARD INFORMATION

Award Type: Scholarship
Average Amount: Varies
Number of Awards: Varies
Award Coverage: Tuition

ELIGIBILITY REQUIREMENTS

- Contact or visit website for eligibility requirements

APPLICATION INFORMATION

Instructions: Visit our website or contact for additional information

CONTACT
Indiana University School of Law
Assistant Director of Student Financial Services for McKinney School of Law
530 West New York St.
Indianapolis, IN 46202
Tel: +1 (317) 278-2880
Email: lawadmit@iupui.edu
Web: www.indylaw.indiana.edu/llm

Indiana University-Purdue University Fort Wayne IPFW
IPFW Chancellor's Merit Award

PROGRAM INFORMATION

Description: IPFW is a joint campus of 2 of the world's most prestigious universities, Indiana University and Purdue University. IPFW grants internationally-recognized undergraduate and graduate degrees from both IU and Purdue. International students with strong academic background may be considered for the IPFW Chancellor's Merit Award Scholarship which covers approximately $8,740/year undergrad student or $7,288/year grad student tuition. Minimum 87 TOEFL or 7.0 IELTS is required for consideration.
Levels of Study: Undergraduate, Graduate
Field of Study: All
Nationality: Any Region
Location of Study: Indiana University-Purdue University Fort Wayne (IPFW)
Fort Wayne, IN

AWARD INFORMATION

Award Type: Scholarship, Tuition Reduction
Average Amount: Approx $9000
Number of Awards: 25 per year
Award Coverage: Non-resident portion of tuition
Award Duration: 4 years (undergraduate)

ELIGIBILITY REQUIREMENTS

- Must have TOEFL score of 87 IBT, or a 7.0 on the IELTS and a 3.0 GPA

APPLICATION INFORMATION

Award Deadline: Jun
Instructions: No scholarship application is required, international students may apply for admission online

CONTACT
Indiana University-Purdue University Fort Wayne IPFW
Director of International Education
2101 E Coliseum Blvd
Walb Student Union 145
Fort Wayne, IN 46845
Tel: +1 (260) 481-6034
Fax: +1 (260) 481-6674
Email: iss@ipfw.edu
Web: www.ipfw.edu/international

Institute for Advanced Study

School of Historical Studies Memberships

PROGRAM INFORMATION

Description: The Institute for Advanced Study is a community of scholars focused on intellectual inquiry, free from teaching and other university obligations. Scholars of all nationalities are offered membership for up to a year, either with or without a stipend. Extensive resources are provided including offices, libraries, restaurant and housing facilities, and support services. The School of Historical Studies' principal interests are the history of Western, Near Eastern and Asian civilizations, with particular emphasis upon Greek and Roman civilization, the history of Europe (medieval, early modern, and modern), the Islamic world, East Asian studies, art history, the history of science and philosophy, modern international relations and music.

Levels of Study: Post Doctorate, Professional

Field of Study: Archaeology, Art History, Asian Studies, Classics, European Studies/EU Studies, History, Humanities, International Law, International Relations, Islamic Studies, Music, Philosophy and Religion, Political Science, Translation and Interpretation

Nationality: Any Region

Location of Study: Institute for Advanced Study Princeton, NJ

AWARD INFORMATION

Award Type: Fellowship

Average Amount: Up to $70,000

Number of Awards: Approximately 40 per year

Award Coverage: Salary replacement, up to $70,000, some travel reimbursement for getting to and from the Institute

Award Duration: Maximum of 1 academic year

ELIGIBILITY REQUIREMENTS

- Must have a PhD at the time of application
- Must have substantial publications, taking into account the applicant's stage of academic career

APPLICATION INFORMATION

Award Deadline: Nov 1

Instructions: Instructions are posted on the web at: www.hs.ias.edu/instructions

CONTACT

Institute for Advanced Study
Administrative Officer
School of Historical Studies
Einstein Drive
Princeton, NJ 08540
Tel: +1 (609) 734-8300
Email: mzelazny@ias.edu
Web: www.hs.ias.edu

James Madison University

James Madison University International Student Grant/Aid Program

PROGRAM INFORMATION

Description: James Madison University offers grants to undergraduate international students. Students may major in any program, but a minimum GPA must be maintained to remain eligible. These grants cover full tuition room and board. In addition, JMU offers academic merit scholarships for international students.

Levels of Study: Undergraduate

Field of Study: All

Nationality: Any Region

Location of Study: James Madison University Harrisonburg, VA

AWARD INFORMATION

Award Type: Award, Grant, Scholarship

Average Amount: $500-$13,000

Number of Awards: Varies

Award Coverage: Tuition, room, board

Award Duration: 4 years

ELIGIBILITY REQUIREMENTS

- Must demonstrate a financial need
- Must demonstrate academic merit
- Must be enrolled or planning to enroll at JMU as an undergraduate

APPLICATION INFORMATION

Award Deadline: Feb 15

Instructions: Complete the James Madison University international application, complete the supplemental financial aid for international students form. Visit our website for more information.

CONTACT

James Madison University
Sonner Hall- MSC 0108
481 Bluestone Drive
Harrisonburg, VA 22807
Tel: +1 (540) 568-5681
Fax: +1 (540) 568-3332
Email: international@jmu.edu
Web: www.jmu.edu/admissions

Johnson Wales University

Johnson & Wales University Awards for International Students

PROGRAM INFORMATION

Description: Our undergraduate and graduate degree programs in business, hospitality, culinary arts, technology, and education are career-focused, to provide the knowledge and skills that employers have identified as necessary for career success Industry-experienced faculty who bring real-life knowledge, hands-on learning, and networking opportunities into small classroom settings.

Levels of Study: Undergraduate, Graduate, Doctorate, Professional

Field of Study: Accounting, Biology, Business and Management, Communications and Journalism, Computer Science, Education, English as a Second Language, Equestrian Studies, Family and Consumer Sciences/ Human Sciences, Fashion Marketing & Management, Health Professions, Information Technology, International Management, International Relations, Liberal/General Studies, Management, Marketing, Master of Business Administration (MBA), Parks and Recreation, Psychology, Security and Protective Services, Social Science, Urban Planning

Nationality: Any Region

Location of Study: Johnson & Wales University Providence, RI

AWARD INFORMATION

Award Type: Award, Fellowship, Grant, Internship, Loan, Scholarship, Student Exchange, Study Abroad, Tuition Reduction

Average Amount: $1,000 - $5,000

Number of Awards: Varies

Award Coverage: Tuition

Award Duration: Renewable up to 4 years

ELIGIBILITY REQUIREMENTS

- Must complete admissions application
- Must submit official transcripts of high school completion
- Must have TOEFL scores of 550 PBT/210 CBT/80 IBT
- Must submit bank statement
- Must submit a copy of biographical portion of passport

APPLICATION INFORMATION

Award Deadline: Rolling

Instructions: Apply online: admissions.jwu.edu

CONTACT

Johnson & Wales University
8 Abbott Park Place
Providence, RI 02903
Tel: +1 (401) 598-1074
Fax: +1 (401) 598-4901
Email: JSchwarz@jwu.edu
Web: admissions.jwu.edu

Kalamazoo College

Kalamazoo College Undergraduate Study Scholarships

PROGRAM INFORMATION

Description: Kalamazoo College considers every student for merit based scholarships as well as granting supplementary awards for leadership in social activism and community engagement, creative expression, international activism, and environmental activism. Additionally, the social justice award is given to a student who shows a commitment to pursuing human rights work.

Levels of Study: Undergraduate

Field of Study: All

Nationality: Any Region

Location of Study: Kalamazoo College
Kalamazoo, MI

AWARD INFORMATION

Award Type: Scholarship, Student Exchange, Study Abroad

Average Amount: $5,000-$24,000

Number of Awards: Unlimited

Award Coverage: Tuition, housing, board.

Award Duration: Maximum of 4 years

ELIGIBILITY REQUIREMENTS

- Must submit a completed application including the Kalamazoo College Certification of Finances Form
- English language proficiency is required, if English is a second language, students must have a minimum TOEFL score of 550 PBT/213 CBT/79-95 IBT

APPLICATION INFORMATION

Award Deadline: Feb

Instructions: Visit our website or contact for additional information.

CONTACT

Kalamazoo College
1200 Academy Street
Kalamazoo, MI 49006
Tel: +1 (269) 337-7166
Email: admission@kzoo.edu
Web: www.kzoo.edu

Kansas State University

Kansas State University Funding

PROGRAM INFORMATION

Description: Kansas State University is a 150-year-old public research university in the middle of the US

Levels of Study: Undergraduate, Graduate, Doctorate, Post Doctorate

Field of Study: All

Nationality: Any Region

Location of Study: Kansas State University
Manhattan, KS

AWARD INFORMATION

Award Type: Associateship, Award, Fellowship, Grant, Scholarship, Tuition Reduction

Average Amount: Varies

Number of Awards: Varies

Award Duration: Varies

ELIGIBILITY REQUIREMENTS

- Students must meet all Kansas State University admission requirements and show academic accomplishment
- Undergraduate scholarships are limited. A few global diversity scholarships are granted each year to students who have a 3.5/4.0 GPA, submit a letter of reference, personal statement and proof of English
- Graduate and post-doctoral students should consult their individual departments for reward availability and requirements

APPLICATION INFORMATION

Instructions: Please visit the undergraduate admissions website, or graduate department website for more information on how to apply

CONTACT

Kansas State University
International Admissions and Recruiting
304 Fairchild Hall
Manhattan, Kansas
Tel: +1 (785) 532-7277
Fax: +1 (785) 532-4311
Email: intladmit@ksu.edu
Web: www.k-state.edu

Kennesaw State University

Kennesaw Academic Out-of-State Fee Waiver

PROGRAM INFORMATION

Description: Will offer In-state tuition for entering undergraduate and graduate applicants.

Levels of Study: Undergraduate, Graduate

Field of Study: All

Nationality: Any Region

Location of Study: Kennesaw State University
Kennesaw, GA

AWARD INFORMATION

Award Type: Tuition Reduction

Average Amount: Varies

Number of Awards: Varies

Award Coverage: Out-of-state tuition

Award Duration: Undergraduate: maximum of 4 years; graduate: maximum of 2 years

ELIGIBILITY REQUIREMENTS

- Freshmen: Must have a 3.25 GPA, 550 critical reading, 550 math on the SAT, and TOEFL score of 80 IBT or equivalent
- Graduate students: Must have a 3.5 GPA, 550 GMAT or 550 verbal, 550 quantitative, 4 analytical writing, and TOEFL score of 80 IBT or equivalent

APPLICATION INFORMATION

Award Deadline: Rolling

Instructions: Please visit the website for further application instructions

CONTACT

Kennesaw State University
Global Admissions
3391 Town Point Dr. NW
Suite 1300
Kennesaw, GA 30144-5591
Tel: +1 (470) 578-3002
Fax: +1 (470) 578-9170
Email: internationaladmissions@kennesaw.edu
Web: www.kennesaw.edu/globaladmissions/index.shtml

Kent State University

International Freshman Scholarship Program

PROGRAM INFORMATION

Description: The International Freshman Scholarship program is available to any nonimmigrant to the US who is an incoming undergraduate student to Kent State University. This merit-based scholarship may vary in amount awarded to the student. The maximum award covers non-resident tuition ($18,000+) for 4 years. All eligible applicants will automatically be considered for an award.

Levels of Study: Undergraduate

Field of Study: All

Nationality: Any Region

Location of Study: Kent State University
Kent, OH

AWARD INFORMATION

Award Type: Scholarship

Average Amount: Varies.

Number of Awards: 5-8 awards per year

Award Coverage: Full or partial tuition

Award Duration: Maximum 4 years

ELIGIBILITY REQUIREMENTS

- Must have a 3.5 or higher grade point average on a 4.0 scale
- Must have a 27 ACT Composite or 1210 SAT Reading and Math

APPLICATION INFORMATION

Award Deadline: Feb 15

Instructions: Submit an online application for admission and include the scholarship application with supporting materials

CONTACT

Kent State University
Office of Global Education
625 Loop Rd
106 Van Campen Hall
Kent, OH 44242
Tel: +1 (330) 672-7980
Fax: +1 (330) 672-4025
Email: intladm@kent.edu
Web: www2.kent.edu/admissions/international/cost/financial-assistance.cfm

Kenyon College

Kenyon College International Scholarship

PROGRAM INFORMATION

Description: Kenyon attempts to meet the full financial need of admitted international students through scholarships, a loan, and an on-campus job. Since we have a limited international aid budget, those with low need or no need are more likely to gain admission.

Levels of Study: Undergraduate

Field of Study: All

Nationality: Any Region

Location of Study: Kenyon College
Gambier, OH

AWARD INFORMATION

Award Type: Grant, Scholarship

Average Amount: $40,000

Number of Awards: 20-25 per entering class

Award Coverage: Tuition, room, board, required fees, books, funds for 1 round-trip travel

Award Duration: Maximum of 4 years

ELIGIBILITY REQUIREMENTS

- Preference is given to those who present the strongest secondary school record and exam results
- Must have high standardized test scores (SAT I, GRE, or ACT); IELTS or TOEFL can be submitted if your language of instruction has not been English

APPLICATION INFORMATION

Award Deadline: Jan 15

Instructions: Candidates must complete all testing and application parts by Jan 15

CONTACT

Kenyon College
Director of International Admissions
Ransom Hall
Gambier, OH 43022
Tel: +1 (740) 427-5776
Fax: +1 (740) 427-5770
Email: admissions@kenyon.edu
Web: www.kenyon.edu

Kettering University

Kettering University International Undergraduate Scholarships

PROGRAM INFORMATION

Description: Kettering University is a world-class institution that has been preparing leaders in the Engineering, Technology, Science and Business fields for more than 90 years. All Kettering students participate in our nationally recognized cooperative education, a program where students alternate between academic and professional terms. All cooperative education assignments are paid and connected to each student's field of study.

Levels of Study: Undergraduate

Field of Study: Biochemistry, Biology, Biotechnology, Business and Management, Chemistry, Computer Science, Engineering, Mathematics, Physics

Nationality: Any Region

Location of Study: Kettering University
Flint, MI

AWARD INFORMATION

Award Type: Scholarship

Average Amount: $2,500-$15,500

Number of Awards: Varies

Award Coverage: Partial tuition

Award Duration: Maximum of 4.5 years

ELIGIBILITY REQUIREMENTS

- Must be enrolled at Kettering University

APPLICATION INFORMATION

Award Deadline: Varies

Instructions: Application form is available online at www.kettering.edu/apply; there is no application fee and students are encouraged to apply 1 year prior to desired enrollment date

CONTACT

Kettering University
Assistant Director of International Admissions
Admissions
1700 University Avenue
Flint, MI 48504
Tel: +1 (810) 762-7961
Fax: +1 (810) 762-9837
Email: InternationalAdmissions@kettering.edu
Web: www.kettering.edu/intladmissions

Lafayette College

Lafayette College Financial Aid for International Students

PROGRAM INFORMATION

Description: Each year Lafayette College offers need-based financial aid to approximately 70 international students. The students who are chosen for financial aid are among the top-ranked students in their high school and often have outstanding SAT/TOEFL scores. Students seeking financial aid are required to complete either the recommended CSS Profile or the International Student Financial Aid Application. The amount of a student's award is directly related to the student's family's need. Lafayette is committed to meeting the full demonstrated need of each accepted student. Lafayette does offer a limited number of academic-based merit awards to highly competitive candidates. International students will automatically be considered for this award; no separate application is required.

Levels of Study: Undergraduate

Field of Study: All

Nationality: Any Region

Location of Study: Lafayette College
Easton, PA

AWARD INFORMATION

Award Type: Grant, Loan, Scholarship

Average Amount: Varies

Number of Awards: Approx 55

Award Coverage: Tuition, room, board, incidental expenses

Award Duration: 4 years

ELIGIBILITY REQUIREMENTS

- Must have As, Bs, or 90s plus on transcript
- Must have an SAT score above 2000
- Must have a TOEFL score above 600 PBT/250 CBT/80 IBT

APPLICATION INFORMATION

Award Deadline: Jan

Instructions: International applicants who are seeking financial aid must complete the preferred CSS Profile (online) or we will accept the International Student Financial Aid Application and submit it along with their application

CONTACT

Lafayette College
Office of Admissions
118 Markle Hall
Easton, PA 18042
Tel: +1 (610) 330-5100
Fax: +1 (610) 330-5355
Email: internatl@lafayette.edu
Web: www.admissions.lafayette.edu

Leeward Community College

International Student Scholarship

PROGRAM INFORMATION

Description: A scholarship for non-resident students (not a US citizen) pursuing their first degree.

Location of Study: Leeward Community College
Pearl City, HI

ELIGIBILITY REQUIREMENTS

- Students must be enrolled for at least 6 credits and have a cumulative GPA of at least 2.5

CONTACT

Leward Community College
96-045 Ala Ike
Pearl CIty, HI 96782
Tel: +1 (808) 455-0011
Email: leeward@hawaii.edu
Web: www.leeward.hawaii.edu/finaid-award-policies-2014-2015

Lewis & Clark College

Lewis & Clark College International Student Grant

PROGRAM INFORMATION

Description: International Student Grants are available to academically qualified applicants based on need, merit, and geographic diversity.

Levels of Study: Undergraduate

Field of Study: All

Nationality: Any Region

Location of Study: Lewis & Clark College
Portland, OR

AWARD INFORMATION

Award Type: Grant

Average Amount: $24,000

Number of Awards: Unlimited

Award Coverage: Partial tuition

Award Duration: Academic year, renewable if academic requirements are met

ELIGIBILITY REQUIREMENTS

- Must qualify for admission to university in their home country
- Must have a minimum TOEFL score of 575 PBT/232 CBT/91 IBT for direct admission
- Must have a minimum TOEFL score of 61 IBT for admission with Academic English

APPLICATION INFORMATION

Award Deadline: Jan 15

Instructions: Apply online for admission or submit a Common Application; applicants must also submit a Lewis & Clark International Financial Aid Application or College Board International Financial Aid Application

CONTACT

Lewis & Clark College - MSC 192
International Students & Scholars
0615 SW Palatine Hill Road
Portland, OR 97219
Tel: +1 (503) 768-7305
Fax: +1 (503) 768-7301
Email: iso@lclark.edu
Web: www.lclark.edu/dept/iso

Lewis University

Lewis University International Student Scholarship

PROGRAM INFORMATION

Description: Lewis University awards academic scholarships to international Bachelor's students (F1 student visa for undergraduate majors) based on grade point average (GPA). International students are automatically considered for this program upon submitting an application.

Levels of Study: Undergraduate

Field of Study: All

Nationality: Any Region

Location of Study: Lewis University
Romeoville, IL

AWARD INFORMATION

Award Type: Scholarship

Average Amount: $5,500-$4,000

Number of Awards: Unlimited

Award Coverage: Tuition

Award Duration: Academic year, renewable

ELIGIBILITY REQUIREMENTS

- Must submit transcripts via a credential evaluation, such as One Earth Evaluations, EdPerpectives, ECE or WES
- Must meet all admission criteria
- Must have the minimal GPA required, between 3.0 and 4.0 for $5,500 per year, or between 2.5 and 2.9 for $4,000 per year

APPLICATION INFORMATION

Award Deadline: Jul and Nov

Instructions: There is no need to apply for the scholarship, as it will be automatically given to the student if the grades on the transcript evaluation (from either One Earth Evaluations, EdPerpectives, ECE or WES) meet the minimal criteria

CONTACT

Lewis University
Assistant Director of International Admission & Recruitment
One University Parkway #297
Romeoville, IL 60446
Tel: +1 (815) 836-5635
Fax: +1 (815) 836-5002
Email: maloneycl@lewisu.edu
Web: www.lewisu.edu/admissions/international/

Lewis-Clark State College

Lewis-Clark State College International Student Scholarships

PROGRAM INFORMATION

Description: LCSC offers scholarships to qualified international students.

Levels of Study: Undergraduate

Field of Study: All

Location of Study: Lewis-Clark State College
Lewiston, ID

AWARD INFORMATION

Award Type: Scholarship

Average Amount: $3,500-$5,000

Number of Awards: Unlimited

Award Coverage: Tuition

Award Duration: Duration of Study

ELIGIBILITY REQUIREMENTS

- 2.5 GPA from high school or transfer institution
- Complete 12 or more credits per semester
- Volunteer a minimum of 10 hours per semester
- Maintain 2.5 grade point average at LCSC each semester

APPLICATION INFORMATION

Instructions: Scholarships will be granted after transcripts are evaluated at time of admission, no further scholarship application is needed

CONTACT

Lewis-Clark State College
Director, International Programs
500 8th Ave.
Lewiston, ID 83501, US
Tel: +1 (208) 792-2177
Fax: +1 (208) 792-2824
Email: internationaladmissions@lcsc.edu
Web: www.lcsc.edu/international/cost.html

Linfield College

Linfield College International Scholarship

PROGRAM INFORMATION

Description: Linfield College International Scholarships are awarded to qualified international students at the time of admission to the college. The award is renewable for up to 5 years as long as the student continues to meet Linfield's standards for enrollment.

Levels of Study: Undergraduate

Field of Study: All

Nationality: Any Region

Location of Study: Linfield College
McMinnville, OR

AWARD INFORMATION

Award Type: Grant, Scholarship

Average Amount: $25,000

Number of Awards: Unlimited

Award Coverage: Up to 50% of the total cost of attendance

Award Duration: Maximum of 5 years

ELIGIBILITY REQUIREMENTS

- Must have completed high secondary (high) school and have qualified for admission to Linfield College

APPLICATION INFORMATION

Award Deadline: Apr

Instructions: Complete the application for admission for Linfield College through the Common Application online

CONTACT

Linfield College
Assistant Director of International Recruitment
900 SE Baker Street
McMinnville, OR 97128
Tel: +1 (503) 883-2213
Fax: +1 (503) 883-2472
Email: admission@linfield.edu
Web: www.linfield.edu

Lock Haven University

Lock Haven University Scholarship

PROGRAM INFORMATION

Description: International students pursuing an undergraduate degree at Lock Haven are eligible to receive a tuition reduction scholarship.

Levels of Study: Undergraduate

Field of Study: All

Nationality: Any Region

Location of Study: Lock Haven University
Lock Haven, PA

AWARD INFORMATION

Award Type: Tuition Reduction

Average Amount: Varies

Number of Awards: Varies

Award Coverage: Partial tuition

Award Duration: Maximum of 4 years

ELIGIBILITY REQUIREMENTS

- Must have high academic credentials
- Must demonstrate financial need

CONTACT

Lock Haven University
Institute for International Studies
401 North Fairview Street, LHU
Lock Haven, PA 17745
Tel: +1 (570) 484-2140
Email: international@lhup.edu
Web: www.lhup.edu

Long Beach City College

Long Beach City College Associate Degree Program Scholarship

PROGRAM INFORMATION

Description: Long Beach City College is accredited by the Western Association of Schools and Colleges. Best known for helping students transfer to top universities including UC Irvine, UCLA, USC, and California State University, Long Beach, LBCC is also well known for international business, radio/television and film, music recording, aviation, nursing (RN), and the sciences. The American Language and Culture Institute offers 9-week terms for students who need to become proficient in English. The International Student Center offers special resources and services designed to assist foreign students. The International Friends program matches new international students with experienced students for advice, friendship, and tutoring.

Levels of Study: Undergraduate

Field of Study: All

Nationality: Any Region

Location of Study: Long Beach City College
Long Beach, CA

AWARD INFORMATION

Award Type: Scholarship

Average Amount: Varies

Number of Awards: Varies

Award Coverage: Tuition, books, educational supplies.

Award Duration: Academic year

ELIGIBILITY REQUIREMENTS

- Must be a full-time student attending Long Beach City College at the time of applying for the award and when the award is received; some awards may be used for further study at 4-year universities

APPLICATION INFORMATION

Award Deadline: Dec

Instructions: Apply online between Sep and Dec each year. Faculty references are required

CONTACT

Long Beach City College
Administrative Assistant, Scholarships
4901 E. Carson St.
Long Beach, CA 90808
Tel: +1 (562) 938-4267
Email: rdamaso@lbcc.edu
Web: www.lbcc.edu/international

Loras College

Loras College International Scholarship

PROGRAM INFORMATION

Description: Loras offers qualified international students academic merit scholarships upon acceptance.

Levels of Study: Undergraduate

Field of Study: Accounting, Biochemistry, Biology, Business and Management, Chemistry, Economics, Education, Engineering, Finance, Journalism, Music, Natural Sciences, Neuroscience, Psychology, Science

Nationality: Any Region

Location of Study: Loras College
Dubuque, IA

AWARD INFORMATION

Award Type: Scholarship

Average Amount: $10,000

Number of Awards: 10

Award Coverage: Tuition

Award Duration: Maximum of 8 semesters

APPLICATION INFORMATION

Instructions: Apply for admissions here www.loras.edu/Admission-and-Financial-Aid/Undergraduate-Students/International-Students/The-Application-Process.aspx

CONTACT

Loras College
Admissions
1450 Alta Vista
Dubuque, IA
Tel: +1 (563) 588-7234
Email: Rebecca.Ohnesorge@loras.edu
Web: www.loras.edu/Admission-and-Financial-Aid/Undergraduate-Students/International-Students.aspx

Loyola U. Chicago Civitas ChildLaw Center

Civitas ChildLaw Center Scholarships

PROGRAM INFORMATION

Description: University-affiliated center for the study of child and family law.

Levels of Study: Graduate, Professional

Field of Study: Law

Nationality: Any Region

Location of Study: Loyola U. Chicago School of Law
Chicago, IL

AWARD INFORMATION

Award Type: Scholarship

Average Amount: $3000

Number of Awards: 5

Award Coverage: Tuition remission

Award Duration: 1 year or equivalent

ELIGIBILITY REQUIREMENTS

- Admission to LLM

APPLICATION INFORMATION

Award Deadline: Jul

CONTACT

Loyola. U. Chicago Civitas ChildLaw Center
Program Coordinator
gsanch3@luc.edu
25 E. Pearson, Chicago, IL
60611 Chicago IL
Tel: +1 (312) 915-6481
Fax: +1 (312) 915-6485
Email: gsanch3@luc.edu
Web: www.luc/childlaw

Loyola University Chicago

Loyola University Graduate Assistantships

PROGRAM INFORMATION

Description: International students are eligible for graduate assistantships offered by academic departments. Students should contact their department directly to inquire about these opportunities.

Levels of Study: Graduate

Field of Study: All

Nationality: Any Region

Location of Study: Loyola University Chicago
Chicago, IL

AWARD INFORMATION

Award Type: Award

Average Amount: Varies

Number of Awards: Varies

Award Coverage: Varies

ELIGIBILITY REQUIREMENTS

- Varies by department

APPLICATION INFORMATION

Award Deadline: Varies
Instructions: Check department application guidelines

CONTACT

Loyola University Chicago
1032 W. Sheridan Road
Chicago, IL 60660
Tel: +1 (773) 508-8840
Email: DSDgrads@luc.edu
Web: www.luc.edu/studentdevelopment/assistantships/

Loyola University Chicago
Loyola University Scholarships

PROGRAM INFORMATION

Description: Committed to preparing people to lead extraordinary lives, Loyola University Chicago was founded in 1870 and is the largest of the 28 Jesuit colleges and universities in the US. Loyola has a total enrollment of more than 15,000 students, which includes 10,000 undergraduates hailing from all 50 states, as well as 82 foreign countries. The University has 4 campuses, 3 in the greater Chicago area and 1 in Rome, Italy. Recognizing Loyola's excellence in education, US News and World Report has ranked Loyola consistently among the "top national universities" and "best values" in its annual publications.
Levels of Study: Graduate, Doctorate
Field of Study: All
Nationality: Any Region
Location of Study: Loyola University Chicago
Chicago, IL

AWARD INFORMATION

Award Type: Tuition Reduction
Average Amount: Varies
Number of Awards: 4
Award Coverage: Tuition
Award Duration: Duration of program

ELIGIBILITY REQUIREMENTS

- Must be a sponsored student (eg, Fulbright)
- Must be accepted into an academic program at Loyola University, Chicago

APPLICATION INFORMATION

Instructions: Please contact the Graduate School

CONTACT

Loyola University Chicago
The Graduate School
1032 W. Sheridan Road
Chicago, IL 60660
Tel: +1 (773) 508-7704
Email: emoore@luc.edu
Web: www.luc.edu

Loyola University Chicago
Loyola University Undergraduate Merit Scholarships

PROGRAM INFORMATION

Description: International students are eligible for undergraduate merit scholarships. The Presidential, Damen, Loyola, and Trustee scholarships are offered on a competitive basis to admitted freshman applicants. These scholarships are awarded without consideration of financial need.
Levels of Study: Undergraduate
Field of Study: All
Nationality: Any Region
Location of Study: Loyola University Chicago
Chicago, IL

AWARD INFORMATION

Award Type: Tuition Reduction
Average Amount: $13,000-$18,000
Number of Awards: Varies
Award Coverage: Tuition
Award Duration: 4 years

ELIGIBILITY REQUIREMENTS

- Must be admitted by Feb 1 to be considered
- Must submit an SAT or ACT score

APPLICATION INFORMATION

Award Deadline: Dec
Instructions: Students are considered for merit awards at time of application to the university; no separate scholarship application is required.

CONTACT

Loyola University Chicago
Assistant Director of International Admission
1032 W. Sheridan Road
Chicago, IL 60660
Tel: +1 (773) 508-3922
Email: lsimon2@luc.edu
Web: www.luc.edu/finaid/scholarships_auto.shtml

Loyola University New Orleans
Loyola University New Orleans Partial Tuition Scholarships

PROGRAM INFORMATION

Description: Founded by the Jesuits in 1912, Loyola University New Orleans has graduated more than 35,000 graduates who have excelled in innumerable professions. The total enrollment is approximately 4,900 students, 2,900 of whom are undergraduates. Loyola's student body represents all 50 states and 41 different countries. Loyola offers more than 60 majors in its colleges of business, humanities & natural sciences, music & fine arts, social sciences, and college of law.
Levels of Study: Undergraduate
Field of Study: All
Nationality: Any Region
Location of Study: Loyola University New Orleans
New Orleans, LA

AWARD INFORMATION

Award Type: Scholarship
Average Amount: Varies
Number of Awards: Unlimited
Award Coverage: Partial tuition
Award Duration: Maximum of 4 years

ELIGIBILITY REQUIREMENTS

- Must submit standardized test scores for the SAT or ACT and TOEFL or IELTS if English is a non-native language
- Must submit a certified and translated copy of the candidate's secondary school academic record
- Certification of Finances Form must be submitted
- Must submit the Loyola Application for Undergraduate Admission or Common Application

APPLICATION INFORMATION

Award Deadline: Jan
Instructions: For further information on how to apply, please visit the website.

CONTACT

Center for International Education
Assistant Director for International Student & Scholar Services
6363 St. Charles Ave, Box 205
New Orleans, LA 70118
Tel: +1 (504) 864-7550
Fax: +1 (504) 864-7548
Email: kmagner@loyno.edu
Web: www.loyno.edu/cie/

Luther College
Luther College Academic Scholarships and Diversity Enrichment Awards

PROGRAM INFORMATION

Description: Luther College offers awards that are granted to selected students from distinctive and broadly diverse backgrounds based on their potential to enrich the educational environment on campus and make positive contributions to the larger world. In addition, a number of merit-based academic scholarships are offered for international student applicants. Diversity Enrichment Awards are granted at time of admission to international students. There is no separate application process, other than applying and being admitted to Luther College. Diversity Enrichment Awards may be combined with Luther academic scholarships (Founders, President's, Dean's), music scholarships, and special endowed scholarships.
Levels of Study: Undergraduate
Field of Study: All
Nationality: Any Region
Location of Study: Luther College
Decorah, IA

AWARD INFORMATION

Award Type: Grant, Scholarship
Average Amount: Varies
Number of Awards: Varies
Award Coverage: Tuition, fees, housing, food
Award Duration: Up to 4 years

ELIGIBILITY REQUIREMENTS

- Scholarship amounts vary depending on the strength of the candidate's academic background
- Complete the Common Application
- Must submit 2 letters of recommendation, International Student Financial Aid Application, secondary school transcripts, final secondary school exams, SAT scores (recommended), TOEFL or IELTS scores (if language of instruction is not English)

APPLICATION INFORMATION

Award Deadline: Mar 1 for fall semester; Nov 1 for spring semester

Instructions: Music Scholarships are awarded to promising music students based on the outcome of a music audition, contact the International Admissions Office for music audition guidelines

CONTACT

Luther College
700 College Drive
Decorah, IA 52101
Tel: +1 (563) 387-1062
Fax: +1 (563) 387-1060
Email: global@luther.edu
Web: www.luther.edu/admissions/international/

Lynn University

Lynn University Annual Academic Awards

PROGRAM INFORMATION

Description: Located on 123 lushly landscaped acres in beautiful south Florida, Lynn University is a small liberal arts university that awards baccalaureate, master's, and doctoral degrees. With a small student body of undergraduate and graduate students, Lynn is committed to supporting students' journeys of self-discovery.

Levels of Study: Undergraduate

Field of Study: All

Nationality: Any Region

Location of Study: Lynn University
Boca Raton, FL

AWARD INFORMATION

Award Type: Scholarship

Average Amount: $6,000-$12,000

Number of Awards: Varies

Award Coverage: Tuition

ELIGIBILITY REQUIREMENTS

- International students: it is not necessary for you to fill out a FAFSA or apply for financial aid
- Lynn offers partial academic scholarships to qualified undergraduate international students with exceptional grades, SAT, ACT and TOEFL scores

APPLICATION INFORMATION

Award Deadline: Mar for fall semester, Oct for spring semester

Instructions: For more information on how to apply, please visit the website

CONTACT

Lynn University
Schmidt College Center
3601 North Military Trail
Boca Raton, FL 33431
Tel: +1 (561) 237-7900
Fax: +1 (561) 237-7900
Email: admission@lynn.edu
Web: www.lynn.edu

Marquette University

Ignatius/Magis Scholarships for Undergraduates

PROGRAM INFORMATION

Description: Ignatius/Magis Scholarships are awarded to qualified new undergraduate students who demonstrate academic excellence or leadership in previous studies. The award is to recognize students with high academic achievement, leadership skills, or outstanding prior service to their community.

Levels of Study: Undergraduate

Field of Study: All

Nationality: Any Region

Location of Study: Marquette University
Milwaukee, WI

AWARD INFORMATION

Award Type: Scholarship

Average Amount: $4,000-$14,000

Number of Awards: Varies

Award Coverage: Partial tuition

Award Duration: Academic year, renewable up to 4 years

ELIGIBILITY REQUIREMENTS

- Must meet all requirements for undergraduate admission The Ignatius/Magis Scholarship is based on evidence of academic achievement, not on financial need

APPLICATION INFORMATION

Award Deadline: Rolling

Instructions: No separate financial aid or scholarship application is needed, all international undergraduate applicants are considered for the Ignatius Scholarship and notified at the time of the admission decision

CONTACT

Marquette University
Holthusen Hall, 4th floor
PO Box 1881
Milwaukee, WI 53201-1881
Tel: +1 (414) 288-7289
Fax: +1 (414) 288-3701
Email: world@marquette.edu
Web: www.marquette.edu/oie/

Marquette University

Marquette University International Jesuit High School Scholarship

PROGRAM INFORMATION

Description: The International Jesuit High School Scholarship is awarded to qualified new undergraduate students who will enroll at Marquette University directly after completing secondary studies at a Jesuit High School outside the US Students must demonstrate academic excellence in previous studies.

Levels of Study: Undergraduate

Field of Study: All

Nationality: Any Region

Location of Study: Marquette University
Milwaukee, WI

AWARD INFORMATION

Award Type: Scholarship

Number of Awards: Varies

Award Coverage: 50% of tuition

Award Duration: Academic year, renewable up to 4 years

ELIGIBILITY REQUIREMENTS

- Must enroll at Marquette University directly after completion of senior secondary studies at a school operated by the Jesuits outside of the US
- Must meet all requirements for undergraduate admission

APPLICATION INFORMATION

Award Deadline: Mar

Instructions: Complete all admission procedures for international undergraduates, no separate financial aid or scholarship application is required, but applicants are encouraged to provide additional documentation about the quality of their previous achievement

CONTACT

Marquette University
Holthusen Hall, 4th Floor
PO Box 1881
Milwaukee, WI 53201
Tel: +1 (414) 288-7289
Fax: +1 (414) 288-3701
Email: world@marquette.edu/
Web: www.marquette.edu/oie

Marquette University

Kimberly-Clark International Scholar Award

PROGRAM INFORMATION

Description: The Kimberly-Clark International Scholar Award is granted to highly qualified new international students who enroll at Marquette University from countries where Kimberly-Clark Corp. maintains a presence. Students must demonstrate academic excellence in previous studies.

Levels of Study: Undergraduate

Field of Study: All

Nationality: Any Region

Location of Study: Marquette University
Milwaukee, WI

AWARD INFORMATION

Award Type: Scholarship
Average Amount: $6,000-$10,000
Number of Awards: Varies
Award Coverage: Partial tuition
Award Duration: Academic year, renewable up to 4 years

ELIGIBILITY REQUIREMENTS

- Must meet all requirements for undergraduate admission, the Kimberly-Clark International Scholar Award is based on evidence of high academic achievement, not on financial need
- Must be a citizen of a country where Kimberly-Clark Corp. has a presence

APPLICATION INFORMATION

Award Deadline: Mar
Instructions: Complete all admission procedures for international undergraduates, no separate financial aid or scholarship application is required, but applicants are encouraged to provide additional documentation about the quality of their previous achievement

CONTACT

Marquette University
Holthusen Hall, 4th Floor
PO Box 1881
Milwaukee, WI 53201
Tel: +1 (414) 288-7289
Fax: +1 (414) 288-3701
Email: world@marquette.edu
Web: www.marquette.edu/oie/

Marshall University

Marshall University Academic Scholarships for Undergraduate Students

PROGRAM INFORMATION

Description: Incoming freshmen and transfer international students are automatically considered for scholarship assistance. Visit the website for a list of all the academic scholarships with more details about eligibility and renewal of the awards.
Levels of Study: Undergraduate
Field of Study: All
Nationality: Any Region
Location of Study: Marshall University Huntington, WV

AWARD INFORMATION

Award Type: Scholarship
Average Amount: Varies
Award Coverage: Tuition waiver
Award Duration: Varies

ELIGIBILITY REQUIREMENTS

- For updated information on scholarships and requirements, visit the Marshall University Office of Student Financial Assistance website

APPLICATION INFORMATION

Award Deadline: Same as application deadline
Instructions: For more information on how to apply, please visit the website

CONTACT

Marshall University
Center for International Programs
Old Main 320
One John Marshall Drive
Huntington, WV 25755
Tel: +1 (304) 696-6265
Fax: +1 (304) 696-6353
Email: cip@marshall.edu
Web: www.marshall.edu/admissions/international_undergrad.asp

Mary Baldwin College

Baldwin Scholarships

PROGRAM INFORMATION

Description: International students are eligible for merit-based scholarships.
Levels of Study: Undergraduate
Field of Study: All
Nationality: Any Region
Location of Study: Mary Baldwin College Staunton, VA

AWARD INFORMATION

Award Type: Scholarship
Average Amount: Varies
Number of Awards: Unlimited
Award Coverage: Tuition
Award Duration: Maximum of 4 years

ELIGIBILITY REQUIREMENTS

- Must be admitted to Mary Baldwin College
- Must submit TOEFL or SAT scores
- Satisfaction of F-1 visa requirements for study in the US

APPLICATION INFORMATION

Award Deadline: Rolling
Instructions: Submit a completed application for admission to Mary Baldwin College, including TOEFL or SAT scores

CONTACT

Mary Baldwin College
Assistant Director of Admissions
Staunton, VA 24401
Tel: +1 (540) 887-7181
Fax: +1 (540) 887-7185
Email: admit@mbc.edu
Web: www.mbc.edu/international

Marymount College of Fordham University

Marymount College International Award

PROGRAM INFORMATION

Description: Marymount College is the women's college of Fordham University. All international students are eligible for merit-based scholarships.
Levels of Study: Undergraduate
Field of Study: All
Nationality: Any Region
Location of Study: Marymount College Tarrytown, NY

AWARD INFORMATION

Award Type: Scholarship
Average Amount: Varies
Number of Awards: Unlimited
Award Coverage: Partial tuition
Award Duration: Academic year, renewable as long as academic requirements are met

ELIGIBILITY REQUIREMENTS

- Must have a minimum TOEFL score of 190 CBT
- Must have strong academic background
- SAT scores are recommended

APPLICATION INFORMATION

Award Deadline: Apr for fall semester; Nov for spring semester
Instructions: Apply for admission online or contact to request application materials

CONTACT

Marymount College of Fordham
International Student Advisor
Marymount Avenue
Tarrytown, NY 10591
Tel: +1 (914) 332-8295
Fax: +1 (914) 332-7442
Email: ois@fordham.edu
Web: www.fordham.edu

Maryville College

Maryville College Undergraduate Scholarships

PROGRAM INFORMATION

Description: Scholarships of $19,000 to $22,000 are available to incoming international students. Scholarships cover approximately half of the total cost of attendance.
Levels of Study: Undergraduate
Field of Study: All
Nationality: Any Region
Location of Study: Maryville College Maryville, TN

AWARD INFORMATION

Award Type: Scholarship
Average Amount: $19,000 - $22,000
Number of Awards: Unlimited
Award Coverage: Partial tuition
Award Duration: Maximum of 4 years

ELIGIBILITY REQUIREMENTS

- Any international student who wishes to pursue a bachelor's degree at Maryville College is eligible
- Students must complete all admission requirements
- Should write a brief personal statement
- Must complete volunteer hours with the Maryville College Cultural Ambassadors program
- Can be awarded to students admitted via conditional admission

APPLICATION INFORMATION

Award Deadline: Rolling

Instructions: File an international student application, following the directions on the website for international admissions, and file all associated required items

CONTACT

Maryville College
Assistant Director, International Admissions
502 E Lamar Alexander Pkwy
International House
Maryville, TN 37804
Tel: +1 (865) 981-8183
Fax: +1 (865) 981-8187
Email: brian.todd@maryvillecollege.edu
Web: www.maryvillecollege.edu/international/costs

Maryville College

Maryville College Full Tuition International Diversity Scholarship

PROGRAM INFORMATION

Description: Full tuition scholarship for 1 student each academic year.

Levels of Study: Undergraduate

Field of Study: All

Nationality: Any Region

Location of Study: Maryville College
Maryville, TN

AWARD INFORMATION

Award Type: Scholarship

Number of Awards: 1

Award Coverage: Tuition

Award Duration: Maximum of 4 years

ELIGIBILITY REQUIREMENTS

- Must be admitted to the college.
- TOEFL IBT score of at least 74 or IELTS of 6.5 unless the student is a native English speaker
- SAT or ACT scores are recommended

APPLICATION INFORMATION

Award Deadline: Mar 1

Instructions: Students admitted to Maryville College, must submit the scholarship application form and a scholarship essay of 1-2 pages, International Diversity Scholarship Form available online at www.maryvillecollege.edu/media/dsx/manager/CIE/International%20Admissions/International-Diversity-Scholarship%20App2015.pdf

CONTACT

Maryville College
Center for International Education
502 E Lamar Alexander Pkwy
Center for International Education
Maryville, TN 37804
Tel: +1 (865) 981-8183
Fax: +1 (865) 981-8187
Email: brian.todd@maryvillecollege.edu
Web: www.maryvillecollege.edu/international

Menlo College

Menlo College International Student Scholarship

PROGRAM INFORMATION

Description: International students are an important part of Menlo College, making up about 20 percent of the student body. Scholarships for international students are available based on merit.

Levels of Study: Undergraduate

Field of Study: Business and Management, Communications and Journalism, Liberal/General Studies

Nationality: Any Region

Location of Study: Menlo College
Atherton, CA

AWARD INFORMATION

Award Type: Scholarship

Average Amount: Varies

Number of Awards: 20

Award Coverage: Partial tuition

Award Duration: Academic year, renewable as long as academic requirements are met

ELIGIBILITY REQUIREMENTS

- Must submit transcripts in English
- Transcripts must show strong academic achievement
- Must have a minimum TOEFL score of 550 PBT
- Must provide certificate of finance

APPLICATION INFORMATION

Award Deadline: Rolling

Instructions: Apply for admission online or contact to request application materials

CONTACT

Menlo College
International Student Advisor
1000 El Camino Real
Atherton, CA 94027
Tel: +1 (650) 543-3831
Fax: +1 (650) 543-4496
Email: admission@menlo.edu
Web: www.menlo.edu/offices/international-student-office

Methodist University

Methodist University Presidential Scholarship

PROGRAM INFORMATION

Description: Methodist University offers Presidential Scholarships to incoming freshman and transfer students who meet the eligibility requirements.

Levels of Study: Undergraduate

Field of Study: All

Nationality: Any Region

Location of Study: Methodist University
Fayetteville, NC

AWARD INFORMATION

Award Type: Scholarship, Tuition Reduction

Average Amount: $18,500

Award Coverage: Tuition, room and board

Award Duration: Maximum of 4 years

ELIGIBILITY REQUIREMENTS

- Must have a GPA of 3.1 and above (on 4.0 scale)
- Must submit TOEFL scores of 500 PBT/200 CBT/60 IBT or minimum score of 900 on SAT in Math and Critical Reading sections
- Must submit official academic records

APPLICATION INFORMATION

Instructions: Please submit all required documents in original form, visit our website for more information

CONTACT

Methodist University
International Programs Director
5400 Ramsey Street
Fayetteville, NC 28311
Tel: +1 (910) 630-7042
Fax: +1 (910) 630-7672
Email: lsheppard@methodist.edu
Web: www.methodist.edu/int

Miami University

Miami University Merit Scholarships

PROGRAM INFORMATION

Description: This is a merit-based, competitive scholarship to qualified first-year students. It is renewable for 4 years. Submit all required college application materials on or before the deadline; separate scholarship application form is not required.

Levels of Study: Undergraduate

Field of Study: All

Nationality: Any Region

Location of Study: Miami University
Oxford, OH

AWARD INFORMATION

Award Type: Scholarship
Average Amount: $500-$29,000
Number of Awards: Varies
Award Coverage: Partial tuition and fees
Award Duration: 4 years

ELIGIBILITY REQUIREMENTS

- Must have a US GPA of 3.5 (4.00 grading scale) or the international equivalent
- Must have a minimum SAT I (CR+M) score of 1170, or ACT score of 26
- Must have acceptable proof of English language proficiency (TOEFL or IELTS)
- Must be admitted into a degree program

APPLICATION INFORMATION

Award Deadline: Feb 1
Instructions: Take and submit official test scores on or before Feb 1

CONTACT

Miami University
Assistant Director
301 South Campus Avenue
Oxford, Ohio
Oxford, OH 45056
Tel: +1 (513) 529-2288
Fax: +1 (513) 529-0682
Email: goglobal@miamioh.edu
Web: www.miamioh.edu/apply

Miami University

Miami University Graduate Assistantships

PROGRAM INFORMATION

Description: Students working towards a master's degree, a specialist in education degree, or a doctorate may be awarded an assistantship at the discretion of the academic department. Assistantships provide a tuition waiver for either full, 3-quarter, 1-half, or 1-quarter of the graduate comprehensive fee for the period of appointment. In addition, students receive a stipend amount set by the individual departments, in exchange for work in their academic department. Recipients of Graduate Assistantships are determined by individual academic departments.
Levels of Study: Graduate
Field of Study: All
Nationality: Any Region
Location of Study: Miami University Oxford, OH

AWARD INFORMATION

Award Type: Associateship
Average Amount: Varies
Number of Awards: Varies by department
Award Coverage: Tuition, partial fees, living expenses
Award Duration: Length of graduate degree program

ELIGIBILITY REQUIREMENTS

- Determined by each academic department

APPLICATION INFORMATION

Instructions: Indicate on the international graduate application for admission that you would like to be considered for an assistantship, additional items may be required by the academic department

CONTACT

Miami University
Graduate School
102 Roudebush Hall
Oxford, OH 45056
Tel: +1 (513) 529-3734
Fax: +1 (513) 529-3762
Email: applygrad@miamioh.edu
Web: www.miamioh.edu/graduate-studies/index.html

Miami University

Miami University International Graduate Grants-in-Aid

PROGRAM INFORMATION

Description: F or J status students awarded a Grants-in-Aid will receive a 58 percent tuition waiver for 1 year's total cost of study. There are no duties associated with this aid.
Levels of Study: Graduate
Field of Study: All
Nationality: Any Region
Location of Study: Miami University Oxford, OH

AWARD INFORMATION

Award Type: Grant
Average Amount: $26,000
Number of Awards: 20
Award Coverage: 86 percent of comprehensive fees, and 100 percent of out-of-state surcharge
Award Duration: 1 year, eligible for renewal

ELIGIBILITY REQUIREMENTS

- Must have received an undergraduate degree from an accredited/recognized university
- Must have received admission into a graduate degree program
- Minimum GPA 3.0 out of 4.0
- TOEFL IBT total score equal to or greater than 87, with speaking score of 20. IELTS band score equal to or greater than 7.0, with speaking score of 6.5
- F or J visa

APPLICATION INFORMATION

Award Deadline: Mar
Instructions: Eligible applicants will be automatically reviewed by the Graduate School, there is no separate application.

CONTACT

Miami University Graduate School
Director of International Graduate Admission
501 E High St
102 Roudebush Hall
Oxford, OH 45056
Tel: +1 (513) 529-3734
Fax: +1 (513) 529-3762
Email: applygrad@miamioh.edu
Web: www.miamioh.edu/graduate-studies/index.html

Miami University

Miami University International Education Scholarships

PROGRAM INFORMATION

Description: Competitive, merit-based scholarship program for international degree-seeking students who will enroll at Miami University on an F-1 or J-1 visa. Submit all required application materials on or before the deadline; separate scholarship application form is not necessary.
Levels of Study: Undergraduate
Field of Study: All
Nationality: Any Region
Location of Study: Miami University Oxford, OH

AWARD INFORMATION

Award Type: Scholarship
Average Amount: $6,710
Number of Awards: 500
Award Coverage: Partial tuition and fees
Award Duration: 4 years

ELIGIBILITY REQUIREMENTS

- Must be admitted to a degree program
- Must hold equivalent of US high school diploma with above-average results
- Must have proof of English proficiency (TOEFL, or IELTS)

APPLICATION INFORMATION

Award Deadline: Feb 1
Instructions: Apply for admission on-line at www.miamioh.edu/apply

CONTACT

Miami University
Assistant Director
Office of Admissions
301 South Campus Avenue
Oxford, OH 45056
Tel: +1 (513) 529-2288
Fax: +1 (513) 529-0682
Email: goglobal@miamioh.edu
Web: www.miamioh.edu/apply

Miami University

Miami University MUDEC Scholarships

PROGRAM INFORMATION

Description: Scholarship for students from Luxembourg seeking an undergraduate or graduate degree.
Levels of Study: Undergraduate, Graduate
Field of Study: All
Nationality: Luxembourg
Location of Study: Miami University Oxford, OH

AWARD INFORMATION

Award Type: Scholarship
Average Amount: $16,107-$27,780
Number of Awards: 3-5
Award Coverage: Partial or full tuition
Award Duration: Academic year, renewable as long as academic requirements are met

ELIGIBILITY REQUIREMENTS

- Must hold equivalent of US secondary school diploma (for undergraduate) or bachelor's degree (for graduate) with above-average results
- Must have proof of English proficiency (TOEFL, IELTS, SAT)

APPLICATION INFORMATION

Award Deadline: Mar
Instructions: Contact MUDEC for more information

CONTACT

MUDEC
Assistant to the Director
Chateau de Differedange
1 Impasse de Chateau
L-4524 Differdange
Luxembourg
Email: manesr@miamioh.edu
Web: www.units.muohio.edu/luxembourg

Michigan State University

Michigan State University International Undergraduate Scholarships

PROGRAM INFORMATION

Description: MSU has a comprehensive program of merit scholarships made possible by the generosity of alumni and friends of the university. All admitted students are automatically considered for scholarships.
Levels of Study: Undergraduate
Field of Study: All
Nationality: Any Region
Location of Study: Michigan State University East Lansing, MI

AWARD INFORMATION

Award Type: Scholarship
Average Amount: $1,000-$6,000 per year. Students with exceptional academic records and test scores may be eligible for in-state tuition as well
Number of Awards: Varies
Award Coverage: Tuition
Award Duration: Up to 4 years

ELIGIBILITY REQUIREMENTS

- Must complete application with all supporting documentation
- Strongly encourage submission of SAT or ACT

APPLICATION INFORMATION

Instructions: All admitted students are automatically considered for this scholarship, for optimal consideration, apply for admission by Nov 1; in most cases, the application and required personal statement suffice for scholarship consideration; eligible students will be notified if additional materials are needed; to apply for admission please go to beaspartan.msu.edu

CONTACT

Michigan State University
Office of Admissions
426 Auditorium Road, Room 250
East Lansing, MI 48824
Tel: +1 (517) 355-8332
Fax: +1 (517) 353-1647
Email: admis@msu.edu
Web: admissions.msu.edu

Michigan Technological University

Michigan Technological University International Ambassador Scholarship

PROGRAM INFORMATION

Description: International Ambassador Scholarships are awarded to international students seeking to enroll in a full-time course of undergraduate study. Recipients of the maximum award pay the Michigan resident tuition rate.
Levels of Study: Undergraduate
Field of Study: All
Nationality: Any Region
Location of Study: Michigan Technological University Houghton, MI

AWARD INFORMATION

Award Type: Scholarship
Average Amount: $6,000
Number of Awards: 100 per semester
Award Coverage: Tuition
Award Duration: Up to 4 years

ELIGIBILITY REQUIREMENTS

- Must have record of academic achievement and evidence of leadership
- Must demonstrate English language competency
- Renewable as long as academic requirements are met

APPLICATION INFORMATION

Award Deadline: Rolling
Instructions: Apply for admission online or contact to request application materials

CONTACT

Michigan Technological University
International Programs & Services
1400 Townsend Drive
Houghton, MI 49931
Tel: +1 (906) 487-2160
Fax: +1 (906) 487-1891
Email: ips@mtu.edu
Web: www.mtu.edu/international

Middle Tennessee State University

Middle Tennessee State University Graduate Assistantships

PROGRAM INFORMATION

Description: With an enrollment of more than 25,000 students, MTSU is the largest undergraduate university in the state of Tennessee. With a wide variety of nationally recognized academic degree programs at the baccalaureate, master's, and doctoral levels, MTSU takes pride in educating the best and the brightest students from Tennessee and around the world.
Levels of Study: Graduate, Doctorate
Field of Study: Biochemistry, Biology, Biotechnology, Chemistry, Computer Science, Economics, Education, History, Mathematics, Molecular Biology
Nationality: Any Region
Location of Study: Middle Tennessee State University Murfreesboro, TN

AWARD INFORMATION

Award Type: Associateship
Average Amount: Varies
Number of Awards: Varies
Award Coverage: Tuition, stipend.
Award Duration: Renewable annually for a maximum of 4 years

ELIGIBILITY REQUIREMENTS

- Contact individual departments for requirements.
- TOEFL:- computer-based minimum score 195, paper-based minimum score 525, IBT minimum score 71 (We ONLY accept ETS official test scores for the TOEFL)
- IELTS- overall score of 6 UMELI- minimum score 85 ELS Level 112 Certificate of Completion

APPLICATION INFORMATION

Award Deadline: Mar
Instructions: International students should apply online, information regarding admission requirements and graduate assistantships may be found on the program's website

CONTACT

Middle Tennessee State University
College of Graduate Studies
MTSU Box 42
Murfreesboro, TN 37132
Tel: +1 (615) 898-2840
Fax: +1 (615) 904-8080
Email: graduate@mtsu.edu
Web: www.mtsu.edu/graduate/

Mildred Elley

Mildred Elley International Student Scholarships

PROGRAM INFORMATION

Description: International students may request their applications to be reviewed for scholarship award upon application to the college. Awards generally cover up to 25 percent of the tuition amount. The college's tuition is 1 of the lowest among private colleges in New York and Massachusetts.

Levels of Study: Undergraduate

Field of Study: All

Nationality: Any Region

Location of Study: Mildred Elley College
Albany, NY

AWARD INFORMATION

Award Type: Internship, Scholarship, Tuition Reduction

Average Amount: Varies

Number of Awards: Up to 20

Award Coverage: Tuition

Award Duration: Maximum of 2.5 years

ELIGIBILITY REQUIREMENTS

- Must have a minimum high school GPA of 2.5 out 4.0 or equivalent
- Must demonstrate English proficiency (TOEFL 173 CBT or higher)
- Must maintain 3.0 or higher cumulative GPA throughout duration of studies
- May be required to intern with the college or its community partners

APPLICATION INFORMATION

Award Deadline: Rolling

Instructions: Please contact the Admissions Office for more information

CONTACT

Mildred Elley
Office of Financial Aid
855 Central Avenue
Albany, NY 12206
Tel: +1 (518) 786-0855
Fax: +1 (518) 786-0011
Email: admissions-albany@mildred-elley.edu
Web: www.mildred-elley.edu

Mills College

Mills College Merit Scholarships

PROGRAM INFORMATION

Description: Undergraduate international students may be eligible for a Mills College merit-based scholarship. The scholarship award is based on academic performance, examination results, and the results of standardized tests. All undergraduate students who submit an admissions application and all required credentials by the published deadlines are considered for the scholarship.

Levels of Study: Undergraduate

Field of Study: All

Nationality: Any Region

Location of Study: Mills College
Oakland, CA

AWARD INFORMATION

Award Type: Scholarship

Average Amount: $10,000-$22,000

Number of Awards: Varies

Award Coverage: Partial tuition

Award Duration: Maximum of 4 years

ELIGIBILITY REQUIREMENTS

- The merit scholarship awards are based on academic performance, school examination results and the results of standardized tests; there is no separate application form, admissions application and supporting documents are used to determine scholarship eligibility.
- Must submit official SAT or ACT results (first year applicants)
- Must submit official TOEFL or IELTS results

APPLICATION INFORMATION

Award Deadline: Jan 15

Instructions: Must submit the admissions application using the Common Application at commonapp.org and all supporting documents, for more information on our application process, go to www.mills.edu/international

CONTACT

Mills College
Office of Admissions
5000 MacArthur Blvd.
Oakland, CA 94613
Tel: +1 (510) 430-2135
Fax: +1 (510) 430-3298
Email: admission@mills.edu
Web: www.mills.edu/international

Minnesota State University Moorhead

Minnesota State University International Student Scholarships

PROGRAM INFORMATION

Description: Multiple scholarships are offered to upper class international students of Minnesota State University. These scholarships are awarded to students who maintain a high GPA and who engage in apprentice relations with their department. The Marjorie Sanders Scholarship is available to incoming African students who are seeing their first undergraduate degree.

Levels of Study: Undergraduate

Field of Study: All

Nationality: Any Region

Location of Study: Minnesota State University Moorhead
Moorhead, MN

AWARD INFORMATION

Award Type: Scholarship

Average Amount: Varies

Number of Awards: Varies

Award Coverage: Tuition reduction

Award Duration: up to 4.5 years of enrollment

ELIGIBILITY REQUIREMENTS

- All new international students MUST attend mandatory international student orientation (all the assigned days) during their first semester. Please check the international student orientation page for more information
- Standard academic progress: this is defined as maintaining a 2.0 Cumulative GPA
- Contribute 10 hours of volunteer work per semester, a minimum of 3 volunteer hours must be at MSU Moorhead event on or off-campus, only professional staff and graduate assistants can sign as supervisors on the volunteer hour form NOT your friend or students from other campuses

APPLICATION INFORMATION

Award Deadline: Commencement Day of each term

Instructions: Visit website or contact to request application materials

CONTACT

Minnesota State University Moorhead
International Student Services
1104 7th Ave South
Moorhead, MN 56563
Tel: +1 (218) 477-2956
Fax: +1 (218) 477-5928
Email: international@mnstate.edu
Web: www.mnstate.edu/international

Minnesota State University, Mankato

Cultural Contribution Resident Tuition Scholarship

PROGRAM INFORMATION

Description: Minnesota State University, Mankato's environment of big ideas, global solutions, and real world thinking equips students to go beyond expectations and into exciting, rewarding futures. New international students receive an in-state, resident tuition scholarship that can be renewed each semester. Each year the university is selected to host US Government-sponsored students on Fulbright, IREX, BSMP, and other scholarship programs.

Levels of Study: Undergraduate, Graduate, Doctorate

Field of Study: All

Nationality: Any Region

Location of Study: Minnesota State University Mankato, MN

AWARD INFORMATION

Award Type: Tuition Reduction

Average Amount: Varies

Number of Awards: Available to all F-1 & J-1 students

Award Coverage: Resident in-state tuition rates

Award Duration: Undergraduate: 4.5 years; graduate: 2.5 years

ELIGIBILITY REQUIREMENTS

- Awarded to all new international admits their first semester
- Maintain specific GPA and 25-hour cultural contribution requirement each term to maintain the resident tuition each subsequent semester

APPLICATION INFORMATION

Award Deadline: Rolling

Instructions: Scholarship awarded automatically with either undergraduate (bachelor's) or graduate (master's/doctoral) admission

CONTACT

Minnesota State University, Mankato
Elizabeth and Wynn Kearney International Center
250 Centennial Student Union
Mankato, MN 56001
Tel: +1 (507) 389-1281
Fax: +1 (507) 389-2790
Email: isss@mnsu.edu
Web: www.mnsu.edu/international/scholarship/instate.html

Monmouth College

Monmouth College International Merit Scholarships

PROGRAM INFORMATION

Description: Monmouth College offers the International Merit Scholarship to qualified undergraduate international students. Awards are based upon the academic strength, leadership capacity, and future potential of each applicant. Financial assistance is awarded only after a student has been officially accepted into Monmouth.

Levels of Study: Undergraduate

Field of Study: All

Nationality: Any Region

Location of Study: Monmouth College Monmouth, IL

AWARD INFORMATION

Award Type: Scholarship

Average Amount: $21,000

Number of Awards: 40

Award Coverage: Tuition

Award Duration: 4 years

ELIGIBILITY REQUIREMENTS

- Must complete the application process and be accepted into Monmouth College
- Must submit official copies of all transcripts/grade reports from each institution attended
- Must submit official copies of TOEFL or IELTS scores sent directly to Monmouth College (if the applicant's first language is not English); this is waived with IB, A-level, or English-medium high school diploma or exam results
- Students with external scholarships or private or governmental sponsorship should provide documentation of the award or the Sponsor's Affidavit of Support and copy of bank statement

APPLICATION INFORMATION

Award Deadline: Rolling

Instructions: See www.monmouthcollege.edu/admissions/international for guidelines to the application process at Monmouth College, you will find a link to an information page for international students here, and much more

CONTACT

Monmouth College
Associate Dean for Academic Affairs and Director of International Recruitment
700 East Broadway
Monmouth, IL 61462
Tel: +1 (309) 457-2277
Fax: +1 (309) 457-2335
Email: international@monmouthcollege.edu
Web: www.monmouthcollege.edu/admissions/international

Monmouth College

Monmouth College Undergraduate Scholarships for Syrian Students

PROGRAM INFORMATION

Description: Monmouth College is pleased to offer 1 full tuition scholarship and up to 8 partial tuition scholarships to academically-strong Syrian students.

Levels of Study: Undergraduate

Field of Study: All

Nationality: Syria

Location of Study: Monmouth College Monmouth, IL

AWARD INFORMATION

Award Type: Scholarship

Average Amount: Varies

Number of Awards: 9

Award Coverage: The College will award 1 full scholarship (tuition waivers) to an academically outstanding Syrian student, the College will reserve merit scholarships ($21,000 tuition waivers/year) for Syrian students and will have up to 8 of these available

Award Duration: 2 years or more

ELIGIBILITY REQUIREMENTS

- SAT scores of at least 1100 (ACT 24+) or other clear documentation of academic achievement (high TOEFL or IETLS scores and strong high school grades in rigorous classes, for example)
- TOEFL scores must be at least 80 IBT/550 PBT. IELTS score must be at least 6
- Scholarships are offered to students upon their admission to Monmouth College
- All undergraduate scholarships for Syrian students require documentation of academic achievement and future promise (course records/transcripts; letter of recommendation from an EducationUSA advisor or high school teacher or counselor)

APPLICATION INFORMATION

Award Deadline: Rolling

Instructions: Visit our website at www.monmouthcollege.edu/admissions/international for more information

CONTACT

Monmouth College
Associate Dean for Academic Affairs
700 East Broadway
Monmouth, IL 61462
Tel: +1 (309) 457-2277
Fax: +1 (309) 457-2335
Email: btooley@monmouthcollege.edu
Web: www.monmouthcollege.edu/admissions/international/

Monmouth University

Monmouth University Academic Excellence and Graduate Scholarships

PROGRAM INFORMATION

Description: Scholarship opportunities are available at the undergraduate and graduate levels. Undergraduate awards range from $2,000 to $17,000 and are based on a student's cumulative GPA and test scores. Graduate students awards are based on cumulative GPA and the number of credits taken each semester.

Levels of Study: Undergraduate, Graduate

Field of Study: All

Nationality: Any Region

Location of Study: Monmouth University West Long Branch, NJ

AWARD INFORMATION

Award Type: Scholarship

Average Amount: $2,000-$17,000 for undergraduate students; varies for graduate students

Number of Awards: Varies

Award Coverage: Partial tuition

Award Duration: Academic year, renewable as long as academic requirements are met

ELIGIBILITY REQUIREMENTS

- Undergraduates: Minimum score: TOEFL of 550 PBT/213 CBT/79 IBT; 6 IELTS; 77 MELAB; B2 CAE; minimum combined SAT score of 1400 (3 sections); must hold equivalent of secondary school diploma
- Graduate students: Must have minimum undergraduate grade point average of 3.0 on a 4.0 scale. Minimum score: TOEFL - 550 PBT/213 CBT/79 IBT: 6 IELTS; 77 MELAB; B2 CAE

APPLICATION INFORMATION

Award Deadline: Undergraduates: Jun for fall semester, Nov for spring semester; Graduates: Jul for fall semester, Nov for spring semester

Instructions: Apply for admission online or contact the admissions office to request application materials

CONTACT

Monmouth University
Assistant Director of Undergraduate Admission
400 Cedar Avenue
West Long Branch, NJ 07764
Tel: +1 (732) 263-5869
Fax: +1 (732) 263-5166
Email: ortiz-torres@monmouth.edu
Web: www.monmouth.edu/international

Montana State University

MSU Freshman Achievement Scholarships

PROGRAM INFORMATION

Description: Montana State University will offer millions of dollars in scholarships to non-resident freshmen who apply for admission in the fall and have a minimum total score of a 1560 on the SAT or 23 on the ACT.

Levels of Study: Undergraduate

Field of Study: All

Nationality: Any Region

Location of Study: Montana State University Bozeman, MT

AWARD INFORMATION

Award Type: Scholarship

Average Amount: $8,000-$50,000

Number of Awards: Unlimited

Award Coverage: Partial tuition

Award Duration: Academic year, renewable for up to 4 years

ELIGIBILITY REQUIREMENTS

- $8,000 Achievement Award ($2,000 per year renewable for 4 years): SAT score 1560-1610 or ACT score 23. $10,000 Achievement Award ($2,500 per year renewable for 4 years): SAT score 1620-1670 or ACT score 24
- $14,000 Achievement Award ($3,500 per year renewable for 4 years): SAT score 1680-1730 or ACT score 25. $16,000 Achievement Award ($4,000 per year renewable for 4 years): SAT score 1740-1790 or ACT score 26
- $20,000 Achievement Award ($5,000 per year renewable for 4 years): SAT score 1800-1850 or ACT score 27. $24,000 Achievement Award ($6,000 per year renewable for 4 years): SAT score 1860-1910 or ACT score 28
- $30,000 Achievement Scholarship ($7,500 per year renewable for 4 years): SAT score 1920-2130 or ACT 29-32. $50,000 Achievement Award ($12,500 per year renewable for 4 years): SAT score 2140 and higher or ACT of 33 and higher
- Must be entering as a freshman with no previous college study

APPLICATION INFORMATION

Award Deadline: Aug

Instructions: Apply to the university and then request that your SAT or ACT scores be sent directly to MSU; your score will automatically determine the scholarship amount to be awarded once we receive it; MSU will take your best SAT/ACT score up until the day classes begin

CONTACT

Montana State University
Director for International Student and Scholar Services
Office of International Programs
400 Culbertson Hall
Bozeman, MT 59717-2260
Tel: +1 (406) 994-4031
Fax: +1 (406) 994-1619
Email: globalstudy@montana.edu
Web: www.montana.edu/international/admissions/scholarshipsfresh.htm

Montana State University

MSU Office of International Programs Scholarship

PROGRAM INFORMATION

Description: All international undergraduate applicants will automatically be considered for new student scholarships valued at up to $4,000. These scholarships are available to qualified international students, freshmen or transfer, applying to begin their studies either fall or spring semester. Documents required in the international undergraduate application will determine eligibility, and no separate scholarship application is required. SAT exam score results are not required to compete for these scholarships. These scholarships are available only to new students during their first year of study at MSU and are renewable, depending on availability of funds and student achievement at MSU demonstrated with a CGPA of at least 3.0/4.0. Selection is based on previous academic achievement, test scores, potential for success at MSU, and overall fit with the institution and its academic programs. Scholarships will be available until all are awarded; therefore, students are encouraged to submit their MSU application early.

Levels of Study: Undergraduate

Field of Study: All

Nationality: Any Region

Location of Study: Montana State University Bozeman, MT

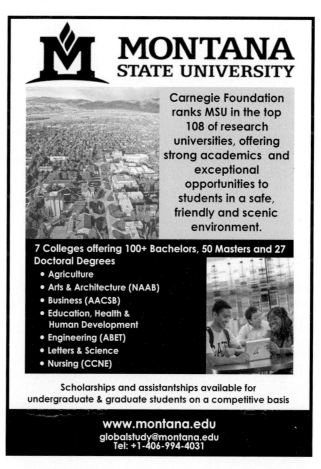

AWARD INFORMATION

Award Type: Scholarship
Average Amount: up to $3,500
Number of Awards: Approx 50 per semester
Award Coverage: Partial tuition
Award Duration: Academic year

ELIGIBILITY REQUIREMENTS

- Must have a minimum equivalent cumulative grade point average of 3.0/4.0 scale or 80 percent or "very good" or "B" in A = excellent system

APPLICATION INFORMATION

Award Deadline: May 15 for fall semester, Oct 15 for spring semester
Instructions: All undergraduate international students are automatically considered for this scholarship based on their MSU application, no special application is necessary

CONTACT

Montana State University
International Representative
Office of International Programs
400 Culbertson Hall
Bozeman, MT 59717-2260
Tel: +1 (406) 994-6462
Fax: +1 (406) 994-1619
Email: globalstudy@montana.edu
Web: www.montana.edu/international/admissions/scholarshipstransfer.htm

Montclair State University
Montclair State University Graduate Assistantship

PROGRAM INFORMATION

Description: The Office of Graduate Admissions & Support Services offers approximately 200 assistantships for first-time master's and doctoral degree students who are interested in an opportunity to gain an academic experience that directly complements the student's degree program curriculum. All assistantships are diverse in nature and encompass a wide variety of responsibilities and duties while allowing students to also achieve their academic goals. Assistantships will offer opportunities to work with faculty on research, assist faculty with instructional support, and/or be related to the student's clinical or field work.
Levels of Study: Graduate, Doctorate
Field of Study: All
Nationality: Any Region
Location of Study: Montclair State University Montclair, NJ

AWARD INFORMATION

Award Type: Associateship
Average Amount: Varies
Number of Awards: Varies
Award Coverage: Covers full tuition; monthly stipend paycheck in exchange for 20 hours work per week
Award Duration: Master's students: maximum 2 years; doctoral students: maximum 3 years

ELIGIBILITY REQUIREMENTS

- Must be fully matriculated in a master's or doctoral degree program at MSU
- Must be a full-time student, maintaining a minimum of 9 credits per semester, maximum of 12 credits per semester
- Must maintain at least a 3.0 GPA during each semester of the assistantship
- Must fulfill 20 hours per week of assigned on-campus work during the academic year

APPLICATION INFORMATION

Award Deadline: Feb
Instructions: Master's students should be sure to mark the appropriate area on the graduate admission application if interested in a graduate assistantship; doctoral students must complete a separate assistantship application; graduate assistantships will be considered as part of the admission process to a graduate master's degree program; applying early is recommended. For complete instructions visit our website

CONTACT

Montclair State University
1 Normal Avenue
Montclair, NJ 07043
Tel: +1 (973) 655-5147
Fax: +1 (973) 655-7869
Email: graduate.school@montclair.edu
Web: www.montclair.edu

Montclair State University
Montclair State University Freshman Merit Scholarships

PROGRAM INFORMATION

Description: The Office of Undergraduate Admissions is pleased to present these merit-based scholarships to a select number of international freshman applicants who receive the required scores on the SAT or ACT. Please note that all GPA requirements are based on a standard 4.0 scale. Consideration for these scholarships is automatic upon applying. Official letters of notification will be sent out to students who have already applied.
Levels of Study: Undergraduate
Field of Study: All
Nationality: Any Region
Location of Study: Montclair State University Montclair, NJ

AWARD INFORMATION

Award Type: Scholarship
Average Amount: Varies
Number of Awards: Limited
Award Coverage: Tuition
Award Duration: Maximum 4 years

ELIGIBILITY REQUIREMENTS

- $5,000 a year for 8 sequential, full-time semesters (student must maintain a 3.25 GPA at Montclair State): applicant must have attained a 3.5 secondary school GPA and a combined SAT score of 1800 or ACT score of 26
- $10,000 a year for 8 sequential semesters (student must maintain a 3.25 GPA at Montclair State): applicant must have attained a 3.75 secondary school GPA and a combined SAT score of 1850 or ACT score of 27
- Please note: meeting the eligibility requirements described above does not guarantee awarding of a merit scholarship, the admissions committee reviews each application holistically

APPLICATION INFORMATION

Award Deadline: Admission application deadline
Instructions: For more information on how to apply, please visit the website

CONTACT

Montclair State University
Undergraduate Admissions Office
1 Normal Avenue
Montclair, NJ 07043
Tel: +1 (973) 655-4444
Fax: +1 (973) 655-7700
Email: msuadm@mail.montclair.edu
Web: www.montclair.edu/global-education/international-services/resources/financial-information/visa-application/freshman-merit-scholarship/

Montclair State University
Montclair State University International Partner Award

PROGRAM INFORMATION

Description: The MSU International Partner Award is available to any student who comes to MSU from a partner institution abroad. Students from partner schools receive a 35 percent tuition discount.
Levels of Study: Undergraduate, Graduate, Doctorate
Field of Study: All
Nationality: Australia, Austria, China, Japan, Korea, Republic of, Mexico, Norway, Russia, Slovakia, Spain, Thailand, Ukraine
Location of Study: Montclair State University Montclair, NJ

AWARD INFORMATION

Award Type: Tuition Reduction
Average Amount: 35 percent discount
Number of Awards: Unlimited
Award Coverage: Tuition
Award Duration: Duration of studies

ELIGIBILITY REQUIREMENTS

- Must be a graduate with a bachelor's or a master's degree from 1 of Montclair State University's Global Partner Schools, for a complete list of global partner schools, please visit the website
- Must apply and be admitted into a degree program at Montclair State University
- Must maintain the minimum academic requirements for retention in the program

APPLICATION INFORMATION

Award Deadline: Varies

Instructions: Download and complete the application on our website. Email the completed application

CONTACT

Montclair State University
International Services
22 Normal Avenue
Montclair, NJ 07043
Tel: +1 (973) 655-6862
Fax: +1 (973) 655-7726
Email: international.services@montclair.edu
Web: www.montclair.edu

Monterey Institute of International Studies

Graduate School of International Policy and Management Merit Scholarship

PROGRAM INFORMATION

Description: At the Graduate School of International Policy and Management (GSIPM), over 45 percent of our student body is comprised of international students and nearly all GSIPM students have professional experience abroad. We emphasize immersive and open-architectural learning inside and outside of the classroom. Opportunities for field experience are plentiful through our practica, International Professional Service Semester, Development Project Management Institute, the International Business Plan, and the GLOBE Center. In addition, our students receive individualized career advice from the Center for Advising and Career Services. Professional master's degrees are offered in nonproliferation & terrorism studies, MPA, international policy studies (with tracks in human security and development or trade, investment & development), international environmental policy and MBA.

Levels of Study: Graduate

Field of Study: Business and Management, Environmental Policy, International Development, International Management, Master of Business Administration (MBA)

Nationality: Any Region

Location of Study: Monterey Institute of International Studies Monterey, CA

AWARD INFORMATION

Award Type: Scholarship

Average Amount: Varies

Number of Awards: Awarded by merit

Award Duration: 2 years

ELIGIBILITY REQUIREMENTS

- We consider all admitted applicants for the Monterey Institute Merit Scholarship, a separate application is not required
- Must be admitted to a degree program at the Monterey Institute to qualify

APPLICATION INFORMATION

Award Deadline: Fall semester: Dec 1, Feb 1, Mar 15

Instructions: We carefully examine both past academic performance and professional experience in assessing candidates to our programs, we do not adhere to a strict formula for admission, each year we strive to enroll candidates with strong intellectual and professional backgrounds who will add to the diverse and international community on our campus, please see our website for full application details

CONTACT

Monterey Institute of International Studies
Recruiting Department
460 Pierce St.
Monterey, CA 93940
Tel: +1 (831) 647-4123
Web: www.miis.edu/academics/programs/gsipm

Monterey Institute of International Studies

Monterey Institute of International Studies Merit Scholarship

PROGRAM INFORMATION

Description: Located in Monterey, California, the Monterey Institute was founded in 1955 with a mission of improving international understanding through education in languages, cross-cultural communications, and a detailed study of the complex relations between nations and peoples. In its first 5 decades, the Institute has grown to become a unique and irreplaceable training ground for professionals in specialized fields crucial to the international community. Our graduates go forth to become diplomats, negotiators, business leaders, language teachers, translators and interpreters, and other key players in today's global environment. No other institution of higher learning covers the same ground or turns out a more important cadre of trained professionals.

Levels of Study: Undergraduate, Graduate

Field of Study: Accounting, Asian Studies, Business and Management, Conflict Management, Conflict Resolution, Economics, Education, Environmental Studies, Finance, Foreign Languages, French, Human Rights, Intensive English, International Development, International Education, International Management, International Relations, Management, Marketing, Political Science, Public Administration, Public Policy, Spanish, TESOL, US Foreign Policy, Women's Studies

Nationality: Any Region

Location of Study: Monterey Institute of International Studies Monterey, CA

AWARD INFORMATION

Award Type: Scholarship

Average Amount: $4,000-$16,000

Number of Awards: Varies

Award Coverage: Tuition

Award Duration: 1-2 years

ELIGIBILITY REQUIREMENTS

- Varies based on scholarship

APPLICATION INFORMATION

Award Deadline: Rolling

Instructions: Visit our website at www.miis.edu/admissions/financialaid/scholarships for information on our merit-based scholarships

CONTACT

Monterey Institute of International Studies
Admission Office
460 Pierce Street
Monterey, CA 93940
Tel: +1 (831) 647-4123
Fax: +1 (831) 647-6405
Email: admit@miis.edu
Web: www.miis.edu

Monterey Institute of International Studies

The FUHU-Danish Scholarship

PROGRAM INFORMATION

Description: This half-tuition scholarship is made available by collaboration between the Monterey Institute of International Studies and FUHU-IA.

Levels of Study: Graduate

Field of Study: Master of Business Administration (MBA)

Nationality: Denmark

Location of Study: Monterey Institute of International Studies Monterey, CA

AWARD INFORMATION

Award Type: Scholarship

Average Amount: Half tuition

Number of Awards: Varies

Award Coverage: Tuition

ELIGIBILITY REQUIREMENTS

- Available to all qualified residents of Denmark and people closely associated with Danish businesses and/or organizations
- The scholarship can only be used toward obtaining an MBA degree at the Monterey Institute

APPLICATION INFORMATION

Award Deadline: Rolling

Instructions: To apply to the Monterey Institute MBA program and the FUHU International Alumni Scholarship, you must submit the following documents to the Monterey Institute Admissions Office: completed application for admission; official transcripts showing courses, grades, and diploma earned and date (in English); GMAT score; TOEFL score; 2 letters of recommendation; resume or CV

CONTACT

Monterey Institute of International Studies
460 Pierce Street
Monterey, CA 93940
Tel: +1 (831) 647-4123
Fax: +1 (831) 647-6405
Email: admit@miis.edu
Web: www.miis.edu

Monterey Institute of International Studies

Monterey Institute of International Studies Kathryn Davis Fellowship for Peace

PROGRAM INFORMATION

Description: The Monterey Institute of International Studies is pleased to announce full fellowships or attend Middlebury Language Schools. These fellowships link 2 affiliated institutions known internationally for language and international study: the Monterey Institute and Middlebury College. These fellowships are made possible by a gift from Kathryn Davis to address today's critical need for more effective language proficiency. This intense study, equivalent to a full year of college-level language learning, will allow students to enhance language skills to meet enrollment prerequisites at the Monterey Institute. Fellowships for Peace recipients will be chosen on the basis of academic credentials, experience, and commitment to building a more peaceful world.

Levels of Study: Undergraduate, Graduate

Field of Study: Conflict Resolution, Foreign Languages, International Development, International Management, International Relations, Peace Studies, Public Administration, Security and Protective Services

Location of Study: The Monterey Institute of International Studies

AWARD INFORMATION

Award Type: Fellowship

Number of Awards: 100

Award Coverage: Tuition, room, board

Award Duration: Summer (3 months)

ELIGIBILITY REQUIREMENTS

- Must be admitted for fall to a degree program in international policy, international business, or teaching a foreign language
- Teaching foreign language students must be at a minimum of the fourth year of college-level study of their desired teaching language
- By the time of enrollment at the Monterey Institute in fall, students must demonstrate that they meet the language proficiency requirements for their program of study

APPLICATION INFORMATION

Award Deadline: Jan 14

Instructions: Visit our website for more information

CONTACT

Monterey Institute of International Studies
Admissions Office
460 Pierce Street
Monterey, CA 93940
Tel: +1 (831) 647-4123
Email: admit@miis.edu
Web: www.miis.edu/admissions/financialaid/scholarships/davis

Monterey Institute of International Studies

Betty and David Jones Scholarship

PROGRAM INFORMATION

Description: The Monterey Institute seeks individuals committed to rigorous language study, master's-degree training, and professional skill development to address global issues of development, international commerce, environmental preservation, nuclear nonproliferation, and other critical issues of our time. The Betty and David Jones scholarships offer students the opportunity to take advantage of the combined language and international study resources of the Monterey Institute and Middlebury Language Schools. To be eligible for the Betty and David Jones scholarships, candidates must be admitted to a degree program at the Monterey Institute of International Studies. Scholarship recipients will be chosen on the basis of academic credentials, experience, and commitment to building a more peaceful world.

Levels of Study: Undergraduate, Graduate, Professional

Field of Study: Conflict Resolution, Economics, Environmental Policy, Environmental Studies, Foreign Languages, Intensive English, International Development, International Education, International Management, International Relations, Management, Master of Business Administration (MBA), Natural Resources and Conservation, Ocean and Resource Management, Policy Research, Political Science, Public Administration, Public Policy, TESOL, Translation and Interpretation, US Foreign Policy

Nationality: Any Region

Location of Study: Monterey Institute of International Studies Monterey, CA

AWARD INFORMATION

Award Type: Scholarship

Number of Awards: Up to 50 Scholarships

Award Coverage: 2 types of Awards: Scholarships for tuition, room and board will be awarded for the Middlebury Language Schools program; scholarships for tuition only will be awarded for the Monterey Institute Summer Intensive Language Program or the English Preparation for Graduate Students Program

Award Duration: Duration of Language Program

ELIGIBILITY REQUIREMENTS

- By the time of enrollment in a degree program at the Monterey Institute, students must demonstrate that they meet the language proficiency requirements for their program of study
- For the following degrees: MBA, MAIPS, MAIEP, MAIEM, MPA, MANPTS, BAIS— students are required to be at the following levels by the time of enrollment at the Monterey Institute: Arabic and Spanish: ready to begin studies at the second college level minimum; Chinese (Mandarin), English, French, Japanese, and Russian: ready to begin studies at the third-year college level
- Teaching Foreign Language students must be at the minimum fourth year college-level in their desired teaching language
- 1 summer of intensive language training is the equivalent of 1 full year of college language study during the regular academic year for Spanish and French; and is the equivalent of at least 1 semester of college language study for Arabic, Chinese, Japanese, Russian; students who successfully complete their summer language studies should meet the Monterey Institute entry requirements
- Note that before the first semester begins, students must pass a placement test that indicates the student is ready to begin studies at the appropriate level

APPLICATION INFORMATION

Award Deadline: Feb 1

Instructions: Applicants to the Betty & David Jones Language Scholarship must submit the following in order to be considered for the scholarship: complete the application form online for the Jones Language Scholarship by Feb 1, submit a complete application to a Monterey Institute degree program by Feb 1 (For Monterey Institute degree program application, go to www.miis.edu/admissions/apply/instructions; all application materials must be received (not postmarked) by Feb 1

CONTACT

Admissions
460 Pierce St.
MIIS OFFICE SERVICES
Monterey, CA 93940
Tel: +1 (831) 647-4123
Email: admit@miis.edu
Web: www.miis.edu/admissions/financialaid/scholarships/jones

Murray State University

Murray State University International Leadership Scholarship

PROGRAM INFORMATION

Description: Murray State University, founded in 1922, is a public university offering 118 bachelor's and master's programs. The university receives high rankings for its academic excellence and low tuition fees. As an international student, you will feel welcome in the city of Murray which is 1 of the friendliest and safest places in America.

Levels of Study: Undergraduate, Graduate

Field of Study: All

Nationality: Any Region

Location of Study: Murray State University Murray, KY

AWARD INFORMATION

Award Type: Scholarship

Average Amount: $11,500

Number of Awards: 5 per year

Award Coverage: Tuition

Award Duration: 4 years for undergrads, 2 years for graduate students

ELIGIBILITY REQUIREMENTS

- Must write a 500 word essay describing community service experience and past leadership roles in community or school activities
- Must obtain a minimum of 2 letters of recommendation

APPLICATION INFORMATION

Award Deadline: Mar 15 for fall admission; Sept 15 for spring admission

Instructions: Complete application and email required documents to msu.intl@murraystate.edu

CONTACT

Murray State University
International Admissions
168 Woods Hall
Murray, KY 42071
Tel: 270-809-4223
Email: msu.intl@murraystate.edu
Web: www.murraystate.edu/iis

Murray State University

Murray State University English as a Second Language Scholarship

PROGRAM INFORMATION

Description: The International ESL Scholarship is available for all international students who take the ESL program at Murray State University for at least 1 term prior to their degree program of study.

Levels of Study: Undergraduate, Graduate

Field of Study: All

Nationality: Any Region

Location of Study: Murray State University
Murray, KY

AWARD INFORMATION

Award Type: Tuition Reduction

Average Amount: $4,000 for Undergraduates, $2,000 for Graduates

Number of Awards: Unlimited

Award Coverage: Tuition

Award Duration: 4 years for undergrads, 2 years for graduate students

APPLICATION INFORMATION

Award Deadline: No Deadline

Instructions: Automatically awarded to student that complete 1 term of intensive English language study before beginning their bachelor's or master's degree

CONTACT

Murray State University
International Admissions
168 Woods Hall
Murray, KY 42071
Tel: 270-809-4223
Email: msu.intl@murraystate.edu
Web: www.murraystate.edu/iis

Neumann University

Neumann University Presidential Scholarships

PROGRAM INFORMATION

Description: These scholarships are awarded based on a student's cumulative high school GPA.

Levels of Study: Undergraduate

Field of Study: All

Nationality: Any Region

Location of Study: Neumann University
Aston, PA

AWARD INFORMATION

Award Type: Scholarship

Average Amount: $8,500-$12,500

Number of Awards: Unlimited

Award Coverage: Tuition

Award Duration: Up to 4 years

ELIGIBILITY REQUIREMENTS

- Must have cumulative GPA of 3.5 or higher to receive the full $12,500 scholarship
- Must have cumulative GPA of 3.0-3.49 to receive $10,500 scholarship
- Must have cumulative GPA of 2.0-2.99 to receive $8,500 scholarship
- Must meet regular admissions standards

APPLICATION INFORMATION

Award Deadline: Jul

Instructions: Apply online at www.neumann.edu

CONTACT

Neumann University
Coordinator, International Studies Education
1 Neumann Drive
Aston, PA 19014
Tel: +1 (610) 558-5616
Fax: +1 (610) 361-5214
Email: neumann@neumann.edu
Web: www.neumann.edu

New School University

New School International Student Fellowships and Scholarships

PROGRAM INFORMATION

Description: International students are eligible for various fellowships and scholarships. Some scholarships are available to applicants from specific countries. See website for list of awards.

Levels of Study: Graduate

Field of Study: Social Science

Nationality: Any Region

Location of Study: The New School for Social Research
New York, NY

AWARD INFORMATION

Award Type: Fellowship, Scholarship

Average Amount: Varies

Award Coverage: Varies by award

Award Duration: Academic year

ELIGIBILITY REQUIREMENTS

- Vary by award. Contact or go to the website for more information

APPLICATION INFORMATION

Award Deadline: Dec

Instructions: Download application materials, for most scholarships and fellowships there is no separate application, check website for information on specific awards and notify your prospective academic department

CONTACT

The New School
Director of Admissions, The New School for Social Research
72 Fifth Avenue, 3rd Floor
Room 101
New York, NY 10011
Tel: +1 (800) 862-5039
Fax: +1 (212) 627-2695
Email: SocialResearchAdmit@newschool.edu
Web: www.newschool.edu/nssr/subpage.aspx?id=14574

New York Film Academy

New York Film Academy Grants and Scholarships

PROGRAM INFORMATION

Description: The New York Film Academy offers the most hands-on and intensive programs in the world. NYFA offers Master of Fine Arts, Master of Arts, Bachelor of Fine Arts, and Associate of Fine Arts degree programs. Additionally, the Academy offers 1 and 2-Year Conservatory Programs NYFA offers need-based tuition assistance and talent-based scholarships to qualified international students.

Levels of Study: Undergraduate, Graduate, Professional

Field of Study: Film, Photography, Visual and Performing Arts

Nationality: Any Region

Location of Study: New York Film Academy
New York, NY

AWARD INFORMATION

Award Type: Grant, Scholarship

Average Amount: $2,500-$15,000

Number of Awards: Unlimited

Award Coverage: Tuition

Award Duration: Maximum of 3 years

ELIGIBILITY REQUIREMENTS

- Tuition Assistance is determined based on financial need. Completion of a NYFA Tuition Assistance application is required
- Household financial information is required for dependent students
- Must submit an essay discussing the household financial situation and a specific financial need for tuition assistance is required. Please include information about how the remaining tuition balance will be paid
- Students applying for performance-based programs must submit an audition via YouTube links to admissions@nyfa.edu

APPLICATION INFORMATION

Award Deadline: Within 60 days from application

Instructions: All applicants requesting tuition assistance must complete the NYFA Tuition Assistance Application available from www.nyfa.edu/admissions/financial_aid.php; performing arts students must then submit an audition via YouTube links to admissions@nyfa.edu

CONTACT

New York Film Academy
Director of Financial Aid
100 East 17th Street
New York, NY 10003
Tel: +1 (212) 674-4300
Fax: +1 (212) 477-1414
Email: financialaid@nyfa.edu
Web: www.nyfa.edu

New York University School of Law

Hauser Global Scholars Program

PROGRAM INFORMATION

Description: The Hauser Global Scholarship is the most prestigious honor awarded to exceptional LLM students. The Hauser Global Scholars reflect the breadth, diversity and achievement of NYU School of Law's graduate student body. Scholars are chosen on the basis of their intellectual and leadership ability and their capacity to participate productively in a global community of scholars and practitioners. Hauser Global Scholar candidates must be graduates of a law school outside of the US.

Levels of Study: Graduate

Field of Study: Law

Nationality: Any Region

Location of Study: New York University New York, NY

AWARD INFORMATION

Award Type: Scholarship

Average Amount: Varies

Number of Awards: Varies

Award Coverage: Full tuition and reasonable living expenses

Award Duration: Academic year

ELIGIBILITY REQUIREMENTS

- Must be graduates of a law school outside of the US
- The Committee requires that applicants who take the TOEFL achieve a minimum total score of at least 100, for applicants who take the IELTS, the Committee requires a minimum overall band score of at least a 7

APPLICATION INFORMATION

Award Deadline: Dec

Instructions: Apply online via the NYU application available on LSAC; in addition to completing the application for admission to the full-time LLM program (including a personal statement), candidates must electronically attach to their online application an essay of 500 to 750 words that briefly describes a current legal dilemma, controversy, or issue facing a country, a region, or the world, and suggests a strategy to address the problem

CONTACT

New York University
Office of Graduate Admissions
139 MacDougal Street
Suite C-10
New York, NY 10012
Tel: +1 (212) 998-6060
Fax: +1 (212) 995-4883
Email: law.grad.moreinfo@nyu.edu
Web: www.law.nyu.edu/llmjsd

Niagara University

Niagara University Scholarships, Grants, and Assistantships

PROGRAM INFORMATION

Description: Located in Western New York, nestled between the city of Buffalo and Niagara Falls, Niagara University welcomes students from around the world and is appreciative of the contributions and diversity they bring to our campus. Niagara University offers 4 year merit-based scholarships, achievement awards and grants to incoming first year international undergraduate students. For graduate students, Niagara University offers assistantships in various departments.

Levels of Study: Undergraduate, Graduate

Nationality: Any Region

Location of Study: Niagara University Niagara Falls, NY

AWARD INFORMATION

Award Type: Award, Fellowship, Grant, Scholarship

Average Amount: Varies

Number of Awards: Varies

Award Coverage: Tuition, monthly stipend

Award Duration: Maximum of 4 years

ELIGIBILITY REQUIREMENTS

- Must complete the following: Complete an approved application, accompanied by a $30 processing fee
- Native English speakers: submit SAT or ACT scores; Nonnative English Speakers: submit a TOEFL exam and SAT or ACT; Transcripts: if you live in an English-speaking country or attend an American or English-speaking school abroad, you can directly submit all of your secondary school and college transcripts to Niagara University for review
- Transcripts: If you live in an English-speaking country or attend an American or English-speaking school abroad, you can directly submit all of your secondary school and college transcripts to Niagara University for review
- An essay or written statement is required of every applicant for undergraduate admission
- Nonnative English speakers seeking admission to Niagara University must verify their proficiency in English by taking the TOEFL, a TOEFL score of 550+ (paper exam) is required for admission

APPLICATION INFORMATION

Award Deadline: Rolling admissions

CONTACT

Niagara University
Admissions Advisor
14109 Niagara Falls NY, US
Tel: +1 (716) 286-8700
Fax: +1 (716) 286-8710
Email: tkeigley@niagara.edu
Web: www.niagara.edu/international-admissions

North Central College

North Central College International Scholarship

PROGRAM INFORMATION

Description: North Central College International Scholarships of up to $20,000 per year are awarded to new undergraduate international students demonstrating a strong academic history. North Central grants bachelor's degrees in over 55 majors and pre-professional programs and offers 7 master's degree programs.

Levels of Study: Undergraduate

Field of Study: All

Nationality: Any Region

Location of Study: North Central College Naperville, IL

AWARD INFORMATION

Award Type: Scholarship

Average Amount: $17,000

Number of Awards: Varies

Award Coverage: Partial tuition

Award Duration: Academic year, renewable for additional years

ELIGIBILITY REQUIREMENTS

- Must meet all requirements for undergraduate admission to North Central College
- Award decisions are based primarily on academic history (transcripts), English proficiency test score (TOEFL, IELTS), recommendation letters, personal essay are also considered

APPLICATION INFORMATION

Award Deadline: Rolling

Instructions: Complete the undergraduate international student application and provide all required supporting documentation. For details, please visit the North Central website at www.northcentralcollege.edu/admission/international.

CONTACT

North Central College
Assistant Director of International Admission
30 N. Brainard St.
Naperville, IL 60540
Tel: +1 (630) 637-5800
Fax: +1 (630) 637-5819
Email: inadm@noctrl.edu
Web: www.northcentralcollege.edu

North Central Missouri College

NCMC Scholarships for International Students

PROGRAM INFORMATION

Description: North Central Missouri College is seeking international students who would like to study in the US in a safe rural environment. A community college with an enrollment of 1900 students, North Central Missouri College offers associate's degrees in arts, university transfer degrees, as well as associate's degrees in science.

Levels of Study: Undergraduate

Field of Study: All

Nationality: Any Region

Location of Study: North Central Missouri College Trenton, MO

AWARD INFORMATION

Award Type: Scholarship

Average Amount: Up to $500 a semester

Number of Awards: 10

Award Coverage: Tuition or housing

Award Duration: Up to 2 years

ELIGIBILITY REQUIREMENTS

- Must be accepted to North Central Missouri College
- Must be on a F-1 student visa
- Students must live in the residence halls to receive the scholarship
- Renewal of the scholarship each semester is based on maintaining F-1 visa status, satisfactory academic progress, no disciplinary actions for conduct, continued residence in the residence halls

APPLICATION INFORMATION

Award Deadline: Jul 1

Instructions: Apply online

CONTACT

North Central Missouri College
Office of Admission
1301 Main Street
Trenton, MO 64683
Tel: +1 (660) 359-3948 ext: 1401
Fax: +1 (660) 359-7856
Email: kmccollum@mail.ncmissouri.edu
Web: www.ncmissouri.edu

North Dakota State University

Lorraine Murphy New Student Global Diversity Scholarship

PROGRAM INFORMATION

Levels of Study: Undergraduate

Nationality: Any Region

Location of Study: North Dakota State University, ND

AWARD INFORMATION

Award Type: Scholarship

Average Amount: $500

Number of Awards: Varies

Award Coverage: 1-time award towards tuition, housing, or other NDSU student expenses

Award Duration: 1 semester

ELIGIBILITY REQUIREMENTS

- Must be newly admitted to an undergraduate degree or the Intensive English Language Program (IELP)
- Must hold a SEVIS Form I-20
- Minimum cumulative grade average of 3.0/4.0 (or equivalent, based on specific education system)

APPLICATION INFORMATION

Award Deadline: Aug 1-fall term, Jan 1-spring term

Instructions: Please submit your online scholarship application after receiving acceptance to NDSU, but no later than the posted deadline

CONTACT

North Dakota State University
Office of Global Outreach
Dept 4640, PO Box 6050
Putnam Hall, Lower Level
Fargo, ND 58108
Tel: +1 (701) 231-8761
Fax: +1 (701) 231-8556
Email: ndsu.intl.admissions@ndsu.edu
Web: www.ndsu.edu/intladmissions/scholarships

North Dakota State University

Academic and Cultural Sharing Scholarship

PROGRAM INFORMATION

Levels of Study: Undergraduate

Nationality: Africa, Asia, Europe, Latin America, Middle East, American Samoa, Australia, Bermuda, Cook Islands, Fed. States of Micronesia, Fiji, French Polynesia, Guam, Kiribati, Marshall Islands, Nauru, New Caledonia, New Zealand, Niue, Norfolk Island, Palau, Papua New Guinea, Samoa, Solomon Islands, Tonga, Tuvalu, United States, Vanuatu

Location of Study: North Dakota State University, ND

AWARD INFORMATION

Award Type: Scholarship

Average Amount: $8,816

Award Coverage: 50% discount of the non-resident base rate tuition

Award Duration: 1 year, eligible for renewal

ELIGIBILITY REQUIREMENTS

- Minimum 2.50/4.0 or higher cumulative GPA (grade point average) for initial award and maintenance after each semester
- Demonstrated commitment to cultural sharing and outreach through volunteer, extra-curricular, community, and on-campus activities/organizations
- Hold (or will hold) valid F-1 student status with a valid I-20, and continued enrollment in a minimum of 12 undergraduate credits each semester
- Complete 10 hours of qualified cultural sharing each semester

APPLICATION INFORMATION

Award Deadline: Jun 1-Fall term; Nov 1-Spring term

Instructions: Please submit your online scholarship application with recommendation letter no later than the admission deadlines for the Fall or Spring terms; interested students must apply for this scholarship prior to admission; applications after acceptance or enrollment at NDSU cannot be considered

CONTACT

North Dakota State University
Office of Global Outreach
Dept 4640, PO Box 6050
Putnam Hall, Lower Level
Fargo, North Dakota 58108-6050
Tel: +1 (701) 231-8761
Fax: +1 (701) 231-8556
Email: ndsu.intl.admissions@ndsu.edu
Web: www.ndsu.edu/intladmissions/scholarships

Northeastern Illinois University

Northeastern Illinois University

PROGRAM INFORMATION

Description: Northeastern Illinois University, a fully-accredited, state university attracts students from more than 40 countries from around the world. In fact, our university is consistently ranked as the most ethnically diverse university in the Midwestern US. Northeastern is located in Chicago, America's third largest city; despite the urban surroundings, our 67-acre main campus is a welcoming oasis to the nearly 12,000 commuter students who attend and study in 1 of our more than 80 undergraduate and graduate programs.

Levels of Study: Undergraduate, Graduate

Field of Study: All

Nationality: Any Region

Location of Study: Northeastern Illinois University Chicago, IL

AWARD INFORMATION

Award Type: Associateship, Award, Scholarship, Student Exchange

Average Amount: Varies

Number of Awards: Varies

Award Coverage: Tuition and fees (part or whole)

Award Duration: Depends on type of award

ELIGIBILITY REQUIREMENTS

- For a BA/BS degree: Official high school transcripts translated and submitted to ECE (www.ece.org) for course-by-course evaluation; must be top 50% of graduating class or ACT 19 (composite score) or SAT 890 (combined score)
- For an MA/MS degree: Official university transcripts translated and submitted to ECE (www.ece.org) for course-by-course evaluation (BA equivalent under Bologna Accord accepted); there is no GRE requirement, (but MBA & MSA require GMAT 450)
- For a BA/BS degree: TOEFL 500 PBT/173 CBT/61 IBT or IELTS 6.0
- For an MA/MS degree: TOEFL 550 PBT/213 CBT/79 IBT or IELTS 6.0
- All degrees require a Northeastern Financial Statement (notarized) and official bank letter(s) from each sponsor, in USD

APPLICATION INFORMATION

Award Deadline: Varies

Instructions: Visit www.neiu.edu/scholarships for more information, apply online at www.neiu.edu/Admissions/Admissions.html

CONTACT

Northeastern Illinois University
International Programs
5500 N. St. Louis Avenue
Chicago, IL 60625
Tel: +1 (773) 442-6013
Fax: International-Programs@neiu.edu
Email: International-Programs@neiu.edu
Web: www.neiu.edu

Northern Arizona University

NAU International Student Presidential Scholarships

PROGRAM INFORMATION

Description: New F-1 undergraduate international students seeking admission as a degree seeking student at the Northern Arizona University Flagstaff campus may be eligible for a $10,000 per academic year award applicable to their tuition costs. Students will be notified of this award at the time of admission to the university. Award letters will be sent with students' admissions packets.

Levels of Study: Undergraduate

Field of Study: All

Nationality: Any Region

Location of Study: Northern Arizona University Flagstaff, AZ

AWARD INFORMATION

Award Type: Scholarship, Tuition Reduction
Average Amount: $10,000
Number of Awards: Varies
Award Coverage: Tuition
Award Duration: 2 semesters

ELIGIBILITY REQUIREMENTS

- New F-1 degree-seeking student
- Must be admitted to a university major at Northern Arizona University
- Students should have at least a "B" average in their secondary and postsecondary studies

APPLICATION INFORMATION

Award Deadline: Mar
Instructions: All international applicants for undergraduate admission are automatically considered, for more information on how to apply, please visit the website

CONTACT

Northern Arizona University
Center for International Education
PO Box 5598
Blome Hall, Room 200
Flagstaff, AZ 86011
Tel: +1 (928) 523-2409
Fax: +1 (928) 523-9489
Email: studynau@nau.edu
Web: www.nau.edu/provost/cie/international-admissions

Northern Arizona University
NAU Continuing International Student Presidential Scholarship

PROGRAM INFORMATION

Description: The Continuing International Student Presidential Scholarship is a merit-based tuition waiver for enrolled F-1 undergraduate, degree-seeking international students enrolled in a bachelor's degree program at the Flagstaff campus.
Levels of Study: Undergraduate
Nationality: Any Region
Location of Study: Northern Arizona University Flagstaff, AZ

AWARD INFORMATION

Award Type: Tuition Reduction
Average Amount: Up to $10,000
Award Coverage: Tuition

ELIGIBILITY REQUIREMENTS

- Must be an F-1 visa holder
- Must have completed at least 1 semester of university-level coursework at Northern Arizona University by the end of the semester when you apply
- Must meet Northern Arizona University's English proficiency requirement
- Must be in good academic standing and making good progress towards your first bachelor's degree
- Must have at least a 2.5 cumulative GPA at the end of the semester of application and should show evidence of involvement in campus activities/organizations

APPLICATION INFORMATION

Award Deadline: May

CONTACT

Northern Arizona University
International Student & Scholar Services (ISSS)
PO Box 5598
Flagstaff, AZ 86011-5598
Tel: +1 (928) 523-2409
Fax: +1 (928) 523-9489
Email: isss@nau.edu
Web: nau.edu/cie/study-at-nau/

Northern Arizona University
NAU Indonesian Student Scholarship

PROGRAM INFORMATION

Description: New F-1 Indonesian students seeking admission as a degree-seeking student at the Flagstaff campus can apply for a scholarship. This can apply to tuition costs for up to 4 years during a bachelor's degree.
Levels of Study: Undergraduate
Nationality: Indonesia
Location of Study: Northern Arizona University Flagstaff, AZ

AWARD INFORMATION

Award Type: Tuition Reduction
Award Coverage: 20% of tuition
Award Duration: 1 year

CONTACT

Northern Arizona University
International Admissions & Recruitment (IAR)
PO Box 5598
Flagstaff, AZ 86011
Tel: +1 (928) 523-2409
Fax: +1 (928) 523-9489
Email: studynau@nau.edu
Web: nau.edu/cie/study-at-nau/

Northern Arizona University
International Baccalaureate Scholarship

PROGRAM INFORMATION

Description: If you are a student receiving an International Baccalaureate diploma and are admitted to Northern Arizona University as an undergraduate, first-degree seeking student, you are eligible to receive $5,000 per year for tuition. You may not combine this award with other tuition awards. It is renewable for up to 8 semesters if you maintain a 2.5 GPA and complete 30 credit hours per year.
Levels of Study: Undergraduate
Nationality: Any Region
Location of Study: Northern Arizona University Flagstaff, AZ

AWARD INFORMATION

Award Type: Tuition Reduction
Average Amount: $5,000 per year
Award Coverage: Tuition
Award Duration: Maximum of 8 semesters

ELIGIBILITY REQUIREMENTS

- Receiving a IB diploma
- Maintain a 2.5 GPA
- Complete 30 credit hours per year
- You may not combine this award with other tuition awards

APPLICATION INFORMATION

Instructions: nau.edu/cie/study-at-nau/

CONTACT

Northern Arizona University
International Admissions & Recruitment (IAR)
PO Box 5598
Flagstaff, Arizona 86011-5598
Tel: 1-928-523-2409
Fax: 1-928-523-9489
Email: studynau@nau.edu
Web: nau.edu/cie/study-at-nau/

Northern Arizona University
Khursheed Fatima Scholarship

PROGRAM INFORMATION

Description: This fund is established by Samia Ashraf in memory of her mother, Khursheed Fatima. The scholarship, up to $11,000 for 2 semesters at Northern Arizona University, is awarded to 1 student to cover tuition and fees, then books and supplies.
Levels of Study: Undergraduate
Nationality: South/Central Asia
Location of Study: Northern Arizona University Flagstaff, AZ

AWARD INFORMATION

Award Type: Scholarship
Average Amount: up to $11,000
Award Coverage: Tuition, fees, books, supplies
Award Duration: 2 semesters

ELIGIBILITY REQUIREMENTS

- Must be an enrolled, degree-seeking undergraduate
- Must have a cumulative GPA of at least 2.8
- Must demonstrate financial need
- Must demonstrate academic promise
- preference shall be given to a female student from South Asia (Pakistan, India, Nepal, Sri Lanka, Bangladesh, Bhutan, or Afghanistan)

APPLICATION INFORMATION

Instructions: nau.edu/cie/study-at-nau/

CONTACT

Northern Arizona University
International Student & Scholar Services (ISSS)
PO Box 5598
Flagstaff, Arizona 86011-5598
Tel: 1-928-523-2409
Fax: 1-928-523-9489
Email: isss@nau.edu
Web: nau.edu/cie/study-at-nau/

Northern Arizona University
Phi Theta Kappa Scholarship

PROGRAM INFORMATION

Description: Open to Phi Theta Kappa students who are currently attending a 2-year college and who will be attending Northern Arizona University the following semester as an undergraduate, first-degree-seeking student.

Levels of Study: Undergraduate

Nationality: Any Region

Location of Study: Northern Arizona University Flagstaff, AZ

ELIGIBILITY REQUIREMENTS

- Full time undergraduate student
- Admitted to NAU as a first degree seeking student
- Member of Phi Theta Kappa
- Currently enrolled at a community college and transferring to NAU immediately (no break in enrollment between schools)
- Not participating in Western Undergraduate Exchange (WUE) or Worldwide University (WWU) program

APPLICATION INFORMATION

Instructions: Visit the website for more information on applying at nau.edu/uploadedFiles/Administrative/FinAid/Forms/PTKApp.pdf

CONTACT
Northern Arizona University
PO Box 5598
Flagstaff, AZ 86011-5598
Tel: +1 (928) 523-2409
Fax: +1 (928) 523-9489
Email: studynau@nau.edu
Web: nau.edu/cie/study-at-nau/

Northern Illinois University
Northern Illinois University Graduate Assistance

PROGRAM INFORMATION

Description: Located in 1 of the most dynamic regions of the country, NIU is a comprehensive teaching and research institution with a diverse and international student body.

Levels of Study: Graduate

Field of Study: All

Nationality: Any Region

Location of Study: Northern Illinois University DeKalb, IL

AWARD INFORMATION

Award Type: Award, Fellowship, Scholarship, Tuition Reduction

Average Amount: Varies

Number of Awards: Varies

Award Coverage: Varies

ELIGIBILITY REQUIREMENTS

- Varies by award

APPLICATION INFORMATION

Instructions: For more information on how to apply, please visit the website

CONTACT
Northern Illinois University
The Graduate School
223 Adams Hall
DeKalb, IL 60115
Tel: +1 (815) 753-6112
Email: internationalgrads@wpo.cso.niu.edu
Web: www.niu.edu/admissions

Northern Kentucky University
Northern Kentucky University International Student Award

PROGRAM INFORMATION

Description: Award for high achieving international students wishing to study at Northern Kentucky University entering as freshmen.

Levels of Study: Undergraduate

Field of Study: All

Nationality: Any Region

Location of Study: Northern Kentucky University Highland Heights, KY

AWARD INFORMATION

Award Type: Award

Average Amount: $1,000

Number of Awards: Approx 10 per semester

Award Coverage: Partial tuition

Award Duration: Academic year, renewable for additional years

ELIGIBILITY REQUIREMENTS

- Must be a freshman
- Must have an SAT score of 1060 or better
- Must have a GPA (4.0 scale) of 2.5 or higher
- Must have high secondary school rank
- A levels and other academic achievements considered

APPLICATION INFORMATION

Award Deadline: Rolling

Instructions: When you apply for admission you are automatically considered for the scholarship if you meet the minimum requirements

CONTACT
Northern Kentucky University
International Students and Scholars
University Center 405
Highland Heights, KY 41099
Tel: +1 (859) 572-6517
Fax: +1 (859) 572-6178
Email: oiss@nku.edu
Web: oiss.nku.edu

Northern Kentucky University
Northern Kentucky University Non-resident Award for Transfer Students

PROGRAM INFORMATION

Description: Award for students transferring from an accredited institution of higher education to Northern Kentucky University.

Levels of Study: Undergraduate

Field of Study: All

Nationality: Any Region

Location of Study: Northern Kentucky University Highland Heights, KY

AWARD INFORMATION

Award Type: Award

Average Amount: $2,000

Number of Awards: Varies

Award Coverage: Varies

Award Duration: Academic year, renewable up to 6 terms

ELIGIBILITY REQUIREMENTS

- Must receive a final transfer evaluation of at least 60 semester credit hours or 90 quarter hours; that is, equal to or greater than junior status from a regionally accredited institutions
- Must be academically eligible to return to institution previously attended and have earned a minimum 2.0 cumulative GPA
- Must be admitted to an undergraduate bachelor's degree program at NKU with no restrictions or academic deficiencies
- Must be a resident of any US state except Kentucky or be an international student
- Must enroll in a minimum of 12 semester hours

APPLICATION INFORMATION

Award Deadline: Aug

Instructions: No application required, transcripts are reviewed with application for admission

CONTACT
Northern Kentucky University
Nunn Drive, UC 366
Highland Heights, KY 41099
Tel: +1 (859) 572-6517
Fax: +1 (859) 572-6178
Email: oiss@nku.edu
Web: oiss.nku.edu

Northern Michigan University

Northern Michigan University International Student Academic Award

PROGRAM INFORMATION

Description: The International Academic Award is available for international students who receive a cumulative grade point average (GPA) of 3.0 or higher (on a 4.0 scale) at NMU. These students will receive the award, which reduces their tuition. This reduction can amount to a savings of $1,100 per spring semester, $1,100 per winter semester, $1,000 per spring/summer semester, or up to $3,200 per calendar year. The student must maintain his or her full-time status and a cumulative GPA of 3.0 or higher to continue to receive the International Academic Award.

Levels of Study: Undergraduate

Field of Study: All

Nationality: Any Region

Location of Study: Northern Michigan University Marquette, MI

AWARD INFORMATION

Award Type: Tuition Reduction

Average Amount: $1,100 per semester

Number of Awards: Unlimited

Award Coverage: Partial tuition

Award Duration: 7 semesters

ELIGIBILITY REQUIREMENTS

- Must hold a valid F-1 visa
- Must achieve a minimum cumulative GPA of 3.0 during the first 4 semesters of study at NMU, with a minimum of 12 credit hours per semester, 16 credit hours per semester are needed to complete most degree programs within 8 semesters
- Recipients of the International Academic Award will be provided the opportunity to perform up to 15 hours of community service for each semester the award is received

APPLICATION INFORMATION

Award Deadline: End of the semester

Instructions: No application process necessary, if an NMU international student meets the requirements, then the scholarship is awarded

CONTACT

Northern Michigan University
International Program Director
Hedgcock 2101
1401 Presque Ilse Avenue
Marquette, MI 49855-5301
Tel: +1 (906) 227-2510
Fax: +1 (906) 227-2533
Email: ipo@nmu.edu
Web: www.nmu.edu/iao

Northern State University

Wolfpact Scholarship

PROGRAM INFORMATION

Description: Northern State University's WolfPACT scholarship is the largest guaranteed scholarship in South Dakota. Incoming freshmen with ACT scores over 21 or an SAT Critical Reading + Math score over 980 are eligible for the WolfPACT scholarship.

Field of Study: Accounting, Agriculture and Related Sciences, American History, Art History, Arts and Culture, Chemistry, Communication Technologies, Communications and Journalism, Creative Writing, Engineering, Engineering 3-2, Engineering-Related Technologies, Finance, Fine Arts, Foreign Languages, Geography, Government, Information Technology, Journalism, Law, Marine Engineering, Music, Nursing, Physics, Spanish, Theater

Nationality: Any Region

Location of Study: Northern State University Aberdeen, SD

ELIGIBILITY REQUIREMENTS

- Students with an ACT of 30 or higher are guaranteed $12,000 over 4 years
- Students with ACT scores of 28 or 29 qualify for $11,000 for 4 years
- Students with ACT scores of 24 to 27 qualify for $7,000 for 4 years
- Students with ACT scores of 21 to 23 receive $5,000 for 4 years

APPLICATION INFORMATION

Award Deadline: Mar

Instructions: To apply for WolfPACT, send a completed admission application, application fee, high school transcript, ACT score, and be accepted for admission

CONTACT

Northern State University
International Recruiter and Advisor
1200 S. Jay St., Box 1103
Aberdeen, SD 57401
Tel: +1 (605) 626-2637
Email: international@northern.edu
Web: www.northern.edu/admissions/Pages/fa/wolfpact.aspx

Northwest Missouri State University

Carolyn Houts International Student Scholarship

PROGRAM INFORMATION

Description: The scholarship shall be awarded to a full time international student who exemplifies positive contributions to Northwest through campus involvement, solid academic performance and leadership.

Levels of Study: Undergraduate

Nationality: Any Region

Location of Study: Northwest Missouri State University Maryville, MO

AWARD INFORMATION

Award Type: Scholarship

Average Amount: $500.00

Number of Awards: 1

ELIGIBILITY REQUIREMENTS

- Student must exemplify positive contributions to Northwest through campus involvement, academic performance, and leadership
- First preference for the award shall be given to a student from Africa
- The recipient shall maintain enrollment to be considered as a full-time student by the University

APPLICATION INFORMATION

Award Deadline: Feb 1

Instructions: Return completed application to Dr. Jeffrey Foot at the Student Engagement Center

CONTACT

Northwest Missouri State University
International Affairs
800 University Drive
Student Engagement Center, UN 2380
64468 Maryville Missouri
Tel: 660-562-1367
Email: iic@nwmissouri.edu
Web: www.nwmissouri.edu

Northwest Missouri State University

Northwest Missouri State University Society of International Ambassadors Scholarship

PROGRAM INFORMATION

Description: This scholarship recognizes outstanding contributions made by an international student (a foreign national student in F-1 or J-1 visa status only) to promote and create a pluralistic campus climate. Awarded to a continuing undergraduate international student who is enrolled on a full-time basis at Northwest Missouri State University, the applicant will demonstrate leadership or merit in promoting intercultural programs or experiences or will have demonstrated skill educating the general student population about the personal and professional importance of understanding international issues and possessing different perspectives thus marking the traits of a globally prepared citizen.

Levels of Study: Undergraduate

Field of Study: All

Nationality: Any Region

Location of Study: Northwest Missouri State University Maryville, MO

AWARD INFORMATION

Award Type: Award, Scholarship, Tuition Reduction

Average Amount: $500

Number of Awards: 1

Award Coverage: Applied toward tuition

Award Duration: Awarded each year

ELIGIBILITY REQUIREMENTS

- Must be a continuing student with a minimum GPA of 2.75
- Must have demonstrated merit and involvement within the Northwest campus and community

APPLICATION INFORMATION

Award Deadline: Feb 1

Instructions: To apply for the Society of International Ambassadors Scholarship please visit the website at www.nwmissouri.edu/finaid/PDF/scholarships/SIA.pdf to download the application.

CONTACT

Northwest Missouri State University
Director of International Affairs & ESL
800 University Drive
Student Engagement Center, 2nd Floor Student Union
Maryville, MO 64468
Tel: +1 (660) 562-1367
Fax: +1 (660) 562-1546
Email: iic@nwmissouri.edu
Web: www.nwmissouri.edu/admissions/intl/index.htm

Northwest Missouri State University
Northwest Missouri State University Graduate Non-Resident Waiver

PROGRAM INFORMATION

Description: Extra out-of-state fees and charges are waived. Students are only responsible for paying in-state tuition prices.

Levels of Study: Graduate

Field of Study: All

Nationality: Any Region

Location of Study: Northwest Missouri State University Maryville, MO

AWARD INFORMATION

Award Type: Award, Scholarship, Tuition Reduction

Average Amount: $4,000

Number of Awards: Unlimited

Award Coverage: Extra out-of-state fees and charges are waived, leaving the students only responsible for paying in-state tuition prices

Award Duration: Awarded yearly. Eligible for renewal

ELIGIBILITY REQUIREMENTS

- Automatically awarded to continuing graduate students who maintain a minimum GPA of 3.30

APPLICATION INFORMATION

Instructions: The Graduate Non-Resident Waiver is automatically awarded to eligible students.

CONTACT

Northwest Missouri State University
Director of International Affairs & ESL
800 University Drive
Student Engagement Center, Student Union 2380
Maryville, MO 64468
Tel: +1 (660) 562-1367
Fax: +1 (660) 562-1546
Email: iic@nwmissouri.edu
Web: www.nwmissouri.edu/admissions/intl/index.htm

Northwest Missouri State University
International Graduate Achievement Scholarship

PROGRAM INFORMATION

Description: Northwest Missouri State University has been offering students a dynamic learning environment for over 100 years. Through energetic lectures and hands-on experience our faculty and staff produce successful graduates.

Levels of Study: Graduate

Field of Study: All

Nationality: Any Region

Location of Study: Northwest Missouri State University Maryville, MO

AWARD INFORMATION

Award Type: Award, Scholarship, Tuition Reduction

Average Amount: $1,000

Number of Awards: Unlimited

Award Coverage: Partial tuition

Award Duration: First semester

ELIGIBILITY REQUIREMENTS

- Awarded to first semester graduate students accepted to Northwest who have high levels of achievement in their academic background

APPLICATION INFORMATION

Instructions: Scholarship is automatically awarded to eligible students who apply to Northwest Missouri State University

CONTACT

Northwest Missouri State University
Director of International Affairs & ESL
800 University Drive
Student Engagement Center, Student Union 2380
Maryville, MO 64468
Tel: +1 (660) 562-1367
Fax: +1 (660) 562-1546
Email: iic@nwmissouri.edu
Web: www.nwmissouri.edu/admissions/intl/index.htm

Northwest Missouri State University
Northwest Missouri State University Northwest Academic Merit Scholarship

PROGRAM INFORMATION

Description: Scholarships ranging from $1,000-$3,500 for freshman students with an ACT score above 21 or an SAT I score above 980.

Levels of Study: Undergraduate

Field of Study: All

Nationality: Any Region

Location of Study: Northwest Missouri State University Maryville, MO

AWARD INFORMATION

Award Type: Award

Average Amount: $1,000-$3,500

Number of Awards: Unlimited

Award Duration: Awarded on a yearly basis, renewable

ELIGIBILITY REQUIREMENTS

- Students with an SAT I* Score of 980-1040/ACT 21-22 will receive $1,000 per year
- Students with an SAT I* Score of 1050-1200/ACT 23-26 will receive $2,500 per year
- Students with an SAT I* Score of 1210-1600/ACT 27-36 will receive $3,500 per year
- Combination of SAT Critical Reading and SAT Mathematics Scores

APPLICATION INFORMATION

Instructions: No application needed

CONTACT

Northwest Missouri State University
Director of International Affairs & ESL
800 University Drive
Student Engagement Center, Student Union 2380
Maryville, MO 64468
Tel: +1 (660) 562-1367
Fax: +1 (660) 562-1546
Email: iic@nwmissouri.edu
Web: www.nwmissouri.edu/admissions/intl/index.htm

Northwest Missouri State University
Northwest Missouri State Academic Merit Scholarship for Transfer Students

PROGRAM INFORMATION

Description: Awards of $1,000-$2,500 for transfer students with a transferable GPA of 3.0 or above.

Levels of Study: Undergraduate

Field of Study: All

Nationality: Any Region

Location of Study: Northwest Missouri State University Maryville, MO

AWARD INFORMATION

Award Type: Award, Scholarship

Average Amount: $1,000-$2,500

Number of Awards: Unlimited

Award Coverage: Awards of $1,000-$2,500 for transfer students with a transferable GPA of 3.0 or above

ELIGIBILITY REQUIREMENTS

- Students with 3.00-3.29 transferable GPA will receive $1,000 per year
- Students with 3.30-3.49 transferable GPA will receive $1,500 per year
- Students with 3.50-4.00 transferable GPA will receive $2,500 per year

APPLICATION INFORMATION

Instructions: Visit the website.

CONTACT

Northwest Missouri State University
Director of International Affairs & ESL
800 University Drive
Student Engagement Center, Student Union 2380
Maryville, MO 64468
Tel: +1 (660) 562-1367
Fax: +1 (660) 562-1546
Email: iic@nwmissouri.edu
Web: www.nwmissouri.edu/admissions/intl/index.htm

Northwest Missouri State University
Northwest International Achievement Scholarship

PROGRAM INFORMATION

Description: This award will serve as a tuition waiver that represents the value of the difference in price between in-state and out-of-state tuition.

Levels of Study: Undergraduate

Field of Study: All

Nationality: Any Region

Location of Study: Northwest Missouri State University Maryville, MO

AWARD INFORMATION

Award Type: Award, Scholarship, Tuition Reduction

Average Amount: $6,252

Number of Awards: Unlimited

Award Coverage: This award will serve as a tuition waiver that represent the value of the difference in price between in-state and out-of-state tuition

ELIGIBILITY REQUIREMENTS

- Must be accepted into Northwest's undergraduate program
- Must have TOEFL 65 IBT/513 PBT, 6.0 on Academic IELTS, or 43 on Pearson Test of English

APPLICATION INFORMATION

Instructions: No application needed, visit website for more information

CONTACT

Northwest Missouri State University
Director of International Affairs & ESL
800 University Drive
Student Engagement Center, Student Union 2380
Maryville, MO 64468
Tel: +1 (660) 562-1367
Fax: +1 (660) 562-1546
Email: iic@nwmissouri.edu
Web: www.nwmissouri.edu/admissions/intl/index.htm

Northwest Missouri State University
Northwest International Achievement Scholarship for Transfers

PROGRAM INFORMATION

Description: No application needed. This award is a tuition waiver that will represent the value of the difference in price between in-state and out-of-state tuition for transfer students.

Levels of Study: Undergraduate

Field of Study: All

Nationality: Any Region

Location of Study: Northwest Missouri State University Maryville, MO

AWARD INFORMATION

Award Type: Award, Scholarship, Tuition Reduction

Average Amount: $6,252

Number of Awards: Unlimited

Award Coverage: This award is a tuition waiver that will represent the value of the difference in price between in-state and out-of-state tuition

ELIGIBILITY REQUIREMENTS

- Must have a 3.0 GPA in at least 24 hours of transferable credit
- Must be accepted into a Northwest undergraduate program
- Must meet the standard English proficiency levels for international acceptances
- Transfer students with less than 24 transferrable hours will be eligible based on freshman criteria

APPLICATION INFORMATION

Instructions: No application needed

CONTACT

Northwest Missouri State University
Director of International Affairs & ESL
800 University Drive
Student Engagement Center, Student Union 2380
Maryville, MO 64468
Tel: +1 (660) 562-1367
Fax: +1 (660) 562-1546
Email: iic@nwmissouri.edu
Web: www.nwmissouri.edu/admissions/intl/index.htm

Northwestern University
McCormick School of Engineering and Applied Science

PROGRAM INFORMATION

Description: MS and PhD programs.

Levels of Study: Graduate, Doctorate

Field of Study: Biotechnology, Cognitive Science, Communication Technologies, Computer and Information Sciences, Computer Science, Engineering, Environmental Studies, Information Technology, Management, Mathematics, Metallurgy

Nationality: Any Region

Location of Study: Northwestern University Evanston, IL

AWARD INFORMATION

Award Type: Fellowship, Tuition Reduction

Average Amount: Varies

Number of Awards: Varies

Award Coverage: Tuition, stipend for living expenses, health insurance for PhD students

Award Duration: Varies

ELIGIBILITY REQUIREMENTS

- Bachelor's degree
- GRE scores
- TOEFL or IELTS scores, unless BS or MS degree has been earned where English is the language of instruction

APPLICATION INFORMATION

Award Deadline: Varies

CONTACT

Northwestern University
Assistant Dean for Graduate Studies
2145 Sheridan Road
L-261
Evanston, IL 60208
Tel: +1 (847) 491-4547
Fax: +1 (847) 491-5341
Email: b-lindvall@northwestern.edu
Web: www.mccormick.northwestern.edu/

Notre Dame Law School
Notre Dame JSD Program in International Human Rights Law

PROGRAM INFORMATION

Description: Geared toward human rights practitioners who would like to teach and pursue research at the university level, the JSD program provides specialized study in international human rights law. Students in this program analyze human rights issues with members of the faculty who are specialists in the field, while also drawing upon the resources of Notre Dame's Kellogg Institute for International Studies, Kroc Institute for International Peace Studies, and Department of Political Science. Our students engage with a rich interdisciplinary curriculum that prepares them to defend human rights and to transform the legal, social, and economic contexts in which they are violated. With its long tradition of human rights education and generous scholarship opportunities, The Center for Civil and Human Rights at Notre Dame Law School prepares graduates to join a powerful alumni network of over 300 lawyers promoting human dignity in more than 80 countries.

Levels of Study: Graduate, Doctorate, Professional

Field of Study: Human Rights, International Law, Law

Nationality: Any Region

Location of Study: Notre Dame Law School Notre Dame, IN

AWARD INFORMATION

Award Type: Scholarship, Tuition Reduction

Average Amount: $22,500 to $45,000

Number of Awards: Typically 1 full scholarship

Award Coverage: This award covers full tuition for 1 student or partial tuition for 2 students. Does not cover living expenses

Award Duration: Academic year

ELIGIBILITY REQUIREMENTS

- Eligible applicants must possess a JD, LLB, or equivalent law degree
- Eligible applicants must demonstrate English language competency

APPLICATION INFORMATION

Instructions: Visit our website at www.humanrights.nd.edu for more information

CONTACT

Notre Dame Law School
Center for Civil and Human Rights
P.O. Box 780
Notre Dame, Indiana 46556
Tel: +1 (574) 631-8555
Fax: +1 (574) 631-8702
Email: cchr@nd.edu
Web: www.humanrights.nd.edu

Notre Dame Law School
Center for Civil and Human Rights

PROGRAM INFORMATION

Description: The Center provides scholarship funding for lawyers from around the world (including the US) to pursue LLM and J.S.D. degrees in international human rights law at Notre Dame Law School.

Levels of Study: Graduate, Doctorate, Professional

Field of Study: Human Rights, International Law

Nationality: Any Region

Location of Study: University of Notre Dame, Notre Dame Law School
Notre Dame, IN

AWARD INFORMATION

Award Type: Fellowship, Scholarship, Tuition Reduction

Average Amount: Varies

Number of Awards: Varies

Award Coverage: Tuition, housing and other living expenses

Award Duration: Varies

ELIGIBILITY REQUIREMENTS

- Must possess a JD, LLB or equivalent degree from an accredited law school in the US or any foreign country for the LLM applicants
- Must possess an LLM or equivalent degree from an accredited law school in the US or any foreign country for the J.S.D. applicants

APPLICATION INFORMATION

Instructions: The application is available at our website: humanrights.nd.edu

CONTACT
Notre Dame Law School
LLM Program Director, Center for Civil and Human Rights
2161 Eck Hall of Law
Notre Dame, Indiana 46556
Tel: +1 (574) 631-8544
Fax: +1 (574) 631-8702
Email: sobrien2@nd.edu
Web: humanrights.nd.edu

Oberlin College
Oberlin College Financial Aid

PROGRAM INFORMATION

Description: Need-based financial aid for admitted international students. Aid consists primarily of grants, but may also include loans and/or campus employment.

Levels of Study: Undergraduate

Field of Study: All

Nationality: Any Region

Location of Study: Oberlin College
Oberlin, OH

AWARD INFORMATION

Award Type: Grant

Average Amount: Varies

Award Coverage: Tuition, housing, food, books

Award Duration: Maximum of 4 years (5 years for double degree students)

ELIGIBILITY REQUIREMENTS

- Must complete the College Board's CSS Profile
- Must complete the International Certification of Finances form

APPLICATION INFORMATION

Award Deadline: Jan

Instructions: Students who have been accepted and who have submitted both of the above forms will be considered for need-based financial aid

CONTACT
Oberlin College
Assistant Director of Admissions
Office of Admissions
101 North Professor Street
Oberlin, OH 44074
Tel: +1 (440) 775-8411
Fax: +1 (440) 775-6905
Email: international.admissions@oberlin.edu
Web: new.oberlin.edu/applying

Oberlin Conservatory of Music
Oberlin Conservatory of Music International Student Financial Aid

PROGRAM INFORMATION

Description: The Performance Diploma is a 4-semester program, offered only in certain performance departments, and is designed for the very small number of gifted performers who have not yet obtained a Bachelor of Music degree. Performance Diploma students may apply to the Bachelor of Music program before the end of the first year of the program. The graduate level Artist Diploma is a 4 semester program, offered only in certain performance departments, which is intended for a limited number of exceptionally gifted performers who have obtained a Bachelor of Music degree or equivalent and who wish to concentrate on private applied study without additional course requirements.

Levels of Study: Undergraduate, Graduate

Field of Study: Music

Nationality: Any Region

Location of Study: Oberlin Conservatory of Music
Oberlin, OH

AWARD INFORMATION

Award Type: Grant, Scholarship

Average Amount: Varies

Number of Awards: Varies

ELIGIBILITY REQUIREMENTS

- Must submit the application for admission and complete a formal audition
- Must submit International Student Financial Aid Application and Declaration of Finances Form

APPLICATION INFORMATION

Award Deadline: Dec

Instructions: For more information on how to apply, please visit the website

CONTACT
Oberlin Conservatory of Music
39 West College St.
Oberlin, OH 44074
Tel: +1 (440) 775-8413
Fax: +1 (440) 775-6972
Email: michael.manderen@oberlin.edu
Web: new.oberlin.edu/conservatory/

Ohio Dominican University
Ohio Dominican International Student Scholarships and Awards

PROGRAM INFORMATION

Location of Study: Ohio Dominican University
Columbus, OH

ELIGIBILITY REQUIREMENTS

- Successful completion of ELS Level 112 intensive program
- Official TOEFL score of at least 550 (79- internet based); official STEP EIKEN score of 1st and Pre-1st for Japanese students, official IELTS band score of at least 6.5

CONTACT
Griffin Student Center
1216 Sunbury Road
Columbus, OH 43219
Tel: +1 (614) 251-4500
Fax: +1(614) 251-0156
Email: international@ohiodominican.edu
Web: https://www.ohiodominican.edu/Admissions/Undergraduate-Admissions/International-Students/Financial-Aid-and-Scholarships/

Ohio Northern University
Ohio Northern University International Student Scholarships and Awards

PROGRAM INFORMATION

Description: Ohio Northern University is a private, comprehensive university with approximately 3,600 students. Students are offered a supportive environment with faculty and staff dedicated to fostering personal growth and intellectual curiosity. International students will find a strong set of support services and programs. Scholarships are available to admitted freshman and transfer international students.

Levels of Study: Undergraduate

Field of Study: All

Nationality: Any Region

Location of Study: Ohio Northern University
Ada, OH

AWARD INFORMATION

Award Type: Scholarship

Average Amount: $10,000

Number of Awards: Available to all admitted students

Award Coverage: Tuition

Award Duration: Renewed annually

ELIGIBILITY REQUIREMENTS

- Must have a minimum secondary school grade point average of 2.8 on 4.0 scale
- Must have a minimum IELTS exam score of 6.0 with no sub score below 5.5 or a TOEFL score of 550 PBT/78 IBT to take full schedule of academic courses; students with a 5.5 IELTS with no sub score below 5.0 or 460 PBT/50 IBT TOEFL can qualify for admission into their College and placement in the International Scholar Transition Program
- The student or sponsor of the student must show adequate funds or financial resources to cover expenses associated with attendance at ONU

APPLICATION INFORMATION

Award Deadline: Rolling

Instructions: Apply on-line at www.onu.edu using the international student application for freshmen or transfer students; send documents supporting application to the address below, transcripts from high school should be sent directly to ONU from the high school; students are automatically considered for international scholarships after they are admitted to ONU, no separate scholarship application is required

CONTACT

Ohio Northern University
Office of International Admissions
Weber Hall
525 S. Main Street
Ada, OH 45810
Tel: +1 (419) 772-2483
Fax: +1 (419) 772-2484
Email: int-adm@onu.edu
Web: www.onu.edu

Ohio Northern University

Ohio Northern University International Scholar Transition Program

PROGRAM INFORMATION

Description: The International Scholar Transition Program is designed for students who meet all admission requirements but lack an adequate level of English proficiency to take a full schedule of academic courses. Students admitted into ISTP take coursework half time in ESL classes, while simultaneously enrolled in regular academic classes. Academic classes are taken for credit toward 1's degree.

Levels of Study: Undergraduate

Field of Study: All

Nationality: Any Region

Location of Study: Ohio Northern University
Ada, OH

AWARD INFORMATION

Award Type: Award

Average Amount: $10,000

Number of Awards: Varies

Award Coverage: Tuition

Award Duration: Academic year

ELIGIBILITY REQUIREMENTS

- Must meet the academic requirements for admission into their program of study
- Must meet the financial requirements for admission into ONU
- Must score a minimum TOEFL 460 PBT/50 IBT, IELTS 5.5 with no sub score below 5.0, completion of Level 109 at an ELS Language Center

APPLICATION INFORMATION

Award Deadline: Jul 15

Instructions: Complete international student application on line at www.onu.edu and send supporting documents to International Admissions at ONU

CONTACT

Ohio Northern University
Office of International Admissions
525 S. Main Street
Ada, OH 45810
Tel: +1 (419) 772-2483
Fax: +1 (419) 772-2484
Email: int-adm@onu.edu
Web: www.onu.edu/admission/international_admissions

Ohio University

Ohio University Graduate Assistantships

PROGRAM INFORMATION

Description: Awarded by individual Ohio University schools or academic departments. Provides a tuition scholarship (full or partial) plus a stipend for services as prescribed by the individual department.

Levels of Study: Graduate, Doctorate

Field of Study: All

Nationality: Any Region

Location of Study: Ohio University
Athens, OH

AWARD INFORMATION

Award Type: Associateship, Scholarship

Average Amount: Varies

Number of Awards: Varies

Award Coverage: Stipend plus tuition scholarship, which covers instructional fees up to 18 quarter hours per quarter (does not cover general fee or health insurance)

ELIGIBILITY REQUIREMENTS

- Varies by department
- Candidates may apply for up to 5 Graduate Assistantships

APPLICATION INFORMATION

Instructions: Visit website or contact for more information

CONTACT

Ohio University
Graduate Studies
McKee House
44 University Terrace
Athens, OH 45701
Tel: +1 (740) 597-1540
Fax: +1 (740) 597-3005
Email: internationalgrad@ohio.edu
Web: www.ohio.edu/studentaffairs/gas.cfm

Ohio University

Ohio University Graduate Tuition Scholarships

PROGRAM INFORMATION

Description: Awarded by individual Ohio University schools or departments on the basis of scholarly merit.

Levels of Study: Graduate, Doctorate

Field of Study: All

Nationality: Any Region

Location of Study: Ohio University
Athens, OH

AWARD INFORMATION

Award Type: Scholarship

Average Amount: Varies

Number of Awards: Varies

Award Coverage: Instructional fees up to 18 quarter hours per quarter (does not cover general fee or health insurance costs)

ELIGIBILITY REQUIREMENTS

- Varies by department

APPLICATION INFORMATION

Instructions: Visit website or contact for more information

CONTACT

Ohio University
Graduate Studies
McKee House
44 University Terrace
Athens, OH 45701
Tel: +1 (740) 597-1540
Fax: +1 (740) 597-3005
Email: internationalgrad@ohio.edu
Web: www.ohio.edu/graduate/finaid.cfm

Ohio Wesleyan University

Ohio Wesleyan University Scholarships

PROGRAM INFORMATION

Description: Ohio Wesleyan University provides financial assistance to international students out of its commitment for international educational exchange and its desire to provide educational opportunity to academically talented students from around the world. Ohio Wesleyan University was founded in 1842 and has an unusual synthesis of liberal arts learning and pre-professional preparation. The University is strongly committed to developing the service ethic in students, fusing theory with its practical applications, and confronting specific issues of long-range public importance.

Levels of Study: Undergraduate

Field of Study: All

Nationality: Any Region

Location of Study: Ohio Wesleyan University
Delaware, OH

AWARD INFORMATION

Award Type: Grant, Scholarship

Average Amount: Up to $25,000

Number of Awards: Varies

Award Coverage: Tuition

Award Duration: 4 years

ELIGIBILITY REQUIREMENTS

- Must have an outstanding academic profile
- Must submit SAT I, TOEFL/IELTS
- Must submit an essay and 2 letters of recommendation

APPLICATION INFORMATION

Award Deadline: Jan 1

Instructions: Please visit the website for details of application process

CONTACT

Ohio Wesleyan University
Office of Admission and Financial Aid
61 S. Sandusky Street
Delaware, OH 43015
Tel: +1 (740) 368-3020
Fax: +1 (740) 368-3314
Email: owuintl@owu.edu
Web: www.owu.edu

Oklahoma City University

Freshman Undergraduate University and Department Awards

PROGRAM INFORMATION

Description: All Freshman applicants for any program in Business, Arts & Sciences, and Nursing are eligible.

Levels of Study: Undergraduate

Field of Study: Accounting, Art History, Arts and Culture, Biochemistry, Business and Management, Communications and Journalism, Computer and Information Sciences, Economics, Environmental Studies, Finance, Government, Health Professions, Humanities, Information Technology, Journalism, Marketing, Master of Business Administration (MBA), Mathematics, Photography, Physics, Psychology, Science

Nationality: Any Region

Location of Study: Oklahoma City University
Oklahoma City, OK

AWARD INFORMATION

Award Type: Scholarship

Average Amount: $10,000

Award Coverage: Tuition

Award Duration: 4 years

ELIGIBILITY REQUIREMENTS

- SAT score 1020 (reading + math) and higher combined with HS GPA 3.0 or better on a 4.0 scale

APPLICATION INFORMATION

Award Deadline: Mar

Instructions: Award is automatic, there are no special application instructions

CONTACT

Oklahoma City University
Associate Vice President of International Admissions
Tel: +1 (405) 208-5130
Email: ia@okcu.edu
Web: www.okcu.edu/admissions/freshmen/scholarships/

Oklahoma City University

Oklahoma City University Undergraduate and Graduate Scholarships

PROGRAM INFORMATION

Description: Each year Oklahoma City University awards scholarships to more than 80 percent of eligible and promising freshman, transfer, and graduate students. The application for admission is also the application for most scholarships. Scholarships are based on academic merit or performance. Interest in scholarships may be marked on the International Application form.

Levels of Study: Undergraduate, Graduate

Field of Study: All

Nationality: Any Region

Location of Study: Oklahoma City University
Oklahoma City, OK

AWARD INFORMATION

Award Type: Scholarship, Tuition Reduction

Average Amount: Varies

Number of Awards: Varies

Award Coverage: Tuition

Award Duration: Varies

ELIGIBILITY REQUIREMENTS

- Freshmen: Minimum High School GPA 3.0, SAT 1020 or ACT 22
- International freshmen who do not take SAT or ACT: Minimum High School GPA 3.0, TOEFL 80/IELTS 6.0
- Transfer: Minimum transfer GPA 3.0
- Students with a minimum 3.85 GPA and minimum ACT 31 are invited to apply for the full-tuition Trustee Scholarship, Applications must be received by Dec 4
- Scholarship requirements vary and are subject to change without notice, for the most specific and up to date information, please check the website: www.okcu.edu/financialaid/scholarships/undergrad/

APPLICATION INFORMATION

Award Deadline: Nov for early awards; Mar is the final deadline

Instructions: Most scholarships are awarded automatically. For Trustee Scholarship instructions, please visit our website: www.okcu.edu/financialaid/scholarships/undergrad/freshmen/#trustee

CONTACT

Oklahoma City University
Assistant Director of International Admissions
2501 N. Blackwelder Street
Oklahoma City, OK 73106
Tel: +1 (405) 208-5358
Fax: +1 (405) 208-5279
Email: ia@okcu.edu
Web: www.okcu.edu

Oklahoma State University Institute of Technology

Oklahoma State University Institute of Technology International Student Tuition Waiver

PROGRAM INFORMATION

Description: Oklahoma State University Institute of Technology offers a competitive non-resident tuition waiver for international students. This is a discount of up to $500 of non-resident tuition per term. Eligibility is based on course grades for previous academic work and prior student leadership experience.

Levels of Study: Undergraduate

Field of Study: All

Nationality: Any Region

Location of Study: Oklahoma State University Institute of Technology
Okmulgee, OK

AWARD INFORMATION

Award Type: Tuition Reduction

Average Amount: Up to $500 per semester

Number of Awards: 5

Award Coverage: Portion of non-resident tuition

Award Duration: Until graduation

ELIGIBILITY REQUIREMENTS

- Must have and maintain a 3.0 GPA or higher to be eligible
- Must be degree seeking and maintain full-time enrollment (12 credit hours per semester)
- Must live on campus
- Student should maintain proper status according to US Citizenship & Immigration Services and US Department of Homeland Security regulations
- Students must provide a transcript evaluation to certify GPA. Contact the OSUIT international office for a list of approved evaluation agencies; exception: evaluation is not required of students transferring in from another US institution

APPLICATION INFORMATION

Instructions: Contact the international office to request an application, or download at go.osuit.edu/advancement/international/admissions

CONTACT

Oklahoma State University Institute of Technology
OSUIT International Office
Suite 108, Donald W. Reynolds Technology Center
1801 E 4th Street
Okmulgee, OK 74447
Tel: +1 (918) 293-4998
Fax: +1 (918) 293-4633
Email: osuit.international@okstate.edu
Web: go.osuit.edu/advancement/international/admissions

Old Dominion University
Old Dominion University International Undergraduate Student Scholarship

PROGRAM INFORMATION

Description: Competitive and merit based, Old Dominion University's International Student Scholarship covers partial tuition up to $10,000 per year. The scholarship is renewable for up to 4 years based on continued academic performance. This scholarship is available to undergraduate international students only.

Levels of Study: Undergraduate

Nationality: Any Region

Location of Study: Old Dominion University Norfolk, VA

AWARD INFORMATION

Award Type: Scholarship

Average Amount: Up to $10,000 per year

Number of Awards: 45

Award Coverage: Partial tuition and fees

Award Duration: Maximum of 4 years

ELIGIBILITY REQUIREMENTS

- Must be a new international undergraduate student holding a non-immigrant visa (F1 Visa), must not have previously enrolled at ODU Must be Ineligible for in-state tuition
- Must have a minimum US-equivalent GPA of "B+"
- Must have TOEFL (Test of English as a Foreign Language) score of 550 PBT/79 IBT, or other demonstrated English proficiency as described on university website
- 1 page essay indicating academic intent and personal goals
- 1 letter of recommendation from previous teacher or advisor; leadership ability through school and community activities should be addressed

APPLICATION INFORMATION

Award Deadline: Fall semester, Apr 15; Spring semester, Oct 1

Instructions: Apply online

CONTACT
Old Dominion University
Office of International Admissions
2101 Dragas Hall
Norfolk, Virginia 23529
Tel: +1 (757) 683-3701
Fax: +1 (757) 683-3651
Email: intladm@odu.edu
Web: www.odu.edu/admission/international/process/undergraduate-international-checklist/iss-scholarship

Oregon State University
Oregon State University International Cultural Service Program

PROGRAM INFORMATION

Description: The International Cultural Service Program (ICSP) began at OSU in 1983 and offers scholarships to international students in exchange for helping their academic college internationalize. Recipients will act as ambassadors for their countries and participate in cultural awareness-building activities.

Levels of Study: Undergraduate, Graduate

Field of Study: All

Nationality: Any Region

Location of Study: Oregon State University Corvallis, OR

AWARD INFORMATION

Award Type: Scholarship

Average Amount: Up to $13,500

Number of Awards: 30 - 35

Award Coverage: Tuition

Award Duration: Maximum of 4 years

ELIGIBILITY REQUIREMENTS

- Must be a non-citizen on an F-1 or J-1 visa, with the intention of studying full-time
- Must submit a complete application, including 2 letters of reference, by the deadline
- Must complete an application to OSU in full by Mar 1
- Must be willing to speak in the community about country and culture of origin
- Must maintain a G.P.A. of 2.5 for undergraduates or 3.0 for graduates (on a 4.0 scale)

APPLICATION INFORMATION

Award Deadline: Feb 1

Instructions: Please visit our website and download all application materials, application may be faxed or mailed, but should be received at OSU, Office of International Programs, no later than Mar 1

CONTACT
Oregon State University
2900 SW Jefferson Way
Corvallis, OR 97331
Email: intlonline@oregonstate.edu
Web: oregonstate.edu/admissions/international/scholarships

Oregon State University
Oregon State University - International Provost Scholarship

PROGRAM INFORMATION

Description: Competitive scholarships are offered to exceptional international students. Award amounts vary and are renewable for up to 4 years of undergraduate study if renewal requirements are met. No separate scholarship application is required.

Levels of Study: Undergraduate

Field of Study: All

Nationality: Any Region

Location of Study: Oregon State University Corvallis, OR

AWARD INFORMATION

Award Type: Grant, Scholarship, Tuition Reduction

Average Amount: $6,000-$9,000

Number of Awards: 9 - 15

Award Coverage: Tuition remission.

Award Duration: Maximum of 4 years

ELIGIBILITY REQUIREMENTS

- Must be an international student
- Must have a 3.5 GPA or greater
- Must meet the English language proficiency requirements for full admission
- No separate scholarship application is required, qualified applicants automatically considered

APPLICATION INFORMATION

Award Deadline: Feb

Instructions: For more information on the scholarship, please visit the website or email financial.aid@oregonstate.edu

CONTACT
Office of Financial Aid and Scholarships
218 Kerr Administration Building
Corvallis, OR 97331-2120
Tel: +1 (541) 737-2241
Fax: +1 (541) 737-4494
Email: financial.aid@oregonstate.edu
Web: oregonstate.edu/financialaid/international-provost-scholarship

Oregon State University
INTO OSU Merit-Based Scholarship

PROGRAM INFORMATION

Description: Designed to help INTO OSU Pathway students finance their programs, the Merit-Based Scholarship will be awarded to those students who excel academically. A Pathway is a 1-year program that happens during a student's first year at OSU where they'll receive additional support with academics, English, and transition to life in the US. This scholarship is for students entering the Pathway.

Levels of Study: Undergraduate, Graduate

Field of Study: All

Nationality: Any Region

Location of Study: Oregon State University Corvallis, OR

AWARD INFORMATION

Award Type: Scholarship

Average Amount: $9,000

Number of Awards: 15

Award Coverage: Tuition

Award Duration: Maximum of 1 year

ELIGIBILITY REQUIREMENTS

- 3.0 overall GPA for graduates 2.9 overall GPA for undergraduates
- Fully admitted to an INTO OSU Pathway
- Must be an international student

APPLICATION INFORMATION

Award Deadline: Jul

Instructions: Apply to a Pathway program and contact intlonline@oregonstate.edu for consideration if you meet the requirements, for more information on how to apply, please visit website

CONTACT

INTO OSU
1701 SW Western Blvd.
Corvallis, OR 97333
Email: intlonline@oregonstate.edu
Web: oregonstate.edu/admissions/international/scholarships

Oregon State University

INTO OSU Continued Success Scholarship

PROGRAM INFORMATION

Description: The INTO OSU Continued Success Scholarship helps students finance studies in a full OSU graduate or undergraduate program after a pathway program. Regardless of academic performance prior to the pathway, this scholarship allows students to start anew and earn recognition for performing well in the US. This applies only to the year immediately following a Pathway program.

Nationality: Any Region

Location of Study: Oregon State University Corvallis, OR

ELIGIBILITY REQUIREMENTS

- 3.6 overall GPA during Pathway
- Meet all progression requirements within a 3-term Pathway program
- Fully admitted to an OSU program

APPLICATION INFORMATION

Award Deadline: Qualified applicants are automatically awarded

Instructions: No action required. Qualified applicants are automatically awarded

CONTACT

Oregon State University
INTO OSU
1701 SW Western Blvd.
Corvallis, OR 97333
Email: intlonline@oregonstate.edu
Web: www.oregonstate.edu/admissions/international/continued-success

Oregon State University

INTO OSU Regional Scholarship

PROGRAM INFORMATION

Description: The INTO OSU Regional Scholarship is designed to help students financially access award-winning academic and English programs in the US.

Nationality: Any Region

Location of Study: Oregon State University Corvallis, OR

ELIGIBILITY REQUIREMENTS

- Must be an international student

APPLICATION INFORMATION

Award Deadline: 4 weeks prior to start

Instructions: Contact intlonline@oregonstate.edu; for more information on how to apply, please visit website

CONTACT

INTO OSU
1701 SW Western Blvd.
Corvallis, OR 97333
Email: intlonline@oregonstate.edu
Web: oregonstate.edu/admissions/international/scholarships

Our Lady of the Lake University

Our Lady of the Lake University International Undergraduate Scholarships

PROGRAM INFORMATION

Description: Our Lady of the Lake University (OLLU), located in San Antonio, Texas, offers up to $10,000 in scholarships per year to undergraduate international students who want a bachelor's degree. Scholarships are not available if you already have a bachelor's degree. OLLU is a private, Catholic university for men and women founded in 1895. OLLU competes in the NAIA sports league and scholarships are available under conditions.

Levels of Study: Undergraduate

Field of Study: All

Nationality: Any Region

Location of Study: Our Lady of the Lake University San Antonio, TX

AWARD INFORMATION

Award Type: Scholarship

Average Amount: Up to $10,000

Number of Awards: Unlimited

Award Coverage: Partial tuition, fees, books, living expenses

Award Duration: 4 years

ELIGIBILITY REQUIREMENTS

- To be eligible for the $10,000 scholarship students must have a minimum GPA of 3.5 on a 4.0 scale
- To be eligible for the $7,500 scholarship students must have a GPA between 3.0-3.49 on a 4.0 scale
- To be eligible for the $5,000 scholarship students must have a GPA between 2.5-2.99 on a 4.0 scale
- OLLU does not offer the above scholarships to graduate students, a $1,500 per academic year is offered to international graduate students in our Weekend College programs
- The scholarship is limited to undergraduate students for the first bachelor's degree

APPLICATION INFORMATION

Award Deadline: Rolling

Instructions: Send an email to International Admissions to indicate your desire to apply to OLLU; undergraduate applicants are welcome to scan/email transcript[s] of secondary school, transfer student will have to obtain a credential evaluation, instructions will be given.

CONTACT

Our Lady of the Lake University
International Admissions
411 SW 24th St.
San Antonio, TX 78207
Tel: +1 (210) 431-3978
Fax: +1 (210) 431-4036
Email: international@lake.ollusa.edu
Web: www.ollusa.edu

Pacific Lutheran University

Pacific Lutheran University International Student Scholarships

PROGRAM INFORMATION

Description: Renewable international student scholarships. Amount varies up to full tuition per year. Must enroll at PLU to qualify

Levels of Study: Undergraduate, Graduate

Field of Study: All

Nationality: Any Region

Location of Study: Pacific Lutheran University Tacoma, WA

AWARD INFORMATION

Award Type: Scholarship

Average Amount: Varies

Number of Awards: Unlimited

Award Coverage: Tuition and fees

Award Duration: Up to 4 years

ELIGIBILITY REQUIREMENTS

- Must be enrolled at Pacific Lutheran University
- Must meet all admission requirements, including English proficiency

APPLICATION INFORMATION

Award Deadline: Rolling

Instructions: For more information, please visit the website, or email kuroiwalewis@plu.edu

CONTACT

Pacific Lutheran University
Director of International Admission
Office of Admission
Tacoma, WA 98447-0003
Tel: +1 (253) 535-8177
Fax: +1 (253) 536-5136
Email: kuroiwalewis@plu.edu
Web: www.plu.edu/admission/international/home.php

Pacific Lutheran University
Pacific Lutheran University Nordic Scholarship

PROGRAM INFORMATION

Description: Renewable International student scholarship that covers $10,000 per year for undergraduate scholarship for students from Scandinavia.

Levels of Study: Undergraduate, Graduate

Field of Study: All

Nationality: Denmark, Finland, Iceland, Norway, Sweden

Location of Study: Pacific Lutheran University Tacoma, WA

AWARD INFORMATION

Award Type: Scholarship

Average Amount: Approx $10,000

Number of Awards: Unlimited

Award Coverage: Tuition and fees

Award Duration: Up to 4 years

ELIGIBILITY REQUIREMENTS

- Must be enrolled at Pacific Lutheran University
- Must be a citizen of a Nordic country
- Must be a degree seeking student
- Must live on campus

APPLICATION INFORMATION

Award Deadline: Rolling

Instructions: For more information, please visit the website or email kuroiwalewis@plu.edu

CONTACT

Pacific Lutheran University
Director of International Admission
Office of Admission
Tacoma, WA 98447-0003
Tel: +1 (253) 535-8177
Fax: +1 (253) 536-5136
Email: kuroiwalewis@plu.edu
Web: www.plu.edu/admission/international/home.php

Pacific Lutheran University
Pacific Lutheran University Scholarships

PROGRAM INFORMATION

Description: Renewable International student scholarships, amount varies up to $22,000 per year; must be enrolled at Pacific Lutheran University to qualify.

Levels of Study: Undergraduate, Graduate

Field of Study: All

Nationality: Asia, Europe, Latin America, Middle East, North America, Oceania, Namibia, South Africa

Location of Study: Pacific Lutheran University Tacoma, WA

AWARD INFORMATION

Award Type: Tuition Reduction

Average Amount: Varies

Number of Awards: Unlimited

Award Coverage: Tuition and fees

Award Duration: Up to 4 years

ELIGIBILITY REQUIREMENTS

- Must be enrolled at Pacific Lutheran University
- Must meet all admission requirements including English proficiency

APPLICATION INFORMATION

Award Deadline: Rolling

Instructions: For more information, please visit the website or email kuroiwalewis@plu.edu

CONTACT

Pacific Lutheran University
Director of International Admission
Office of Admission
Tacoma, WA 98447-0003
Tel: +1 (253) 535 8177
Fax: +1 (253) 536-5136
Email: kuroiwalewis@plu.edu
Web: www.plu.edu

Pacific University Oregon
Pacific University Oregon Honors Scholarship

PROGRAM INFORMATION

Description: Pacific University offers automatic merit scholarships to international students studying at the undergraduate level.

Levels of Study: Undergraduate

Field of Study: All

Nationality: Any Region

Location of Study: Pacific University Forest Grove, OR

AWARD INFORMATION

Award Type: Scholarship

Average Amount: $19,000

Number of Awards: Unlimited

Award Coverage: Tuition

Award Duration: Maximum of 4 years

ELIGIBILITY REQUIREMENTS

- Must have a minimum GPA at his/her previous school of 3.7 on a 4.0 scale, grades from outside US will be converted to US grading system, then amount of scholarship will be determined

APPLICATION INFORMATION

Award Deadline: No deadline

Instructions: Apply online or download application packet, application can be submitted by fax, email, or postal mail

CONTACT

Pacific University
International Admissions
2043 College Way UC A151
Forest Grove, OR 97116
Tel: +1 (503) 352-2851
Fax: +1 (503) 352-2975
Email: johnharn@pacificu.edu
Web: www.pacificu.edu

Pacific University Oregon
Pacific University Oregon Presidential Scholarship

PROGRAM INFORMATION

Description: Pacific University offers automatic merit scholarships to international students studying at the undergraduate level.

Levels of Study: Undergraduate

Field of Study: All

Nationality: Any Region

Location of Study: Pacific University Forest Grove, OR

AWARD INFORMATION

Award Type: Scholarship

Average Amount: $15,500

Number of Awards: Unlimited

Award Coverage: Tuition

Award Duration: Maximum of 4 years

ELIGIBILITY REQUIREMENTS

- Recipients average a 3.6 GPA on a 4.0 scale from previous school; grades from outside US will be converted to US grading system, then amount of scholarship will be determined

APPLICATION INFORMATION

Instructions: Apply online or download application packet

CONTACT

Pacific University
International Student Admissions
2043 College Way UC A151
Forest Grove, OR 97116
Tel: +1 (503) 352-2851
Fax: +1 (503) 352-2970
Email: johnharn@pacificu.edu
Web: www.pacificu.edu

Pacific University Oregon
Pacific University Oregon Trustee Scholarship

PROGRAM INFORMATION

Description: Pacific University offers automatic merit scholarships to international students studying at the undergraduate level.

Levels of Study: Undergraduate

Field of Study: All

Nationality: Any Region

Location of Study: Pacific University Forest Grove, OR

AWARD INFORMATION

Award Type: Scholarship

Average Amount: $11,500

Number of Awards: Unlimited

Award Coverage: Tuition

Award Duration: Maximum of 4 years

ELIGIBILITY REQUIREMENTS

- Recipients average a 3.39 GPA, grades from outside US will be converted to US grading system, then amount of scholarship will be determined
- Recipients average a combined Math and Critical Reading SAT score of 1070 or ACT score of 23

APPLICATION INFORMATION

Instructions: Apply online or download application packet

CONTACT

Pacific University
International Student Admissions
2043 College Way UC A151
Forest Grove, OR 97116
Tel: +1 (503) 352-2851
Fax: +1 (503) 352-2970
Email: johnharn@pacificu.edu
Web: www.pacificu.edu

Pacific University Oregon
Pacific University Oregon University Scholarship

PROGRAM INFORMATION

Description: Pacific University offers automatic merit scholarships to international students studying at the undergraduate level.

Levels of Study: Undergraduate

Field of Study: All

Nationality: Any Region

Location of Study: Pacific University Forest Grove, OR

AWARD INFORMATION

Award Type: Scholarship

Average Amount: $10,500

Number of Awards: Unlimited

Award Coverage: Tuition

Award Duration: Maximum of 4 years

ELIGIBILITY REQUIREMENTS

- Recipients average a 3.19 GPA; grades from outside US will be converted to US grading system, then amount of scholarship will be determined

APPLICATION INFORMATION

Instructions: Apply online or download application packet

CONTACT

Pacific University
International Student Admissions
2043 College Way UC A151
Forest Grove, OR 97116
Tel: +1 (503) 352-2851
Fax: +1 (503) 352-2970
Email: johnharn@pacificu.edu
Web: www.pacificu.edu

Pacific University Oregon
Pacific University Oregon Online Scholarship Competition

PROGRAM INFORMATION

Description: An online scholarship competition, by invitation only, to admitted students with a minimum GPA. It is a math and writing competition that you can complete from any computer.

Levels of Study: Undergraduate

Field of Study: All

Nationality: Any Region

AWARD INFORMATION

Award Type: Tuition Reduction

Average Amount: $2,000-$5,000 per year

Number of Awards: Unlimited

Award Duration: Maximum 4 years

ELIGIBILITY REQUIREMENTS

- Apply and be admitted before Mar 1.

APPLICATION INFORMATION

Award Deadline: Feb before fall start date

Instructions: You will receive an invitation, after you are admitted, if you qualify

CONTACT

Pacific University
International Admissions
2043 College Way
Forest Grove, OR 97116
Email: johnharn@pacificu.edu
Web: www.pacificu.edu/onlinescholarship

Pacific University Oregon
Pacific University Oregon Pacesetters Scholarship Competition

PROGRAM INFORMATION

Description: Applicants must travel to Pacific University Oregon's campus for this event and take a math and writing test. Invitations are offered to fully admitted freshman students only with good high school scores. Applicants must be admitted to Pacific by Feb 1 and start the following fall semester. If you participate, you will receive a minimum scholarship of $2,000 per year, in addition to your merit scholarship. Some students will receive $5,000 per year. The top 2 students will receive full tuition scholarships for 4 years.

Levels of Study: Undergraduate

Field of Study: All

Nationality: Any Region

AWARD INFORMATION

Award Type: Scholarship

Average Amount: $2,000-full tuition per year

Number of Awards: 100

Award Duration: 4 years

ELIGIBILITY REQUIREMENTS

- Must apply and be admitted by Feb 1
- Must be a freshman (transfer students are not eligible)
- Usually must have at least a 3.5 GPA on scale of 4
- Must travel to our campus near Portland, Oregon, for testing
- If you attend Pacific, we will reimburse you $350 toward your airfare (with airline receipt)

APPLICATION INFORMATION

Award Deadline: Feb

CONTACT

Pacific University
International Admissions
2043 College Way
Forest Grove, OR 97116
Tel: +1 (503) 352-2851
Fax: +1 (503) 352-2975
Email: johnharn@pacificu.edu
Web: www.pacificu.edu/pacesetters

Pacific University Oregon
Pacific University Oregon Music Scholarship

PROGRAM INFORMATION

Description: Pacific has an extensive program of grants, scholarships and awards to help students finance their education. Scholarships for music are awarded on the basis of talent, and do not require that the recipient be a music major. All scholarship awards from the music department become part of the total institutional package offered by the University to the student.

Levels of Study: Undergraduate

Field of Study: All

Nationality: Any Region

Location of Study: Pacific University Forest Grove, OR

AWARD INFORMATION

Award Type: Scholarship

Average Amount: $2,000-$6,000 per year

Number of Awards: Approx 30

Award Coverage: Tuition

Award Duration: 4 years

ELIGIBILITY REQUIREMENTS

- Must be skilled in voice or a musical instrument
- If given award, must take music lessons and perform in school symphony, band or choir

APPLICATION INFORMATION

Award Deadline: Feb

Instructions: Future students must apply for the scholarship before they become a student at Pacific University to be eligible for this scholarship, contact or see website for more information

CONTACT

Pacific University
International Admissions
2043 College Way
Forest Grove, OR 97116
Tel: +1 (503) 352-2851
Fax: +1 (503) 352-2975
Email: johnharn@pacificu.edu
Web: www.pacificu.edu

Pacific University Oregon
Pacific University Founders Scholarship

PROGRAM INFORMATION

Description: Pacific University offers automatic merit scholarships to international students studying at the undergraduate level.

Levels of Study: Undergraduate

Field of Study: All

Nationality: Any Region

Location of Study: Pacific University
Forest Grove, OR

AWARD INFORMATION

Award Type: Scholarship

Average Amount: $22,000

Number of Awards: Unlimited

Award Coverage: Tuition

Award Duration: Maximum of 4 years

ELIGIBILITY REQUIREMENTS

- Must have a minimum GPA at his/her previous school of 3.81 on a 4.0 scale, grades from outside US will be converted to US scale

APPLICATION INFORMATION

Award Deadline: No deadline

Instructions: Apply via Common App or send email for paper form to intladmissions@pacificu.edu

CONTACT

Pacific University
International Admissions
2043 College Way
Forest Grove, OR 97116
Tel: +1 (503) 352-2841
Fax: +1 (502) 352-2975
Email: intladmissions@pacificu.edu
Web: www.pacificu.edu/intl

Penn State University Dickinson School of Law
Penn State Law LLM Merit Scholarships

PROGRAM INFORMATION

Description: The Law School awards merit-based scholarships to its outstanding LLM applicants. Typical awards range in size from $3,000 to $5,000 US All applicants are considered for merit-based scholarships and no separate scholarship form is required.

Levels of Study: Graduate, Professional

Field of Study: Law

Nationality: Any Region

Location of Study: Penn State University Dickinson School of Law
State College, PA

AWARD INFORMATION

Award Type: Scholarship, Tuition Reduction

Average Amount: $3,000-$5,000

Number of Awards: Varies

Award Coverage: Tuition

Award Duration: Length of program

ELIGIBILITY REQUIREMENTS

- Admission criteria apply, upon admission every student is considered for a merit scholarship, no special application is required

APPLICATION INFORMATION

Award Deadline: Jun

Instructions: Application information can be found at law.psu.edu/llm/apply

CONTACT

Penn State Law
Admissions
Lewis Katz Building
16802 University Park, PA
Tel: (814) 867-2373
Email: fcm3@psu.edu
Web: www.law.psu.edu/llm

Pew Latin American Fellows
Pew Latin American Fellows Program in the Biomedical Sciences

PROGRAM INFORMATION

Description: The Pew Charitable Trusts is sponsoring a program to provide support for young scientists from Latin America for postdoctoral training in the US. The program is intended to provide such individuals with an opportunity to further their scientific knowledge, promote scientific exchange and collaboration between investigators in the US and Latin America, and advance basic scientific research in Latin America.

Levels of Study: Doctorate, Post Doctorate, Professional

Field of Study: Biochemistry, Biology, Biotechnology

Nationality: Latin America

Location of Study: University of San Francisco
San Francisco, CA

AWARD INFORMATION

Award Type: Fellowship

Average Amount: $60,000 over 2 years

Number of Awards: Varies

Award Duration: 2 years

ELIGIBILITY REQUIREMENTS

- Must have held a PhD and/or MD degrees, or equivalent, for no more than 5 years
- Applicants who received their degree from schools in the US, Canada, or Europe will not be accepted
- Applicants may not have had previous postdoctoral training outside of Latin America nor may they already hold a postdoctoral position in the US
- Must submit a written statement of intent to return to Latin America. Fellows must have a confirmed position and laboratory space in their home country by the end of the fellowship period in order to obtain the $35,000 portion of the award

APPLICATION INFORMATION

Award Deadline: Oct

Instructions: Applications are available online

CONTACT

University of San Francisco
Center for Health Professions
3333 California Street, Suite 410
San Francisco, CA 94118
Tel: +1 (415) 476-8181
Fax: +1 (415) 476-4113
Email: apepper@pewtrusts.org
Web: www.pewtrusts.org/en/projects/pew-latin-american-fellows

Pine Manor College
Pine Manor College Global Scholarships for International Students

PROGRAM INFORMATION

Description: Consistently ranked as the number 1 most diverse liberal arts college in the US, Pine Manor College offers women from all backgrounds the opportunity to develop leadership skills and study in an inclusive and nurturing environment. A 4-year private college for women founded in 1911, Pine Manor offers 9 majors encompassing over 50 different areas of interest.

Levels of Study: Undergraduate

Field of Study: All

Nationality: Any Region

Location of Study: Pine Manor College
Chestnut Hill, MA

AWARD INFORMATION

Award Type: Scholarship

Average Amount: $2,500-$5,000

Award Coverage: Tuition

ELIGIBILITY REQUIREMENTS

- International scholarships vary in their eligibility criteria

APPLICATION INFORMATION

Instructions: Prospective students should consult the website for more detailed Pine Manor scholarship information

CONTACT

Pine Manor College
Office of Undergraduate Admission
400 Heath Street
Chesnut Hill, MA 02467
Tel: +1 (617) 731-7011
Email: aadmission@pmc.edu
Web: www.pmc.edu/international

Pittsburg State University

Pittsburg State International Scholarships/Assistantships

PROGRAM INFORMATION

Description: Pittsburg State University is a public university located in the southeast corner of the state of Kansas. Serving approximately 7,000 students, PSU has an international population of about 500 students from 40 different countries. Pittsburg State offers more than 100 internationally recognized undergraduate and graduate degrees. Although the university is more than 100 years old, class sizes have remained small and individually focused. Pittsburg State University is very attractive to prospective international students because of the quality of our programs and the comparatively low tuition fees.

Levels of Study: Undergraduate, Graduate

Field of Study: All

Nationality: Any Region

Location of Study: Pittsburg State University, Kansas Pittsburg, KS

AWARD INFORMATION

Award Type: Scholarship, Tuition Reduction

Average Amount: Varies

Number of Awards: Undergraduate: 40; graduate: varies

Award Coverage: Undergraduate scholarships cover partial to full tuition; graduate assistantships can cover tuition, stipend for living expenses

Award Duration: Varies

ELIGIBILITY REQUIREMENTS

- Undergraduate International Advocate Scholarship: Cumulative GPA of 3.25, student may apply for this scholarship after 1 semester at Pittsburg State
- Undergraduate Honors College for Incoming Freshmen: GPA 3.5. Must be admitted to PSU and apply before Feb 1 for fall admission each year, applicants must also submit a SAT or ACT score
- Undergraduate Honors College for Transfer Students: GPA 3.75, must be admitted to PSU and apply before Feb 1 for fall admission each year
- Graduate Assistantships: Must be admitted to the graduate program
- Graduate and undergraduate incoming student scholarships are selected based on academic records submitted with application

APPLICATION INFORMATION

Award Deadline: Varies

Instructions: Visit our website for more information on how to apply

CONTACT

International Programs & Services
International Recruitment & Undergrad Admissions
118 Whitesitt Hall, Pittsburg State University
1701 S Broadway
Pittsburg, KS 66762
Tel: +1 (620) 235-4680
Fax: +1 (620) 235-4962
Email: iss@pittstate.edu
Web: www.pittstate.edu/iss

Polytechnic Institute of New York University

Polytechnic Institute of New York University Merit Scholarships in Technology, Science and Engineering

PROGRAM INFORMATION

Description: Founded in 1854 in New York City, Polytechnic Institute of New York University is a unique technology institution dedicated to promoting hands-on education. Students receive a firm grounding in science and technology before embarking on team projects around the globe that allow students to apply their knowledge to real problems. Its New York City location is ideal for such an approach to education. Immersed in 1 of the world's most diverse and exciting cities, students have ample opportunities to learn from professionals and develop unique projects. Top companies visit the campus twice a year to recruit students. Class student/teacher ratio is 12:1. Polytechnic takes pride in its international student body. The university holds more than 500 international students from more than 60 countries.

Levels of Study: Undergraduate, Graduate

Field of Study: Engineering, Science

Nationality: Any Region

Location of Study: Polytechnic Institute of New York University
New York, NY

AWARD INFORMATION

Award Type: Loan, Scholarship

Average Amount: Varies

Number of Awards: Varies

APPLICATION INFORMATION

Instructions: For more detailed information, please visit our website

CONTACT

Polytechnic Institute of New York University
Wunsch Building- MetroTech Campus
Brooklyn, NY 11201
Tel: +1 (718) 637-5955
Fax: +1 (718) 260-3446
Email: uadmit@poly.edu
Web: www.poly.edu/admissions/undergrad/scholarships_and_air/merit_scholarships.php

Portland State University

Portland State University International Achievement Scholarship

PROGRAM INFORMATION

Description: The International Achievement Scholarship is awarded to incoming international undergraduate students on the basis of their academic achievement. Students who maintain high academic standing will receive renewed funding for up to 4 years. All admitted students automatically will be considered for the scholarship.

Levels of Study: Undergraduate

Field of Study: All

Nationality: Any Region

Location of Study: Portland State University
Portland, OR

AWARD INFORMATION

Award Type: Scholarship

Average Amount: Up to $4,500

Number of Awards: Unlimited

Award Coverage: Tuition, not applicable for ESL courses or summer term coursework

Award Duration: Maximum of 4 years

ELIGIBILITY REQUIREMENTS

- Must have entering grade point averages (GPA) of at least 3.2 out of a possible 4.0 grading scale
- Must be enrolled in full-time coursework; at least 12 undergraduate credits

APPLICATION INFORMATION

Award Deadline: Rolling

Instructions: Application for admission is also the scholarship application; no separate form is required, scholarship notification is typically within 3 weeks of admission to the university

CONTACT

Portland State University
Office of Admissions, Registration & Records
PO Box 751
Portland, OR 97207-0751
Tel: +1 (503) 725-5535
Fax: +1 (503) 725-5525
Email: intladm@pdx.edu
Web: www.pdx.edu/scholarships/future-international

Portland State University

Fulbright Matching Grant

PROGRAM INFORMATION

Description: Fulbright Scholars who are admitted and enroll in Portland State University degree programs will receive a matching grant of $4,500 per year. This renewable matching scholarship is available to all Fulbright Scholars. The grant is applicable to PSU instructional fees in each eligible term of enrollment. Portland State also waives application fees for Fulbright Scholars who apply for admission.

Levels of Study: Graduate, Doctorate, Post Doctorate, Professional

Field of Study: All

Nationality: Any Region

Location of Study: Portland State University
Portland, OR

AWARD INFORMATION

Award Type: Scholarship

Average Amount: $4,500

Award Coverage: Tuition remission

ELIGIBILITY REQUIREMENTS

- Must be a recipient of a Fulbright Scholarship/Fellowship
- Must be admitted to a Portland State University degree program (non-ESL)
- Minimum enrollment of 12 credit hours per term for undergraduate students and 9 hours per term for graduate students
- Must maintain continued satisfactory academic standing

APPLICATION INFORMATION

Award Deadline: Rolling

Instructions: No separate application is required, all Fulbright Scholars who apply for admission are automatically awarded this scholarship

CONTACT

Portland State University
Office of Admissions, Registration & Records
P.O. Box 751
Portland, OR 97201-0751
Tel: +1 (503) 725-5535
Fax: +1 (503) 725-5525
Email: intladm@pdx.edu
Web: www.pdx.edu/admissions/international-scholarship-opportunities

Portland State University

Portland State University International Student Retention Scholarship

PROGRAM INFORMATION

Description: The International Student Retention Scholarship, made possible through funding from the State of Oregon, offers partial tuition scholarships each year to a number of deserving students from countries throughout the world. Recipients receive a $1,000 tuition waiver for a maximum of 6 terms and awards are given in fall, winter, and spring terms.

Levels of Study: Undergraduate, Graduate

Field of Study: All

Nationality: Any Region

Location of Study: Portland State University Portland, OR

AWARD INFORMATION

Award Type: Tuition Reduction

Average Amount: $1,000 per term

Number of Awards: 30

Award Coverage: Tuition remission

Award Duration: Maximum of 2 years

ELIGIBILITY REQUIREMENTS

- Undergraduate students (at least sophomore standing) must have been enrolled at PSU for at least 3 terms; undergraduate transfer students (at least sophomore standing) must have been enrolled at PSU for at least 1 term; post-baccalaureate and graduate students must have been enrolled at PSU for at least 1 term
- Undergraduates must have a minimum GPA of 2.75. Graduates must have a minimum GPA of 3.0

APPLICATION INFORMATION

Award Deadline: Jul, Oct, Feb

Instructions: To apply you must submit the application form (www.pdx.edu/international-students/international-student-retention-scholarship-isrs) and documents listed on the application form

CONTACT

Portland State University
Office of International Affairs
P.O. Box 751
Portland, OR 97201-0751
Tel: +1 (503) 725-5943
Email: hondy@pdx.edu
Web: www.pdx.edu/international-students/international-student-scholarships

Portland State University

Portland State University Graduate Assistantship

PROGRAM INFORMATION

Description: Graduate assistantships are offered by academic and administrative departments at the university. They may include work such as Graduate Teaching Assistants (GTA), Graduate Research Assistants (GRA), or Graduate Administrative Assistants (GAA). Students will work approximately 19 hours per week and receive both a tuition remission and a salary.

Levels of Study: Graduate, Doctorate, Post Doctorate, Professional

Field of Study: All

Nationality: Any Region

Location of Study: Portland State University Portland, OR

AWARD INFORMATION

Award Type: Associateship, Tuition Reduction

Average Amount: Varies

Award Coverage: Full tuition, living stipend

ELIGIBILITY REQUIREMENTS

- Must be admitted to a graduate degree program at PSU
- Must complete a minimum of 9 graduate credits each term and maintain a cumulative GPA of 3.0 or higher

APPLICATION INFORMATION

Instructions: Students should contact their academic departments and program coordinator for more information

CONTACT

Portland State University
Office of Graduate Studies
P.O. Box 751
OGS Portland, OR
Tel: +1 (503) 725-8410
Fax: +1 (503) 725-3416
Email: grad@pdx.edu
Web: www.pdx.edu/ogs/graduate-assistantships

Portland State University

Portland State University International Cultural Service Program

PROGRAM INFORMATION

Description: International Cultural Service Program (ICSP) is a scholarship program for international students. ICSP students complete 90 hours of cultural service per academic year. This service generally takes the form of giving cultural presentations to local schools and community groups. PSU students selected as ICSP participants receive a partial tuition remission scholarship equal to approximately half of the non-resident tuition charged during fall, winter, and spring terms.

Levels of Study: Undergraduate, Graduate, Doctorate

Field of Study: All

Nationality: Any Region

Location of Study: Portland State University Portland, OR

AWARD INFORMATION

Award Type: Scholarship

Average Amount: $3000 per term for undergraduate students, $2500 per term for graduate students

Number of Awards: 25

Award Coverage: Tuition remission

Award Duration: Maximum of 1 degree level

ELIGIBILITY REQUIREMENTS

- In order to apply to ICSP, undergraduate students (at least sophomore standing) must have been enrolled on a full-time basis at PSU for at least 3 terms; undergraduate transfer students (at least sophomore standing) must have been enrolled at PSU for at least 1 term; post-baccalaureate and graduate students must have been enrolled at PSU for at least 1 term
- Must perform 90 hours of cultural service per academic year in the Portland community

APPLICATION INFORMATION

Award Deadline: May, Oct, Feb

Instructions: Submit the application found here: www.pdx.edu/international-students/international-cultural-service-program-icsp, be sure to include all of the supporting documents listed on the application

CONTACT

Portland State University
Office of International Affairs
P.O. Box 751
Portland, OR 97201-0751
Tel: +1 (503) 725-9766
Email: rkrueger@pdx.edu
Web: www.pdx.edu/international-students/international-student-scholarships

Princeton University

Princeton University Postdoctoral Fellowships in Hellenic Studies

PROGRAM INFORMATION

Description: These fellowships are intended for scholars in Hellenic Studies, with a special emphasis on Modern Greek or Byzantine Studies, including their relation to the Classical tradition. The goal of this postdoctoral research fellowship program is to advance the scholarship of outstanding Hellenists at an early stage of their career, and thus to strengthen the field of post-Classical Greek Studies in the US and abroad.

Levels of Study: Post Doctorate

Field of Study: Classics, Greek Studies

Nationality: Any Region

Location of Study: Princeton University Princeton, NJ

AWARD INFORMATION

Award Type: Fellowship

Average Amount: Up to $49,000 plus reimbursement of research-related expenses

Number of Awards: 3

Award Coverage: Stipend, research-related expenses

Award Duration: Academic year

ELIGIBILITY REQUIREMENTS

- Must complete all the requirements for the doctoral degree by Mar of the year prior to commencement of fellowship, but no earlier than 4 years prior to the commencement of the fellowship

APPLICATION INFORMATION

Award Deadline: Jan

Instructions: Contact to request application materials

CONTACT

Scheide Caldwell House
Program in Hellenic Studies
Princeton University
Princeton, NJ 08544
Tel: +1 (609) 258-3339
Email: hlsapp@princeton.edu
Web: www.princeton.edu/~hellenic

Ramapo College of New Jersey

Ramapo College Presidential Scholarship

PROGRAM INFORMATION

Description: Established in 1969, Ramapo College is distinguished by its innovative mission, the 4 Pillars of Learning – International, Intercultural, Interdisciplinary, and Experiential. Ramapo College provides an International focus in nearly all fields of study, preparing students to become globally well versed and to take advantage of new opportunities in an increasing interdependent world. Currently most of Ramapo's international students are receiving the Foundation scholarships.

Levels of Study: Undergraduate

Nationality: Any Region

Location of Study: Ramapo College
Mahwah, NJ

AWARD INFORMATION

Award Type: Scholarship

Average Amount: Varies

Number of Awards: Varies

Award Coverage: Tuition

Award Duration: 4 years

ELIGIBILITY REQUIREMENTS

- Must have minimum of 3.5 GPA in high school
- Must have SAT scores of at least 1330 in Critical Reading and Mathematics

APPLICATION INFORMATION

Award Deadline: Dec 1 for spring semester; Mar 1 for fall semester

Instructions: No separate application for the scholarship is necessary

CONTACT

Ramapo College of New Jersey
Roukema Center for International Education
505 Ramapo Valley Road
ASB 123,
Mahwah, NJ 07430
Tel: +1 (201) 684-7533
Fax: +1 (201) 684-7989
Email: radhikar@ramapo.edu
Web: www.ramapo.edu/intl

Ramapo College of New Jersey

Ramapo College Provost Scholarship

PROGRAM INFORMATION

Description: Established in 1969, Ramapo College is distinguished by its innovative mission, the 4 Pillars of Learning – International, Intercultural, Interdisciplinary, and Experiential. Ramapo College provides an International focus in nearly all fields of study, preparing students to become globally well versed and to take advantage of new opportunities in an increasing interdependent world. Currently most of Ramapo's international students are receiving the Foundation scholarships.

Levels of Study: Undergraduate

Location of Study: Ramapo College of New Jersey
Mahwah, NJ

ELIGIBILITY REQUIREMENTS

- Must have 3.2 GPA at high school
- Must have SAT scores of at least 1300 in Critical Reading and Mathematics

APPLICATION INFORMATION

Award Deadline: Dec

CONTACT

Ramapo College of New Jersey
Director, International Student and Scholar Services
505 Ramapo Valley Road
ASB 123
Mahwah, NJ 07430
Tel: +1 (201) 684-7530
Fax: +1 (201) 684-7989
Email: radhikar@ramapo.edu
Web: www.ramapo.edu/international/students/

Randolph College

Randolph College Merit Scholarship Program

PROGRAM INFORMATION

Description: Randolph College is a private, co-educational, 4-year liberal arts and science college located in the mountains of Lynchburg, Virginia. The college offers a strong academic component with 28+ majors and 50 minors. A strong commitment to international students is reflected in the services the college provides as well as in the diversity found on campus.

Levels of Study: Undergraduate

Field of Study: All

Nationality: Any Region

Location of Study: Randolph College
Lynchburg, VA

AWARD INFORMATION

Award Type: Scholarship

Average Amount: $6,000-$20,000

Number of Awards: Varies

Award Coverage: Partial tuition

Award Duration: Academic year, renewable all 4 years as long as requirements are met

ELIGIBILITY REQUIREMENTS

- Must have a strong academic record
- Must have a minimum TOEFL score of 79 IBT or IELTS 6.5
- Must have a minimum SAT I Critical Reading score of 500
- Must be committed to the goals of a liberal arts & science educational environment

APPLICATION INFORMATION

Award Deadline: Feb for fall semester; Nov for spring semester

Instructions: Apply online or apply using Common Application

CONTACT

Randolph College
Admissions Office
2500 Rivermont Avenue
Lynchburg, VA 24503
Tel: +1 (434) 947-8100
Fax: +1 (434) 947-8996
Email: jmcgrath@randolphcollege.edu
Web: www.randolphcollege.edu

Randolph-Macon College

Randolph-Macon College Presidential Scholarships

PROGRAM INFORMATION

Description: Randolph-Macon College Presidential Scholarships range from $13,500 up to $21,000 or more for outstanding applicants.

Levels of Study: Undergraduate

Field of Study: All

Nationality: Any Region

Location of Study: Randolph-Macon College
Ashland, VA

AWARD INFORMATION

Award Type: Scholarship

Average Amount: $17,000

Number of Awards: No limit

Award Coverage: Tuition

Award Duration: Maximum of 4 years

ELIGIBILITY REQUIREMENTS

- Strong high school grades and coursework
- Competitive test scores (SAT or TOEFL accepted)
- Minimum accepted English-proficiency test scores: TOEFL (Internet iBT Test): 80; TOEFL (Paper Test): 550; IELTS: 6.5

APPLICATION INFORMATION

Award Deadline: Feb 1

Instructions: All applicants are considered for Presidential Scholarships. Apply for admission at www.rmc.edu/apply

CONTACT

Randolph-Macon College
Admissions
PO Box 5005
Ashland, VA 23005
Tel: +1 (804) 752-7305
Fax: +1 (804) 752-4707
Email: admissions@rmc.edu
Web: www.rmc.edu/financial-aid/scholarshipsfornewfreshmen.aspx

Reed College
Reed College Financial Aid

PROGRAM INFORMATION

Description: Need-based financial aid for international students. Reed College offers 36 undergraduate majors with 1,400 students and a 10:1 student faculty ratio. Small discussion-based classes are the focus of education at Reed. Reed students are smart, creative thinkers that are excited about their education.

Levels of Study: Undergraduate

Field of Study: All

Nationality: Any Region

Location of Study: Reed College
Portland, OR

AWARD INFORMATION

Award Type: Grant, Loan

Average Amount: Varies

Number of Awards: 20-25

Award Coverage: Varies

Award Duration: Academic year, renewable all 4 years

ELIGIBILITY REQUIREMENTS

- Must have completed a secondary school curriculum
- Must submit SAT or ACT scores
- Must submit a transcript of secondary school work
- If you are a non–US citizen and plan to apply for financial aid from the college, you must complete the College Scholarship Service (CSS) PROFILE

APPLICATION INFORMATION

Award Deadline: Jan

Instructions: Apply online using Common Application. Note that there is a Reed Supplement, which includes a "Why Reed" essay

CONTACT

Reed College
Office of Admission
3203 SE Woodstock Blvd.
Portland, OR 97202
Tel: +1 (503) 777-7511
Fax: +1 (503) 777-7553
Email: admission@reed.edu
Web: web.reed.edu/apply/applying_to_reed/international.html

Rhodes College
Rhodes College International Admission

PROGRAM INFORMATION

Description: Academic programs at Rhodes College combine the best of the classroom and the outside world, involving our students in the larger Rhodes and Memphis communities through a variety of intellectual, service, social, and cultural opportunities. Merit-based scholarships are offered to international students with a strong academic record. Need based scholarships are also offered to international students, however they are more limited.

Levels of Study: Undergraduate

Field of Study: All

Nationality: Any Region

Location of Study: Rhodes College
Memphis, TN

AWARD INFORMATION

Award Type: Fellowship, Grant, Scholarship

Average Amount: $15,000 - full tuition

Number of Awards: Varies

Award Coverage: Scholarships and grants range from $15,000 up to full tuition

Award Duration: Renewable for 4 years

ELIGIBILITY REQUIREMENTS

- Strong academics and rigor of curriculum

APPLICATION INFORMATION

Award Deadline: Jan 15

Instructions: Students may apply online with the common application

CONTACT

Rhodes College
Rhodes Coordinator for International Recruitment
2000 North Parkway
Memphis, TN 38112
Tel: +1 (901) 843-3700
Fax: +1 (901) 843-3631
Email: adminfo@rhodes.edu
Web: www.rhodes.edu/admission/68.asp

Rice University
Rice University Graduate Fellowships

PROGRAM INFORMATION

Description: Rice offers substantial financial support to new and continuing graduate students enrolled in graduate programs in the Schools of Engineering, the Natural Sciences, Humanities, Social Sciences, Architecture and Music. Fellowships are often accompanied by a tuition waiver

Levels of Study: Graduate

Field of Study: All, American History, Anthropology, Architecture and Environmental Design, Art History, Astronomy, Biology, Biotechnology, Chemistry, Computer Science, Earth Science, Education, Engineering, Engineering-Related Technologies, Finance, History, Management, Metallurgy, Natural Sciences, Physical Sciences, Political Science, Psychology, Religion/Theology, Science Technologies, Sociology, Statistics

Nationality: Any Region

Location of Study: Rice University
Houston, TX

AWARD INFORMATION

Award Type: Fellowship

Average Amount: Varies

Award Coverage: Tuition

Award Duration: Academic year

APPLICATION INFORMATION

Instructions: Apply for admission to our graduate programs. See graduate.rice.edu/for information on all programs

CONTACT

Rice University
Graduate & Postdoctoral Studies, MS-13
P.O. Box 1892
Houston, TX 77251
Tel: +1 (713) 348-4002
Fax: +1 (713) 348-4806
Email: graduate@rice.edu
Web: graduate.rice.edu

Rider University
Rider University Merit Scholarships for First-Year Students

PROGRAM INFORMATION

Description: Rider University is pleased to offer scholarships up to $21,000 per academic year to undergraduate international students.

Levels of Study: Undergraduate

Field of Study: All

Nationality: Any Region

Location of Study: Rider University
Lawrenceville & Princeton, NJ

AWARD INFORMATION

Award Type: Scholarship

Average Amount: $8,000-$21,000

Number of Awards: Unlimited

Award Coverage: Partial tuition

Award Duration: Academic year, renewable

ELIGIBILITY REQUIREMENTS

- Criteria are published annually. Please visit our website for updated list of requirements
- Must be a full-time student

APPLICATION INFORMATION

Award Deadline: Jan 15

Instructions: Complete the application for admission and submit all required documentation by the deadline

CONTACT

Rider University
Office of Admission
2083 Lawrenceville Road
Lawrenceville, NJ 08648
Tel: +1 (609) 896-5042
Fax: +1 (609) 895-5680
Email: global@rider.edu
Web: www.rider.edu/global

Rider University
Rider University Merit Scholarships for Transfer Students

PROGRAM INFORMATION

Description: Rider University is pleased to offer scholarships up to $17,500 per academic year to undergraduate transfer students.

Levels of Study: Undergraduate

Field of Study: All

Location of Study: Rider University
Lawrenceville and Princeton, NJ

AWARD INFORMATION

Award Type: Scholarship

Average Amount: $5,000-$17,500

Number of Awards: Unlimited

Award Coverage: Partial tuition

Award Duration: Academic year, renewable

ELIGIBILITY REQUIREMENTS

- Criteria are published annually. Please visit our website for updated list of requirements
- Must be a full-time student

APPLICATION INFORMATION

Award Deadline: Dec 1 for spring semester; Apr 1 for fall semester

Instructions: Complete the application for admission and submit all required documentation by the deadline

CONTACT

Rider University
Office of Admission
2083 Lawrenceville Road
Lawrenceville, NJ 08648
Tel: +1 (609) 896 5042
Fax: +1 (609) 895-5680
Email: global@rider.edu
Web: www.rider.edu/admissions

Roanoke College

Roanoke College Merit Scholarship & Financial Aid

PROGRAM INFORMATION

Description: An unlimited number of partial tuition merit scholarships are available to international candidates who meet Roanoke's admissions requirements and who demonstrate a strong academic record. Financial need is considered in the awarding of Roanoke College Loans and Roanoke College Supplemental Grant Awards.

Levels of Study: Undergraduate

Field of Study: All

Nationality: Any Region

Location of Study: Roanoke College Salem, VA

AWARD INFORMATION

Award Type: Grant, Loan, Scholarship

Average Amount: Varies

Number of Awards: Unlimited

Award Coverage: Partial tuition

Award Duration: Up to 4 years

ELIGIBILITY REQUIREMENTS

- Must submit a completed Roanoke College application, official secondary school transcripts and standardized testing such as SAT, TOEFL, IELTS and/or national examinations
- Must submit Roanoke's International Student Financial Aid Application

APPLICATION INFORMATION

Award Deadline: Apr

Instructions: For more information on how to apply, please visit the website

CONTACT

Roanoke College
Director of International Recruitment
Admissions Office
221 College Lane
Salem, VA 24153
Tel: +1 (540) 375-2270
Fax: +1 (540) 375-2267
Email: bennett@roanoke.edu
Web: www.roanoke.edu

Robert Morris University

Robert Morris University Master of Information Systems Scholarships

PROGRAM INFORMATION

Description: Students pay the same tuition as students from the US. After the first degree from MGSM, the second has no additional tuition cost. Students apply knowledge of technology and skills in problem solving to meet business challenges and anticipate future needs. The curriculum provides a solid foundation of communication skills and applies them to IS applications including database management, information security, mobile computing and networking. The MIS Degree concentrates on 5 key areas of competency: professionalism; analytical skills; ethics and social responsibility; database management; information assurance and networking.

Levels of Study: Graduate

Field of Study: Information Technology, Management

Nationality: Any Region

Location of Study: Robert Morris University Chicago & Orland Park, IL

AWARD INFORMATION

Award Type: Grant

Average Amount: No tuition increase for international students

Number of Awards: 10 awards per quarter

Award Coverage: Tuition

Award Duration: Maximum of 2 years

ELIGIBILITY REQUIREMENTS

- Must apply and be accepted to Robert Morris University's Graduate School
- Must have completed a Bachelor's Degree with statistics coursework
- Review the International Student Checklist for further requirements at: www.robertmorris.edu/masters/MGSM%20Checklist%20Flyer_International_2%20(2)%20(3)%20(1).pdf

APPLICATION INFORMATION

Award Deadline: Sep

Instructions: Apply online at www.robertmorris.edu/masters

CONTACT

Robert Morris University
Senior Vice President Enrollment
401 S. State St.
Chicago, IL 60605
Tel: +1 (312) 935-6640
Fax: +1 (312) 935-6660
Email: clockwood@robertmorris.edu
Web: www.robertmorris.edu/masters

Robert Morris University

Robert Morris University Masters of Business Administration

PROGRAM INFORMATION

Description: The Robert Morris University Master of Business Administration program has been designed to prepare students to not just survive, but to thrive, in challenging environments. Our curriculum is structured to allow students to apply what they learn and to create leaders in business functions including accounting, economics, finance, information systems, management, and marketing.

Levels of Study: Graduate

Field of Study: Accounting, Finance, Health Studies, Human Resource Development, Information Technology, Management

Nationality: Any Region

Location of Study: Robert Morris University Chicago, IL

AWARD INFORMATION

Award Type: Grant

Average Amount: Same as instate tuition

Number of Awards: 10 awards per term

Award Coverage: Tuition

Award Duration: Maximum of 2 years

ELIGIBILITY REQUIREMENTS

- Must complete first master's degree at Robert Morris University Graduate School of Management
- Once degree is granted, the student is eligible to take the second degree with no tuition charges
- Students must attend the day program and take 4 classes per quarter

APPLICATION INFORMATION

Award Deadline: Sep

Instructions: Apply online at masters.robertmorris.edu

CONTACT

Robert Morris University
Senior Vice President Enrollment
401 S. State St.
Chicago, IL 60605
Tel: +1 (312) 935-6640
Fax: +1 (312) 935-6660
Email: clockwood@robertmorris.edu
Web: www.masters.robertmorris.edu

Robert Morris University

Robert Morris University Masters in Sports Administration Scholarships

PROGRAM INFORMATION

Description: The Masters in Sports Administration takes leadership experience gained from the field or in coaching to the next level. It prepares students to achieve management level administrative skills to pursue a career in sports administration.

Levels of Study: Graduate

Field of Study: Management

Nationality: Any Region

Location of Study: Robert Morris University, Illinois Chicago, IL

AWARD INFORMATION

Award Type: Grant
Average Amount: $9,200
Number of Awards: 8 awards per quarter
Award Coverage: Tuition
Award Duration: 2 years

ELIGIBILITY REQUIREMENTS

- Must apply and be accepted in to the Graduate School
- Must have a bachelor's degree
- Please see the International Student Checklist for further requirements: www.robertmorris.edu/masters/MGSM%20Checklist%20Flyer_International_2%20(2)%20(3)%20(1).pdf

APPLICATION INFORMATION

Award Deadline: Aug
Instructions: Apply online at robertmorris.edu/masters

CONTACT

Robert Morris University
Admissions
401 S. State Street
Chicago, Chicago IL
Tel: +1 (815) 603-4380
Email: clockwood@robertmorris.edu
Web: www.masters.robertmorris.edu

Robert Morris University
Robert Morris University Higher Education Administration Scholarships

PROGRAM INFORMATION

Description: The master's in higher education administration prepares students for positions of management and leadership in this field.
Levels of Study: Graduate
Field of Study: Education
Location of Study: Robert Morris University Chicago, IL

AWARD INFORMATION

Award Type: Grant
Average Amount: $9,200
Number of Awards: 8 awards per quarter
Award Coverage: Tuition
Award Duration: 2 years

ELIGIBILITY REQUIREMENTS

- Must apply and be accepted to Robert Morris Graduate School of Management
- Must have 3 years' experience in area of education and/or degree in any area of education

APPLICATION INFORMATION

Award Deadline: Aug
Instructions: Visit www.robertmorris.edu/masters for more information and the International Student Checklist at:/ www.robertmorris.edu/masters/MGSM%20Checklist%20Flyer_International_2%20(2)%20(3)%20(1).pdf for further instructions

CONTACT

Robert Morris University
Admissions
401 S. State Street
Chicago, Chicago IL
Tel: +1 (815) 603-4380
Email: clockwood@robertmorris.edu
Web: www.masters.robertmorris.edu

Robert Morris University
Robert Morris University Health Care Administration Scholarships

PROGRAM INFORMATION

Description: Gives students a manager-level understanding of the complicated health care field. Health care has seen the highest growth in job opportunities during the last few years. With constant change in healthcare law and administration, there is a great need for higher level skills. This program prepares students to function at the critical decision-making level.
Levels of Study: Graduate
Field of Study: Health Professions
Nationality: Any Region
Location of Study: Robert Morris University Chicago, IL

ELIGIBILITY REQUIREMENTS

- Must apply and be accepted to Morris Graduate School of Management
- Must have 3 years' experience in health care area and/or degree in any area of health care
- Must submit TOEFL documentation with a minimum score of 550 paper based, 213 computer based, or 80 internet based

APPLICATION INFORMATION

Award Deadline: Aug
Instructions: Visit the website: www.robertmorris.edu/masters for more information and the International Student Checklist for further application instructions: www.robertmorris.edu/masters/MGSM%20Checklist%20Flyer_International_2%20(2)%20(3)%20(1).pdf

CONTACT

Robert Morris University
Admissions
401 S. State Street
Chicago, IL 60605
Tel: +1 (312) 935-6640
Fax: (312) 935-6660
Email: clockwood@robertmorris.edu
Web: www.robertmorris.edu/masters

Rochester Institute of Technology
RIT International Undergraduate Scholarships

PROGRAM INFORMATION

Description: Tuition scholarships for academically qualified students studying toward the bachelor's degree.
Levels of Study: Undergraduate
Field of Study: All
Nationality: Any Region
Location of Study: Rochester Institute of Technology Rochester, NY

AWARD INFORMATION

Award Type: Scholarship
Average Amount: $6,000- $16,000
Number of Awards: Varies
Award Coverage: Tuition
Award Duration: Renewable each year up to 5 years

ELIGIBILITY REQUIREMENTS

- Must complete application for admission with TOEFL or IELTS and SAT scores
- Must submit financial documentation
- Must renew with a 2.5 or higher RIT GPA

APPLICATION INFORMATION

Award Deadline: Feb
Instructions: Complete the application for admission

CONTACT

Rochester Institute of Technology
Associate Director/Coordinator of International Admission
60 Lomb Memorial Drive
Rochester, NY 14623
Tel: +1 (585) 475-6631
Email: admissions@rit.edu
Web: www.rit.edu

Rocky Mountain College
Rocky Mountain College Program

PROGRAM INFORMATION

Description: Upon successful completion of the admissions application, Rocky Mountain College automatically qualifies international students for merit-based scholarships.
Levels of Study: Undergraduate, Graduate
Nationality: Any Region
Location of Study: Rocky Mountain College Billings, MT

AWARD INFORMATION

Award Type: Grant, Scholarship
Average Amount: Up to $11,000
Number of Awards: Varies
Award Coverage: Tuition and fees
Award Duration: Maximum of 4 years

ELIGIBILITY REQUIREMENTS

- Must have 3.0 grade point average on 4.0 scale
- Must submit SAT or ACT results
- For non-traditional students who are non-native speakers of English who do not submit SAT/ACT scores, must have at least a score of TOEFL 525 PBT/197 CBT; or equivalent score on other standardized tests of English-language proficiency

APPLICATION INFORMATION

Award Deadline: Jun

Instructions: All admitted students are automatically considered for scholarships, the end amount depends on grade point average and SAT/ACT scores. Online applications are available at our website

CONTACT

Rocky Mountain College
1511 Poly Drive
Billings, MT 59102
Tel: +1 (406) 657-1107
Fax: +1 (406) 259-9751
Email: michael.west@rocky.edu
Web: www.rocky.edu

Roger Williams University

Roger Williams University International Scholarships

PROGRAM INFORMATION

Description: Roger Williams University is an independent, coeducational liberal arts university. A dynamic educational environment in which students live and learn to be global citizens, the University is committed to its mantra of learning to bridge the world. Roger Williams University offers merit-based institutional scholarships to international students.

Levels of Study: Undergraduate

Nationality: Any Region

Location of Study: Roger Williams University Bristol, RI

AWARD INFORMATION

Award Type: Scholarship

Average Amount: $10,000-$16,000

Award Duration: Renewable annually for up to 4 years

ELIGIBILITY REQUIREMENTS

- International Presidential Excellence Scholarship must have minimum GPA of 3.5 and must be a new freshman
- International Achievement Scholarship must have a minimum GPA of 3.0 and must be a new freshman or transfer student

APPLICATION INFORMATION

Award Deadline: Feb 1 for fall semester and Nov 1 for spring semester

Instructions: Your application for admission will also act as your scholarship application, no additional applications are necessary for scholarship consideration

CONTACT

Roger Williams University
International Admission Counselor
One Old Ferry Road
Bristol, RI 02809
Tel: +1 (401) 254-3411
Fax: +1 (401) 254-3557
Email: mvieira@rwu.edu
Web: www.rwu.edu

Rollins College

Rollins Academic Scholarships

PROGRAM INFORMATION

Description: Rollins College, established in 1885, occupies a lush, 70-acre campus in the dynamic community of Winter Park. The college is characterized by its traditional Spanish-Mediterranean architecture and is the oldest college in the state of Florida. Part of what makes Rollins such a vibrant and renowned learning environment is the international perspective we incorporate into all aspects of our environment. As part of that effort, students that come to Rollins from around the world make up a significant and valued segment of our campus community.

Levels of Study: Undergraduate

Field of Study: American History, American Literature, American Politics, American Studies, Anthropology, Archaeology, Art History, Arts and Culture, Asian Studies, Biochemistry, Biology, Business and Management, Chemistry, Classics, Computer Science, Economics, Education, Engineering 3-2, Fine Arts, Foreign Languages, History, International Relations, Psychology, Social Science, Spanish, Theater

Nationality: Any Region

Location of Study: Rollins College Winter Park, FL

AWARD INFORMATION

Award Type: Scholarship

Average Amount: $5,000 - full tuition

Award Coverage: Tuition

Award Duration: Maximum 4 years

ELIGIBILITY REQUIREMENTS

- Academic scholarships are based on grades and test scores (SAT or ACT). Scholarships are between $5,000 and a full scholarship

APPLICATION INFORMATION

Award Deadline: Jan 5

Instructions: Visit www.rollins.edu/finaid/as/merit.html to apply, each application is reviewed to determine if they are eligible for scholarship and there is no need to fill out any type of scholarship application

CONTACT

Rollins College
Direct of International Admission
1000 Holt Avenue - Box 2720
Winter Park, FL 32707
Tel: +1 (407) 646-2321
Fax: +1 (407) 646-1502
Email: intadmission@rollins.edu
Web: www.rollins.edu/admission/admissioninfo/international-students/

Rowan University

Rowan University International Student Awards

PROGRAM INFORMATION

Description: Rowan University is a public university in New Jersey offering bachelor's, master's and doctoral degrees.

Levels of Study: Undergraduate

Field of Study: All

Nationality: Any Region

Location of Study: Rowan University Glassboro, NJ

AWARD INFORMATION

Award Type: Award

Award Coverage: Reduction of out-of-state tuition fees up to 90%

Award Duration: Academic year

ELIGIBILITY REQUIREMENTS

- Must meet English proficiency
- Must have an SAT/ACT score
- GPA requirements for transfer students studying at US universities

APPLICATION INFORMATION

Instructions: Contact admissions

CONTACT

Rowan University
Admissions
201 Mullica Hill Rd.
Glassboro, NJ 08028
Tel: +1 (856) 256-5190
Email: ballengee@rowan.edu
Web: www.rowan.edu

Sacred Heart University

Sacred Heart University ESL Scholarships

PROGRAM INFORMATION

Description: Sacred Heart University offers 10, $250 scholarships for the Intensive English Language program. Students from around the world study English full time, with highly qualified instructors at the Fairfield campus in Connecticut.

Levels of Study: Undergraduate, Graduate, Professional

Field of Study: English as a Second Language

Nationality: Any Region

Location of Study: Sacred Heart University Fairfield, CT

AWARD INFORMATION

Award Type: Scholarship, Tuition Reduction

Average Amount: $500

Number of Awards: 2 per semester

Award Coverage: Tuition

Award Duration: 1 year

ELIGIBILITY REQUIREMENTS

- Students must complete the Application form for ESL which is on the website
- Students must be accepted into the full time intensive English language program for at least 2 semesters

APPLICATION INFORMATION

Award Deadline: Rolling

Instructions: Visit our website at www.sacredheart.edu/esl for more information and to complete the application

CONTACT

Sacred Heart University
Director, English Language Institute
5151 Park Avenue
Fairfield, Connecticut
06825 Fairfield Connecticut
Tel: +1 (203) 365-7518
Fax: +1 (203) 371-7731
Email: goldam@sacredheart.edu
Web: www.sacredheart.edu/esl

Saint Louis University
Saint Louis University Scholarships

PROGRAM INFORMATION

Description: Saint Louis University is a Jesuit, Catholic university ranked among the top research institutions in the nation. Merit-based scholarships are awarded to incoming freshmen who meet the academic standards.

Levels of Study: Undergraduate, Graduate, Doctorate, Post Doctorate, Professional

Field of Study: All

Location of Study: Saint Louis University
Saint Louis, MO

AWARD INFORMATION

Award Type: Scholarship

Average Amount: $3,000-$16,000 per year

Award Coverage: Tuition and fees

Award Duration: Up to 4 years

ELIGIBILITY REQUIREMENTS

- ACT or SAT test score required for scholarship consideration
- Recommend at least the equivalent to a "B" average in the US grading scale system

APPLICATION INFORMATION

Award Deadline: Dec

Instructions: Students are required to submit: SLU online application; official secondary school or college transcripts; official English Language test scores (IELTS, TOEFL or PTE)

CONTACT

Saint Louis University
International student admission
One Grand Blvd
DuBourg Hall room 150
St. Louis, MO 63103
Tel: +1 (314) 977-2500
Fax: +1 (314) 977-7136
Email: international@slu.edu
Web: www.slu.edu

Saint Mary's College of California
Saint Mary's Funding for US Studies

PROGRAM INFORMATION

Description: Saint Mary's College of California is a Catholic, La Sallian, and liberal arts institution, located 20 miles east of San Francisco. With an undergraduate population of 2,800 students, class sizes are small and every student receives individual attention from professors. International freshman students who apply in the fall are eligible for merit-based scholarships.

Levels of Study: Undergraduate

Field of Study: All

Nationality: Any Region

Location of Study: Saint Mary's College of California
Moraga, CA

AWARD INFORMATION

Award Type: Scholarship

Average Amount: $13,000

Number of Awards: Varies

Award Coverage: Tuition

Award Duration: Up to 4 years

ELIGIBILITY REQUIREMENTS

- Gael Scholars Award - $14,000. Recipients enrolled in demanding university preparatory programs with noteworthy achievement on school marks and/or external examinations
- Honors Scholarship - $18,000, must have a cumulative Grade Point Average 3.7 or equivalent and similarly competitive SAT or ACT exam results
- Presidential Scholarship $24,000, must have GPA of 3.8 and similarly competitive SAT or ACT exam results
- Lasallian Leadership Award - $13,000, must graduate from Lasallian High School with GPA of 3.5 or higher or equivalent

APPLICATION INFORMATION

Award Deadline: Jan

Instructions: Send all mark sheets, transcripts, or exam results with your application packet. SAT, TOEFL, iELTS, or PTE exam results must be sent directly to Saint Mary's College of California, equivalencies will be determined by the college, no additional scholarship application is required

CONTACT

Saint Mary's College of California
1928 St Marys Rd
PMB 4800
Moraga, CA 94575
Tel: +1 (925) 631-4224
Fax: +1 (925) 376-7193
Email: international@stmarys-ca.edu
Web: www.stmarys-ca.edu/node/12417

Salve Regina University
Salve Regina University Merit Based Scholarships

PROGRAM INFORMATION

Description: Salve Regina University has merit based scholarships ranging from $5,000-$18,000 per academic year for qualified applicants.

Levels of Study: Undergraduate

Field of Study: Accounting, American History, American Literature, American Politics, American Studies, Anthropology, Art History, Arts and Culture, Behavioral Sciences, Business and Management, Communications and Journalism, Dance, Economics, Environmental Studies, Finance, Health Professions, Information Technology, Journalism, Literature, Mathematics, Music, Physical Sciences, Psychology, Religion/Theology, Spanish, Theater

Nationality: Any Region

Location of Study: Salve Regina University
Newport, RI

AWARD INFORMATION

Award Type: Scholarship

Average Amount: $14,000

Award Coverage: Tuition

Award Duration: up to 4 years

ELIGIBILITY REQUIREMENTS

- The Common Application form and Salve Regina Common Application Supplement
- Proof of English proficiency (for non-native speakers of English only), submit PTE, TOEFL or IELTS scores

CONTACT

Salve Regina University
Associate Director of International Enrollment
100 Ochre Point Avenue
02840 Newport Rhode Island
Tel: +1 (401) 341-3256
Fax: +1 (401) 341-2972
Email: intladmit@salve.edu
Web: www.salve.edu/admissions/international

San Francisco State University
SFSU Associated Student Scholarships

PROGRAM INFORMATION

Description: San Francisco State Associated Student Association gives scholarships to students every year. International students are eligible to apply for these scholarships.

Levels of Study: Undergraduate, Graduate

Field of Study: All

Nationality: Any Region

Location of Study: San Francisco State University
San Francisco, CA

AWARD INFORMATION

Award Type: Scholarship

Average Amount: $1,000

Award Coverage: Tuition and fees

Award Duration: Academic year

ELIGIBILITY REQUIREMENTS

- Must be an enrolled and demonstrate proof of future enrollment at San Francisco State University
- Must have minimum 2.5 GPA

APPLICATION INFORMATION

Award Deadline: Early Feb

Instructions: Submit application with required documents by deadline, visit our website for more information

CONTACT

San Francisco State University
Associated Student Inc.
1600 Holloway Ave
San Francisco, CA 94132
Tel: +1 (415) 338-2321
Email: faschol@sfsu.edu
Web: www.sfsu.edu/~finaid/scholarships/

San Francisco State University
SFSU Diana Chung Memorial Scholarship

PROGRAM INFORMATION

Description: Both incoming and currently enrolled international students are eligible for this scholarship.

Levels of Study: Undergraduate, Graduate

Field of Study: All

Nationality: Any Region

Location of Study: San Francisco State University San Francisco, CA

AWARD INFORMATION

Award Type: Scholarship

Average Amount: $1,000

Number of Awards: Varies

Award Coverage: Tuition and fees

Award Duration: Varies

ELIGIBILITY REQUIREMENTS

- Must be an F-1/J-1 student, may be incoming or currently enrolled
- Must have a minimum 3.25 GPA for undergraduates, 3.5 GPA for graduates

APPLICATION INFORMATION

Award Deadline: Late Sep

Instructions: Submit application with required documents by deadline, visit the website for more information

CONTACT

San Francisco State University
Office of International Programs
1600 Holloway Ave.
Centennial Village, Bldg. C
San Francisco, CA 94132
Tel: +1 (415) 338-1293
Fax: +1 (415) 338-6234
Web: www.sfsu.edu/~oip

San Francisco State University
SFSU Graduate Fellowships

PROGRAM INFORMATION

Description: International students are encouraged to apply for selective fellowships.

Levels of Study: Graduate

Field of Study: All

Nationality: Any Region

Location of Study: San Francisco State University San Francisco, CA

AWARD INFORMATION

Award Type: Fellowship

Average Amount: Varies

Award Coverage: Tuition, fees

Award Duration: Academic year

ELIGIBILITY REQUIREMENTS

- Must have a 3.0-3.4 GPA (on a 4.0 scale)
- Must be a currently enrolled graduate student

APPLICATION INFORMATION

Award Deadline: Apr

Instructions: Visit website

CONTACT

San Francisco State University
1600 Holloway Ave.
San Francisco, CA 94132
Email: intlgrad@sfsu.edu
Web: www.sfsu.edu/~fellows1/grad_fellowships

San Francisco State University
College of Business Scholarship

PROGRAM INFORMATION

Description: to assist promising College of Business students to continue their studies.

Levels of Study: Undergraduate, Graduate

Field of Study: Accounting, Business and Management

Nationality: Any Region

Location of Study: San Francisco State University San Francisco, CA

AWARD INFORMATION

Award Type: Scholarship

Average Amount: Varies

Number of Awards: Varies

Award Coverage: Tuition & fees

Award Duration: Academic year

ELIGIBILITY REQUIREMENTS

- Must be a currently enrolled student at SF State
- Must show financial need
- Must be in the College of Business
- Must have a minimum of GPA 2.75

APPLICATION INFORMATION

Award Deadline: Early Apr

Instructions: Visit the website for more information: cob.sfsu.edu/

CONTACT

San Francisco State University
1600 Holloway Ave.
San Francisco, CA 94132
Email: cob@sfsu.edu
Web: www.sfsu.edu/~finaid/scholarships/search/387.htm

San Francisco State University
SFSU Alumni Association Scholarships

PROGRAM INFORMATION

Description: The Alumni Association Scholarships are for currently enrolled students at San Francisco State University and 1 scholarship for incoming freshmen. International students are eligible to apply.

Levels of Study: Undergraduate, Graduate

Field of Study: All

Nationality: Any Region

Location of Study: San Francisco State University San Francisco, CA

AWARD INFORMATION

Award Type: Scholarship

Average Amount: $1,500

Number of Awards: Varies

Award Coverage: Tuition and fees

Award Duration: Varies

ELIGIBILITY REQUIREMENTS

- Currently enrolled undergraduate or graduate student, 1 scholarship for incoming freshmen
- Must have a minimum GPA 3.25

APPLICATION INFORMATION

Award Deadline: Varies

Instructions: Visit website

CONTACT

San Francisco State University
Alumni Association
1600 Holloway Ave.
San Francisco, CA 94132
Tel: +1 (415) 338-2217
Email: alumni@sfsu.edu
Web: www.sfsu.edu/~alumni/scholarship.htm

Seattle Central Community College
Seattle Central Community College International Student Scholarships

PROGRAM INFORMATION

Description: Seattle Central offers several scholarships for new students and continuing students.

Levels of Study: Undergraduate

Field of Study: All

Nationality: Any Region

Location of Study: Seattle Central Community College Seattle, WA

AWARD INFORMATION

Award Type: Internship, Scholarship

Average Amount: $250-$4,500

Number of Awards: Varies

Award Coverage: Partial tuition, paid work experience

Award Duration: 3 months-academic year

ELIGIBILITY REQUIREMENTS

- Must submit 2 recommendations, a personal essay, transcripts, and a resume
- Must submit documentation of personal achievements (artistic contests, sports competitions, volunteer positions, etc)
- Must have been fully accepted to Seattle Central Community College by the scholarship application deadline

APPLICATION INFORMATION

Award Deadline: Feb for spring; May for summer; Aug for fall; Nov for winter

Instructions: Visit website

CONTACT

Seattle Central Community College
International Education Programs
1701 Broadway BE 1113
Seattle, WA 98122
Tel: +1 (206) 587-3893
Fax: +1 (206) 587-3868
Email: iepsccc@sccd.ctc.edu
Web: www.seattlecentral.edu/international

Siena Heights University

Siena Heights University International Student Scholarships

PROGRAM INFORMATION

Description: Siena Heights is a Catholic-affiliated, liberal arts university supporting both full-time traditional students and working adults. With a student body of 2,275, Siena Heights offers its students personalized attention from faculty and staff, reinforcing the University's strong sense of community and purpose. With a long history of welcoming international students and a universalized, intercultural curriculum, Siena Heights has much to offer students from abroad.

Levels of Study: Undergraduate, Graduate

Field of Study: All

Nationality: Any Region

Location of Study: Siena Heights University Adrian, MI

AWARD INFORMATION

Award Type: Scholarship

Average Amount: $1,000-$5,000

Number of Awards: Varies

Award Coverage: Tuition

Award Duration: Up to 4 years

ELIGIBILITY REQUIREMENTS

- Must have official transcripts from all prior institutions, documents must be translated in English and evaluated for US equivalence by an approved evaluation service
- Must have a minimum US equivalent GPA of 3.0
- Must have a minimum SAT composite score of 860 in combined verbal and math or ACT composite of 18

APPLICATION INFORMATION

Instructions: Please visit website

CONTACT

Siena Heights University
Office of International Studies
1247 E. Siena Heights Drive
49221 Adrian MI
Tel: +1 (517) 264-7001
Email: international@sienaheights.edu
Web: www.sienaheights.edu

Siena Heights University

Siena Heights University International Transfer Merit Scholarship

PROGRAM INFORMATION

Description: Transfer scholarships are awarded to students that have completed the equivalent of an associate's degree at another accredited institution and are transferring in to Siena Heights University to complete a bachelor of arts degree.

Levels of Study: Undergraduate

Field of Study: All

Nationality: Any Region

Location of Study: Siena Heights University Adrian, MI

AWARD INFORMATION

Award Type: Award, Grant, Scholarship

Average Amount: $2,250-$9,500

Number of Awards: Unlimited

Award Coverage: Tuition

Award Duration: 2 years

ELIGIBILITY REQUIREMENTS

- Must have a minimum 2.0 GPA from a US accredited institution
- Minimum GPA requirements apply for renewal

APPLICATION INFORMATION

Instructions: Visit website

CONTACT

Siena Heights University
Office of International Studies
1247 E. Siena Heights Dr.
Adrian, MI 49221
Web: www.sienaheights.edu

Sierra College

Sierra College International Student Scholarship

PROGRAM INFORMATION

Description: Sierra College is located in the foothills of the beautiful Sierra Nevada mountains of northern California. A large number of our students transfer to the University of California and California State University systems attending schools such as UC Berkeley, UCLA, and UC Santa Barbara. Sierra College offers more than 70 associate degree programs, including business, communication studies, computer science, engineering, marketing, and many more. Sierra College offers scholarships that are specifically targeted to students planning on transferring to a 4-year school. Many of our international students receive these awards. These scholarships offer a wonderful opportunity and are good value as yearly tuition at Sierra College is $5,000.

Levels of Study: Undergraduate

Field of Study: All

Nationality: Any Region

Location of Study: Sierra College Rocklin, CA

AWARD INFORMATION

Award Type: Scholarship, Tuition Reduction

Average Amount: $500-$1,000

Number of Awards: Varies

Award Coverage: Tuition

Award Duration: Approx 1 year

ELIGIBILITY REQUIREMENTS

- Students are only eligible to apply for scholarships once they have attended Sierra College for at least 1 semester. It will not be awarded prior to a student attending Sierra College
- Students may be eligible for a variety of different Sierra College scholarships depending on their major, GPA, or future career plans

APPLICATION INFORMATION

Instructions: For more information on how to apply to the college please visit us at www.sierracollege.edu/int

CONTACT

Sierra College
Program Manager, Outreach and International
5000 Rocklin Road
Rocklin, CA 95677
Tel: +1 (916) 660-7374
Fax: +1 (916) 630-4522
Email: aturner@sierracollege.edu
Web: www.sierracollege.edu/int

Simmons College

Simmons College Merit Scholarship

PROGRAM INFORMATION

Description: Simmons College is a small university in the heart of Boston that integrates liberal arts with professional preparation. For more than 100 years, we have empowered women to become leaders in their careers and in their communities. We also offer coed graduate programs in health studies, education, communications management, social work, library and information science, and liberal arts — plus an MBA program designed for women. Merit-based scholarships and supplementary scholarships for those who qualify and apply

Levels of Study: Undergraduate

Field of Study: All

Nationality: Any Region

Location of Study: Simmons College Boston, MA

AWARD INFORMATION

Award Type: Scholarship

Average Amount: Varies

Number of Awards: Unlimited

Award Duration: 4 years

APPLICATION INFORMATION

Award Deadline: Feb 1

Instructions: Please visit our website or contact us for more information

CONTACT

Simmons College
Senior Assistant Director
300 The Fenway
Boston, MA 02115
Tel: +1 (617) 521-2051
Fax: +1 (617) 521-3190
Email: ugadm@simmons.edu
Web: www.simmons.edu/financialaid/new/undergraduate/scholarships.php

SIT Graduate Institute

SIT Scholarships and Grants for International Students

PROGRAM INFORMATION

Description: SIT offers various different grants and scholarships to international students to partially cover of tuition. SIT grants are based primarily on need, and students are automatically considered for this grant when their application is reviewed. A number of scholarships have also been established to recognize students who reflect the SIT mission through their professional and personal lives. Such awards include the International Aid and Development Scholarship, The Activism and Academy Scholarship, and the Peace Fellowship.

Levels of Study: Graduate, Professional

Field of Study: Conflict Management, Conflict Resolution, English as a Second Language, Human Rights, International Development, International Education, International Management, International Relations, Minority Rights, Peace Studies, Public Policy, Social Justice, Social Movements, TESOL

Nationality: Any Region

Location of Study: SIT Graduate Institute
Brattleboro, VT

AWARD INFORMATION

Award Type: Scholarship

Average Amount: Up to $10,000

Number of Awards: Varies

Award Coverage: Partial tuition

Award Duration: Academic year

ELIGIBILITY REQUIREMENTS

- Must be accepted into 1 of SIT Graduate Institute's master's degree programs in Brattleboro, VT or Washington, DC
- Must have a minimum TOEFL score of 550 PBT/213 CBT/79 IBT with minimum of 24 writing and 23 speaking, or a minimum IELTS score of Band 6.0

APPLICATION INFORMATION

Award Deadline: Mar

Instructions: Application for admissions and financial aid can be found at our website

CONTACT

SIT Graduate Institute
PO Box 676, Kipling Rd
Brattleboro, VT 05302
Tel: +1 (802) 258-3510
Fax: +1 (802) 258-3428
Email: admissions@sit.edu
Web: graduate.sit.edu/sit-graduate-institute/pn/prospective-students/financial-aid/

Slippery Rock University

Slippery Rock University Undergraduate International Student Non-need based financial aid

PROGRAM INFORMATION

Description: Slippery Rock University is pleased to offer eligible international students the out-of-state reduced tuition rate which is a form of non-need based financial assistance.

Levels of Study: Undergraduate

Field of Study: All

Nationality: Any Region

Location of Study: Slippery Rock University
Slippery Rock, PA

AWARD INFORMATION

Award Type: Tuition Reduction

Number of Awards: Awarded to all international students qualifying for admission

Award Coverage: Tuition

Award Duration: Maximum of 4 years

ELIGIBILITY REQUIREMENTS

- Must maintain a cumulative GPA of 3.0 to remain at this tuition level after the first year of enrollment

APPLICATION INFORMATION

Award Deadline: Varies

Instructions: Must submit complete Slippery Rock University application form, for application forms and instructions visit our website

CONTACT

Slippery Rock University
Associate Director for International Student Admissions
Office for Global Engagement
004 Spotts World Culture Building
Slippery Rock, PA 16057
Tel: +1 (724) 738-2057
Fax: +1 (724) 738-2289
Email: international.admissions@sru.edu
Web: www.sru.edu/academics/globalengagement/Pages/CostsandFinancialAid.aspx

Slippery Rock University

Scholarships for Enrolled International Students

PROGRAM INFORMATION

Description: Slippery Rock University offers 4 different scholarships to international students who have completed a minimum of 30 semester hours. The 4 awards are: The Shiron Cooper Memorial Scholarship for Caribbean students, The Carol Holland Scholarship, The Stan Kendziorski International Student Scholarship, and International Student Scholarship.

Levels of Study: Undergraduate, Graduate, Doctorate

Field of Study: All

Nationality: Any Region

Location of Study: Slippery Rock University
Slippery Rock, PA

AWARD INFORMATION

Award Type: Scholarship

Average Amount: Varies

Number of Awards: Varies

Award Coverage: Tuition

Award Duration: Academic year

ELIGIBILITY REQUIREMENTS

- Must have completed a minimum of 2-3 semesters in residence at SRU
- Must demonstrate academic achievement & extra-curricular activities
- Additional requirements are scholarship specific. Visit our website for more information

APPLICATION INFORMATION

Instructions: Applications are made available to current international students at SRU in Feb of each spring semester

CONTACT

Slippery Rock University
Adviser for International and Study Abroad Student
Office for Global Engagement
004 Spotts World Culture Building
Slippery Rock, PA 16057
Tel: +1 (724) 738-2057
Fax: +1 (724) 738-2289
Email: theresa.crispin@sru.edu
Web: www.sru.edu/academics/internationalservices/Pages/internationalScholarships.aspx

Slippery Rock University

Provosts Scholarship for Global Diversity & Academic Achievement

PROGRAM INFORMATION

Description: Award granted upon successful admission and renewable at the end of spring or summer semester each year thereafter based upon merit

Levels of Study: Undergraduate

Field of Study: All

Nationality: Any Region

Location of Study: Slippery Rock University
Slippery Rock, PA

AWARD INFORMATION

Award Type: Scholarship
Average Amount: $1,500
Number of Awards: Unlimited
Award Coverage: Tuition
Award Duration: 1 year

ELIGIBILITY REQUIREMENTS

- Successful admission to Slippery Rock University
- Must be an international student
- 3.0 GPA or higher after spring semester and/or summer sessions each year thereafter

APPLICATION INFORMATION

Instructions: Apply for admission, if accepted, award will automatically be applied to students' account, no application required. For renewable instructions see Office for Global Engagement

CONTACT

Slippery Rock University
Associate Director for International Student Admissions
1 Morrow Way
Slippery Rock, Pennsylvania 16057
Tel: +1 (724) 738-2057
Fax: +1 (724) 738-2289
Email: international.admissions@sru.edu
Web: www.sru.edu/internationaladmissions

Slippery Rock University
Slippery Rock University Presidential Award for Academic Excellence

PROGRAM INFORMATION

Description: Award is granted at the end of an academic year and is based on academic excellence and financial need.
Levels of Study: Undergraduate
Field of Study: All
Nationality: Any Region
Location of Study: Slippery Rock University Slippery Rock, PA

AWARD INFORMATION

Award Type: Scholarship
Average Amount: $500
Number of Awards: Unlimited
Award Coverage: Tuition
Award Duration: 1 year

ELIGIBILITY REQUIREMENTS

- Must be currently enrolled at Slippery Rock University
- Must be an international student
- Upon completion of the spring term and/or summer sessions students with a 3.5 GPA or higher will be considered eligible for this award

APPLICATION INFORMATION

Instructions: See Office for Global Engagement for additional information related to eligibility

CONTACT

Slippery Rock University
Associate Director for International Student Admissions
1 Morrow Way
Slippery Rock, PA 16057
Tel: +1 (724) 738-2057
Fax: +1 (724) 738-2289
Email: international.admissions@sru.edu
Web: www.sru.edu/internationaladmissions

Soka University of America
Soka Opportunity Scholarships

PROGRAM INFORMATION

Description: Meeting the costs of an education represents a significant investment for most students and their families. Soka University of America has been committed to providing comprehensive merit and need-based financial aid programs that make it possible for current and admitted students who meet specific requirements and deadlines to attend. In fact, all admitted students whose annual earned family income is $60,000 or less will receive free tuition (room and board fees will still apply).
Levels of Study: Undergraduate
Field of Study: Liberal/General Studies
Nationality: Any Region
Location of Study: Soka University of America Aliso Viejo, CA

AWARD INFORMATION

Award Type: Scholarship, Tuition Reduction
Average Amount: $2,000
Number of Awards: Varies
Award Coverage: Tuition (room and board fees still apply).
Award Duration: Up to 4 years

ELIGIBILITY REQUIREMENTS

- Must be admitted to Soka University based upon high school grades, SAT scores, essay, recommendations, leadership, activities
- Annual earned family income must be $60,000 or less for full tuition reduction, higher incomes may be eligible for a prorated scholarship
- May not have graduated from college nor completed more than 3/4 of their required coursework towards their first undergraduate degree (eg, BA/BS) at the time of application to SUA

APPLICATION INFORMATION

Award Deadline: Mar 2
Instructions: Apply online at www.soka.edu/apply.

CONTACT

Soka University of America
Financial Aid Manager
1 University Drive
Aliso Viejo, CA 92656
Tel: +1 (949) 480-4000
Fax: +1 (949) 480-4151
Email: financialaid@soka.edu
Web: www.soka.edu/admission_aid

Soka University of America
Merit Scholarship

PROGRAM INFORMATION

Description: Awards range from $2,000 to $20,000 annually. Award levels determined upon admission to Soka are automatically renewed annually, subject to a student's continued satisfactory academic progress of a term GPA of 3.0 or better.
Levels of Study: Undergraduate
Field of Study: Liberal/General Studies
Nationality: Any Region
Location of Study: Soka University of America Aliso Viejo, CA

AWARD INFORMATION

Award Type: Scholarship
Average Amount: $2,000-$20,000
Number of Awards: Unlimited
Award Coverage: All educational expenses
Award Duration: Maximum 4 years

ELIGIBILITY REQUIREMENTS

- Must be academically high achieving
- Must maintain a GPA of 3.0

APPLICATION INFORMATION

Instructions: Students are automatically considered for the award upon acceptance to the university

CONTACT

Soka University of America
Manager of Financial Aid
1 University Drive
Aliso Viejo, CA 92656
Tel: +1 (949) 480-4000
Fax: +1 (949) 480-4151
Email: financialaid@soka.edu
Web: www.soka.edu/admission_aid

Soka University of America
Makiguchi Scholarship for Global Citizens

PROGRAM INFORMATION

Description: Each year an SUA Makiguchi Scholarship for Global Citizens award will be given to 1 international applicant, who has graduated from high school in an African nation, is outstanding both in character and academic standing, and who has difficulty studying at SUA due to financial reasons. This award will consist of tuition, fees, room & board, and incidental costs, including airfare. This award is granted for a period of 4 years.
Levels of Study: Undergraduate
Field of Study: Liberal/General Studies
Nationality: Africa
Location of Study: Soka University of America Aliso Viejo, CA

AWARD INFORMATION

Award Type: Scholarship
Average Amount: $37,000
Number of Awards: 1 per year
Award Coverage: Tuition, room and board, transportation
Award Duration: Up to 4 years

ELIGIBILITY REQUIREMENTS

- Must have graduated from high school in an African nation
- Must have outstanding academic standing

APPLICATION INFORMATION

Award Deadline: Jan

Instructions: Apply for admission (www.soka.edu/apply) and apply for financial aid (www.soka.edu/financial aid)

CONTACT

Soka University of America
Financial Aid Manager
1 University Drive
Aliso Viejo, CA 92656
Tel: +1 (949) 480-4351
Fax: +1 (949) 480-4151
Email: cdadamo@soka.edu
Web: www.soka.edu/admission_aid

Soka University of America

Soka University of America Global Merit Scholarship

PROGRAM INFORMATION

Description: A Global Merit Scholarship is a full-ride scholarship. This scholarship is guaranteed for 4 years, subject to a student's continued satisfactory academic progress of a term GPA of 3.0 or better.

Levels of Study: Undergraduate

Field of Study: Liberal/General Studies

Nationality: Any Region

Location of Study: Soka University of America Aliso Viejo, CA

AWARD INFORMATION

Award Type: Scholarship

Average Amount: $41,842

Number of Awards: 12 per year

Award Coverage: Tuition, room, board, health insurance fee, travel, books and some personal expenses

Award Duration: 4 years

ELIGIBILITY REQUIREMENTS

- This award is given to the top few students of each class when they enter as freshmen
- This award is renewed each year as long as the student meets the satisfactory academic progress requirements

APPLICATION INFORMATION

Award Deadline: Mar 2

Instructions: Students are automatically considered for this award at the time they are accepted

CONTACT

Soka University of America
Financial Aid Manager
1 University Drive
Aliso Viejo, CA 92656
Tel: +1 (949) 480-4351
Fax: +1 (949) 480-4151
Email: financialaid@soka.edu
Web: www.soka.edu/admission_aid

South Dakota State University

Jackrabbit Guarantee Scholarship

PROGRAM INFORMATION

Description: The Jackrabbit Guarantee Scholarship is a commitment by South Dakota State University to award a minimum of $1,000 in academic scholarship aid per year for 4 years to every first-time freshman eligible student.

Levels of Study: Undergraduate

Field of Study: All

Nationality: Any Region

Location of Study: South Dakota State University Brookings, SD

AWARD INFORMATION

Award Type: Scholarship

Average Amount: $1,000

Award Coverage: Tuition

Award Duration: 4 years

ELIGIBILITY REQUIREMENTS

- Must be a new, incoming freshman who has earned an ACT score of 24 or higher (1090 SAT) and who attends the main SDSU campus in Brookings
- All Jackrabbit Guarantee recipients are required to maintain a cumulative grade point average (CGPA) of 3.0
- Students must complete a minimum of 30 credit hours on the Brookings campus each academic year (fall and spring) for continuing eligibility
- A Jackrabbit Guarantee recipient must remain continuously enrolled at SDSU. If a student does not enroll or withdraws during any fall or spring semester, s/he will be dropped from the program
- Students with special circumstances such as participation in National Student Exchange (NSE), study abroad or internships must notify the university scholarship coordinator to obtain approval prior to leaving SDSU

APPLICATION INFORMATION

Award Deadline: Priority is given to applications received on or before Jan 15

Instructions: To be considered for the Jackrabbit Guarantee Scholarship, admitted first-year students must complete the Freshman Academic Scholarship Application at www.sdstate.edu/admissions/financing/aid/upload/ScholarshipApp-2011-12.pdf

CONTACT

South Dakota State University
International Student Coordinator
Briggs Library 119 - Box 2115
1300 N Campus Drive
Brookings, SD 57007-35004
Tel: +1 (800) 827-3198
Fax: +1 (605) 688-6540
Email: sdsu.intlstud@sdstate.edu
Web: www.sdstate.edu/admissions/financing/aid/scholarships.cfm

Southern Illinois University Edwardsville

SIU Edwardsville Competitive Graduate Award

PROGRAM INFORMATION

Description: The Competitive Graduate Award supports highly qualified new students who are accepted into advanced degree programs at SIUE. They will include a monthly stipend, as well as waiver of tuition. Applicants must be new graduate students, whose first term of enrollment as a classified student in a graduate degree program will be no earlier than the summer prior to the distribution of the award.

Levels of Study: Graduate

Field of Study: All

Nationality: Any Region

Location of Study: Southern Illinois University Edwardsville Edwardsville, IL

AWARD INFORMATION

Award Type: Award, Fellowship, Grant, Scholarship, Tuition Reduction

Average Amount: $26,000

Number of Awards: 19

Award Coverage: Monthly stipend (9 months), tuition (2 sem), starting in fall semester of each year

Award Duration: 9 months

ELIGIBILITY REQUIREMENTS

- Must be a new graduate student accepted into master's degree program at SIUE at the time of application
- Application should include: your completed CGA applications and supporting materials (3 letters of recommendation, cover sheet, statement of personal history, statement of goals must be on file in the Graduate School by application deadline
- English language proficiency at University required level

APPLICATION INFORMATION

Award Deadline: Jan

Instructions: Visit our website or contact for more information on how to apply

CONTACT

Southern Illinois University Edwardsville
International Programs
Campus Box 1616
Edwardsville, IL 62026-1616
Tel: +1 (618) 650-3728
Email: graduateschool@siue.edu
Web: www.siue.edu/graduatestudents/fellowshipsandgrants/information.shtml

Southern Illinois University Edwardsville
SIU Edwardsville International GEO Award

PROGRAM INFORMATION

Description: Through a competitive process, Southern Illinois University Edwardsville will award up to 40 new undergraduate freshman and transfer international students a special reduced tuition rate to recognize their outstanding academic achievement.

Levels of Study: Undergraduate

Field of Study: All

Nationality: Any Region

Location of Study: Southern Illinois University Edwardsville Edwardsville, IL

AWARD INFORMATION

Award Type: Tuition Reduction

Average Amount: $28,000 (over 4 years)

Number of Awards: 40

Award Coverage: Tuition

Award Duration: 8 semesters

ELIGIBILITY REQUIREMENTS

- Awardees will be selected, through a competitive process, based on overall high school grade point average, TOFEL or IELTS scores, and/or outstanding talent.
- There is no separate application required to be considered for this scholarship and there is no application fee for undergraduate international applicants

APPLICATION INFORMATION

Award Deadline: Apr

Instructions: Interested students should complete an international undergraduate application; required items for an undergraduate application are: English language verification (official TOEFL or IELTS scores); official academic transcripts/records; copy of Biographical Page from Passport

CONTACT

Southern Illinois University Edwardsville
Office of Admissions
Campus Box 1600
Edwardsville, Illinois 62026
Tel: 618-650-2727
Email: intladm@siue.edu
Web: www.siue.edu/internationalstudents/tuition-reduction_undergrad.shtml

Southern New Hampshire University
Penmen International Student Merit Scholarship

PROGRAM INFORMATION

Description: Eligible undergraduate students may be awarded up to $5,000 per year. Eligible graduate students may be awarded up to $3,000 per year. Eligibility determined by GPA.

Levels of Study: Undergraduate, Graduate

Field of Study: All

Nationality: Any Region

Location of Study: Southern New Hampshire University Manchester, NH

AWARD INFORMATION

Award Type: Scholarship

Average Amount: $3,000-$5,000, depending on level of study

Number of Awards: 25 per level of study

Award Coverage: Tuition

Award Duration: Undergraduate: 1 year, renewable, Graduate: 1-time award

ELIGIBILITY REQUIREMENTS

- Graduate applicants must have GPA of 3.0
- Undergraduate applicants must have GPA of 2.75

APPLICATION INFORMATION

Instructions: Request application form from Director of International Admissions

CONTACT

Southern New Hampshire University
Dir., International Admissions
2500 N. River Rd
Manchester, NH
Tel: +1 (603) 645-9629
Fax: +1 (603) 645-9603
Email: s.harvey@snhu.edu
Web: www.snhu.edu

Southern Oregon University
Southern Oregon University Cascade and Siskiyou International Student Scholarships

PROGRAM INFORMATION

Description: Cascade and Siskiyou International Student Scholarships are for international students attending Southern Oregon University. This scholarship is for international undergraduates, graduates, and graduating IEP students.

Levels of Study: Undergraduate, Graduate

Field of Study: All

Nationality: Any Region

Location of Study: Southern Oregon University Ashland, OR

AWARD INFORMATION

Award Type: Scholarship

Average Amount: $6,525-$8,775

Number of Awards: Approx 5

Award Coverage: Tuition

Award Duration: Academic year with possible renewal

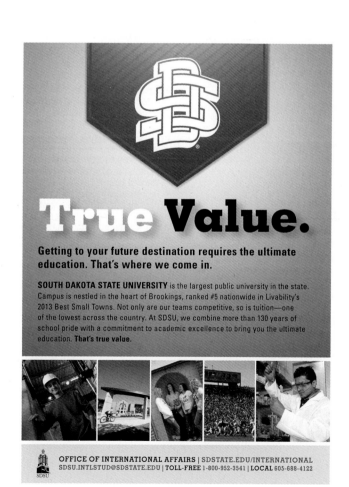

ELIGIBILITY REQUIREMENTS

- International undergraduate applicants must be applying as a new undergraduate and attending Southern Oregon University for the first time
- Returning international graduate applicants must be entering their second quarter of graduate coursework at SOU (students completing foundation coursework will not be considered until after their first quarter of graduate coursework has been completed)
- Must apply for admission and be accepted as a degree-seeking, tuition-paying student; exchange students, government/employer sponsored students, students in special short-term non-degree programs, and IEP students are not eligible
- Undergraduates must have GPA of 3.0 (on a 4.0 scale) and first quarter graduates must have GPA at SOU of 3.2

APPLICATION INFORMATION

Award Deadline: Apr 1

Instructions: For more information, contact the Office of International Programs

CONTACT
Southern Oregon University
Office of International Programs
1250 Siskiyou Blvd
Ashland, OR 97520
Tel: +1 (541) 552-6336
Email: intprogs@sou.edu
Web: www.sou.edu/international

Springfield College

Springfield College International Undergraduate Scholarships

PROGRAM INFORMATION

Description: International undergraduate and transfer applicants are eligible for the Springfield College President's Achievers Award. International undergraduates are eligible for a yearly travel stipend of up to $1500. Students are automatically considered for a scholarship upon admission. International students who visit campus and subsequently apply and enroll will receive an additional 1-time credit of $1500.

Levels of Study: Undergraduate

Nationality: Any Region

Location of Study: Springfield College
Springfield, MA

AWARD INFORMATION

Award Type: Scholarship

Average Amount: $6,000 - $14,000

Number of Awards: Unlimited

Award Coverage: Tuition, travel expenses

Award Duration: President's Achievers Awards and the travel stipend - up to 4 years; award for a visit is a 1-time credit

ELIGIBILITY REQUIREMENTS

- Must demonstrate academic merit as determined by admissions at time of application
- Must be fully admitted into degree program (awards not available for ESL program)
- Not available for students who receive full sponsorship for tuition, fees, living expenses from government/ sponsoring organization
- Award renewal based on making satisfactory academic progress per Springfield College policy
- Awards may be revoked if you fail to meet behavioral standards of the College as established by the Dean of Student Affairs

APPLICATION INFORMATION

Award Deadline: rolling

CONTACT
Springfield College
International Center
263 Alden St.
Springfield, MA 01109
Tel: (413) 748-3206
Fax: (413) 748-3019
Web: www.springfieldcollege.edu

St Olaf College

St. Olaf College Funding

PROGRAM INFORMATION

Description: St. Olaf is a residential, liberal arts and science college with world-class programs in mathematics and music. We're also recognized for our science research, our intensive global focus and the percentage of our alumni who go on to graduate school. St. Olaf offers 45 graduation majors, including 15 teaching certifications, 19 concentrations, and 17 pre-professional fields. St. Olaf enrolls 3,000 students representing 47 states and 39 foreign countries. Financial need-based and merit-based scholarships are offered to international freshmen who qualify.

Levels of Study: Undergraduate

Field of Study: All

Nationality: Any Region

Location of Study: St. Olaf College
Northfield, MN

AWARD INFORMATION

Award Type: Scholarship, Student Exchange

Average Amount: Half tuition

Number of Awards: Varies

Award Coverage: Partial to full tuition

Award Duration: Maximum of 4 years (8 semesters) for degree-seeking students; maximum of 1 year for non-degree, exchange students

ELIGIBILITY REQUIREMENTS

- The need/merit-based awards are for degree-seeking students (transfers may be considered) regardless of their intended major
- Degree-seeking students, including international transfers, may also apply for other St. Olaf merit-based scholarships

APPLICATION INFORMATION

Award Deadline: Feb

Instructions: Students must submit International Student Financial Aid Form or the CSS Profile and Certification of Finance forms, as well as their admissions application; if the student applies for academic, music, or community service merit-based scholarships, he or she must submit the appropriate application and/or audition material

CONTACT
St. Olaf College
Associate Dean of Admissions, International Recruitment
1520 St. Olaf Ave
Northfield, MN 55057
Tel: +1 (507) 786-3025
Fax: +1 (507) 786-3832
Email: howensti@stolaf.edu
Web: www.stolaf.edu/financialaid

St. Catherine University

Catherine T. McNamee International Student Scholarship

PROGRAM INFORMATION

Description: Catherine T. McNamee International Student Scholarship is awarded to female, bachelor's degree-seeking students enrolled at St. Catherine University in any major. Scholarships are based primarily on academic achievement and financial need. Scholarships range up to $20,000 per year while enrolled full time. The largest scholarship covers approximately half of tuition and room and board costs for students who live on campus.

Levels of Study: Undergraduate

Field of Study: All

Nationality: Any Region

Location of Study: St. Catherine University
St. Paul, MN

AWARD INFORMATION

Award Type: Scholarship

Average Amount: $15,000

Number of Awards: 20

Award Coverage: Tuition, room and board

Award Duration: Up to 4 years

ELIGIBILITY REQUIREMENTS

- Must be female
- Must be admissible to the university
- Must have minimum TOEFL score of 500 PBT/61 IBT

APPLICATION INFORMATION

Award Deadline: Mar

Instructions: Request application for admission and scholarships 9 months prior to beginning study

CONTACT
St. Catherine University
Associate Director, International Admission
2004 Randolph Avenue, F-29
St. Paul, MN 55105
Tel: +1 (651) 690-6029
Fax: +1 (651) 690-8824
Email: international@stkate.edu
Web: www.stkate.edu/colleges/undergraduate/

St. Catherine University

Bonnie Hyland Umeh Excellence In Leadership Scholarship

PROGRAM INFORMATION

Description: This scholarship is for female, bachelor's degree-seeking students with Nigerian citizenship for studies at St. Catherine University.

Levels of Study: Undergraduate

Field of Study: All

Nationality: Nigeria

Location of Study: St. Catherine University
St. Paul, MN

AWARD INFORMATION

Award Type: Scholarship

Average Amount: $2,000

Number of Awards: 1

Award Coverage: Tuition

Award Duration: 4 years

ELIGIBILITY REQUIREMENTS

- Must be female
- Must be admissible to the university
- Must have minimum TOEFL score of 500 PBT/61 IBT
- Must have Nigerian citizenship

APPLICATION INFORMATION

Award Deadline: Mar

Instructions: Request application materials from the Office of International Admission

CONTACT

St. Catherine University
Associate Director, International Admission
2004 Randolph Avenue, F-29
St. Paul, MN 55105
Tel: +1 (651) 690-6029
Fax: +1 (651) 690-8824
Email: international@stkate.edu
Web: www.stkate.edu/colleges/undergraduate/

St. Catherine University

St. Catherine EducationUSA Scholarship

PROGRAM INFORMATION

Description: This $1,500 scholarship is awarded to female, bachelor's degree-seeking students in any major who submit a letter of recommendation from the EducationUSA advisor in her home country.

Levels of Study: Undergraduate

Field of Study: All

Nationality: Any Region

Location of Study: St. Catherine University Saint Paul, MN

ELIGIBILITY REQUIREMENTS

- Must be female
- Must be admissible to the university
- Must have minimum TOEFL score of 500 PBT/61 IBT
- Must submit letter of recommendation from EducationUSA advisor in home country

APPLICATION INFORMATION

Award Deadline: Mar

Instructions: Request application for admission and scholarships 9 months prior to beginning study

CONTACT

St. Catherine University
Associate Director, International Admission
2004 Randolph Ave, F-29
St. Paul, MN 55105
Tel: +1 (651) 690-6029
Fax: +1 (651) 690-8824
Email: international@stkate.edu
Web: www.stkate.edu/colleges/undergraduate/

St. Cloud State University

St. Cloud State University: In-State Tuition for International Students

PROGRAM INFORMATION

Description: SCSU offers in-state tuition for international students via the Academic & Cultural Sharing Scholarship, which saves approximately $6,114 per year for undergraduate students and approximately $2,950 per year for eligible graduate students.

Levels of Study: Undergraduate, Graduate

Field of Study: All

Nationality: Any Region

Location of Study: St. Cloud State University St. Cloud, MN

AWARD INFORMATION

Award Type: Scholarship

Average Amount: $6,114 for eligible undergraduates and $3,000 (annually) for eligible graduate programs (doctoral, MBA, MEM in Maple Grove are not part of the scholarship)

Number of Awards: Varies

Award Coverage: In-state tuition

Award Duration: Duration of studies

ELIGIBILITY REQUIREMENTS

- Must check in with the Center for International Studies upon arrival into the US, please note that the ACSS is granted to new international students on their first semester; requirements 2 & 3 only apply to future semesters
- Must maintain a 2.5 cumulative GPA as an undergraduate student or a 3.0 cumulative GPA as a graduate student
- Must complete 2 cultural sharing activities every semester and submit the online Cultural Activities form by May 1 (to be eligible for the summer and fall scholarship) and Dec 15 (to be eligible for the spring scholarship)
- Must maintain active F-1/J-1 status, students with a pending reinstatement or change of status application to F-1/J-1 status are not eligible for the ACSS until the application has been adjudicated by USCIS
- Graduate Assistantship provides 2 year of tuition waiver for eligible graduate students, the awards can be for full time or part time graduate assistants

APPLICATION INFORMATION

Award Deadline: May 1 for fall semester, Dec 15 for spring semester

Instructions: It is not necessary to apply for the scholarship for new international students; the scholarship is granted to you in your first semester, provided that you check in during orientation; you would then need to complete 2 cultural sharing activities each semester and maintain a minimum GPA to qualify for continuous ACSS scholarship for your duration of studies; that is about $24,516 worth of savings for a 4 year program

CONTACT

St. Cloud State University
Center of International Studies
101 Lawrence Hall, 720 Fourth Avenue South
St. Cloud, MN 56301
Tel: +1 (320) 308-4287
Fax: +1 (320) 308-4223
Email: World2scsu@stcloudstate.edu
Web: www.stcloudstate.edu/internationalstudents/students/scholarships/ACS.asp

St. John's University

St. John's University Graduate Awards

PROGRAM INFORMATION

Description: A limited number of Graduate Assistantships and University Fellowships are granted to various departments within each School and College of the University. Administrative Assistantships are also available in the administrative sector.

Levels of Study: Graduate, Doctorate

Field of Study: All

Nationality: Any Region

Location of Study: St. John's University, NY

AWARD INFORMATION

Award Type: Fellowship, Grant, Scholarship

Average Amount: 6-9 credits per semester

Number of Awards: Varies

Award Coverage: Tuition, stipend

Award Duration: 2 years, fellowships longer

ELIGIBILITY REQUIREMENTS

- Awards are given on the basis of academic merit. Graduate Assistants are only expected to submit GRE or GMAT scores if they are required within their primary department of study, and only if they are working within that primary department
- Minimal GMAT scores for the Peter J. Tobin College of Business are 550 or above. If a department or program does not require GRE scores, they are not required for consideration of an assistantship
- All awardees are expected to have an undergraduate overall GPA of at least 3.20; graduate assistants will be expected to show evidence of a 3.20 GPA or above in any previous graduate work
- Doctoral Fellows will be expected to show evidence of 3.5 GPA or above in any previous graduate work, graduate assistants who do not maintain these minimum GPAs will not be eligible to keep their assistantships

APPLICATION INFORMATION

Instructions: Visit www.stjohns.edu/academics/provost/scholarships for application

CONTACT

St. John's University
Director of Graduate Admission
8000 Utopia Parkway
Queens, NY 11439
Email: medranor@stjohns.edu
Web: www.stjohns.edu/admission-aid/graduate-admission

St. John's University

St. John's University Undergraduate Merit-Based Scholarships

PROGRAM INFORMATION

Description: St. John's University offers merit-based scholarships to first-year undergraduate students based on high school average and SAT or ACT test scores.

Levels of Study: Undergraduate

Field of Study: All

Nationality: Any Region

Location of Study: St. John's University, NY

AWARD INFORMATION

Award Type: Scholarship
Average Amount: $5,000 - Full Tuition
Number of Awards: Unlimited
Award Coverage: Tuition
Award Duration: Maximum 4 years

ELIGIBILITY REQUIREMENTS

- Completed undergraduate application with official transcripts, essay and eligible SAT or ACT scores
- High school GPA of 80 or higher on 100-point scale. International student GPAs may be recalculated to reflect US-style grading
- Undergraduate freshmen scholarships are intended for 4 years of continuous, full-time undergraduate study, transfer student scholarships are for 2 or 3 years of continuous undergraduate study

APPLICATION INFORMATION

Award Deadline: Rolling
Instructions: Review for merit-based scholarship is automatic, applicants are notified of any academic scholarships in their acceptance letter

CONTACT

St. John's University
Assistant Director of International Admissions
8000 Utopia Parkway
11439 Queens NY
Tel: (718) 990-2415
Fax: (718) 990-5827
Email: intladm@stjohns.edu
Web: www.stjohns.edu/admission-aid/scholarships/merit-based-scholarships

St. John's University

St. John's University Ozanam Scholars Program

PROGRAM INFORMATION

Description: Committed, passionate, and motivated are just a few words which describe an Ozanam Scholar. Rooted in the themes of Scholarly Research, Vincentian Service, and Global Citizenship, students will have the opportunity to not only grow academically, but elevate their contribution to society through solutions-based research. Required course work, travel, and community service will be the foundation for their activities while exploring local, national, and international concerns and developing the acumen to address the issues of the social justice. This program provides a select group of scholars with a unique and innovative learning experience. The Ozanam Scholars Program connects small student groups with dedicated faculty to contribute to solving real world problems in local, national and international communities.
Levels of Study: Undergraduate
Nationality: Any Region
Location of Study: St. John's University Queens, NY

AWARD INFORMATION

Award Type: Scholarship
Average Amount: Up to $10,000
Number of Awards: Approx 30 annually
Award Coverage: Tuition
Award Duration: Maximum 4 years

ELIGIBILITY REQUIREMENTS

- Must live on campus during the first 2 years, complete service requirements, participate in all Ozanam Scholars program events
- Must participate in a study abroad experience in Rome at your own expense, complete an independent study in junior year, complete a capstone project in senior year
- Students must complete a social justice minor

APPLICATION INFORMATION

Award Deadline: Feb 6
Instructions: Complete Ozanam Scholarship online application: https://www.stjohnsadmin.org/ozanam

CONTACT

St. John's University
Assistant Director of International Admissions
8000 Utopia Parkway
11439 Queens New York
Tel: +1 (718) 990-2415
Fax: + (718) 990-5827
Email: arcarioa@stjohns.edu
Web: www.stjohns.edu/ozanam

St. Norbert College

St. Norbert College Academic Scholarships and Funding Grants

PROGRAM INFORMATION

Description: St. Norbert is a nationally recognized 4-year liberal arts college offering bachelor and master degrees. We offer over 40 academic majors and programs. International students are welcome to attend as full-time degree seeking students. St. Norbert offers academic scholarships for worthy students from around the world. Additionally, St. Norbert offers additional funding if the student qualifies. We also offer conditional admission with our on campus ESL program.
Levels of Study: Undergraduate
Field of Study: All
Nationality: Any Region
Location of Study: St. Norbert College De Pere, WI

AWARD INFORMATION

Award Type: Grant, Scholarship
Average Amount: $5,000-$12,000
Number of Awards: Unlimited
Award Coverage: Tuition and fees
Award Duration: Maximum of 4 years

APPLICATION INFORMATION

Award Deadline: Rolling
Instructions: See website for complete instructions

CONTACT

St. Norbert College
Admission
100 Grant St.
De Pere, WI 54115
Tel: +1 (920) 403-3942
Fax: +1 (920) 403-4072
Email: international@snc.edu
Web: www.snc.edu/go/iapply

State University of New York - Plattsburgh

SUNY Plattsburgh - Scholarships & Grants

PROGRAM INFORMATION

Description: SUNY Plattsburgh is home to a vibrant community of renowned teachers and nationally recognized scholars, dedicated to engaging students and helping them to succeed. Our students arrive from diverse backgrounds and places. But once enrolled, they have 1 particularly important thing in common: a college experience with the power to transform their lives. SUNY Plattsburgh offers scholarships to each accepted international student. We award scholarships based on a student's academic merit (high school average or transfer GPA), student type (Freshman or Transfer), and country of permanent residence.
Levels of Study: Undergraduate
Field of Study: All
Nationality: Any Region
Location of Study: SUNY Plattsburgh Plattsburgh, NY

AWARD INFORMATION

Award Type: Grant, Scholarship
Average Amount: $2,500-$11,000
Number of Awards: Unlimited
Award Coverage: Partial tuition and fees (up to 33% of total cost of attendance)
Award Duration: Academic year, renewable for additional year

ELIGIBILITY REQUIREMENTS

- Must be accepted and enrolled full-time at SUNY Plattsburgh
- Must possess superior academic achievement as evidenced by high school grades, college/university grades, and/or results on nationally standardized exams
- Must submit evidence of English language proficiency (for example, TOEFL, IELTS, completion of recognized ESL program)
- Freshman applicants are encouraged to provide SAT or ACT results

APPLICATION INFORMATION

Instructions: Download, complete, submit application along with required academic documents, visit our website for further information

CONTACT

SUNY Plattsburgh
Global Education Office
101 Broad Street
Kehoe 210
Plattsburgh, NY 12901
Tel: +1 (518) 564-3287
Fax: +1 (518) 564-3292
Email: geo@plattsburgh.edu
Web: www.plattsburgh.edu/international/scholarships

State University of New York at Cortland
SUNY Cortland International Student Award

PROGRAM INFORMATION

Description: SUNY Cortland is located in a small Central New York city. The location allows easy access to many major cities in the northeast that offer students the opportunity to expand their cultural experience.

Levels of Study: Undergraduate, Graduate

Field of Study: All

Nationality: Any Region

Location of Study: State University of New York College at Cortland
Cortland, NY

AWARD INFORMATION

Award Type: Award

Average Amount: $4,900

Number of Awards: Unlimited

Award Coverage: Partial tuition and fees

Award Duration: Up to 4 years

ELIGIBILITY REQUIREMENTS

- Must be accepted and matriculated into any SUNY Cortland graduate or undergraduate academic program

CONTACT

SUNY Cortland
International Programs Office
1 Gerhart Drive
Old Main, Room 219
Cortland, NY 13045
Tel: +1 (607) 753-2209
Fax: +1 (607) 753-5989
Email: studyabroad@cortland.edu
Web: www2.cortland.edu/admissions/

State University of New York at Geneseo
SUNY Geneseo International Student Scholarships

PROGRAM INFORMATION

Description: Renewable undergraduate tuition scholarships of $5,000 per year are awarded to excellent students at the time of their admission to Geneseo. Students with extraordinary academic achievements may receive both a tuition scholarship of $5,000 per year and a residence scholarship (valued at $7,000), which covers the cost of a room on-campus for the year. All tuition and room scholarships are awarded to recognize superior academic achievements. In addition, a small number of named scholarships ranging from $500 to $1,000 are awarded each year to continuing international students in recognition of their contributions to the Geneseo campus community.

Levels of Study: Undergraduate

Field of Study: All

Nationality: Any Region

Location of Study: State University of New York - Geneseo
Geneseo, NY

AWARD INFORMATION

Award Type: Scholarship

Average Amount: $4,000

Number of Awards: 140

Award Coverage: Partial tuition and/or campus room fee

Award Duration: Up to 4 years

ELIGIBILITY REQUIREMENTS

- Must have a minimum grade point average, this varies by country/education system
- Must provide completed application, including all official transcripts and TOEFL, Pearson or IELTS score

APPLICATION INFORMATION

Award Deadline: Jun

Instructions: Submit the Common Application Form, or SUNY Geneseo International Student Application form, official academic records and evidence of English language proficiency. No separate scholarship form is required. Visit our website for more information

CONTACT

State University of New York at Geneseo
Director, International Student and Scholar Services
Erwin Building Room 218
SUNY Geneseo
Geneseo, NY 14454
Tel: +1 (585) 245-5404
Fax: +1 (585) 245-5405
Email: hope@geneseo.edu
Web: iss.geneseo.edu

Susquehanna University
Susquehanna University International Student Scholarship

PROGRAM INFORMATION

Description: Successful international applicants are considered for the same academic scholarships offered to admitted American students. The scholarship program considers past academic and social achievement, potential for continued success at the college level, and demonstrated financial need. The awards are renewable for up to 4 years, dependent on satisfactory academic and social standing.

Levels of Study: Undergraduate

Field of Study: All

Nationality: Any Region

Location of Study: Susquehanna University
Selinsgrove, PA

AWARD INFORMATION

Award Type: Scholarship

Average Amount: up to $22,000

Number of Awards: 90%

Award Coverage: Tuition

Award Duration: Up to 4 academic years

ELIGIBILITY REQUIREMENTS

- Must meet international admission requirements and have a minimum TOEFL 79 or IELTS 6

APPLICATION INFORMATION

Award Deadline: Feb

Instructions: All international applicants found to be admissible to the University will be considered for scholarship funding, no additional scholarship application is required, visit our website for further application details

CONTACT

Susquehanna University
Associate Director of Admissions
514 University Avenue
Selinsgrove, PA 17870
Tel: +1 (570) 372-4044
Fax: +1 (570) 372-2722
Email: sunw@susqu.edu
Web: www.susqu.edu/admissions/international.htm

Syracuse University
Syracuse University Hursky Fellowship

PROGRAM INFORMATION

Description: Award is given to a full-time, matriculated or admitted graduate student of Ukrainian background, enrolled in either the Maxwell School of Citizenship and Public Affairs or the College of Arts and Sciences, or to a Syracuse University graduate student whose area of study is the Ukraine or includes Ukrainian topics. Preference is given to students whose study includes Ukrainian language and literature, Ukrainian linguistics, and/or culture.

Levels of Study: Graduate

Field of Study: Conflict Management, Government, Humanities, International Relations, Policy Research, Public Affairs, Social Science

Nationality: Ukraine

Location of Study: Syracuse University
Syracuse, NY

AWARD INFORMATION

Award Type: Fellowship

Average Amount: Varies

Number of Awards: 1

Award Coverage: Stipend and tuition scholarship for 24 credits

Award Duration: Academic year and the following summer

ELIGIBILITY REQUIREMENTS

- Must be a graduate student of Ukrainian background enrolled in either the Maxwell School of Citizenship and Public Affairs or the College of Arts and Sciences, or a Syracuse University graduate student whose area of study is the Ukraine
- Preference is given to students whose study includes Ukrainian language and literature, Ukrainian linguistics, and/or culture
- Prospective students must submit an application for graduate study in order to receive consideration by a nominating department

APPLICATION INFORMATION

Award Deadline: Varies

Instructions: There is no separate application form for the Hursky Fellowship; the Graduate School solicits nominations from academic departments each winter for this award, which is granted for each new academic year, beginning in the fall semester; current or prospective graduate students who are interested in being considered for this award and who qualify should contact their academic department

CONTACT

Syracuse University
Academic department
Syracuse, NY 13244
Tel: +1 (315) 443-4492
Fax: +1 (315) 443-3423
Email: Grad@syr.edu
Web: www.syr.edu/gradschool

Tallahassee Community College

Tallahassee Community College Housing Scholarships

PROGRAM INFORMATION

Description: Tallahassee Community College, located in the capital of the State of Florida, serves over 15,000 students of all ages and ethnic backgrounds each year. Ranked among the top community colleges in the nation, TCC is a 2-year, comprehensive college. Its average class size of 25 students ensures successful teacher-student interactions. Technology-driven classrooms, a state-of-the art library, computer labs and a newly-created academic support center, the Learning Commons, complement the academic environment. TCC offers the Associate in Arts for students planning on transferring to a 4-year university, the Associate in Science in more than 50 different specific areas, and Certificate programs in 25 specific areas.

Levels of Study: Undergraduate

Nationality: Any Region

Location of Study: Tallahassee Community College Tallahassee, FL

AWARD INFORMATION

Award Type: Scholarship

Average Amount: $7,000

Number of Awards: 10

Award Coverage: Housing Scholarship - furnished apartment with private bedroom and bath

Award Duration: 1 year, maximum 2

ELIGIBILITY REQUIREMENTS

- Must have at least 2.8 GPA on any previous college work or high school
- Must participate in minimum of 20 hours of volunteer work for fall and spring semesters with events sponsored by the International Student Services Office or the International Student Organization, including participation in all the fundraising activities sponsored by these 2 entities
- Expected to abide by all the terms of the apartment lease
- Be expected to cooperate with assigned apartment mate in affairs related to the upkeep of the apartment and be responsible for half of the utilities bill

APPLICATION INFORMATION

Award Deadline: Aug for fall entry; Dec for spring entry

Instructions: Applicants will have to have been admitted to TCC before applying for this scholarship can be awarded

CONTACT

Tallahassee Community College
International Student Services Coordinator
444 Appleyard Drive
Tallahassee, Florida 32312, US
Tel: +1 (850) 201-8457
Fax: +1 (850) 201-8468
Email: iss@tcc.fl.edu
Web: www.tcc.fl.edu/internationalstudent

Temple University

Temple University Merit Scholarships for International Undergraduate Students

PROGRAM INFORMATION

Description: Merit Scholarships are available to incoming international undergraduate students of high academic caliber. Scholarship awards for freshmen range from $7,500 up to full tuition

Levels of Study: Undergraduate

Field of Study: All

Nationality: Any Region

Location of Study: Temple University Philadelphia, PA

AWARD INFORMATION

Award Type: Scholarship

Average Amount: $10,000

Number of Awards: Unlimited

Award Coverage: Scholarship awards are distributed annually for up to 4 years, the scholarship amount will be deducted from the student's tuition bill each semester

Award Duration: Up to 4 years

ELIGIBILITY REQUIREMENTS

- Minimum high school GPA of 3.4
- Minimum TOEFL 88 or IELTS 7.0

APPLICATION INFORMATION

Award Deadline: Mar 1

Instructions: All applicants will be considered for scholarships, a separate application is not necessary, awards will be announced at the time of acceptance

CONTACT

Temple University
International Admissions Counselor
1803 N. Broad St
714 Carnell Hall
Philadelphia, PA 19122
Tel: +1 (215) 204-4900
Fax: +1 (215) 204-4990
Email: international.admissions@temple.edu
Web: admissions.temple.edu/international

Tennessee Tech University

Tennessee Tech University Undergraduate Honors Academic Scholarship

PROGRAM INFORMATION

Description: This scholarship is available only to undergraduate students who are not official residents of the state of Tennessee.

Field of Study: All

Nationality: Any Region

Location of Study: Tennessee Tech University Cookeville, TN

AWARD INFORMATION

Award Type: Award, Grant, Tuition Reduction

Average Amount: $15,000

Number of Awards: 50

Award Coverage: Tuition

Award Duration: 8 semesters

ELIGIBILITY REQUIREMENTS

- Prerequisites: 26 ACT, 3.5 high school GPA
- Must complete 60 hours of service each semester through the Honors Program Enrichment Options (HPEO)
- Must take at least 1 honors course each semester until all requirements for graduation in cursu honorum are completed
- Must maintain a GPA of 3.5. while at TTU
- Must have out-of-state residency

APPLICATION INFORMATION

Award Deadline: Aug 1

Instructions: Instructions can be found here: www.tntech.edu/honors/home/

CONTACT

Tennessee Tech University
Honors
P.O. Box 5124
38505 Cookeville TN
Tel: +1 (931) 372-3797
Fax: +1 (931) 372-3674
Email: cwilkerson@tntech.edu
Web: www.tntech.edu/honors/has

Tennessee Tech University

Tennessee Tech University International Undergraduate Legacy/Alumni Scholarship

PROGRAM INFORMATION

Description: This annual scholarship awards $1,000 ($500 for each term) to an international high school graduate whose parent, grandparent, or step-parent graduated from TTU.

Levels of Study: Undergraduate

Field of Study: All

Nationality: Africa, Asia, Europe, Latin America, Australia, Bermuda, Canada, Cook Islands, Fed. States of Micronesia, Fiji, French Polynesia, Kiribati, Marshall Islands, Nauru, New Caledonia, New Zealand, Niue, Norfolk Island, Palau, Papua New Guinea, Samoa, Solomon Islands, Tonga, Tuvalu, Vanuatu

Location of Study: Tennessee Tech University Cookeville, TN

ELIGIBILITY REQUIREMENTS

- Student must have attended an international high school and must have a parent, grandparent, or step-parent who graduated from TTU, spouses and brothers/sisters can be taken into consideration
- Be admitted to TTU as a fulltime, degree -seeking student, students are encouraged to submit scholarship applications as soon as they are admitted to TTU
- Must have or plan to have an F -1 or J -1 student visa.
- Must have a 3.0 GPA out of 4.0
- Must fill out the scholarship application form

APPLICATION INFORMATION

Award Deadline: 1 month prior to enrollment

Instructions: Students are encouraged to apply for scholarships as soon as they are fully admitted to TTU

CONTACT

Tennessee Tech University
Director
1 William L Jones Dr, Rm 135
Cookeville, TN 38505
Tel: +1 (931) 372-3634
Fax: +1 (931) 372-3674
Email: cwilkerson@tntech.edu
Web: www.tntech.edu/internationaladmissions/

Tennessee Tech University

Tennessee Tech University International Undergraduate Multinational Enhancement Scholarship

PROGRAM INFORMATION

Description: This scholarship is designed to promote TTU 's commitment to a multinational student body. This scholarship promotes multicultural and diversity among the international student body. This scholarship is a competitive scholarship designed to attract students from under-represented countries at TTU who are academically gifted or who have special talents that can contribute to the TTU campus.

Levels of Study: Undergraduate

Field of Study: All

Nationality: Africa, Asia, Europe, Latin America, Australia, Bermuda, Canada, Cook Islands, Fed. States of Micronesia, Fiji, French Polynesia, Kiribati, Marshall Islands, Nauru, New Caledonia, New Zealand, Niue, Norfolk Island, Palau, Papua New Guinea, Samoa, Solomon Islands, Tonga, Tuvalu, Vanuatu

Location of Study: Tennessee Tech University Cookeville, TN

AWARD INFORMATION

Award Type: Scholarship

Average Amount: $2,000

Number of Awards: 80

Award Duration: 4 years

ELIGIBILITY REQUIREMENTS

- Must be admitted to TTU as fulltime, degree-seeking student
- Must have or plan to have an FF-1 or J-1 visa.
- Must possess a minimum 3.0 GPA out of 4.0 GPA
- Must submit the scholarship application form with reference letters (at least 2)
- Recipients must maintain fulltime status

APPLICATION INFORMATION

Award Deadline: Student must submit the application 1 month prior to the semester of enrollment

Instructions: Students must apply to TTU first before they can be considered for scholarship, only those admitted will be given priority

CONTACT

Tennessee Tech University
Director
1 William L Jones Dr, Rm 135
Cookeville, TN 38505
Tel: +1 (931) 372-3634
Fax: +1 (931) 372-3674
Email: cwilkerson@tntech.edu
Web: www.tntech.edu/internationaladmissions/

Tennessee Tech University

Tennessee Tech University International Undergraduate Merit Awards

PROGRAM INFORMATION

Description: Awarded to the best international students at Tennessee Tech University. Students must have a minimum 3.3 GPA and must be admitted to be eligible. Students who have an athletic scholarship, honors scholarship or scholarship from their home country are not eligible.

Levels of Study: Undergraduate

Field of Study: All

Nationality: Any Region

Location of Study: Tennessee Tech University Cookeville, TN

AWARD INFORMATION

Award Type: Scholarship

Average Amount: $8,664

Number of Awards: 20

Award Coverage: 55 percent of out-of-state tuition costs

Award Duration: Until student graduates

ELIGIBILITY REQUIREMENTS

- 3.3 GPA
- 1 recommendation letter from a colleague or friend
- 1 recommendation letter from an instructor or professor
- Full admission
- Students may not have an athletic scholarship, honors scholarship or scholarship from their home country

APPLICATION INFORMATION

Award Deadline: 1 month prior to start of semester

Instructions: Contact the Director of International Education for application, at cwilkerson@tntech.edu

CONTACT

Tennessee Tech University
Director
1 William L Jones Dr room 135
Cookeville, TN 38505
Tel: +1 (931) 372-3634
Fax: +1 (931) 372-3674
Email: cwilkerson@tntech.edu
Web: www.tntech.edu/internationaladmissions

Tennessee Tech University

Tennessee Tech University Graduate Assistant

PROGRAM INFORMATION

Description: Assistants are assigned research and support duties. The workload for a full-time assistant is 20 hours per week. All full assistantships provide tuition and fee payments, in addition to a salary stipend during the period of appointment.

Levels of Study: Graduate

Field of Study: Biology, Business and Management, Chemistry, Education, Engineering, Environmental Studies, Multi/Interdisciplinary Studies, Psychology

Nationality: Any Region

Location of Study: Tennessee Tech University Cookeville, TN

AWARD INFORMATION

Award Type: Fellowship, Grant, Tuition Reduction

Average Amount: Varies

Number of Awards: Approx 15

Award Coverage: Tuition and fees, monthly stipend.

Award Duration: Academic year

ELIGIBILITY REQUIREMENTS

- Must enroll full-time
- Must hold a bachelor's degree with a minimum grade point average of 2.5 on a 4.0 scale
- Must have a minimum GMAT score of 450

APPLICATION INFORMATION

Award Deadline: Apr

Instructions: Apply online

CONTACT

Tennessee Tech University
Director of MBA Studies
1105 N. Peachtree, TTU Box 023
Cookeville, TN 38505
Tel: +1 (931) 372-3600
Fax: +1 (931) 372-6544
Email: mbastudies@tntech.edu
Web: www.tntech.edu/mba

Texas Wesleyan University

Texas Wesleyan University International Student Scholarships

PROGRAM INFORMATION

Description: Scholarships are awarded for 1 year based on grade point average with renewal for up to 4 years, provided the student continues to meet the eligibility requirements.

Levels of Study: Undergraduate

Field of Study: All

Nationality: Any Region

Location of Study: Texas Wesleyan University Fort Worth, TX

AWARD INFORMATION

Award Type: Scholarship

Average Amount: $3,000-$10,000

Number of Awards: Varies

Award Coverage: Tuition and fees

Award Duration: Maximum 4 years

ELIGIBILITY REQUIREMENTS

- Must be admitted to the university

APPLICATION INFORMATION

Award Deadline: None

Instructions: Apply through www.ApplyTexas.org; scholarships awarded automatically upon admission

CONTACT

Texas Wesleyan University
International Programs
1201 Wesleyan St
Fort Worth, TX 76105-1536
Tel: +1 (817) 531-5868
Fax: +1 (817) 531-4499
Email: oneworld@txwes.edu
Web: www.txwes.edu/admissions

The College of Saint Rose

College of Saint Rose Graduate Scholarship

PROGRAM INFORMATION

Description: This scholarship is a partial-tuition award to support the master's degree studies of outstanding international students at the College of Saint Rose. There are no limitations on the areas of study this award may cover.

Levels of Study: Graduate

Field of Study: All

Nationality: Any Region

Location of Study: The College of Saint Rose Albany, NY

AWARD INFORMATION

Award Type: Scholarship

Average Amount: Half tuition

Number of Awards: 3 - 4

Award Coverage: Covers 1 half of tuition charges each semester while student is enrolled full time

Award Duration: Maximum of 2 years

ELIGIBILITY REQUIREMENTS

- Must have unconditional admission to a graduate program at the College of Saint Rose
- Must register for full-time study (minimum of 9 credits) per semester
- Must maintain a 3.3 GPA throughout graduate studies

APPLICATION INFORMATION

Award Deadline: May 1 for fall; Oct 15 for spring

Instructions: Complete the application for International Scholarship on the website, applicants to graduate study may submit application for admission and scholarship application at the same time

CONTACT

The College of Saint Rose
432 Western Avenue
Albany, NY 12203
Tel: +1 (518) 454-5143
Fax: +1 (518) 458-5479
Email: grad@strose.edu
Web: www.strose.edu/grad

The College of Saint Rose

College of Saint Rose Guaranteed Undergraduate Scholarships

PROGRAM INFORMATION

Description: The College of Saint Rose offers guaranteed scholarships to first-year undergraduate students.

Levels of Study: Undergraduate

Field of Study: All

Nationality: Any Region

Location of Study: The College of Saint Rose Albany, NY

AWARD INFORMATION

Award Type: Scholarship

Number of Awards: Unlimited

Award Coverage: Tuition: from $5,000 to $14,000 per year

Award Duration: Maximum of 4 years

ELIGIBILITY REQUIREMENTS

- High school GPA of 85 or higher on 100-point scale. (International student GPAs may be recalculated to reflect US-style grading
- Test score on SAT, ACT, TOEFL or IELTS, refer to website (www.strose.edu for current test score requirements
- Complete application with transcripts, letter of recommendation, essay and test scores

APPLICATION INFORMATION

Award Deadline: Rolling

Instructions: All first-year applicants who provide test scores 1 of the following: SAT, ACT, TOEFL, IELTS - are considered for scholarship funding

CONTACT

The College of Saint Rose
International Recruitment & Admissions
432 Western Avenue
Albany, NY 12203
Tel: +1 (518) 454-5143
Fax: +1 (518) 458-5479
Email: international@strose.edu
Web: www.strose.edu/admissions/undergraduateadmissions/financingandcosts/article2387

The College of Saint Rose

College of Saint Rose Guaranteed Transfer Scholarships

PROGRAM INFORMATION

Description: The College of Saint Rose offers guaranteed scholarships to transfer students, based on GPA in previous post-secondary education.

Field of Study: All

Nationality: Any Region

Location of Study: The College of Saint Rose Albany, NY

AWARD INFORMATION

Award Type: Scholarship

Number of Awards: Unlimited

Award Coverage: Tuition — scholarships range from $5,000 to $7,500 per year

Award Duration: 2 years (may be renewable for a third year)

ELIGIBILITY REQUIREMENTS

- GPA in previous post-secondary studies of at least 3.0 on 4-point scale
- WES or ECE evaluation for non-US institutions prior to enrollment at Saint Rose
- Members of Phi Theta Kappa honor society are eligible for an additional $3,000 award, in addition to the transfer scholarship

APPLICATION INFORMATION

Award Deadline: Rolling

Instructions: Provide completed application.

CONTACT

The College of Saint Rose
International Recruitment & Admissions
432 Western Avenue
Albany, NY 12203
Tel: +1 (518) 454-5143
Fax: +1 (518) 458-5479
Email: international@strose.edu
Web: www.strose.edu/admissions/applying/transferstudent

The Fletcher School of Law and Diplomacy - Tufts University

Master of Arts in Law and Diplomacy (MALD)

PROGRAM INFORMATION

Description: The MALD is a 2-year, highly flexible, interdisciplinary professional degree in international affairs. Other degrees include a 2-year Master of International Business (MIB), a 1-year MA in International Affairs for mid-career professionals, a 1-year LLM for lawyers and legal professionals, and a PhD program.

Levels of Study: Graduate, Doctorate, Professional

Field of Study: Conflict Resolution, Economics, Governance/Civil Society, Government, International Development, International Law, International Relations, Social Justice

Nationality: Any Region

Location of Study: Tufts University Medford, MA

AWARD INFORMATION

Award Type: Scholarship

Average Amount: $10,000

Number of Awards: Approx $7 million awarded annually to all applicants

Award Coverage: Tuition

Award Duration: Academic year, renewable for second year

ELIGIBILITY REQUIREMENTS

- Bachelor's degree or equivalent; 1-year MA requires minimum 8 years professional experience; LLM requires law degree or equivalent; PhD requires prior 2-year MA in a relevant field, and submission of MA thesis
- Professional experience strongly recommended (average 2-3 years)
- Economics and statistics coursework strongly recommended
- Second language proficiency strongly recommended; intermediate professional proficiency exams required for graduation (or TOEFL exam during application process for non-native English speakers)
- Demonstrated international experience/exposure strongly recommended

APPLICATION INFORMATION

Award Deadline: Jan

Instructions: Application and all necessary instructions available at fletcher.tufts.edu/Admissions/Apply-to-Fletcher

CONTACT

The Fletcher School of Law and Diplomacy
Admissions Coordinator
160 Packard Ave.
Medford, MA 02155
Tel: +1 (617) 627-3040
Fax: +1 (617) 627-2929
Email: fletcheradmissions@tufts.edu
Web: www.fletcher.tufts.edu

The Juilliard School

Juilliard Scholarships

PROGRAM INFORMATION

Description: The Juilliard School is committed to educating talented performing artists and helping them achieve their highest potential. To that end, we wish to enable all admitted students to attend the school, regardless of their ability to pay. Juilliard's admissions policies are need-blind, meaning that applying for financial aid will not hurt your chances of being admitted. In fact, 80 percent of our admitted students receive scholarship support through Juilliard. Juilliard Scholarships are available to all Juilliard students, including international students. Students who receive scholarships are asked to submit a brief biographical statement to the Financial Aid Office.

Levels of Study: Undergraduate, Graduate, Doctorate

Field of Study: Dance, Music, Theater

Nationality: Any Region

Location of Study: The Juilliard School
New York, NY

AWARD INFORMATION

Award Type: Scholarship

Average Amount: $1,000 up to full need

ELIGIBILITY REQUIREMENTS

- Undergraduates must submit scores of: TOEFL 533 PBT/200 CBT/73 IBT
- Graduates must submit scores of: TOEFL 570 PBT/230 CBT/89 IBT
- Doctoral students must submit scores of: TOEFL 610 PBT/253 CBT/102 IBT

APPLICATION INFORMATION

Award Deadline: Mar 1

Instructions: Please see the website for instructions

CONTACT

The Juilliard School
60 Lincoln Center Plaza
New York, NY 10023
Tel: +1 (212) 799-5000
Email: financialaid@juilliard.edu
Web: www.juilliard.edu

The Ohio State University

The Ohio State University International Undergraduate Scholarships

PROGRAM INFORMATION

Description: The Ohio State University scholarships are offered on a competitive basis.

Levels of Study: Undergraduate

Field of Study: All

Nationality: Any Region

Location of Study: The Ohio State University
Columbus, OH

AWARD INFORMATION

Award Type: Scholarship, Tuition Reduction

Average Amount: $4,000

Number of Awards: Varies

Award Coverage: Partial tuition

Award Duration: Maximum of 8 semesters or equivalent

ELIGIBILITY REQUIREMENTS

- Must be qualified full-time, Columbus campus international freshmen who are admitted for the autumn semester and pay the nonresident tuition surcharge
- Must be an admitted international student with a competitive profile
- All admissions application material must be submitted by Nov 1 in order to be considered, no separate application is needed
- Transfer students are not eligible for these scholarships

APPLICATION INFORMATION

Award Deadline: Nov 1

Instructions: No additional application is necessary, visit our website for application information

CONTACT

The Ohio State University
International Admissions Coordinator
281 W. Lane Ave.
Student Academic Services Bldg
Columbus, OH 43210
Tel: +1 (614) 292-3980
Fax: +1 (614) 292-4818
Email: bibler.27@osu.edu
Web: undergrad.osu.edu

The Ohio State University

The Ohio State University Moritz College of Law's LLM Scholarship

PROGRAM INFORMATION

Description: The Moritz College of Law is part of one of the largest universities in the US: The Ohio State University. The Moritz Master of Laws (LLM) Program is designed for foreign lawyers who wish to advance their legal education in a stimulating academic environment. The College offers the dual advantages of a highly regarded law curriculum at a major US university and an LLM program of limited size that allows for individualized attention and support. The LLM program is pleased to announce a new scholarship initiative for Fulbright Scholars and Muskie Fellows. Fulbright Scholars and Muskie Fellows who are admitted to the LLM program will be granted partial tuition waivers reducing their tuition costs to in-state tuition levels.

Levels of Study: Graduate

Field of Study: Law

Nationality: Any Region

Location of Study: The Ohio State University Moritz College of Law
Columbus, OH

AWARD INFORMATION

Award Type: Scholarship

Average Amount: Approx $23,000

Award Coverage: Partial tuition

ELIGIBILITY REQUIREMENTS

- Must be a Fulbright Scholar or Muskie Fellow admitted to the LLM program
- Must have obtained an LLB from a foreign country; or completed in a foreign country the university-based legal education required to take the equivalent of the bar examination in that foreign country; or is qualified to practice law in a foreign country
- Must take and submit the TOEFL examination if English is not applicants' first language

APPLICATION INFORMATION

Instructions: While our application is to be completed online, other materials must be submitted by mail, some to more than 1 office, please read instructions for each section carefully

CONTACT

The Ohio State University Moritz College of Law
341 Drinko Hall
55 West 12th Avenue
Columbus, OH 43210
Tel: +1 (614) 688-5328
Email: MoritzLLM@osu.edu
Web: moritzlaw.osu.edu/admissions/llm/

The University of Illinois at Urbana-Champaign
Beckman Institute Fellows

PROGRAM INFORMATION

Description: The Beckman Institute Fellows program provides an opportunity for young scientists to spend several years doing independent research before launching formal academic careers. During the term of appointment, there are no teaching or administrative duties required, other than a brief written annual report to the director of the Institute.

Levels of Study: Post Doctorate

Field of Study: All

Nationality: Any Region

Location of Study: University of Illinois at Urbana-Champaign Urbana, IL

AWARD INFORMATION

Award Type: Fellowship

Average Amount: $52,000

Number of Awards: 4-6

Award Coverage: Relocation expenses ($2,000 maximum, first year only), health insurance, research supplies, facility use/service charges, equipment, training, workshops, support for interdisciplinary collaborations, travel between collaborating institutions

Award Duration: Up to 3 years

ELIGIBILITY REQUIREMENTS

- Fellows are selected on the basis of their professional promise, capacity for independent work, interdisciplinary interests, outstanding achievement to date
- Must have a recent PhD in an area of research relevant to Beckman Institute research
- Must be involved in interdisciplinary studies related to 1 of the Beckman Institute's research themes
- Must be eligible for J-1 visa sponsorship for the full 3 year period of the fellowship

APPLICATION INFORMATION

Award Deadline: Nov

Instructions: Please see the website for application information

CONTACT

University of Illinois at Urbana-Champaign
Beckman Institute for Advanced Science and Technology
405 North Mathews Avenue M/C 251
Urbana, IL 61801
Tel: +1 (217) 244-1176
Fax: +1 (217) 333-2922
Email: communications@beckman.illinois.edu
Web: www.beckman.illinois.edu/research/fellows-and-awards/postdoctoral

The University of Michigan Law School
Michigan Grotius Fellowships

PROGRAM INFORMATION

Description: Michigan Law has been known internationally since the 1890s when its first LLMs graduated. The breadth and applicability of Michigan's education is unwaveringly mirrored in the distinction of our alumni who serve as leaders in public, private and academic sectors in the US and beyond.

Levels of Study: Graduate, Professional

Field of Study: Law

Nationality: Any Region

Location of Study: The University of Michigan Law School Ann Arbor, MI

AWARD INFORMATION

Award Type: Fellowship

Average Amount: Varies widely

Number of Awards: 10 - 14 awards per year

Award Coverage: Partial tuition; in rare cases fellowship will cover full tuition

Award Duration: 1 year

ELIGIBILITY REQUIREMENTS

- JD, LLB, or equivalent degree
- Minimum TOEFL scores of 98 or 100; or minimum IELTS scores of 7.0

APPLICATION INFORMATION

Award Deadline: Apply by Jan 30

Instructions: Please visit our website for a more in-depth description of the school and programs, and for detailed application instructions. www.law.umich.edu/prospectivestudents/graduate/Pages/admission.aspx

CONTACT

The University of Michigan Law School
Assistant Director of Admissions
Admissions Office
701 South State Street
Ann Arbor, MI 48109
Tel: +1 (734) 764-0537
Fax: +1 (734) 647-3218
Email: law.grad.admissions@umich.edu
Web: www.law.umich.edu/prospectivestudents/graduate

The University of Michigan Law School
Johnston LLM Fellowship

PROGRAM INFORMATION

Description: Michigan Law has been known internationally since the 1890s when its first LLMs graduated. The breadth and applicability of Michigan's education is unwaveringly mirrored in the distinction of our alumni who serve as leaders in public, private and academic sectors in the US and beyond.

Levels of Study: Graduate, Professional

Field of Study: Comparative Law, Corporate Law, Law

Nationality: Any Region

Location of Study: The University of Michigan Law School Ann Arbor, MI

AWARD INFORMATION

Award Type: Fellowship

Average Amount: Up to $20,000

Number of Awards: 1

Award Coverage: Tuition

Award Duration: 1 year

ELIGIBILITY REQUIREMENTS

- LLB or JD degree within the top 10% of the graduating class
- Proven focus and success in field of legal interest related to corporate laws

APPLICATION INFORMATION

Award Deadline: Jan 30

Instructions: Please visit our website for a detailed description of the school and programs, and for complete application instructions at www.law.umich.edu/prospectivestudents/graduate

CONTACT

The University of Michigan Law School
Assistant Director of Admissions
Admissions Office
701 South State Street
Ann Arbor, Michigan 48109
Tel: +1 (734) 763-6802
Fax: +1 (734) 647-3218
Email: law.grad.admissions@umich.edu
Web: www.law.umich.edu

The University of Michigan Law School
Joris LLM Fellowship

PROGRAM INFORMATION

Description: Michigan Law has been known internationally since the 1890s when its first LLMs graduated. The breadth and applicability of Michigan's education is unwaveringly mirrored in the distinction of our alumni who serve as leaders in public, private and academic sectors in the US and beyond.

Levels of Study: Graduate, Professional

Field of Study: Comparative Law, Corporate Law, Law

Nationality: Western Europe

Location of Study: The University of Michigan Law School Ann Arbor, MI

AWARD INFORMATION

Award Type: Fellowship

Average Amount: $10,000

Number of Awards: 1

Award Coverage: Partial tuition

Award Duration: 1 year

ELIGIBILITY REQUIREMENTS

- LLB or JD degree award within the top 10% of the graduating class

APPLICATION INFORMATION

Award Deadline: Jan 30

Instructions: Please visit our website for a detailed description of the school and programs, and for complete application instructions at www.law.umich.edu/prospectivestudents/graduate

CONTACT

The University of Michigan Law School
Assistant Director of Admissions
Admissions Office
701 South State Street
Ann Arbor, Michigan 48109
Tel: +1 (734) 763-6802
Fax: +1 (734) 647-3218
Email: law.grad.admissions@umich.edu
Web: www.law.umich.edu/prospectivestudents/graduate/degreeprograms

The University of Michigan Law School
Michigan Italian Alumni Law Fellowship

PROGRAM INFORMATION

Description: Michigan Law has been known internationally since the 1890s when its first LLMs graduated. The breadth and applicability of Michigan's education is unwaveringly mirrored in the distinction of our alumni who serve as leaders in public, private and academic sectors in the US and beyond.

Levels of Study: Graduate, Professional

Field of Study: Law

Nationality: Italy

Location of Study: The University of Michigan Law School Ann Arbor, MI

AWARD INFORMATION

Award Type: Fellowship

Average Amount: Up to $40,000

Number of Awards: 1-2

Award Coverage: Partial tuition

Award Duration: 1 year

ELIGIBILITY REQUIREMENTS

- Laurea specialistica or laurea magistrale in law (at least 110/110)
- TOEFL scores of at least 100, or IELTS scores of at least 7.0

APPLICATION INFORMATION

Award Deadline: Jan 30

Instructions: Please visit our website for a more detailed description of the school, programs, and for the application instructions: www.law.umich.edu/prospectivestudents/graduate/Pages/advanced-index.aspx

CONTACT

The University of Michigan Law School
Assistant Director of Admissions
Admissions Office
701 South State Street
Ann Arbor, Michigan 48109
Tel: +1 (734) 764-0537
Fax: +1 (734) 647-3218
Email: law.grad.admissions@umich.edu

The University of Michigan Law School
DeWitt Fellowship

PROGRAM INFORMATION

Description: Michigan Law has been known internationally since the 1890s when its first LLMs graduated. The breadth and applicability of Michigan's education is unwaveringly mirrored in the distinction of our alumni who serve as leaders in public, private and academic sectors in the US and beyond.

Levels of Study: Graduate, Professional

Field of Study: Law

Nationality: Philippines

Location of Study: The University of Michigan Law School Ann Arbor, MI

AWARD INFORMATION

Award Type: Fellowship

Average Amount: Varies

Number of Awards: 1

Award Coverage: Tuition

Award Duration: 1 year

ELIGIBILITY REQUIREMENTS

- LLB or JD degree award within the top 10% of the graduating class

APPLICATION INFORMATION

Award Deadline: Jan 30

Instructions: Please visit our website for a more in-depth description of the school and programs, and for detailed application instructions www.law.umich.edu/prospectivestudents/graduate/Pages/admission.aspx

CONTACT

The University of Michigan Law School
Assistant Director of Admissions
Admissions Office
701 South State Street
Ann Arbor, Michigan 48109
Tel: +1 (734) 764-0537
Fax: + 1 (734) 647-3218
Email: www.law.grad.admissions@umich.edu
Web: www.law.umich.edu/prospectivestudents/graduate/Pages/advanced-index.aspx

The University of Mississippi
University of Mississippi Graduate Teaching and Research Assistantships

PROGRAM INFORMATION

Description: Graduate teaching or research assistantships may be available to admitted/enrolled graduate students in master's or doctoral programs per the discretion of the academic department to which they are admitted. Graduate assistantships generally require part-time teaching, laboratory assistance, or research. Students who hold qualifying graduate assistantships at their departments may qualify for full or partial tuition support by the graduate school.

Levels of Study: Graduate, Doctorate, Professional

Field of Study: All

Nationality: Any Region

Location of Study: The University of Mississippi Oxford, MS

AWARD INFORMATION

Award Type: Award, Tuition Reduction

Average Amount: Varies

Number of Awards: Varies

Award Coverage: Graduate assistantships cover basic living expenses; tuition support covers all or partial tuition costs

Award Duration: 1 year, renewable

ELIGIBILITY REQUIREMENTS

- Must be admitted to a graduate (master's or doctoral) program to be considered for graduate assistantships by graduate department, and for tuition support by the Graduate School
- Application requirements include: online application, application fee, official transcripts and degree certificates, English language proficiency test scores, graduate exams (GRE, GMAT), statement of purpose, letters of recommendation

APPLICATION INFORMATION

Award Deadline: Apr 1

Instructions: Please see gradschool.olemiss.edu/prospective-students/for more information

CONTACT

The University of Mississippi
Director, Office of International Programs
Martindale 331
Oxford, MS 38677
Tel: +1 (662) 915-7404
Fax: +1 (662) 915-7486
Email: intladmg@olemiss.edu
Web: gradschool.olemiss.edu/prospective-students/financial-aid-information/

The University of Mississippi
Academic Excellence Scholarships (International Freshman only)

PROGRAM INFORMATION

Description: For incoming international freshman students who graduated from high school outside of the US Academic Excellence Scholarships - International range from 15%-90% of tuition. Such scholarships may not be combined with International Undergraduate International Student Scholarships.

Levels of Study: Undergraduate **Field of Study:** All

Nationality: Any Region

Location of Study: The University of Mississippi Oxford, MS

AWARD INFORMATION

Award Type: Scholarship

Average Amount: $3,250-$17,048

Award Coverage: Tuition

Award Duration: Maximum of 4 years

ELIGIBILITY REQUIREMENTS

- Academic Excellence Scholarship: International of $17,048 per academic year requires cum GPA of 3.90/4.00 or higher on high school credentials, and minimum 6.00 IELTS; 79 IBT; 53 PTE-A, applicant must be "freshman"
- Academic Excellence Scholarship: International of $9,000 per academic year requires cum GPA of 3.75-3.89/4.00 on high school credentials and minimum 6.00 IELTS; 79 IBT; 53 PTE-A, applicant must be "freshman"
- Academic Excellence Scholarship: International of $6,000 per academic year requires cum GPA of 3.50-3.74/4.00 on high school credentials and minimum 6.00 IELTS; 79 IBT; 53 PTE-A, applicant must be "freshman"
- Academic Excellence Scholarship: International of $3,250 per academic year requires cum GPA of 3.25-3.49/4.00 on high school credentials and minimum 6.00 IELTS; 79 IBT; 53 PTE-A, applicant must be "freshman"
- If Academic Excellence Scholarship: International was awarded, the scholarship is renewable for 3 additional years provided the student maintains a 3.00 cum GPA at the University of Mississippi and remains in valid legal standing in the US

APPLICATION INFORMATION

Instructions: Separate Scholarship Application is not required. Apply at: international.olemiss.edu/apply/

CONTACT

The University of Mississippi
Director, Office of International Programs
331 Martindale
Oxford, MS 38677
Tel: +1 (662) 915-7404
Fax: +1 (662) 915-7486
Email: intladmu@olemiss.edu
Web: international.olemiss.edu/scholarships-undergraduate/

The University of Mississippi

University of Mississippi International Undergraduate Transfer Student Scholarships

PROGRAM INFORMATION

Description: Competitive Award. Must submit International Student Scholarship Application and be admitted prior to Apr 1 for Fall enrollment.

Levels of Study: Undergraduate

Field of Study: All

Nationality: Any Region

Location of Study: University of Mississippi
Oxford, MS

ELIGIBILITY REQUIREMENTS

- Cumulative college/university GPA of 3.00/4.00 on 30 credits or more (generally at least 1 year of full-time study), or its equivalent
- English proficiency test requirements: i-TOEFL-79; IETLS-6.00; or PTE-A-53
- Compelling aspirations and promise of success

APPLICATION INFORMATION

Award Deadline: Apr 1 for fall enrollment

Instructions: Apply for admission in Jan/Feb prior to Fall enrollment. Apply for Scholarship in Jan/Feb prior to Fall enrollment.

CONTACT

The University of Mississippi
Director, Office of International Programs
Martindale 331
Oxford, Mississippi
38677 Oxford Mississippi
Tel: +1 (662) 915-7404
Fax: +1 (662) 915-7486
Email: gprovoos@olemiss.edu
Web: international.olemiss.edu/scholarships-undergraduate/

The University of Montana

University of Montana Entering Student Scholarships

PROGRAM INFORMATION

Description: The University of Montana Scholarship Program has many scholarships for new international freshman and transfer students. Students only need to apply for admission to the University of Montana to be considered for the scholarships. A scholarship committee matches academically-qualified applicants with the scholarship that best fits them.

Levels of Study: Undergraduate

Field of Study: All

Nationality: Any Region

Location of Study: The University of Montana
Missoula, MT

AWARD INFORMATION

Award Type: Scholarship

Average Amount: Up to $10,000 per year

Number of Awards: Varies

Award Coverage: Housing or Tuition & Fees

Award Duration: Renewable up to 4 years as long as academic requirements are met

ELIGIBILITY REQUIREMENTS

- Must be an incoming freshman or transfer student
- Must have minimum score of TOEFL 525 PBT/70 IBT or 6.0 IELTS or 74 MELAB
- ACT or SAT is optional, but if you have these scores we encourage you to submit them

APPLICATION INFORMATION

Award Deadline: May 15

Instructions: Applicants must submit a completed UM application for International Admissions, please visit our website to apply

CONTACT

The University of Montana
Associate Director, International Recruitment
Office of International Programs
International Center
Missoula, MT 59812
Tel: +1 (406) 243-5844
Fax: +1 (406) 243-6194
Email: julie.cahill@umontana.edu
Web: www.admissions.umt.edu/admissions/scholarships

The University of Montana

Davidson Honors College Presidential Leadership Scholarship

PROGRAM INFORMATION

Description: The Presidential Leadership Scholarship is University of Montana's premier academic scholarship, recognizing outstanding talent, academic performance and contribution to the community.

Levels of Study: Undergraduate

Field of Study: All

Nationality: Any Region

Location of Study: The University of Montana
Missoula, MT

AWARD INFORMATION

Award Type: Scholarship

Average Amount: $9,000-$11,000

Number of Awards: 24

Award Coverage: Stipend, tuition

Award Duration: 4 years or until graduation

ELIGIBILITY REQUIREMENTS

- 1 letter of recommendation from a teacher speaking to your academic and personal qualities, this letter should be obtained in a sealed envelope from your reference, must be included in your application or mailed to the Davidson Honors College
- Must submit an unofficial transcript of your high school record and ACT or SAT results
- List all honors, activities, accomplishments, and community service
- Must submit an essay of 2-3 pages (double spaced) on 1 of 3 assigned topics
- Must submit the University of Montana International Application for Undergraduate Admission

APPLICATION INFORMATION

Award Deadline: Dec 31

Instructions: Complete the Davidson Honors College application form online, you may also download the application form from the website

CONTACT

The University of Montana
The Davidson Honors College
Missoula, MT 59812
Tel: +1 (406) 243-2541
Fax: +1 (406) 243-6446
Email: dhc@umontana.edu
Web: www.dhc.umt.edu/scholarships/dhcScholarships.php

The University of Texas at San Antonio

UT San Antonio Border County Program

PROGRAM INFORMATION

Description: This is a student tuition assistance program that allows eligible F-1 and J-1 students from Mexico an opportunity to pay Texas in-state tuition. Both graduate students and undergraduates are eligible to apply.

Levels of Study: Undergraduate, Graduate

Field of Study: All

Nationality: Mexico

Location of Study: University of Texas at San Antonio
San Antonio, TX

AWARD INFORMATION

Award Type: Award
Average Amount: In-state tuition
Number of Awards: Unlimited
Award Coverage: Tuition
Award Duration: Academic year, renewable

ELIGIBILITY REQUIREMENTS

- Must be a citizen or permanent resident of Mexico
- Must be admitted to UTSA and have been issued an I-20 or DS-2019 Form by UTSA
- Must be a full-time student
- Must demonstrate financial need for past 12 months with receipts attached
- Must plan to return to Mexico after finishing the educational program

APPLICATION INFORMATION

Award Deadline: Jul
Instructions: Go to our website for more information, print the application form, complete the form, and return it with the supporting documentation to the address on the form

CONTACT

The University of Texas at San Antonio
Office of International Programs, International Student Services
One UTSA Circle
San Antonio, TX 78249-0616
Tel: +1 (210) 458-7995
Email: IntlAdmissions@utsa.edu
Web: international.utsa.edu/financial-aid-resources/border-county-program/

The Wharton School of the University of Pennsylvania

Joseph Wharton Fellowships and European Fellowship

PROGRAM INFORMATION

Description: Every student who is admitted to the school is eligible for fellowship support and the criteria for selection of awards may include academic achievement, compelling leadership, exceptional professional development, and unique personal qualities. There is no formal fellowship application, and notification of fellowship support is included with the admissions decision. Global content is integrated throughout the curriculum and the school offers a wide variety of international business programs including the Lautner Institute's dual MBA/MA in international studies.
Levels of Study: Professional
Field of Study: Business and Management
Nationality: Any Region
Location of Study: University of Pennsylvania
Philadelphia, PA

AWARD INFORMATION

Award Type: Scholarship
Average Amount: Varies
Number of Awards: Varies
Award Coverage: Varies

APPLICATION INFORMATION

Award Deadline: With admission application
Instructions: For more information on how to apply, please visit the website

CONTACT

The Wharton School, University of Pennsylvania
Office of MBA Admissions and Financial Aid
Vance Hall, Suite 111
3733 Spruce Street
Philadelphia, PA 19104
Tel: +1 (215) 898-6183
Fax: +1 (215) 898-0120
Email: mbaoperations@wharton.upenn.edu
Web: www.wharton.upenn.edu

Thomas Jefferson School of Law

Master of Laws, Juris Doctorate

PROGRAM INFORMATION

Description: Scholarship availability for law students
Levels of Study: Graduate, Doctorate, Post Doctorate, Professional
Field of Study: Business Law, Comparative Law, Corporate Law, International Law, Law, Tax Law
Nationality: Any Region
Location of Study: Thomas Jefferson School of Law
San Diego, CA

AWARD INFORMATION

Award Type: Fellowship, Internship, Scholarship
Average Amount: $14.000
Number of Awards: 522
Award Coverage: Tuition
Award Duration: Maximum 3 years

ELIGIBILITY REQUIREMENTS

- GPA and LSAT determine award on a fixed matrix

APPLICATION INFORMATION

Award Deadline: Apr
Instructions: contact admissions

CONTACT

Thomas Jefferson School of Law
Associate Dean
1155 Island Avenue
San Diego, California 92101, US
Tel: +1 (619) 961-4211
Fax: +1 (619) 961-1211
Email: profbyrnes@gmail.com
Web: www.tjsl.edu/admissions/scholarships

Towson University

Towson University International Merit Scholarships

PROGRAM INFORMATION

Description: Towson University is pleased to continue a merit scholarship program for new undergraduate international students. The scholarships are for students who demonstrate a strong record of academic achievement and proficient English skills.
Levels of Study: Undergraduate
Field of Study: All
Nationality: Any Region
Location of Study: Towson University
Towson, MD

AWARD INFORMATION

Award Type: Scholarship
Average Amount: $9,000
Award Coverage: Partial tuition
Award Duration: 4 years maximum

ELIGIBILITY REQUIREMENTS

- Must be an international (F-1) undergraduate student
- Must have cumulative grade point average of 3.50 or equivalent when converted to the US 4.0 scale
- Must have a minimum TOEFL score of 550 PBT/213 CBT/77 IBT; IELTS score of 6.5

APPLICATION INFORMATION

Award Deadline: May 1 for fall semester; Dec 1 for spring semester
Instructions: There is no separate application for the International Merit Scholarship, please print an International Student Application from our website and submit it to our office with supporting documents

CONTACT

Towson University
8000 York Road
Towson, MD 21252
Tel: +1 (410) 704-6069
Fax: +1 (410) 704-6070
Email: intladm@towson.edu
Web: www.towson.edu/intladm

Troy University

Troy University Prepared Scholarship

PROGRAM INFORMATION

Description: This scholarship is granted to all new international undergraduate students who shows advance English proficiency prior to starting their semester.
Levels of Study: Undergraduate
Field of Study: All
Nationality: Any Region
Location of Study: Troy University
Troy, AL

AWARD INFORMATION

Award Type: Scholarship
Average Amount: $5,000
Number of Awards: Unlimited
Award Coverage: Tuition
Award Duration: First year

ELIGIBILITY REQUIREMENTS

- Must submit a score of 6.5 on the IELTS or 550 PBT/213 CBT/80 IBT on the TOEFL
- Students may substitute the TOEFL or IELTS scores with SAT scores (1000 CR+MATH with minimum with 500 on the critical reading part)

APPLICATION INFORMATION

Award Deadline: Rolling

Instructions: This scholarship is awarded automatically to all international undergraduate students that submit scores as required before their enrollment, review our online brochure: troy.mkttracker.com/index.php?t=troy-40

CONTACT

Troy University
Center for International Programs
Pace Hall 123
Troy, AL 36082
Tel: +1 (334) 670-3335
Fax: +1 (334) 670-3735
Email: intlrecruit@troy.edu
Web: admissions.troy.edu/international/undergraduate-scholarships.html

Troy University

Troy University Graduate Assistantships

PROGRAM INFORMATION

Description: Troy University is a public institution comprised of a network of campuses throughout Alabama and worldwide. International in scope, Troy University provides a variety of educational programs at the undergraduate and graduate levels for a diverse student body in traditional, nontraditional, and emerging electronic formats. Academic programs are supported by a variety of student services, which promote the welfare of the individual student. Troy University's dedicated faculty and staff promote discovery and exploration of knowledge and its application to lifelong success through effective teaching, service, creative partnerships, scholarship, and research.

Levels of Study: Graduate

Field of Study: All

Nationality: Any Region

Location of Study: Troy University Troy, AL

AWARD INFORMATION

Award Type: Scholarship

Average Amount: $7,500, in-state tuition

Number of Awards: 20

Award Coverage: Varies

ELIGIBILITY REQUIREMENTS

- Must have full admission to graduate program
- The assistantship requires 20 hours of work per week

APPLICATION INFORMATION

Award Deadline: Rolling

Instructions: For more information on how to apply, please visit the website, and review our online brochure: www.troy.mkttracker.com/index.php?t=troy-40

CONTACT

Troy University
Center for International Programs
Troy, AL 36082
Tel: +1 (334) 670-3534
Fax: +1 (334) 670-3735
Email: intladm@troy.edu
Web: www.troy.edu/academics/graduate-programs.html

Troy University

Troy University International Education Scholarship (IES)

PROGRAM INFORMATION

Description: Troy University is a public institution comprised of a network of campuses throughout Alabama and worldwide. International in scope, Troy University provides a variety of educational programs at the undergraduate and graduate levels for a diverse student body in traditional, nontraditional and emerging electronic formats.

Levels of Study: Undergraduate

Field of Study: All

Nationality: Any Region

Location of Study: Troy University Troy, AL

AWARD INFORMATION

Award Type: Scholarship

Average Amount: $5,000

Award Duration: 1 year

ELIGIBILITY REQUIREMENTS

- Complete the scholarship application form
- Have home GPA equal to 2.0 US GPA or approximately 70%
- Submit a 1 page resume/cv of their accomplishments
- Complete the remaining admission requirements by the time of enrollment
- Must participate in various international activities

APPLICATION INFORMATION

Award Deadline: Rolling

Instructions: Request application form from International Office, review online brochure here: www.troy.mkttracker.com/index.php?t=troy-40

CONTACT

Troy University
Center for International Programs
Troy, AL 36082
Tel: +1 (334) 670-3335
Fax: +1 (334) 670-3735
Email: intlrecruit@troy.edu
Web: admissions.troy.edu/international/undergraduate-scholarships.html

Troy University

Troy University International Honors Student Scholarships

PROGRAM INFORMATION

Description: Troy University is a public institution comprised of a network of campuses throughout Alabama and worldwide. International in scope, Troy University provides a variety of educational programs at the undergraduate and graduate levels for a diverse student body in traditional, nontraditional and emerging electronic formats.

Levels of Study: Undergraduate

Field of Study: All

Nationality: Any Region

Location of Study: Troy University Troy, AL

AWARD INFORMATION

Award Type: Scholarship

Average Amount: $8,000

Number of Awards: Unlimited

Award Coverage: Half tuition waiver

Award Duration: 3 years

ELIGIBILITY REQUIREMENTS

- Must have minimum GPA of 3.0 (on the 4.0 scale) after earning 30 hours at Troy University
- Must continue to maintain GPA of 3.0 (on the 4.0 scale) to recover the scholarship each semester

APPLICATION INFORMATION

Award Deadline: Rolling

Instructions: Contact the Director of International Admission. Review the online brochure here: troy.mkttracker.com/index.php?t=troy-40

CONTACT

Troy University
Center for International Programs
Troy, AL 36082
Tel: +1 (334) 670-3335
Fax: +1 (334) 670-3735
Email: intlrecruit@troy.edu
Web: admissions.troy.edu/international/undergraduate-scholarships.html

Troy University

Troy University International Elite Scholarships

PROGRAM INFORMATION

Description: Troy University is a public institution comprised of a network of campuses throughout Alabama and worldwide. International in scope, Troy University provides a variety of educational programs at the undergraduate and graduate levels for a diverse student body in traditional, nontraditional, and emerging electronic formats. Troy University offers a limited number of full and partial scholarships to students with exceptionally high academic achievements.

Levels of Study: Undergraduate

Field of Study: All

Nationality: Any Region

Location of Study: Troy University Troy, AL

AWARD INFORMATION

Award Type: Scholarship
Average Amount: Varies
Number of Awards: Varies
Award Coverage: Tuition, room and board.
Award Duration: 8 semesters

ELIGIBILITY REQUIREMENTS

- The Millennium Scholars Award requires a 31 ACT and/or 1380 (CR+MT only) SAT 1, and high school GPA equal to an American 3.7 GPA (4.0 scale); the Chancellor's Award requires a 27 ACT and/or 1220 (CR+MT only) SAT 1, and high school GPA equal to 3.5
- Must carry a full academic load (minimum 12 hours) for each semester
- Must be available to assist the International office during various activities
- Must be prepared and able to document the ability to sustain the remaining cost associated with studying at Troy University

APPLICATION INFORMATION

Award Deadline: Mar for fall semester, Oct for spring semester
Instructions: Request scholarship application. Review the online brochure here: troy.mkttracker.com/index.php?t=troy-40

CONTACT

Troy University
Center for International Programs
Pace Hall 123
Troy, AL
36082 Troy AL
Tel: +1 (334) 670-3335
Fax: +1 (334) 670-3735
Email: intlrecruit@troy.edu
Web: admissions.troy.edu/international/undergraduate-scholarships.html

Truman State University

Truman State University International Baccalaureate Scholarships

PROGRAM INFORMATION

Description: Scholarships are awarded at the time of admission and are renewable up to 8 semesters. Scholarship amount is $2,000 and is awarded to students who have successfully completed the IB diploma. Truman has been ranked as the #1 Public University in the Midwest for 18 consecutive years by US News and World Report, 1998-2015.
Levels of Study: Undergraduate
Field of Study: All
Nationality: Any Region
Location of Study: Truman State University Kirksville, MO

AWARD INFORMATION

Award Type: Scholarship
Average Amount: $2,000
Number of Awards: Unlimited at this time
Award Coverage: Scholarships are applied to tuition, fees, and on-campus housing
Award Duration: Academic year, renewable up to 8 semesters

ELIGIBILITY REQUIREMENTS

- Scholarships are awarded based on successful completion of the IB diploma

APPLICATION INFORMATION

Award Deadline: Jun 1 for fall semester; Nov 1 for spring semester
Instructions: Submit an online application for admission and scholarship at www.truman.edu, there is not a separate application for the scholarship

CONTACT

Truman State University
International Admissions Coordinator
Baldwin Hall 129
100 E Normal Avenue
Kirksville, MO 63501
Tel: +1 (660) 785-4215
Fax: +1 (660) 785-7473
Email: intladmit@truman.edu
Web: www.truman.edu

Truman State University

Truman State University Advanced Level Examination Scholarship

PROGRAM INFORMATION

Description: Scholarship is awarded at the time of admission and renewable up to 8 semesters. Scholarship award is $2,000 and awarded to students who have successfully completed 3 A-Level subjects with a grade of B or higher. Truman has been ranked as the #1 Public University in the Midwest for 18 consecutive years by US News and World Report, 2008-2015.
Levels of Study: Undergraduate
Field of Study: All
Nationality: Any Region
Location of Study: Truman State University Kirksville, MO

AWARD INFORMATION

Award Type: Scholarship
Average Amount: $2,000
Number of Awards: Unlimited at this time.
Award Coverage: Scholarships are applied to tuition, fees, and on-campus housing.
Award Duration: Academic year, renewable up to 8 semesters

ELIGIBILITY REQUIREMENTS

- Scholarships are awarded based on successful completion of 3 A-Level subjects with a grade of B or higher

APPLICATION INFORMATION

Award Deadline: Jun 1 for fall semester; Nov 1 for spring semester
Instructions: Submit an online application for admission and scholarship at www.truman.edu, there is not a separate application for the scholarship

CONTACT

Truman State University
International Admissions Coordinator
Baldwin Hall 129
100 E Normal Avenue
Kirksville, MO 63501
Tel: +1 (660) 785-4215
Fax: +1 (660) 785-7473
Email: intladmit@truman.edu
Web: www.truman.edu

Truman State University

Truman State University Caribbean Advanced Proficiency Examination Scholarships

PROGRAM INFORMATION

Description: Scholarships are awarded at the time of admission and renewable up to 8 semesters. Scholarship amount is $2,000 and awarded to students who have successfully completed 6 units of the CAPE with a grade of II (B) or higher. Truman has been ranked as the #1 Public University in the Midwest for 18 consecutive years by US News and World Report, 2008-2015.
Levels of Study: Undergraduate
Field of Study: All
Nationality: Caribbean
Location of Study: Truman State University Kirksville, MO

AWARD INFORMATION

Award Type: Scholarship
Average Amount: $2,000
Number of Awards: Unlimited at this time
Award Coverage: Scholarships are applied to tuition, fees, and on-campus housing
Award Duration: Academic year, renewable up to 8 semesters

ELIGIBILITY REQUIREMENTS

- Scholarships are awarded based on successful completion of 6 units with a grade of II (B) or higher

APPLICATION INFORMATION

Award Deadline: Jun 1 for fall semester; Nov 1 for spring semester
Instructions: Submit an online application for admission and scholarship at www.truman.edu. There is not a separate application for the scholarship

CONTACT

Truman State University
International Admissions Coordinator
Baldwin Hall 129
100 E Normal Avenue
Kirksville, MO 63501
Tel: +1 (660) 785-4215
Fax: +1 (660) 785-7473
Email: intladmit@truman.edu
Web: www.truman.edu

Truman State University

Truman State University International President's Honorary Scholarships

PROGRAM INFORMATION

Description: Scholarships given at the time of admission and renewable up to 8 semesters. Scholarships may exceed 50% of tuition. Multiple awards are offered. 90 percent of incoming international students receive significant scholarship awards. Truman has been ranked as the #1 Public University in the Midwest for 18 consecutive years by US News and World Report, 1998-2015!

Levels of Study: Undergraduate

Field of Study: All

Nationality: Any Region

Location of Study: Truman State University
Kirksville, MO

AWARD INFORMATION

Award Type: Scholarship

Average Amount: $5,500

Number of Awards: Unlimited at this time

Award Coverage: Scholarships are applied to tuition, fees and on-campus housing

Award Duration: Academic year, renewable up to 4 years

ELIGIBILITY REQUIREMENTS

- Scholarships are awarded based on academic accomplishments at the secondary school level, leadership, and service.

APPLICATION INFORMATION

Award Deadline: Jun 1 for fall semester; Nov for spring semester

Instructions: Submit an online application for admission and scholarship at www.truman.edu, there is not a separate application for the scholarship

CONTACT

Truman State University
International Admissions Coordinator
Baldwin Hall 129
100 East Normal Avenue
Kirksville, MO 63501
Tel: +1 (660) 785-4215
Fax: +1 (660) 785-7473
Email: intladmit@truman.edu
Web: www.truman.edu

Tulane University

Tulane University Financial Assistance for International Undergraduate Students

PROGRAM INFORMATION

Description: All international student are eligible for need based financial aid if they qualify, and can also compete for merit-based scholarships as well. Undergraduate students can qualify for up to $20,000 in need-based financial aid and up to full-tuition for merit-based financial aid. Furthermore, Tulane offers a Global Scholarship which awards a renewable full-tuition award for outstanding international students.

Levels of Study: Undergraduate

Field of Study: All

Nationality: Any Region

Location of Study: Tulane University
New Orleans, LA

AWARD INFORMATION

Award Type: Scholarship

Average Amount: $21,254

Number of Awards: Varies

Award Coverage: Tuition

Award Duration: 4 years

ELIGIBILITY REQUIREMENTS

- Standardized test scores for the SAT1 or ACT, and TOEFL or IELTS if English is a non-native language
- Must submit a certified and translated copy of the candidate's secondary school academic record and government examination certificates
- Certification of Finances Form must be completed and turned in
- Recommendation letter from school counselor or teacher

APPLICATION INFORMATION

Award Deadline: Jan 15

Instructions: For further information on how to apply and for additional scholarships, please visit the website: admission.tulane.edu/international/intlscholarships.php

CONTACT

Tulane University
Office of Undergraduate Admission
6823 St. Charles Ave.
210 Gibson Hall
New Orleans, LA 70118
Tel: +1 (504) 865-5208
Fax: +1 (504) 865-5209
Email: interns@tulane.edu
Web: www.admission.tulane.edu/international

Unity College

Unity College Undergraduate International Students Tuition Waiver

PROGRAM INFORMATION

Description: Unity College seeks to admit international students with exemplary academic records. International students are eligible to qualify for the waiver, which is based on international students' declared financial need.

Levels of Study: Undergraduate

Field of Study: Agriculture and Related Sciences, Biology, Ecology, Education, Environmental Policy, Environmental Studies, Life Sciences, Mathematics, Multi/Interdisciplinary Studies, Natural Resources and Conservation, Parks and Recreation

Location of Study: Unity College
Unity, ME

AWARD INFORMATION

Award Type: Tuition Reduction

Award Coverage: Tuition waiver up to 50%

CONTACT

Unity College
Assistant Director of Admissions/International Counselor
90 Quaker Hill Rd
Unity Maine
Tel: (207) 509-7262
Fax: (207) 509-7262
Email: evamcvicar@unity.edu
Web: www.unity.edu/

University at Buffalo, The State University of New York SUNY

University at Buffalo International Undergraduate Freshmen Scholarships

PROGRAM INFORMATION

Description: SUNY Buffalo offers a number of different merit-based scholarships for high achieving secondary/high school students applying for freshman admission with high grades/marks and SAT scores.

Levels of Study: Undergraduate

Field of Study: All

Nationality: Any Region

Location of Study: University at Buffalo, The State University of New York
Buffalo, NY

AWARD INFORMATION

Award Type: Scholarship

Average Amount: Varies

Number of Awards: Varies

Award Duration: Maximum of 4 years

ELIGIBILITY REQUIREMENTS

- Must have high secondary school grades
- Must submit SAT scores

APPLICATION INFORMATION

Award Deadline: Feb

Instructions: Download undergraduate international application at the website, all international freshmen applicants are considered for this scholarship

CONTACT

University at Buffalo, The State University of New York (SUNY)
International Enrollment Management
411 Capen Hall
Buffalo, NY 14260
Tel: +1 (716) 645-2368
Fax: +1 (716) 645-2528
Email: intiem@buffalo.edu
Web: www.buffalo.edu/InternationalAdmissions.html

University of Arizona

University of Arizona Undergraduate Tuition Scholarships

PROGRAM INFORMATION

Description: As a public research university serving the diverse citizens of Arizona and beyond, the mission of the University of Arizona is to provide a comprehensive, high-quality education that engages our students in discovery through research and broad-based scholarship. We aim to empower our graduates to be leaders in solving complex societal problems.

Levels of Study: Undergraduate

Field of Study: All

Nationality: Any Region

Location of Study: University of Arizona
Tucson, AZ

AWARD INFORMATION

Award Type: Scholarship
Average Amount: $6,000
Number of Awards: 45 awards per semester
Award Coverage: Tuition
Award Duration: Maximum of 4 years

ELIGIBILITY REQUIREMENTS

- Visit www.admissions.arizona.edu/international/steps-to-apply to submit an application
- Be fully admitted to any undergraduate program

APPLICATION INFORMATION

Award Deadline: Feb 1 for fall semester; Oct 1 for spring semester
Instructions: www.admissions.arizona.edu/international/steps-to-apply

CONTACT

University of Arizona
International Recruitment Manager
PO Box 210073
Tucson, AZ 85721
Tel: +1 (520) 621-3237
Fax: +1 (520) 621-9799
Email: askuainternational@gmail.com
Web: www.arizona.edu

University of Arkansas
Chancellor's Scholarship

PROGRAM INFORMATION

Description: Highly competitive annual award for outstanding freshman level international and domestic students.
Levels of Study: Undergraduate
Field of Study: All
Nationality: Any Region
Location of Study: University of Arkansas Fayetteville, AR

AWARD INFORMATION

Award Type: Scholarship
Average Amount: Up to $8,000
Number of Awards: Varies
Award Coverage: $8,000, plus non-resident tuition waiver
Award Duration: Up to 4 years; 5 years for architecture and MAT students

ELIGIBILITY REQUIREMENTS

- Must have a 1350 SAT or better and 4.0 high school GPA or better to receive consideration
- Must meet University of Arkansas admission criteria and be accepted as a degree-seeking student, available only for incoming freshmen (students who completed high school, but not enrolled in any university level program)

APPLICATION INFORMATION

Award Deadline: Jan
Instructions: Students must complete and submit the University of Arkansas Academic Scholarship Application, the application is available online or from the University of Arkansas Scholarship Office

CONTACT

University of Arkansas
Office of Academic Scholarships
101 Old Main
Office of Academic Scholarships
Fayetteville, AR 72701
Tel: +1 (479) 575-4464
Fax: +1 (479) 575-4329
Email: iao@uark.edu
Web: www.scholarships.uark.edu

University of Arkansas
Honors College Fellowship

PROGRAM INFORMATION

Description: The University of Arkansas Honors College provides exceptional resources for students who are intellectually curious, engaged, and committed to making a difference. Fellows can take advantage of the various resources available to them through the Honors College. Each year, more than 90 new freshmen receive fellowship support (plus non-resident tuition, if applicable), exceeding the direct costs of tuition, room and board, and fees. The additional funding may be used for other educational expenses. Honors College Fellowship applicants will also be considered for Chancellor's, University, and Honors College Academy Scholarships without a separate application.
Levels of Study: Undergraduate
Field of Study: All
Nationality: Any Region
Location of Study: University of Arkansas Fayetteville, AR

AWARD INFORMATION

Award Type: Fellowship
Average Amount: $12,500
Number of Awards: Varies
Award Coverage: Tuition and fees, books, room and board, travel expenses
Award Duration: 4 years (5 years for architecture and MAT students)

ELIGIBILITY REQUIREMENTS

- Must complete their application for admission to the University of Arkansas and be accepted as a degree-seeking student
- Must submit the University of Arkansas Honors College Prestigious Fellowships Application
- Must provide official high school transcript including seventh semester grades, official ACT/SAT scores in a sealed envelope signed by the high school registrar or appropriate school official
- Must submit 2 letters of recommendation along with the fellowship application
- Must show strong academic performance with high school GPA of 3.9 or higher and ACT/SAT scores of at least ACT 32/SAT 1400

APPLICATION INFORMATION

Award Deadline: Nov
Instructions: Apply for admission online or contact to request application materials

CONTACT

University of Arkansas
Honors College
Honors College Office
244 Ozark Hall
Fayetteville, AR 72701
Tel: +1 (479) 575-7678
Fax: +1 (479) 575-4882
Email: honorscollege@uark.edu
Web: honorscollege.uark.edu/index.php/prest_links

University of Arkansas
University of Arkansas Bolivian Tuition Advantage Award

PROGRAM INFORMATION

Description: Waives the out-of-state portion of tuition for all qualifying undergraduate and graduate level students from Bolivia. The State of Arkansas partnered with the country of Bolivia through the Partners of the Americas program.
Levels of Study: Undergraduate, Graduate
Field of Study: All
Nationality: Bolivia
Location of Study: University of Arkansas Fayetteville, AR

AWARD INFORMATION

Award Type: Award
Award Coverage: Non-resident portion of tuition
Award Duration: Renewable

ELIGIBILITY REQUIREMENTS

- Must meet all admissions criteria and be accepted as a degree-seeking student
- Must be a citizen and permanent resident of Bolivia
- Must be a student at the freshman, transfer, or graduate level
- Must be enrolled full-time in your degree program at the University of Arkansas (12 credit hours for undergraduate students; 9 credit hours for graduate students)
- For scholarship renewal, undergraduates must earn a 2.0 GPA each semester and successfully complete 24 credit hours each academic year (Aug-May); graduate students must earn at least a 2.85 semester GPA each semester and successfully complete 18 credit hours in degree program each academic year (Aug-May)

APPLICATION INFORMATION

Award Deadline: Mar
Instructions: Apply for admission online or contact to request application materials

CONTACT

University of Arkansas
Office of Graduate and International Admissions
340 N. Campus Drive, Ozark Hall 213
1 University of Arkansas
Fayetteville, AR 72701
Tel: +1 (479) 575-6246
Fax: +1 (479) 575-5246
Email: iao@uark.edu
Web: iao.uark.edu/scholarships.html

University of Arkansas
Silas Hunt Distinguished Scholarship

PROGRAM INFORMATION

Description: Awarded to new freshman students from under-represented communities who have demonstrated outstanding academic leadership qualities and potential. Underrepresented communities include, but are not limited to, underrepresented ethnic or minority groups, a student with an interest in a field that does not typically attract members of his/her ethnicity or gender, or a first-generation college student.

Levels of Study: Undergraduate

Field of Study: All

Nationality: Any Region

Location of Study: University of Arkansas
Fayetteville, AR

AWARD INFORMATION

Award Type: Scholarship

Average Amount: $5,000-$8,000

Number of Awards: Varies

Award Coverage: Tuition, housing, any expenses related to education

Award Duration: Renewable for 4 years (5 years for architecture and MAT students)

ELIGIBILITY REQUIREMENTS

- Must be a new freshman applicant.
- Must have strong SAT/ACT scores of at least 28 ACT/1240 SAT and strong high school GPA of at least 3.75.
- Candidates should exhibit strong writing skills, demonstrated leadership, other areas of achievement.

APPLICATION INFORMATION

Award Deadline: Nov

Instructions: Students must complete and submit the University of Arkansas Academic Scholarship Application, the application is available online or from the University of Arkansas Scholarship Office

CONTACT

University of Arkansas
Office of Academic Scholarships
101 Old Main
1 University of Arkansas
Fayetteville, AR 72701
Tel: +1 (479) 575-4464
Fax: +1 (479) 575-4329
Email: scholars@uark.edu
Web: www.scholarships.uark.edu

University of Arkansas
University of Arkansas Caribbean Tuition Advantage Award

PROGRAM INFORMATION

Description: Award waives non-resident tuition differential for undergraduate freshman applicants and transfer students from participating Caribbean nations.

Levels of Study: Undergraduate

Field of Study: All

Nationality: Anguilla, Antigua, Bahamas, Barbados, Belize, British Virgin Islands, Cayman Islands, Dominica, Grenada, Jamaica, Martinique, Montserrat, St. Kitts-Nevis, St. Lucia, St. Vincent, Trinidad & Tobago, Turks & Caicos Islands

Location of Study: University of Arkansas
Fayetteville, AR

AWARD INFORMATION

Award Type: Award

Average Amount: 80%-90% of the difference between in-state and out-of-state tuition, depending upon incoming grade point average

Award Coverage: Non-resident portion of tuition

Award Duration: May be renewed for the duration of undergraduate studies

ELIGIBILITY REQUIREMENTS

- Must meet all admissions criteria and be accepted as a degree-seeking student
- Must be a citizen and permanent resident of the Caribbean nations listed
- Must be a recent high school graduate or transfer student from a college or university
- Must be enrolled full-time, minimum of 12 credit hours per semester in a degree program at the University of Arkansas
- For scholarship renewal, must earn a 2.5 GPA each semester and successfully complete 24 credit hours each academic year (Aug-May)

APPLICATION INFORMATION

Award Deadline: Mar

Instructions: Apply for admission online or contact to request application materials

CONTACT

University of Arkansas
Office of Graduate and International Admissions
340 N. Campus Drive, Ozark Hall 213
1 University of Arkansas
Fayetteville, AR 72701
Tel: +1 (479) 575-6246
Fax: +1 (479) 575-5246
Email: iao@uark.edu
Web: iao.uark.edu/scholarships.html

University of Arkansas
University of Arkansas Foundation for the International Exchange of Students Scholarship

PROGRAM INFORMATION

Description: Incorporated at the University of Arkansas as a non-profit organization in 1949, FIES support comes from the University, from contributions by faculty and interested individuals, and from special fund-raising events. F All recipients of FIES awards are selected by the FIES Scholarship Committee.

Levels of Study: Undergraduate

Field of Study: All

Nationality: Any Region

Location of Study: University of Arkansas
Fayetteville, AR

AWARD INFORMATION

Award Type: Award

Average Amount: Varies

Number of Awards: Varies

Award Coverage: Full tuition and fees

Award Duration: Academic year

ELIGIBILITY REQUIREMENTS

- Must meet all criteria for admission and be accepted as a degree-seeking undergraduate student
- FIES will give preference to children of former FIES Scholarship recipients; awards are based on academic performance, class standing (preference given to juniors/seniors)
- Must be enrolled for at least the required minimum of 12 credit hours in degree program each semester of the academic year (Aug-May)
- No automatic extensions. May be renewed for a second year with re-application of FIES Scholarship requirements through FIES; only 1 renewal is allowed; no preference is given to previous recipients

APPLICATION INFORMATION

Award Deadline: Mar

Instructions: Must submit completed FIES Scholarship application form, available online or by request from the International Admissions office; submit completed FIES application form with copies of all post-secondary transcripts and 3 letters of recommendation.

CONTACT

University of Arkansas
Office of Graduate and International Admissions
340 N. Campus Drive, Ozark Hall 213
1 University of Arkansas
Fayetteville, AR 72701
Tel: +1 (479) 575-6246
Fax: +1 (479) 575-5246
Email: iao@uark.edu
Web: iao.uark.edu/scholarships.html

University of Arkansas
University of Arkansas Panama Tuition Advantage

PROGRAM INFORMATION

Description: Waives the out-of-state portion of tuition for all qualifying undergraduate and graduate level students from Panama.

Levels of Study: Undergraduate, Graduate, Doctorate

Field of Study: All

Nationality: Panama

Location of Study: University of Arkansas
Fayetteville, AR

AWARD INFORMATION

Award Type: Tuition Reduction

Average Amount: 80%-90% of the difference between in-state and out-of-state tuition, depending upon incoming grade point average

Award Coverage: Non-resident portion of tuition

Award Duration: May be renewed for the duration of studies

ELIGIBILITY REQUIREMENTS

- Must be fully admitted to the University of Arkansas
- Must be a citizen and permanent resident of Panama
- Must be a student at the freshman, transfer, or graduate level
- Must be enrolled full-time in your degree program at the University of Arkansas (12 credit hours for undergraduate students; 9 credit hours for graduate students)
- For scholarship renewal, undergraduates must earn a 2.7 GPA each semester and successfully complete 24 credit hours each academic year (Aug-May); graduate students must earn at least a 2.85 semester GPA each semester and successfully complete 18 credit hours in degree program each academic year (Aug-May)

APPLICATION INFORMATION

Award Deadline: May

Instructions: Apply for admission online or contact to request application materials

CONTACT

University of Arkansas
Office of Graduate and International Admissions
340 N. Campus Drive, Ozark Hall 213
1 University of Arkansas
Fayetteville, AR 72701
Tel: +1 (479) 575-6246
Fax: +1 (479) 575-5246
Email: iao@uark.edu
Web: iao.uark.edu/scholarships.html

University of Arkansas
Razorback Bridge Scholarship

PROGRAM INFORMATION

Description: Awarded to students from under-represented communities who have demonstrated outstanding academic leadership qualities and potential. Under-represented communities include, but are not limited to, under-represented ethnic or minority groups, a student with an interest in a field that does not typically attract members of his/her ethnicity or gender, residence in an under-represented county in Arkansas, or a first generation college student. Students selected as Razorback Bridge Scholars will also participate in a peer and faculty-mentoring program. Razorback Bridge Scholars will have many opportunities to get involved in leadership activities on campus.

Levels of Study: Undergraduate

Location of Study: University of Arkansas Fayetteville, AR

AWARD INFORMATION

Award Type: Scholarship

Average Amount: Up to $3,500

Award Duration: 4 years

ELIGIBILITY REQUIREMENTS

- Must provide SAT or ACT scores and strong high school grade average

APPLICATION INFORMATION

Award Deadline: Jan

Instructions: Students must complete and submit the University of Arkansas Academic Scholarship Application, the application is available online or from the University of Arkansas Scholarship Office

CONTACT

University of Arkansas
Office of Academic Scholarships
101 Old Main
1 University of Arkansas
Fayetteville, AR 72701
Tel: +1 (479) 575-4464
Fax: +1 (479) 575-4329
Email: scholars@uark.edu
Web: www.scholarships.uark.edu

University of Arkansas
University of Arkansas Rwandan Tuition Advantage

PROGRAM INFORMATION

Description: Non-resident tuition award to citizens and current residents of Rwanda. Only undergraduate freshman and transfer students.

Levels of Study: Undergraduate

Field of Study: All

Nationality: Rwanda

Location of Study: University of Arkansas Fayetteville, AR

AWARD INFORMATION

Award Type: Tuition Reduction

Average Amount: 80%-90% of the difference between in-state and out-of-state tuition, depending upon incoming grade point average

Award Coverage: Non-resident tuition

Award Duration: Renewable

ELIGIBILITY REQUIREMENTS

- Must meet all admissions criteria and be accepted as a degree-seeking student
- Must be a citizen and permanent resident of Rwanda
- Must be a recent high school graduate or transfer student from a college or university
- Must be enrolled full-time, minimum of 12 credit hours per semester in a degree program at the University of Arkansas
- For scholarship renewal, must earn a 2.0 GPA each semester and successfully complete 24 credit hours each academic year (Aug-May)

APPLICATION INFORMATION

Award Deadline: Mar

Instructions: Apply for admission online or contact to request application materials

CONTACT

University of Arkansas
Office of Graduate and International Admissions
340 N. Campus Drive, Ozark Hall 213
1 University of Arkansas
Fayetteville, AR 72701
Tel: +1 (479) 575-6246
Fax: +1 (479) 575-5246
Email: iao@uark.edu
Web: iao.uark.edu/scholarships.html

University of Arkansas
Chancellor's Community Scholarship

PROGRAM INFORMATION

Description: Awarded to top applicants from the applicant pool who also have a demonstrable commitment to community service.

Levels of Study: Undergraduate

Field of Study: All

Location of Study: University of Arkansas Fayetteville, AR

AWARD INFORMATION

Award Type: Scholarship

Average Amount: Up to $5000

Number of Awards: Varies

Award Coverage: Tuition

Award Duration: 4 years

ELIGIBILITY REQUIREMENTS

- Must have strong SAT scores and excellent high school grade average

APPLICATION INFORMATION

Award Deadline: Jan

Instructions: Students must complete and submit the University of Arkansas Academic Scholarship Application, the application is available online or from the University of Arkansas Scholarship Office

CONTACT

University of Arkansas
Office of Academic Scholarships
101 Main
1 University of Arkansas
Fayetteville, AR 72701
Tel: +1 (479) 575-4464
Fax: +1 (479) 575-4329
Email: scholars@uark.edu
Web: www.scholarships.uark.edu

University of Arkansas
University of Arkansas John and Marie Lavallard International Scholarship

PROGRAM INFORMATION

Description: Annual award for an outstanding international student with financial need. Scholarship will be utilized for tuition plus room and board.

Levels of Study: Undergraduate

Field of Study: All

Nationality: Any Region

Location of Study: University of Arkansas Fayetteville, AR

AWARD INFORMATION

Award Type: Scholarship

Average Amount: Varies

Number of Awards: 1

Award Coverage: Tuition reduction, stipend, room and board

Award Duration: 1 year

ELIGIBILITY REQUIREMENTS

- Must meet University of Arkansas admission criteria
- Must be a citizen and permanent resident of a country other than the US
- Must present a clear statement of objectives to be achieved through study at the University of Arkansas
- Preference will be given to applicants not currently in the US
- Non-degree and degree seeking applicants will be considered

APPLICATION INFORMATION

Award Deadline: Mar

Instructions: Apply for admission online or contact to request application materials

CONTACT

University of Arkansas
Office of Graduate and International Admissions
340 N. Campus Drive, Ozark Hall 213
1 University of Arkansas
Fayetteville, AR 72701
Tel: +1 (479) 575-6246
Fax: +1 (479) 575-5246
Email: iss@uark.edu
Web: iao.uark.edu/scholarships.html

University of Arkansas - Fort Smith

University of Arkansas Honors International Studies Program (HISP) Scholarship

PROGRAM INFORMATION

Description: The Honors International Studies Program Scholarship is a highly competitive scholarship for students who demonstrate strong academic performance. The program consists of a unique honors general education curriculum with international focus, exciting travel study classes, service opportunities, independent study options, and the opportunity to graduate with honors.

Levels of Study: Undergraduate

Field of Study: Accounting, Anthropology, Art History, Arts and Culture, Biology, Business and Management, Chemistry, Communications and Journalism, Computer and Information Sciences, Computer Science, Education, Finance, Foreign Languages, Government, History, Information Technology, Journalism, Liberal/General Studies, Management, Mathematics, Music, Nursing, Physics, Political Science, Psychology, Spanish

Nationality: Any Region

Location of Study: University of Arkansas - Fort Smith Fort Smith, AR

ELIGIBILITY REQUIREMENTS

- 27+ composite ACT score (or 1800+ SAT score)
- 3.5 high school GPA on a 4.0 scale
- 91+ TOEFL (or 6.5 IELTS)
- Submit essay and participate in an interview
- Strong academic performance and international interests

APPLICATION INFORMATION

Award Deadline: Mar

Instructions: All students applying for this scholarship must submit a complete application, students must also be seeking a bachelor's degree through UAFS, recipients are required to live on campus their freshman year

CONTACT

University of Arkansas - Fort Smith
Office of International Relations
5210 Grand Avenue
Fort Smith, AR 72913
Tel: +1 (479) 788-7166
Email: takeo.suzuki@uafs.edu
Web: www.uafs.edu/international

University of Arkansas - Fort Smith

University of Arkansas Chancellor's Leadership Council (CLC)

PROGRAM INFORMATION

Description: The Chancellor's Leadership Council Scholarship is a highly competitive scholarship for students that demonstrate strong leadership capabilities both inside and outside of school as well as demonstrate strong academic performance. They must have the desire to take leadership roles on campus, complete service projects, and serve as active members of the Chancellor's Leadership Council. Students selected for this scholarship have the privilege to enroll in a 3 credit hour leadership course taught by Chancellor Paul B. Beran. Recipients are required to live on campus their freshman and sophomore years. All students applying for this scholarship must submit a complete application. Students must also be seeking a Bachelor Degree through UAFS.

Field of Study: Accounting, Arts and Culture, Biology, Business and Management, Chemistry, Computer Science, Finance, Foreign Languages, History, Information Technology, Marketing, Mathematics, Music, Nursing, Physics, Science, Theater

Nationality: Any Region

Location of Study: University of Arkansas - Fort Smith Fort Smith, AR

AWARD INFORMATION

Award Type: Scholarship, Tuition Reduction

Average Amount: $35,000

Number of Awards: 1-3

Award Coverage: Tuition, room and board, meals

Award Duration: 4 years

ELIGIBILITY REQUIREMENTS

- 25+ composite ACT score
- 3.25 cumulative GPA
- Demonstration of strong leadership and academic performance
- Must be seeking a Bachelor's degree
- TOEFL 91 or more

APPLICATION INFORMATION

Award Deadline: Oct

CONTACT

University of Arkansas - Fort Smith
Executive Director for International Relations
5210 Grand Avenue
Fort Smith, AR 72913-3649
Tel: +1 (479) 788-7166
Email: takeo.suzuki@uafs.edu
Web: uafs.edu/international

University of Arkansas - Fort Smith

UAFS Japanese Student Relief Scholarship (JSRS)

PROGRAM INFORMATION

Description: University of Arkansas Fort Smith is a 4 year public university, which was established in 1928. This highly competitive scholarship program was established to help a Japanese student who was affected by the 2011 Earthquake off the Pacific Coast of Tohoku. UAFS encourages students who are interested in studying abroad, wanting to develop leadership skills and who are willing to serve the community to apply.

Levels of Study: Undergraduate

Field of Study: Accounting, Biology, Business and Management, Chemistry, Computer Science, Education, Finance, Foreign Languages, History, Information Technology, Marketing, Mathematics, Music, Nursing, Spanish, Theater

Location of Study: University of Arkansas Fort Smith Fort Smith, AR

AWARD INFORMATION

Award Type: Scholarship

Average Amount: $100,000

Number of Awards: 1

Award Coverage: $13000 per year for 4 years for tuition and fees, $5000 for campus housing per year, up to $2000 for campus meals per year

Award Duration: 4 years

ELIGIBILITY REQUIREMENTS

- Be a degree seeking student who wishes to complete undergraduate programs at UAFS
- Live in the federally declared disaster area or sustained serious damages from the disaster (First preference will be given to a student whose parents died as a result of the disaster)
- Japanese citizenship
- Sufficient English proficiency of TOEFL IBT 61/CBT173/PBT500
- Be in good health

APPLICATION INFORMATION

Award Deadline: Jan

Instructions: Submit all the application materials to international@uafs.edu, application screening: Feb, 2015; interview: Feb-Mar 2015; result release: Mar 31, 2015

CONTACT

University of Arkansas - Fort Smith (www.uafs.edu/international)
Executive Director for International Relations
5210 Grand Avenue,
Fort Smith, AR 72913-7166
Tel: +1 (479) 788-7166
Email: takeo.suzuki@uafs.edu
Web: uafs.edu/international

University of Bridgeport
University of Bridgeport Scholarship

PROGRAM INFORMATION

Description: Academic scholarships are offered to international undergraduate and graduate students to encourage academic excellence and student leadership and to continue UB's tradition of enrolling a "Community of Scholars" from around the world. Scholarships are available to both first-year undergraduate and undergraduate transfer students seeking an associate or bachelor's degree. Academic scholarships are also available for international graduate students applying to the MBA, MA in Global Development and Peace, and all graduate degrees in the School of Engineering.

Levels of Study: Undergraduate, Graduate

Field of Study: All

Nationality: Any Region

Location of Study: University of Bridgeport Bridgeport, CT

AWARD INFORMATION

Award Type: Scholarship

Average Amount: Undergraduate: $5,000-$15,000; Graduate: $3,000-$5,000

Number of Awards: Available to all qualified applicants

Award Coverage: Partial tuition and fees

Award Duration: Renewable for 4 years (undergraduate) or 2 years (graduate) as long as academic requirements are met

ELIGIBILITY REQUIREMENTS

- Undergraduates must have a minimum TOEFL 61 IBT or 6.0 IELTS score. Graduates must have a minimum TOEFL 81 IBT or 6.5 IELTS
- Graduates must present GMAT (MBA), GRE (Engineering degrees and MA Global Development & Peace)
- Must have strong academic record

APPLICATION INFORMATION

Award Deadline: May for fall semester; Oct for spring semester

Instructions: Apply for admission online or contact to request application materials. All applicants for admission are considered for scholarships.

CONTACT

University of Bridgeport
126 Park Avenue
Bridgeport, CT 06604
Tel: +1 (203) 576-4552
Fax: +1 (203) 576-4941
Email: admit@bridgeport.edu
Web: www.bridgeport.edu

University of Central Florida
Florida-Eastern European Linkage Institute

PROGRAM INFORMATION

Description: Created by the Florida Legislature as a means to develop a relationship between Florida and the Eastern Europe region, this program offers an Out-of-State tuition exemption to eligible citizens of Eastern Europe countries wishing to study in the state of Florida.

Levels of Study: Undergraduate, Graduate, Doctorate

Field of Study: All

Nationality: Eastern Europe

Location of Study: FL

AWARD INFORMATION

Award Type: Tuition Reduction

Average Amount: Varies

Number of Awards: Varies

Award Coverage: The tuition exemption that is offered covers the out-of-state portion of tuition fees, students are responsible for the in-state tuition fees

Award Duration: Varies

ELIGIBILITY REQUIREMENTS

- Must be a resident of an Eastern European country on the list above
- Must be a student at a state university in Florida or a public community college within the State of Florida
- Candidates are evaluated based on their academic record, area of specialization, aspirations for the future
- Must return to their home country within 3 years of the completion of their study

APPLICATION INFORMATION

Instructions: Go to our website for information and application processing

CONTACT

University of Central Florida
Office of International Studies
Barbara Ying Center building 71
suite 106
Orlando, FL 32816-3105
Tel: +1 (407) 823-3647
Fax: +1 (407) 882-0240
Email: eeli@ucf.edu
Web: www.international.ucf.edu/eeli

University of Central Florida
Florida-Canada Linkage Institute

PROGRAM INFORMATION

Description: Created by the Florida Legislature as a means to establish a bilateral relationship between Florida and Canada, this program offers Canadian Citizens the opportunity to attend Florida Public Universities and Colleges at resident tuition rates. It is an Out-of-State tuition exemption for those intending to return to Canada after completing their degree in Florida.

Levels of Study: Undergraduate, Graduate, Doctorate

Field of Study: All

Nationality: Canada

Location of Study: FL

AWARD INFORMATION

Award Type: Tuition Reduction

Average Amount: Varies

Number of Awards: Varies

Award Coverage: The tuition exemption that is offered covers the out-of-state portion of tuition fees, students are responsible for the in-state tuition fees

ELIGIBILITY REQUIREMENTS

- Must be a legal resident of Canada
- Must be a student at a state university in Florida or a public community college within the state of Florida
- Candidates are evaluated based on their academic record, area of specialization, and aspirations for the future
- Must return to Canada within 3 years of the completion of their study

APPLICATION INFORMATION

Award Deadline: Mar 31

Instructions: Go to our website for information and application processing

CONTACT

University of Central Florida
Office of International Studies
4000 Central Florida Blvd
Suite MH107
Orlando, FL 32816-3105
Tel: +1 (407) 823-3647
Fax: +1 (407) 882-0240
Email: fcli@ucf.edu
Web: www.international.ucf.edu/fcli/index.php

University of Central Missouri
University of Central Missouri International Excellence Award

PROGRAM INFORMATION

Description: For entering freshmen.

Levels of Study: Undergraduate

Field of Study: All

Nationality: Any Region

Location of Study: University of Central Missouri Warrensburg, MO

AWARD INFORMATION

Award Type: Scholarship

Average Amount: $3,000

Award Coverage: Tuition and fees, housing, books

Award Duration: 1 year

ELIGIBILITY REQUIREMENTS

- Must be an entering freshman who has secured regular undergraduate admission into the University of Central Missouri
- Must earn a minimum SAT score of 1630 (critical reading, math, and writing) or ACT composite score of 25

APPLICATION INFORMATION

Instructions: Submit official SAT or ACT score report along with international admission application

CONTACT

University of Central Missouri
Ward Edwards 1200
Warrensburg, MO 64093
Tel: +1 (660) 543-4195
Fax: +1 (660) 543-4201
Email: intladmit@ucmo.edu
Web: www.ucmo.edu/international

University of Central Missouri

University of Central Missouri First Year International Award

PROGRAM INFORMATION

Description: For first-year undergraduate students who secure "regular" admission into the University of Central Missouri.

Levels of Study: Undergraduate

Field of Study: All

Nationality: Any Region

Location of Study: University of Central Missouri Warrensburg, MO

AWARD INFORMATION

Award Type: Scholarship

Average Amount: $2,000

Award Coverage: Tuition and fees, housing, books

Award Duration: 1 year

ELIGIBILITY REQUIREMENTS

- Must be a first-year undergraduate students who secures "regular" admission into the University of Central Missouri

APPLICATION INFORMATION

Instructions: Contact or visit our website for more information

CONTACT

University of Central Missouri
Ward Edwards 1200
Warrensburg, MO 64093
Tel: +1 (660) 543-4195
Fax: +1 (660) 543-4201
Email: intladmit@ucmo.edu
Web: www.ucmo.edu/international

University of Central Missouri

University of Central Missouri Webb Chinese American Scholarship

PROGRAM INFORMATION

Description: For academically-inclined undergraduate and graduate students from China.

Levels of Study: Undergraduate, Graduate

Field of Study: All

Nationality: China

Location of Study: University of Central Missouri Warrensburg, MO

AWARD INFORMATION

Award Type: Scholarship

Average Amount: Varies

Number of Awards: Varies

ELIGIBILITY REQUIREMENTS

- Must be a UCM student who has completed a minimum of 2 years of study at UCM
- Must be accepted for study at any accredited University in mainland China
- Must have a minimum overall cumulative grade point average of 2.5
- Must demonstrate financial need
- Must be pursuing a marketable degree

APPLICATION INFORMATION

Award Deadline: May 1 for fall semester; Nov 1 for spring semester

Instructions: Contact or visit our website for more information

CONTACT

University of Central Missouri
Smiser Alumni Center
Warrensburg, MO 64093
Tel: +1 (660) 543-8000
Fax: +1 (660) 543-4705
Email: intladmit@ucmo.edu
Web: www.ucmo.edu/foundation

University of Central Missouri

University of Central Missouri Olaiya Foundation Scholarship

PROGRAM INFORMATION

Description: Scholarship for graduate applicants from Nigeria pursuing a graduate degree in Industrial Hygiene at the University of Central Missouri. Other West African students may be considered.

Levels of Study: Graduate

Nationality: West Africa

Location of Study: University of Central Missouri Warrensburg, MO

AWARD INFORMATION

Award Type: Scholarship

Average Amount: Varies

Award Duration: Varies, non-renewable

ELIGIBILITY REQUIREMENTS

- Must be an incoming graduate student at UCM
- Must be pursuing a degree in Industrial Hygiene at UCM
- Must have a minimum overall cumulative GPA of 2.5
- Must be an international student from Nigeria or be from a US inner city
- Must express an interest in returning to an inner city or African homeland to work and encourage others to seek higher education

APPLICATION INFORMATION

Award Deadline: Mar

Instructions: Contact or visit our website

CONTACT

University of Central Missouri
Department of Safety Sciences
Humpreys 325
Warrensburg, MO 64093
Tel: +1 (660) 543-8000
Fax: +1 (660) 543-4705
Email: intladmit@ucmo.edu
Web: www.ucmo.edu/foundation

University of Central Missouri

University of Central Missouri Taiwan Commemorative Scholarship

PROGRAM INFORMATION

Description: For a prospective or current undergraduate or graduate student from Taiwan pursuing a degree in industrial technology or related field.

Levels of Study: Undergraduate, Graduate

Nationality: Taiwan

Location of Study: University of Central Missouri Warrensburg, MO

AWARD INFORMATION

Award Type: Scholarship

Average Amount: Varies

Award Duration: Varies, non-renewable

ELIGIBILITY REQUIREMENTS

- Must be a full-time student and in good academic standing at UCM
- Must be pursuing a major in industrial technology
- Must be worthy, deserving and of good moral character
- Must show promise of leadership and academic ability

APPLICATION INFORMATION

Award Deadline: Mar

Instructions: Please visit the website for application details

CONTACT

University of Central Missouri
UCM School of Technology
Grinstead 09
Warrensburg, MO 64093
Tel: +1 (660) 543-8000
Fax: +1 (660) 543-4705
Email: intladmit@ucmo.edu
Web: www.ucmo.edu/foundation

University of Central Missouri

University of Central Missouri Diplomatic Scholarship

PROGRAM INFORMATION

Description: The University of Central Missouri will award a Diplomatic Scholarship equal to the non-resident portion of tuition to full-time, degree seeking undergraduate students who are in the US on an A-1 and A-2 visa. Please request Diplomatic Scholarship consideration in writing and attach A-1 or A-2 visa verification.

Levels of Study: Undergraduate

Field of Study: All

Nationality: Any Region

Location of Study: University of Central Missouri Warrensburg, MO

AWARD INFORMATION

Award Type: Scholarship

Award Coverage: Non-resident portion of tuition: tuition, housing, books, fees

Award Duration: Maximum of 8 semesters

APPLICATION INFORMATION

Instructions: Contact or visit our website for more information

CONTACT

University of Central Missouri
Ward Edwards 1200
Warrensburg, MO 64093
Tel: +1 (660) 543-4195
Fax: +1 (660) 543-4201
Email: intladmit@ucmo.edu
Web: www.ucmo.edu/international

University of Central Missouri

University of Central Missouri Scholarships

PROGRAM INFORMATION

Description: The University of Central Missouri has over 130 fully accredited programs at the bachelors and masters level, plus an outstanding CEA-accredited Intensive English Language Program.

Levels of Study: Undergraduate, Graduate

Field of Study: All

Nationality: Any Region

Location of Study: University of Central Missouri Warrensburg, MO

AWARD INFORMATION

Award Type: Tuition Reduction

Average Amount: $5,000

Number of Awards: 20 awards per semester

Award Coverage: Sponsored students are allowed to pay resident tuition only and the non-resident half of the tuition is waived

Award Duration: 2-4 years depending upon degree program

ELIGIBILITY REQUIREMENTS

- Must meet admissions requirements
- Must possess proof of sponsorship by an agency or government will be required
- Our CEA-accredited Intensive English Program will offer reduced tuition as well for government-sponsored students needing IEP instruction

APPLICATION INFORMATION

Award Deadline: Apr or Oct

Instructions: Apply online.

CONTACT

University of Central Missouri
Director, International Center
Ward Edwards 1200
Warrensburg, MO 64093, US
Tel: +1 (660) 543-4195
Fax: +1 (660) 543-4201
Email: stevenson@ucmo.edu
Web: www.ucmo.edu/recruit/intl

University of Charleston

Charleston International Student Scholarship

PROGRAM INFORMATION

Description: The University of Charleston provides merit-based scholarships to qualified international students who are accepted for admission to our undergraduate programs. The scholarships are based on the applicant's academic record at the time of admission or in recognition of special talent (such as athletic, leadership, or musical skill).

Levels of Study: Undergraduate

Field of Study: All

Nationality: Any Region

Location of Study: University of Charleston Charleston, WV

AWARD INFORMATION

Award Type: Scholarship

Average Amount: Varies

Number of Awards: Varies

Award Coverage: Tuition, housing, meals

Award Duration: Academic year, renewable for up to 4 years

ELIGIBILITY REQUIREMENTS

- Must apply and be accepted for undergraduate admission to the University of Charleston
- Must include official copies of final transcript/grade reports from each institution attended, transcripts must be in English

APPLICATION INFORMATION

Award Deadline: Jul for fall semester

Instructions: Visit our website for more information

CONTACT

University of Charleston
Admissions Office
2300 MacCorkle Avenue, SE
Charleston, WV 25304
Tel: +1 (304) 357-4750
Fax: +1 (304) 357-4781
Email: admissions@ucwv.edu
Web: www.ucwv.edu

University of Cincinnati

University of Cincinnati Global Scholarship

PROGRAM INFORMATION

Description: Founded in 1819, the University of Cincinnati (UC) is Ohio's premier urban research university. The University of Cincinnati offers the UC Global Scholarship for qualified international undergraduate students.

Levels of Study: Undergraduate

Field of Study: All

Nationality: Any Region

Location of Study: University of Cincinnati Cincinnati, OH

AWARD INFORMATION

Award Type: Grant, Scholarship

Average Amount: $1,000-$26,000

Number of Awards: Varies

Award Coverage: Between 5-50 percent of tuition

Award Duration: Up to 4 years

ELIGIBILITY REQUIREMENTS

- Must be an international student completing studies at a US high school, US community college, or foreign high school; or an international student transferring from a foreign university; or permanent resident or US citizen completing studies at a foreign high school or transferring from a foreign university
- Must maintain a 3.2 cumulative grade point average
- Must complete the annual 30-hour volunteer service requirement
- Must have TOEFL score of 79 IBT with 15 for each sub score or IELTS score of 6.5 with 5.5 for each sub score

APPLICATION INFORMATION

Award Deadline: Varies

Instructions: Undergraduate applicants submit a complete admissions application by the Priority Deadlines for maximum consideration; all admissions applications are automatically screened for UC Global Scholarship consideration, there is no separate UC Global Scholarship application

CONTACT

University of Cincinnati
Office of International Admission
47 West Corry Blvd.
Edwards One Building, Suite 5150
Cincinnati, OH 45221-0123
Tel: +1 (513) 556-1100
Fax: +1 (513) 556-0351
Email: international.admissions@uc.edu
Web: www.admissions.uc.edu/international

University of Colorado Denver

University of Colorado Denver Presidential Scholar Award

PROGRAM INFORMATION

Description: The Presidential Scholar Award was developed by former University of Colorado Denver President Brown to identify and recognize outstanding students in the freshmen class. As an award recipient, you will receive $2,500 towards tuition that recurs for 8 semesters, totaling $20,000.

Levels of Study: Undergraduate

Nationality: Any Region

Location of Study: University of Colorado Denver Denver, CO

AWARD INFORMATION

Award Type: Award

Average Amount: $20,000

Number of Awards: 3 per year

Award Coverage: Tuition, room, and board

Award Duration: 4 years

ELIGIBILITY REQUIREMENTS

- The international student awardee must be 'outstanding;' the methodology to identify candidates for the award includes an interview, 2 letters of recommendation, strong academic credentials approximating 3.75/4.0 or higher, a committee review

APPLICATION INFORMATION

Award Deadline: Mar 15th

Instructions: Applicants will be automatically reviewed for the Presidential Scholar Award

CONTACT

University of Colorado Denver
Director of International Enrollment Management
Denver, CO 80217
Tel: +1 (303) 315-8232
Email: application@ucdenver.edu
Web: www.internationaladmissions.ucdenver.edu

University of Dayton

University Scholarships

PROGRAM INFORMATION

Description: Our academic merit scholarship program offers awards based on academic performance prior to enrolling. Those applying as a full-time, degree-seeking student will automatically be considered for scholarship, whether entering from high school or transferring from another college. Scholarship notification occurs upon admission to the University of Dayton. Entering first-year student scholarships are renewable for 4 years and transfer student scholarships are renewable for 3, provided the student maintains a 3.0 GPA, is registered full-time and is a responsible member of the University community.

Levels of Study: Undergraduate

Nationality: Any Region

Location of Study: University of Dayton
Dayton, OH

AWARD INFORMATION

Award Type: Scholarship

Average Amount: $13,000

Number of Awards: 500

Award Duration: Up to 4 years (8 semesters)

ELIGIBILITY REQUIREMENTS

- Full-time attendance
- Application, including the essay. International students may complete either the Application for Undergraduate Admission and Scholarship or the Common Application, there is no application fee
- Letter of Recommendation
- Official copy of secondary transcripts (in language of original issue) of all previously attended secondary schools, including dates of attendance, all subjects studied, grades earned and marks achieved on examinations; any transcripts not issued in English should be accompanied by a certified English translation. Must have a minimum high school GPA of 2.5
- TOEFL (or equivalent), for the TOEFL, a minimum score of 70 on the Internet-based (iB) test or 523 on the paper-based (PB) test is required for full admission

APPLICATION INFORMATION

Award Deadline: Fall Term: May 1; Spring Term: Nov 1

Instructions: Those applying as a full-time, degree-seeking student will automatically be considered for scholarship, whether entering from high school or transferring from another college

CONTACT

University of Dayton
Office of International Admission
Albert Emanuel Hall 037
300 College Park
Dayton, OH 45469-1671
Tel: +1 (855) 664-5623
Email: goglobal@udayton.edu
Web: www.udayton.edu/flyersfirst/financialaid/undergrad/scholarships.php

University of Dayton

University of Dayton International Merit Scholarships

PROGRAM INFORMATION

Description: University of Dayton offers international merit scholarships to first-year and transfer undergraduate applicants

Levels of Study: Undergraduate

Field of Study: All

Nationality: Any Region

Location of Study: University of Dayton
Dayton, OH

AWARD INFORMATION

Award Type: Scholarship

Average Amount: $5,000-$25,000

Number of Awards: Varies

ELIGIBILITY REQUIREMENTS

- The University of Dayton does not require international applicants to submit ACT or SAT scores for admission or a limited scholarship review, however applicants are welcome to submit ACT or SAT scores, as good scores may increase scholarship awards

APPLICATION INFORMATION

Instructions: Contact or visit our website for more information

CONTACT

University of Dayton
Office of International Admission
300 College Park
Dayton, OH 45469-1300
Tel: +1 (937) 229-1850
Email: goglobal@udayton.edu
Web: www.udayton.edu/apply/international.php

University of Denver

University of Denver
Merit-Based Scholarships

PROGRAM INFORMATION

Description: The University of Denver's commitment to international students is exemplified by the availability of merit-based scholarships for first-year and transfer undergraduates. All completed undergraduate applications are automatically considered for merit-based scholarships during admission review. There are no additional forms to fill out. Admitted students are notified of scholarship awards in their admission letters.

Levels of Study: Undergraduate

Field of Study: All

Nationality: Any Region

Location of Study: University of Denver
Denver, CO

AWARD INFORMATION

Award Type: Scholarship

Average Amount: $11,044

Number of Awards: Unlimited

Award Coverage: Merit-based scholarships range $8,000-$21,000 per year; our highest merit-based scholarship covers approximately 1/3 of the cost of attendance

Award Duration: 4 years

ELIGIBILITY REQUIREMENTS

- Admission standards for international students vary based on the educational system of the country in which they have attended school; typically, admitted students have earned the equivalent of As and Bs in a demanding, college preparatory curriculum; applicants who have shown academic achievements beyond these criteria will be considered for merit-based scholarships

APPLICATION INFORMATION

Instructions: All completed undergraduate applications are automatically considered for merit-based scholarships during adm Denver, CO 80208 ission review, there are no additional forms to fill out

CONTACT

University of Denver
Associate Dean, Director of International Student Admission
114 University Hall
2197 S. University Blvd
Denver, CO 80208
Tel: +1 (303) 871-2790
Fax: +1 (303) 871-3522
Email: INTLADM@du.edu
Web: www.du.edu/apply/admission/apply/international/index.html

University of Evansville
University of Evansville Emergency Support for Syrian Students

PROGRAM INFORMATION

Description: The University of Evansville Emergency Support for Syrian Students provides up to $24,000 per year in scholarship aid for up to 4 years in any field of study. The university includes ABET accredited engineering and AACSB accredited business programs, numerous health related areas, arts, humanities and natural and social science fields of study.

Levels of Study: Undergraduate

Field of Study: Accounting, Archaeology, Art History, Biochemistry, Biology, Business and Management, Chemistry, Classics, Cognitive Science, Communications and Journalism, Computer Science, Creative Writing, Economics, Education, Engineering, Finance, Foreign Languages, French, Health Professions, Health Studies, History, Humanities, International Management, International Relations, Journalism, Liberal/General Studies, Literature, Management, Marketing, Mathematics, Music, Neuroscience, Nursing, Philosophy and Religion, Physics, Political Science, Psychology, Public Health, Religion/Theology, Spanish, Theater, Visual and Performing Arts

Nationality: Syria

Location of Study: University of Evansville Evansville, IN

AWARD INFORMATION

Award Type: Scholarship

Average Amount: $25,000

Number of Awards: 2

Award Coverage: Scholarship covers a portion of tuition, student is responsible for remaining tuition, room and board, fees, books, incidental expenses

Award Duration: Up to 8 semesters

ELIGIBILITY REQUIREMENTS

- Most be an undergraduate
- Must have a minimum grade point average of 3.5 on a 4.0 scale
- Must have a minimum TOEFL 61 (IBT) or 5.5 IELTS

APPLICATION INFORMATION

Award Deadline: May 1

Instructions: Visit our website at www.evansville.edu for more information

CONTACT

University of Evansville
Director of International Admission & Recruitment
1800 Lincoln Avenue
Evansville, IN 47722
Tel: +1 (812) 488-2146
Fax: +1 (812) 488-6389
Email: syrianscholarship@evansville.edu
Web: www.evansville.edu

University of Evansville
University of Evansville International Student Scholarships

PROGRAM INFORMATION

Description: The University of Evansville has assistance available in the form of academic scholarships awarded to students who display excellent academic credentials. Each applicant is automatically considered for merit-based scholarship based on academic credentials. Need-based financial aid is not offered, therefore, a separate financial aid application is not requested. The University of Evansville also offers supplementary awards to international students who fit the specific criteria.

Levels of Study: Undergraduate

Field of Study: All

Nationality: Any Region

Location of Study: University of Evansville Evansville, IN

AWARD INFORMATION

Award Type: Scholarship

Average Amount: $14,000-$20,000

Number of Awards: Unlimited

Award Coverage: Partial tuition

Award Duration: 4 years

ELIGIBILITY REQUIREMENTS

- Must complete preparatory studies, exit examination and secondary school graduation requirements
- SAT scores are recommended but not required

APPLICATION INFORMATION

Award Deadline: Jun for fall semester, Nov for spring semester

Instructions: Apply online or via the Common Application and then submit supporting documents, visit our website to learn more about supplementary awards

CONTACT

University of Evansville
International Admissions Office,
Schroeder School of Business Building, Rm 21
1800 Lincoln Avenue
Evansville, IN 47722
Tel: +1 (812) 488-1392
Fax: +1 (812) 488-2146
Email: international@evansville.edu
Web: www.evansville.edu/tuitionandaid/international.cfm

University of Georgia
UGA Foreign Language Teaching Associate

PROGRAM INFORMATION

Description: This foreign language teaching associate position is an assistantship for the Portuguese Language Program.

Levels of Study: Graduate

Field of Study: Area and Ethnic Studies, English as a Second Language, Foreign Languages, Linguistics, Literature, Women's Studies

Nationality: Brazil

Location of Study: University of Georgia Athens, GA

AWARD INFORMATION

Award Type: Fellowship, Scholarship, Student Exchange

Average Amount: $14,000

Number of Awards: 1-2 per semester

Award Coverage: Tuition, housing, food

Award Duration: 1 year

ELIGIBILITY REQUIREMENTS

- Must be a Portuguese speaker
- Must pass TOEFL
- GRE scores

APPLICATION INFORMATION

Award Deadline: Feb

Instructions: Apply to the Department of Romance Languages and the Graduate school

CONTACT

Department of Romance Languages
FLTA coordinator
Gilbert Hall
Athens, GA 30602-1815
Tel: +1 (706) 542-3161
Fax: +1 (706) 542-3287
Email: susieq@uga.edu
Web: www.rom.uga.edu

University of Georgia
UGA Graduate Studies Scholarship

PROGRAM INFORMATION

Description: Scholarship for students enrolled in the MA or PhD in Luso-Brazilian Studies

Levels of Study: Graduate

Field of Study: Foreign Languages, Human Rights, Linguistics, Literature, Women's Studies

Nationality: Angola, Brazil, Canada, Cape Verde, East Timor, Guinea-Bissau, Macao, Mozambique, Portugal, São Tomé & Príncipe, US

Location of Study: University of Georgia Athens, GA

AWARD INFORMATION

Award Type: Scholarship, Student Exchange

Average Amount: $12,000-$15,000

Number of Awards: 1-2

Award Coverage: Tuition, housing, food

Award Duration: Maximum of 5 years

ELIGIBILITY REQUIREMENTS

- Must pass TOEFL
- GRE scores
- Must speak Portuguese

APPLICATION INFORMATION

Award Deadline: Jan

Instructions: Visit www.rom.uga.edu and www.gr.uga.edu for more information

CONTACT

University of Georgia
Graduate Coordinator
Gilbert Hall
Athens, GA 30602-1815
Tel: +1 (706) 542-1075
Fax: +1 (706) 542-3287
Web: www.rom.uga.edu

University of Hawaii at Hilo

University of Hawaii at Hilo International Student Scholarship

PROGRAM INFORMATION

Description: The University of Hawaii at Hilo offers scholarships to undergraduate international students who have demonstrated academic excellence and have some degree of financial need.

Levels of Study: Undergraduate

Field of Study: All

Nationality: Any Region

Location of Study: University of Hawaii at Hilo
Hilo, HI

AWARD INFORMATION

Award Type: Scholarship

Average Amount: $3,000

Number of Awards: 15 per semester

Award Coverage: Partial tuition

Award Duration: Maximum of 4 years

ELIGIBILITY REQUIREMENTS

- Outstanding academic achievement, as demonstrated by excellent grades and/or test scores
- Must be admitted as a classified, degree-seeking undergraduate student
- Must be on an F-1 student visa

APPLICATION INFORMATION

Award Deadline: Mar

Instructions: Applicants must apply for admission and get admitted to the University of Hawaii at Hilo; application is usually available in Jan and deadline to apply is usually Mar for the following academic year

CONTACT

University of Hawaii at Hilo
International Student Services & Intercultural Education
200 W. Kawili Street
Hilo, HI, US
Tel: +1 (808) 932-7467
Fax: +1 (808) 932-7471
Email: mellon@hawaii.edu
Web: www.hilo.hawaii.edu//international/scholarships.php

University of Hawai'i Maui College

University of Hawai'i Maui College International Student Scholarships

PROGRAM INFORMATION

Description: International Student Scholarships are available to incoming and continuing full time and hybrid (part-time Maui Language Institute/part-time credit) F-1 visa students.

Levels of Study: Undergraduate

Field of Study: All

Nationality: Any Region

Location of Study: University of Hawai'i Maui College
Maui, HI

AWARD INFORMATION

Award Type: Scholarship

Average Amount: $1,000

Award Coverage: Tuition

Award Duration: 1 semester

ELIGIBILITY REQUIREMENTS

- Must have a minimum 2.0 GPA
- Must be an F-1 visa student

APPLICATION INFORMATION

Award Deadline: Mar

Instructions: Contact or visit our website

CONTACT

UH Maui College Financial Aid Office
310 Kaahumanu Avenue
Kahului, HI 96732
Tel: +1 (808) 984-3277
Fax: +1 (808) 984-3562
Email: mauifa@hawaii.edu
Web: maui.hawaii.edu/financial/

University of Idaho

Discover Idaho International

PROGRAM INFORMATION

Description: To qualify for this scholarship, students must have either a high school or college transfer Grade Point Average (GPA) of at least a 3.25. All qualified students are guaranteed to receive this tuition waiver! No additional application necessary. This scholarship is renewable if a 2.8 cumulative University of Idaho GPA is maintained.

Levels of Study: Undergraduate

Field of Study: All

Nationality: Any Region

Location of Study: University of Idaho
Moscow, ID

AWARD INFORMATION

Award Type: Tuition Reduction

Average Amount: $1,500-$3,500

Award Coverage: Tuition

Award Duration: Renewable for up to 4 years

ELIGIBILITY REQUIREMENTS

- Must gain enrollment to the University of Idaho
- Must be a degree-seeking undergraduate student
- Must have at least a 3.25 GPA

APPLICATION INFORMATION

Award Deadline: May 1

Instructions: No additional application required. Students with COMPLETE undergraduate applications submitted by Feb 15 will be automatically considered

CONTACT

University of Idaho
Assistant Director, International Marketing and Recruitment
875 Perimeter Drive MS 1250
Moscow, ID 83843-1250
Tel: +1 (208) 885-4599
Fax: +1 (208) 885-2859
Email: sgreenfield@uidaho.edu
Web: www.uidaho.edu/internationalstudents

University of Idaho

University of Idaho International Tuition Waiver

PROGRAM INFORMATION

Description: Students must have a 3.0 GPA and be pursuing a bachelor's degree to be eligible. Preference given to underrepresented student populations. The number of awards is dependent on available funding each year.

Levels of Study: Undergraduate

Field of Study: All

Nationality: Any Region

Location of Study: University of Idaho
Moscow, ID

AWARD INFORMATION

Award Type: Tuition Reduction

Average Amount: $6,500

Number of Awards: 30

Award Coverage: Tuition

Award Duration: Renewable for up to 4 years

ELIGIBILITY REQUIREMENTS

- Must have a 3.0 GPA
- Must be studying for a bachelor's degree
- Preference given to students from underrepresented country populations on our campus

APPLICATION INFORMATION

Award Deadline: Feb 15

Instructions: Students with completed undergraduate applications submitted by Feb 15th will automatically be considered. No special scholarship application required

CONTACT

University of Idaho
Assistant Director, International Marketing and Recruitment
International Programs Office
875 Perimeter Drive MS 1250
Moscow, ID 83844-1250
Tel: +1 (208) 885-4599
Fax: +1 (208) 885-2859
Email: sgreenfield@uidaho.edu
Web: www.uidaho.edu/internationalstudents

University of Illinois at Chicago

University of Illinois at Chicago - Graduate College degrees

PROGRAM INFORMATION

Description: UIC provides full tuition and partial fees waivers to grad student fellowship recipients (both international and domestic students). For a complete listing of Graduate College programs, please visit our website.

Levels of Study: Graduate, Doctorate

Location of Study: University of Illinois at Chicago
Chicago, IL

AWARD INFORMATION

Award Type: Tuition Reduction

Average Amount: Varies

Award Coverage: UIC provides full tuition and partial fees coverage to all grad student fellowship recipients, provided their award is at least $18,000 for 12 months or $15,000 for 9 months

ELIGIBILITY REQUIREMENTS

- Applicant must be applying to a graduate college program; this includes most masters and PhD programs, but not professional programs (MPH, MBA, MSW, etc)
- Applicant must be accepted by a graduate college program
- Applicant will receive tuition and fee waiver coverage as long as Fulbright funding status is maintained
- Applicant must remain in good standing with the graduate college program

APPLICATION INFORMATION

Instructions: Notify Marie Khan, Graduate College External Fellowship Coordinator, that you are a Foreign Fulbright grantee who is interested in attending UIC

CONTACT

University of Illinois at Chicago
External Fellowship Coordinator, Graduate College
601 S. Morgan Street, MC 192
University Hall Room 633
Chicago Chicago Illinois, US
Tel: +1 (312) 355-3456
Fax: +1 (312) 413-0185
Email: mkhanj@uic.edu
Web: www.uic.edu/gcat/GPDP

University of Iowa

Financial Assistance for Undergraduate and Graduate Students at the University of Iowa

PROGRAM INFORMATION

Description: US News & World Report ranks The University of Iowa 29th best among the public universities. 32,000 students enroll each year including 4,000 students from over 100 countries.

Levels of Study: Undergraduate, Graduate, Doctorate, Post Doctorate, Professional

Field of Study: All

Nationality: Any Region

Location of Study: The University of Iowa Iowa City, IA

AWARD INFORMATION

Award Type: Associateship, Award, Fellowship, Scholarship, Tuition Reduction

Average Amount: $2,000-$15,000

Number of Awards: Varies

Award Duration: Varies

ELIGIBILITY REQUIREMENTS

- Undergraduates: Must meet all academic requirements for admission and scholarship requirements
- Graduate students: Requirements are determined by each individual department

APPLICATION INFORMATION

Award Deadline: Varies

Instructions: Please visit our website for specific information regarding undergraduate and graduate awards

CONTACT

The University of Iowa
Associate Director, International Outreach & Recruitment
Office of Admissions
116 Calvin Hall
Iowa City, IA 52242-1396
Tel: +1 (319) 335-1529
Fax: +1 (319) 335-1535
Email: admissions@uiowa.edu
Web: admissions.uiowa.edu

University of Kansas

University of Kansas Funding Awards

PROGRAM INFORMATION

Description: The University of Kansas is a major comprehensive teaching and research institution located on a beautiful campus in Lawrence, Kansas. A limited number of competitive, merit-based scholarships are offered to new international undergraduate degree-seeking students each year. Graduate students may be considered for funding opportunities awarded by graduate programs and academic departments.

Levels of Study: Undergraduate, Graduate, Doctorate

Field of Study: All

Nationality: Any Region

Location of Study: University of Kansas Lawrence, KS

AWARD INFORMATION

Award Type: Associateship, Award, Fellowship, Scholarship, Tuition Reduction

Average Amount: $1,000-$23,000

Number of Awards: Varies

Award Duration: Varies

ELIGIBILITY REQUIREMENTS

- Must be admitted to the University of Kansas and show academic distinction, placing in top tier of the applicant pool
- Undergraduate students must generally have a 3.5 GPA or higher
- Undergraduate students must submit letters of reference, essays, activities, leadership, and test scores (TOEFL, IELTS, SAT, or ACT, etc)
- Graduates students should consult their respective academic departments for specific requirements

APPLICATION INFORMATION

Instructions: For more information on how to apply, please visit our website

CONTACT

University of Kansas
International Recruitment & Undergraduate Admissions
1450 Jayhawk Boulevard, Rm. 45 Strong Hall
Lawrence, KS 66045-7518
Tel: +1 (785) 864-2616
Fax: +1 (785) 864-3404
Email: issrecruit@ku.edu
Web: www.ku.edu

University of Kentucky

University of Kentucky - The Provost Scholarship

PROGRAM INFORMATION

Description: Incoming freshmen whose minimum ACT score is 28 or SAT (Math + Reading) is 1250, and achieve a 3.30 unweighted high school GPA on a 4.0 scale, will automatically be offered a Provost Scholarship. Minimum test score requirements are based on the composite or total score from 1 test date. Combined scores, also known as a superscore, from 2 or more tests will not be considered.

Levels of Study: Undergraduate

Field of Study: All

Nationality: Any Region

Location of Study: University of Kentucky Lexington, KY

AWARD INFORMATION

Award Type: Scholarship

Average Amount: $3,000

Award Coverage: Tuition

Award Duration: 4 years

ELIGIBILITY REQUIREMENTS

- Must have an ACT score of 28 or an SAT (math and reading) of 1250
- High school students must have a 3.30 GPA on a 4.0 scale

APPLICATION INFORMATION

Award Deadline: Jan

Instructions: No application is required

CONTACT

University of Kentucky
Office of Academic Scholarships
128-E Funkhouser Building
Lexington, KY 40506-0054
Tel: +1 (859) 257-4198
Email: academicscholar@lsv.uky.edu
Web: www.uky.edu/AcademicScholarships/freshman.htm

University of Kentucky

University of Kentucky - Competitive Scholarships for Freshmen

PROGRAM INFORMATION

Description: The University of Kentucky provides a competitive scholarship application for higher valued scholarships. Students may receive only 1 scholarship through the Academic Scholarship Program. A competitive scholarship offer would replace an automatic scholarship offer. The Presidential Scholarship covers the cost of in-state tuition. The National Excellence Scholarship amounts to $4,500 per year and is for non-resident applicants only.

Levels of Study: Undergraduate

Field of Study: All

Nationality: Any Region

Location of Study: University of Kentucky Lexington, KY

AWARD INFORMATION

Award Type: Scholarship

Average Amount: Varies

Award Coverage: Tuition

Award Duration: 4 years

ELIGIBILITY REQUIREMENTS

- Must have a minimum test score of 31 ACT or 1360 SAT (math and reading)
- Must have a minimum GPA of 3.5 on a 4.0 scale

APPLICATION INFORMATION

Award Deadline: Jan

Instructions: To request application information, please contact: www.uky.edu/AcademicScholarships/contactus.htm

CONTACT

University of Kentucky
Academic Scholarships
128-E Funkhouser Building
Lexington, KY 40506-0054
Tel: +1 (859) 257-4198
Email: academicscholar@lsv.uky.edu
Web: www.uky.edu/AcademicScholarships/freshman.htm

University of Kentucky

University of Kentucky - William C. Parker Scholarship Program

PROGRAM INFORMATION

Description: The University of Kentucky has a mission and commitment to aggressively recruit and retain students from all segments of society. Factors that are considered in the holistic evaluation of William C. Parker scholarship applications include test scores, grades, an essay, leadership experience, extracurricular activities, awards and recognition, community service, and contribution to diversity. The William C. Parker Scholarship Program is available for incoming freshmen, transfer, and UK continuing students. Students may receive only 1 award through the William C. Parker Scholarship Program.

Levels of Study: Undergraduate

Field of Study: All

Nationality: Any Region

Location of Study: University of Kentucky Lexington, KY

AWARD INFORMATION

Award Type: Scholarship

Average Amount: $5,000

Award Coverage: Tuition

Award Duration: 2 years for transfer, 4 years for freshmen

ELIGIBILITY REQUIREMENTS

- Must have a GPA of 2.50 on a 4.00 scale
- Must be admitted to the University of Kentucky

APPLICATION INFORMATION

Award Deadline: Jan

Instructions: Student must submit a 500-word essay on the topic: How I will contribute to diversity at the University of Kentucky?

CONTACT

University of Kentucky
Director, William C. Parker Scholarship Program
100-C Funkhouser Building
Lexington, KY 40506-0054
Tel: +1 (859) 323-6334
Email: joyceb@email.uky.edu
Web: www.uky.edu/AcademicScholarships/WCP.htm

University of Kentucky

University of Kentucky - Freshmen Engineering Scholarships

PROGRAM INFORMATION

Description: Freshman Scholarships are awarded on the basis of the student's high school GPA, ACT or SAT scores, writing ability and leadership potential. The scholarship application gives a good overview of each applicant's development in those areas. The College of Engineering offers dozens of specific scholarships. However, 1 application serves for all Engineering scholarships available to first-year students with the exception of those offered by the Kentucky Department of Transportation.

Levels of Study: Undergraduate

Field of Study: Computer Science, Engineering

Nationality: Any Region

Location of Study: University of Kentucky Lexington, KY

AWARD INFORMATION

Award Type: Scholarship

Average Amount: $1,500-$3,000

Award Coverage: Tuition

Award Duration: Maximum of 2 years

ELIGIBILITY REQUIREMENTS

- Must have a minimum SAT score of 1300 (minimum 740 math and reading) or ACT composite score of 29 (minimum 33 math)
- Must have a minimum 3.5 GPA on a 4.0 scale

APPLICATION INFORMATION

Award Deadline: Jan

Instructions: To apply for a UK College of Engineering scholarship, carefully complete the application form (PDF): www.engr.uky.edu/scholarships/freshman-scholarships

CONTACT

University of Kentucky
College of Engineering
375B Ralph G Anderson Building
Lexington, KY 40506-0503
Tel: +1 (859) 257-0569
Fax: +1 (859) 323-4922
Email: cdillon@engr.uky.edu
Web: www.engr.uky.edu/scholarships/freshman-scholarships

University of Kentucky

University of Kentucky - Gatton College of Business and Economics Scholarships

PROGRAM INFORMATION

Description: The Gatton College of Business and Economics offers scholarships primarily based on academic performance, financial need, program of study, ethnicity, and residency. Scholarships are awarded to 2 distinct groups of students: incoming freshmen and current business students. All intended business majors that have applied and been accepted by University of Kentucky's Office of Admission will be placed in the scholarship applicant pool for Gatton College incoming freshmen.

Levels of Study: Undergraduate

Field of Study: Accounting, Business and Management, Economics, Finance, Management, Marketing

Nationality: Any Region

Location of Study: University of Kentucky Lexington, KY

AWARD INFORMATION

Award Type: Scholarship

Average Amount: $500-$5,000

Award Coverage: Tuition

Award Duration: Maximum of 4 years

APPLICATION INFORMATION

Award Deadline: Jan

Instructions: Please visit our website for further instructions

CONTACT

Tel: +1 (859) 257-4627
Web: www.gatton.uky.edu/Undergraduates/Content.asp?PageName=UScholarships

University of La Verne
University of La Verne Undergraduate Program Scholarships

PROGRAM INFORMATION

Description: The University of La Verne offers 50+ undergraduate majors. Through the Freshman La Verne Experience (FLEX), students explore these programs. The FLEX program introduces freshmen to classes that, among other things, integrate various forms of community engagement into their classes. Faculty design courses that allow students to apply what they learn in real-world situations.

Levels of Study: Undergraduate

Field of Study: Accounting, American History, American Literature, American Politics, Anthropology, Behavioral Sciences, Business and Management, Communication Technologies, Communications and Journalism, Earth Science, Engineering-Related Technologies, Finance, Fine Arts, Government, Journalism, Literature, Mathematics, Music, Natural Sciences, Photography, Physical Sciences, Physics, Psychology, Religion/Theology, Spanish, Speech and Debate

Nationality: Any Region

Location of Study: University of La Verne
La Verne, CA

AWARD INFORMATION

Award Type: Scholarship

Average Amount: $5,000-$20,000

Award Coverage: Tuition

Award Duration: Renewable for up to 4 years

ELIGIBILITY REQUIREMENTS

- Scholarships are available for undergraduate freshmen students only
- Please refer to our web site for test score requirements
- Please refer to our web site for grade point average requirements

APPLICATION INFORMATION

Award Deadline: Feb

Instructions: Students need to complete the application for admission, students that complete the application by 1 Feb will be given first priority, there is no separate scholarship application

CONTACT
University of La Verne
Director of International Admission
1950 Third Street
La Verne, CA 91750, US
Tel: +1 (909) 448-4032
Fax: +1 (909) 392-2714
Email: awu@laverne.edu
Web: www.laverne.edu/international

University of Massachusetts Amherst
University of Massachusetts Amherst Research Assistantship

PROGRAM INFORMATION

Description: The University offers a number of research assistantships in the research programs of various departments. International applicants who are awarded assistantships, and who have no supplemental means of support, must make sure that the assistantship is adequate to meet their minimum financial needs (refer to Estimate of Expenses). Assistantships are awarded for a maximum of 1 academic year at a time. A graduate assistantship is not a scholarship, and a full-assistantship requires a work contribution by the student averaging 20 hours per week. Federal and State income taxes will be withheld from earnings.

Levels of Study: Graduate, Doctorate

Field of Study: All

Nationality: Any Region

Location of Study: University of Massachusetts - Amherst
Amherst, MA

AWARD INFORMATION

Award Type: Associateship, Award, Grant

Average Amount: Varies

Number of Awards: Varies

Award Coverage: Tuition and fees, health insurance, living expenses

Award Duration: Varies

ELIGIBILITY REQUIREMENTS

- Must meet academic qualification and research needs of individual department

APPLICATION INFORMATION

Award Deadline: Feb for fall semester; Oct for spring semester

Instructions: Contact individual department and/or Assistantship and Fellowships Office, visit our website for more information

CONTACT
University of Massachusetts Amherst
Graduate Admissions
530 Goodell Building, University of Massachusetts Amherst
140 Hicks Way
Amherst, MA 01003
Tel: +1 (413) 545-0721
Fax: +1 (413) 577-0010
Email: gradadm@resgs.umass.edu
Web: www.honors.umass.edu/scholarship/research-assistant-fellowships

University of Massachusetts Amherst
University of Massachusetts - Amherst Teaching Assistantship

PROGRAM INFORMATION

Description: The University offers a number of teaching assistantships in the instructional programs of various departments. Stipends vary greatly. International applicants who are awarded assistantships, and who have no supplemental means of support, must make sure that the assistantship is adequate to meet their minimum financial needs. A graduate assistantship is not a scholarship, and a full-assistantship requires a work contribution by the student averaging 20 hours per week. Federal and State income taxes will be withheld from earnings.

Levels of Study: Graduate, Professional

Field of Study: All

Nationality: Any Region

Location of Study: University of Massachusetts - Amherst
Amherst, MA

AWARD INFORMATION

Award Type: Associateship, Award, Grant

Average Amount: Varies

Number of Awards: Varies

Award Coverage: Tuition and fees, health insurance, living expenses

Award Duration: Varies

ELIGIBILITY REQUIREMENTS

- Must meet academic qualifications and departmental needs

APPLICATION INFORMATION

Award Deadline: Feb 1 for fall semester; Oct 1 for spring semester

Instructions: Contact individual department and/or Assistantship and Fellowships Office

CONTACT
University of Massachusetts - Amherst
Graduate Admissions
530 Goodell Building, University of Massachusetts Amherst
140 Hicks Way
Amherst, MA 01003
Tel: +1 (413) 545-5287
Fax: +1 (413) 577-0007
Email: gradadm@resgs.umass.edu
Web: www.umass.edu/grad_catalog/fellowships.html

University of Massachusetts Amherst

University of Massachusetts - Amherst University Fellowship

PROGRAM INFORMATION

Description: These fellowships are awarded to graduate students on a competitive basis and are intended to help superior students pursue graduate study without a work requirement and obtain a degree in the minimum possible time. They are normally awarded only after a graduate student has completed 2 semesters at the University of Massachusetts - Amherst. A tuition waiver accompanies a University Fellowship, and no service is required.

Levels of Study: Graduate, Doctorate, Professional

Field of Study: All

Nationality: Any Region

Location of Study: University of Massachusetts - Amherst Amherst, MA

AWARD INFORMATION

Award Type: Fellowship

Average Amount: Varies

Number of Awards: Varies

Award Coverage: Tuition and fees, insurance, living expenses

Award Duration: Academic year

ELIGIBILITY REQUIREMENTS

- Must have superior academic qualifications

APPLICATION INFORMATION

Instructions: Please email the listed contact

CONTACT

University of Massachusetts Amherst
Graduate Admissions
239 Whitmore Bldg
Amherst, MA 01003
Tel: +1 (413) 545-5287
Fax: +1 (413) 577-0007
Email: gradadm@resgs.umass.edu
Web: www.umass.edu/grad_catalog/fellowships.html

University of Massachusetts Boston

UMass Boston Graduate Assistantships

PROGRAM INFORMATION

Levels of Study: Graduate, Doctorate

Nationality: Any Region

Location of Study: University of Massachusetts Boston Boston, MA

ELIGIBILITY REQUIREMENTS

- International applicants must complete the General Application Requirements.
- Refer to specific department of study for further requirements.

APPLICATION INFORMATION

Award Deadline: May 1, unless otherwise noted by specific department

Instructions: Application Requirements Check List: Official Transcripts, Applicable Test Scores, Letters of Recommendation, Statement of Purpose, Non-refundable, Application Fee, Program Specific Requirement

CONTACT

University of Massachusetts Boston
Office of Graduate Admissions
100 Morrissey Boulevard
Boston, MA 02125-3393
Email: bos.gadm@umb.edu.
Web: www.umb.edu/admissions/grad/international_ga

University of Miami

University of Miami University Scholarship

PROGRAM INFORMATION

Description: Incoming international freshman students are automatically considered for merit-based scholarships when they apply for admission to the university.

Levels of Study: Undergraduate

Field of Study: All

Nationality: Any Region

Location of Study: University of Miami Coral Gables, FL

AWARD INFORMATION

Award Type: Scholarship

Average Amount: $5,000-$24,000

Number of Awards: Varies

Award Coverage: Tuition or partial tuition

Award Duration: 4 or 5 years depending on program

ELIGIBILITY REQUIREMENTS

- The University of Miami takes into account students' high school curriculum, difficulty of course selection (such as AP/IB), extracurricular activities, essay and guidance counselor recommendation(s), as well as the overall qualities of the student
- Must provide a bank letter indicating they will be able to cover the difference between the scholarship award and the total cost of attendance
- Frost School of Music applicants are not eligible for these awards because they undergo separate consideration for music scholarships

APPLICATION INFORMATION

Award Deadline: Nov, Jan

Instructions: To apply online, visit the website, outstanding international undergraduate students are considered for merit scholarships

CONTACT

University of Miami
Office of International Admission
5202 University Drive
214 Merrick Building
Coral Gables, FL 33124-2025
Tel: +1 (305) 284-2271
Fax: +1 (305) 284-6811
Email: admission@miami.edu
Web: www.miami.edu/int-scholarships

University of Michigan-Flint

University of Michigan-Flint Ralph M. and Emmalyn E. Freeman International Student Scholarship

PROGRAM INFORMATION

Levels of Study: Undergraduate, Graduate, Doctorate

Field of Study: All

Nationality: Any Region

Location of Study: University of Michigan-Flint Flint, MI

AWARD INFORMATION

Award Type: Scholarship

Average Amount: Approx $1,000-$2,500

Number of Awards: Varies

Award Coverage: Tuition, only for fall and winter semesters

ELIGIBILITY REQUIREMENTS

- Must have full-time status
- Must be in good standing with the university
- Must be in good standing regarding visa and non-immigrant status
- Must have a GPA of 3.0

APPLICATION INFORMATION

Instructions: See our website for more information

CONTACT

University of Michigan-Flint
International Center
303 East Kearsley Street
219 University Center
Flint, MI 48502
Email: ic@umflint.edu
Web: www.umflint.edu/international

University of Michigan-Flint

University of Michigan-Flint International Freshman Scholarship

PROGRAM INFORMATION

Description: Scholarship for incoming freshmen.

Levels of Study: Undergraduate

Field of Study: All

Nationality: Any Region

AWARD INFORMATION

Award Type: Scholarship

Average Amount: $1,000-$3,000

Number of Awards: Varies

Award Coverage: Tuition

Award Duration: 1 year

ELIGIBILITY REQUIREMENTS

- Must have a minimum of 3.0 GPA on 4.0 scale

CONTACT

University of Michigan-Flint
International Center
303 E. Kearsley St.
Flint, MI 48502
Tel: +1 (810) 762-0867
Fax: +1 (810) 762-0006
Email: ic@umflint.edu
Web: www.umflint.edu/international

University of Minnesota

University of Minnesota Global Excellence Scholarship (GES)

PROGRAM INFORMATION

Description: Covers either all or half the difference between resident and non-resident tuition rates. These competitive, merit-based scholarships are awarded to international freshmen or transfer students for up to 4 years.

Levels of Study: Undergraduate

Field of Study: All

Nationality: Any Region

Location of Study: University of Minnesota-Twin Cities Minneapolis, MN

AWARD INFORMATION

Award Type: Scholarship

Average Amount: $3,125-$6,250

Award Coverage: Tuition

Award Duration: Maximum of 4 years

ELIGIBILITY REQUIREMENTS

- International freshmen or transfer students

APPLICATION INFORMATION

Award Deadline: Dec 15, 2014

Instructions: There is no separate scholarship application required; students are considered based on an overall assessment of their on-time admission application; all awards are made at the time of admission, continuing students who were not initially awarded are not eligible to apply

CONTACT

University of Minnesota-Twin Cities
Office of Admissions
240 Williamson Hall, 231 Pillsbury Dr SE
Minneapolis, MN 55455
Tel: 1-800-752-1000
Fax: 612-626-1693
Email: passport@umn.edu
Web: www.isss.umn.edu/programs/fa/Global-scholarships.html

University of Minnesota, Crookston

University of Minnesota In-State Tuition

PROGRAM INFORMATION

Description: All students pay the same rate and tuition is banded at 13 credits which means every additional credit is free.

Levels of Study: Undergraduate

Nationality: Any Region

Location of Study: University of Minnesota Crookston Crookston, MN

AWARD INFORMATION

Award Type: Tuition Reduction

Average Amount: $10,034

Number of Awards: Unlimited

Award Coverage: Tuition

Award Duration: 5 years

ELIGIBILITY REQUIREMENTS

- Admitted and enrolled at the University of Minnesota Crookston

APPLICATION INFORMATION

Instructions: Application is automatic with application for admissions

CONTACT

University of Minnesota Crookston
Director, International Programs
2900 University Ave
Crookston, MN 56716, US
Tel: (218) 281-8442
Fax: (218) 281-8575
Email: gillette@umn.edu

University of Minnesota, Crookston

University of Minnesota International Student Tuition Waiver

PROGRAM INFORMATION

Description: Scholarship recipients receive a reduction of their tuition by 1/2 for the academic year.

Levels of Study: Undergraduate

Nationality: Any Region

Location of Study: University of Minnesota Crookston Crookston, MN

AWARD INFORMATION

Award Type: Tuition Reduction

Average Amount: $3,694

Number of Awards: 4

Award Coverage: Tuition

Award Duration: Annual/renewable

ELIGIBILITY REQUIREMENTS

- Need to have completed 1 full semester and enrolled in the second semester with a total equivalent to at least 24 credits from UMC, if you are a transfer student, you will have needed to be here for 1 full semester
- Need to be an international student studying at UMC on an F-1 visa
- Must have a cumulative GPA of 3.0 or above
- Must possess leadership skills, be involved with international activities on campus, and be an active UMC student overall

APPLICATION INFORMATION

Award Deadline: Feb

Instructions: An enrolled international student must complete an online specialty scholarship application by the Feb 15 deadline for consideration

CONTACT

University of Minnesota Crookston
International Programs
2900 University Ave
Crookston MN
Tel: +1 (218) 281-8442
Fax: +1 (218) 281-8575
Email: gillette@umn.edu
Web: www.umcrookston.edu

INSTITUTIONS

University of Minnesota, Twin Cities

University of Minnesota Maroon Global Excellence Scholarships

PROGRAM INFORMATION

Description: The Maroon Global Excellence Scholarships are awarded on the basis of academic merit—students selected for awards are among the best in their high school class and show a record of very strong academic preparation. Maroon Global Excellence Scholarships for the 2014-15 academic year, are $3,625 per year for 4 years (total award of about $14,500).

Levels of Study: Undergraduate

Nationality: Any Region

Location of Study: University of Minnesota - Twin Cities Minneapolis/Saint Paul, MN

AWARD INFORMATION

Award Type: Scholarship

Average Amount: $14,500

Number of Awards: 70

Award Coverage: Award is dispersed over 4 years of a bachelor's degree, equal to approximately $3,625 per year towards tuition

Award Duration: Up to 4 years

ELIGIBILITY REQUIREMENTS

- Must be an international student (non-US citizen)
- Must be pursuing a bachelor's degree (award is for undergraduate students only)
- Must maintain a satisfactory grade point average to retain the scholarship

APPLICATION INFORMATION

Award Deadline: Dec

Instructions: No separate application is needed, all international undergraduate students who apply for admission before our Dec 15th deadline are considered for this scholarship

CONTACT

University of Minnesota - Twin Cities
Office of Admissions
240 Williamson Hall
231 Pillsbury Drive S.E.
Minneapolis, MN
Tel: +1 (612) 625-2008
Email: passport@umn.edu
Web: www.passport.umn.edu

University of Minnesota, Twin Cities

University of Minnesota Gold Global Excellence Scholarships

PROGRAM INFORMATION

Description: The Gold Global Excellence Scholarships are awarded on the basis of academic merit—students selected for awards are among the best in their high school class and show a record of very strong academic preparation. Gold Global Excellence Scholarships for the 2014-15 academic year, were 7,250 per year for 4 years (total scholarship of about $29,000). Recipients are selected from the pool of undergraduate applicants to the University of Minnesota each year, no separate scholarship application required.

Levels of Study: Undergraduate

Field of Study: All

Nationality: Any Region

Location of Study: University of Minnesota - Twin Cities Minneapolis, MN

AWARD INFORMATION

Award Type: Scholarship

Average Amount: $29,000

Number of Awards: 55

Award Coverage: Award is dispersed over 4 years of a bachelor's degree, equal to approximately $7,250 per year

Award Duration: Up to 4 years

ELIGIBILITY REQUIREMENTS

- Must be an international student (non-US citizen)
- Must be pursuing a bachelor's degree (award is for undergraduate students only)
- Must maintain a satisfactory grade point average to retain the scholarship

APPLICATION INFORMATION

Award Deadline: Dec

Instructions: No separate application is needed, all international undergraduate students who apply for admission before our deadline of Dec 15th are considered for this scholarship

CONTACT

University of Minnesota - Twin Cities
Office of Admissions
240 Williamson Hall
231 Pillsbury Drive S.E.
Minneapolis, MN 55455
Tel: +1 (612) 625-2008
Fax: +1 (612) 626-1693
Email: passport@umn.edu
Web: www.passport.umn.edu

University of Missouri - Kansas City UMKC

University of Missouri Intensive English Scholarship

PROGRAM INFORMATION

Description: All non-government sponsored students studying in the English as a Second Language Program at UMKC's Applied Language Institute receive an automatic scholarship that waives a portion of the non-resident tuition fees.

Levels of Study: Undergraduate, Graduate

Field of Study: English as a Second Language

Nationality: Any Region

Location of Study: University of Missouri - Kansas City Kansas City, MO

AWARD INFORMATION

Award Type: Award, Tuition Reduction

Average Amount: $672-$9,719

Award Coverage: Covers a portion of the non-resident tuition

ELIGIBILITY REQUIREMENTS

- Must not be sponsored by a government agency
- Must be enrolled in the English as a Second Language program at UMKC

APPLICATION INFORMATION

Instructions: All students enrolled in this program who meet the above requirements automatically receive this award, visit our website for more information

CONTACT

University of Missouri-Kansas City
International Student Affairs Office
5000 Holmes St. G04
Kansas City, MO 64110
Tel: +1 (816) 235-1113
Fax: +1 (816) 235-6502
Email: isao@umkc.edu
Web: www.umkc.edu/ali/

University of Missouri - Kansas City UMKC

Chancellor's Non-Resident Award

PROGRAM INFORMATION

Description: The Chancellor's Non-Resident (CNR) Award is a renewable scholarship for new international students that waives a portion of the non-resident fees.

Levels of Study: Undergraduate, Graduate

Field of Study: Accounting, Architecture and Environmental Design, Art History, Arts and Culture, Astronomy, Business and Management, Chemistry, Communications and Journalism, Dance, Economics, Environmental Studies, Film, Fine Arts, Foreign Languages, Geography, History, Journalism, Management, Master of Business Administration (MBA), Mathematics, Music, Natural Sciences, Psychology, Spanish, Statistics, Theater

Nationality: Any Region

Location of Study: University of Missouri-Kansas City Kansas City, MO

AWARD INFORMATION

Award Type: Award, Tuition Reduction

Average Amount: $4,875-$10,447

Number of Awards: Approx 200

Award Coverage: A portion of the non-resident tuition

Award Duration: Academic year, renewable each year

ELIGIBILITY REQUIREMENTS

- Must be a degree-seeking student with a GPA of at least a 3.0 on a 4.0 scale
- Must have a TOEFL score of 550 PBT/213 CBT/79 IBT or higher. (Students with at least 2 years of academic education in the US are exempt from TOEFL requirement) or minimum IELTS score of 6.0
- Must be an F-1 or J-1 visa holder
- Must be nominated by the UMKC academic unit, new applicants meeting the criteria are automatically recommended to the academic unit for consideration
- Must be in first semester in degree-seeking status with full admission

APPLICATION INFORMATION

Instructions: See our website for further information.

CONTACT

University of Missouri-Kansas City
International Student Affairs Office
5000 Holmes St. G04
Kansas City, MO 64110
Tel: +1 (816) 235-1113
Fax: +1 (816) 235-6502
Email: isao@umkc.edu
Web: www.umkc.edu/isao/cnr_info.cfm

University of Missouri - Kansas City UMKC
Dean's International Scholar Award

PROGRAM INFORMATION

Description: The Dean's International Scholar Award is a renewable scholarship for new international students studying in the School of Computing and Engineering. The DISA Award waives a portion of non-resident fees.

Levels of Study: Undergraduate, Graduate

Field of Study: Computer Science, Engineering, Information Technology

Nationality: Any Region

Location of Study: University of Missouri-Kansas City Kansas City, MO

AWARD INFORMATION

Award Type: Award, Tuition Reduction

Average Amount: $4,000-$8,500

Number of Awards: Approx 260

Award Coverage: A portion of the non-resident tuition

Award Duration: Academic year, renewable each year

ELIGIBILITY REQUIREMENTS

- Must be a degree-seeking student with a GPA of at least a 3.0 on a 4.0 scale
- Must have TOEFL scores of 550 PBT/213 CBT/79 IBT or higher (students with at least 2 years of academic education in the US are exempt from TOEFL requirement) or minimum IELTS score of 6.0
- Must be an F-1 or J-1 visa holder
- Must be nominated by the School of Computing and Engineering, new applicants meeting the criteria are automatically recommended to the academic unit for consideration
- Must be in first semester with degree-seeking status and full admission

APPLICATION INFORMATION

Instructions: See our website for additional information.

CONTACT

University of Missouri-Kansas City
International Student Affairs Office
5000 Holmes St. G04
Kansas City, MO 64110
Tel: +1 (816) 235-1113
Fax: +1 (816) 235-6502
Email: isao@umkc.edu
Web: www.umkc.edu/isao/disa_info.cfm

University of Missouri - Kansas City UMKC
Doctoral Fee Waiver

PROGRAM INFORMATION

Description: All doctoral students are automatically awarded a fee waiver for the non-resident portion of tuition. No separate application or nomination is required.

Levels of Study: Doctorate

Field of Study: All

Nationality: Any Region

Location of Study: University of Missouri-Kansas City Kansas City, MO

AWARD INFORMATION

Award Type: Tuition Reduction

Average Amount: $9,750

Number of Awards: Automatic award made to all doctoral students

Award Coverage: Non-resident portion of tuition

ELIGIBILITY REQUIREMENTS

- Must be a doctoral student attending University of Missouri - Kansas City.

APPLICATION INFORMATION

Instructions: Visit our website at www.umkc.edu/isao for more information

CONTACT

University of Missouri-Kansas City
International Student Affairs Office
5000 Holmes St. G04
Kansas City, MO 64110
Tel: +1 (816) 235-1113
Fax: +1 (816) 235-6502
Email: isao@umkc.edu
Web: www.umkc.edu/isao/phd_waiver.cfm

University of Missouri - Kansas City UMKC
Community College Leadership Award

PROGRAM INFORMATION

Description: Students who have a 3.0 GPA on a 4.0 scale and who have demonstrated leadership roles at a community college may be eligible for the Community College Leadership Award (CCLA). Recipients receive a non-resident fee waiver and an additional $1,500, for a total value of over $11,500 per year.

Levels of Study: Undergraduate

Field of Study: All

Nationality: Any Region

Location of Study: University of Missouri-Kansas City Kansas City, MO

AWARD INFORMATION

Award Type: Scholarship

Average Amount: $11,946

Number of Awards: 10

Award Coverage: Non-resident tuition plus $1,500 stipend per academic year

Award Duration: Academic year, renewable each year

ELIGIBILITY REQUIREMENTS

- Must have TOEFL scores of 550 PBT/213 CBT/79 IBT or higher (students with at least 2 years of academic education in the US are exempt from TOEFL requirement) or minimum IELTS score of 6.0
- Must be pursuing an associate's degree from an accredited community college
- Must have a GPA of at least a 3.0 on a 4.0 scale
- Must be an F-1 or J-1 visa holder
- Must be in first semester with degree-seeking status and full admission

APPLICATION INFORMATION

Instructions: See our website for further information

CONTACT

University of Missouri-Kansas City
International Student Affairs Office
5000 Holmes St. G04
Kansas City, MO 64110
Tel: +1 (816) 235-1113
Fax: +1 (816) 235-6502
Email: isao@umkc.edu
Web: www.umkc.edu/isao/ccla.cfm

University of Nebraska at Omaha
UNO Advantage Scholarship

PROGRAM INFORMATION

Description: UNO Advantage Scholarships allow recipients to pay resident tuition rates. The scholarships typically reduce tuition charges by about 67 percent. They are renewable each year with good academic progress.

Levels of Study: Undergraduate, Graduate, Doctorate

Field of Study: All

Nationality: Any Region

Location of Study: University of Nebraska at Omaha Omaha, NE

AWARD INFORMATION

Award Type: Scholarship

Average Amount: $4,800 - $9,600

Number of Awards: Varies

Award Coverage: Full or partial reduction of tuition from non-resident to resident rates, these scholarships are renewable and can be retained for duration of undergrad or graduate study if GPA remains above 3.0

Award Duration: Duration of degree program

ELIGIBILITY REQUIREMENTS

- Must be eligible for admission
- Must have at least a 3.0 grade point average on a 4.0 scale
- Must be a J-1 or F-1 visa holder or applicant

APPLICATION INFORMATION

Award Deadline: Rolling

Instructions: Apply using online application at www.world.unomaha.edu/admissions/scholarships.php; be sure to fill out the scholarship application completely

CONTACT

University of Nebraska at Omaha
Assistant Director, International Student Recruitment and Admissions
6001 Dodge Street, ASH 241
Omaha, NE 68182-0080
Tel: +1 (402) 554-2293
Fax: +1 (402) 554-2949
Email: world@unomaha.edu
Web: www.world.unomaha.edu

University of Nebraska at Omaha

UNO New International Student Scholarship

PROGRAM INFORMATION

Description: New International Student Scholarships are worth $6,000 per academic year. Partial grants of $3,000 are sometimes awarded for a single semester. These scholarships are not renewable.

Field of Study: All

Nationality: Any Region

Location of Study: University of Nebraska at Omaha Omaha, NE

AWARD INFORMATION

Award Type: Grant

Average Amount: $1,000-$6,000

Number of Awards: Varies

Award Coverage: Tuition and fees

Award Duration: 2 semesters

ELIGIBILITY REQUIREMENTS

- Must be a new international student entrant into UNO
- Must have a 3.0 GPA or better
- Must be an F-1 or J-1 visa holder

APPLICATION INFORMATION

Award Deadline: Rolling

Instructions: Apply online at www.world.unomaha.edu/admissions/scholarships.php

CONTACT

University of Nebraska at Omaha
Assistant Director, International Student Recruitment and Admissions
6001 Dodge St. 241 ASH
Omaha, NE 68182
Tel: +1 (402) 554-2293
Fax: +1 (402) 554-2949
Email: world@unomaha.edu
Web: www.world.unomaha.edu/admissions/scholarships.php

University of Nebraska at Omaha

University of Nebraska at Omaha Academic Department Scholarships

PROGRAM INFORMATION

Description: Individual academic departments at UNO offer scholarship opportunities that are open to all students, including international students. Eligibility, selection criteria, amount, and duration vary by department and program. Additionally, graduate students may be eligible to apply for graduate assistantships, which pay stipends for performing teaching or research duties.

Levels of Study: Undergraduate, Graduate

Field of Study: Business and Management, Computer and Information Sciences

Nationality: Any Region

Location of Study: University of Nebraska at Omaha Omaha, NE

ELIGIBILITY REQUIREMENTS

- Eligible for admission to UNO
- Minimum 3.0 GPA
- F-1 or J-1 visa holder

APPLICATION INFORMATION

Instructions: Contact the College of Information Science Technology: www.ist.unomaha.edu/index.php?p=scholarships, contact the College of Business Administration: cba.unomaha.edu/SCHOLARSHIPS/

CONTACT

University of Nebraska at Omaha
Assistant Director, International Student Recruitment and Admissions
6001 Dodge St. 241 ASH
Omaha, NE 68182
Tel: +1 (402) 554-2293
Fax: +1 (402) 554-2949
Email: world@unomaha.edu
Web: www.world.unomaha.edu/admissions/scholarships.php

University of Nebraska-Lincoln

University of Nebraska-Lincoln Global Scholarships

PROGRAM INFORMATION

Description: All international students who are admitted to the University of Nebraska-Lincoln are evaluated for merit based, Global Scholarships ranging from $3,000-$13,500.

Levels of Study: Undergraduate

Field of Study: All, American History, American Politics, Anthropology, Architecture and Environmental Design, Astronomy, Biomedical Humanities, Biotechnology, Business and Management, Communication Technologies, Communications and Journalism, Earth Science, Engineering, European Studies/EU Studies, Finance, Fine Arts, Food Technologies, Foreign Languages, Government, Horticulture, Human Resource Development, Journalism, Neuroscience, Physical Sciences, Psychology, Religion/Theology, Women's Studies

Nationality: Any Region

Location of Study: University of Nebraska-Lincoln Lincoln, NE

AWARD INFORMATION

Award Type: Scholarship

Average Amount: $3,000-$13,500

Number of Awards: No limit

Award Coverage: Tuition

Award Duration: Scholarships are renewable annually

ELIGIBILITY REQUIREMENTS

- Student must have admission to the University of Nebraska-Lincoln
- Scholarship consideration is based on previous academic achievement

APPLICATION INFORMATION

Award Deadline: Admission deadline

Instructions: Students will be automatically evaluated for merit based scholarships once they are admitted, no additional essays or materials are required for scholarship consideration

CONTACT

University of Nebraska-Lincoln
International Admissions Counselor
Office of Admissions
1410 Q St.
Lincoln, NE 68588
Tel: +1 (402) 472-2023
Fax: +1 (402) 472-0670
Email: admissions@unl.edu
Web: global.unl.edu

University of Nevada, Reno

University of Nevada-Reno, International Student Awards and Scholarships

PROGRAM INFORMATION

Description: Nevada offers international awards for undergraduate students and scholarships for both undergraduate and graduate international students. Selection is based on merit and participation in extracurricular activities.

Levels of Study: Undergraduate, Graduate

Field of Study: All

Nationality: Any Region

Location of Study: University of Nevada-Reno Reno, NV

AWARD INFORMATION

Award Type: Award, Scholarship

Average Amount: $2,000

Number of Awards: 40 awards/scholarships per academic year

Award Coverage: Partial tuition

Award Duration: Academic year

ELIGIBILITY REQUIREMENTS

- Must meet all criteria for admission to the University of Nevada-Reno
- Must submit a completed scholarship application with supporting documentation by the deadline

APPLICATION INFORMATION

Award Deadline: Jun 1

Instructions: Complete the International Student Award application (if undergraduate) and/or International Student Assistance Scholarship, available online at www.unr.edu/oiss under "forms"

CONTACT

University of Nevada, Reno
Office of International Students & Scholars
Fitzgerald Student Services Building
Room 120
Reno, NV 89557-0074
Tel: +1 (775) 784-6874
Fax: +1 (775) 327-5845
Email: international@unr.edu
Web: www.unr.edu/oiss

University of Nevada, Reno
University of Nevada-Reno Graduate Assistantships

PROGRAM INFORMATION

Description: Graduate assistantships are valued at an estimated $33,600 per year and include a monthly stipend, a per-credit grant-in-aid, health insurance, and in-state resident status for tuition purposes. Students would serve as a research assistant or a teaching assistant.

Levels of Study: Graduate

Field of Study: All

Nationality: Any Region

Location of Study: University of Nevada-Reno Reno, NV

AWARD INFORMATION

Award Type: Fellowship, Tuition Reduction

Average Amount: $33,600

Number of Awards: Approx 250

Award Coverage: Much of the cost of tuition, monthly stipend, health insurance, and some fees

Award Duration: 1 to 5 years

ELIGIBILITY REQUIREMENTS

- Must meet all criteria for graduate admission at the University of Nevada, Reno
- Must submit an application for a graduate assistantship by the deadline

APPLICATION INFORMATION

Award Deadline: Varies by department

Instructions: Apply for admission and for graduate assistantship at www.unr.edu/grad/admissions

CONTACT

University of Nevada, Reno
Graduate School
Fitzgerald Student Services Building, Room 225
Reno, NV 89557
Tel: +1 (775) 784-6869
Fax: +1 (775) 784-6064
Email: gradadmissions@unr.edu
Web: www.unr.edu/grad

University of Nevada, Reno
University of Nevada, Reno, Wilter Ocampo Bolivian Student Scholarship

PROGRAM INFORMATION

Description: Wilter Ocampo was an international student from Bolivia who received a BS in Accounting and Computer Information Systems in 1986. He was the Bolivian National Motor Cross Champion for several years before his death in a race on Jun 20, 1999. This partial scholarship pays for a portion of the out-of-state tuition for semester in which the award is given.

Levels of Study: Undergraduate, Graduate

Field of Study: All

Nationality: Bolivia

Location of Study: University of Nevada, Reno Reno, NV

AWARD INFORMATION

Award Type: Scholarship

Average Amount: Varies

Number of Awards: 1

Award Coverage: Partial tuition

ELIGIBILITY REQUIREMENTS

- Must be from Bolivia
- Must have a cumulative GPA of 3.0

APPLICATION INFORMATION

Award Deadline: Apr

CONTACT

University of Nevada, Reno
Office of International Students & Scholars
Fitzgerald Student Services Building, Room 120
Reno, NV 89557-0074
Tel: +1 (775) 784-6874
Fax: +1 (775) 327-5845
Email: international@unr.edu
Web: www.unr.edu/oiss

University of Nevada, Reno
University of Nevada, Reno, Kayoko Okumoto Scholarship

PROGRAM INFORMATION

Description: This partial scholarship is awarded each year to a Japanese undergraduate student pursuing a degree in business or history.

Levels of Study: Undergraduate

Field of Study: Business and Management, History, International Management, Marketing

Nationality: Japan

Location of Study: University of Nevada, Reno Reno, NV

AWARD INFORMATION

Award Type: Scholarship

Average Amount: Varies

Number of Awards: 1 per academic year

Award Coverage: Partial tuition waiver

ELIGIBILITY REQUIREMENTS

- Must be a Japanese undergraduate student pursuing a degree in business or history
- Must have a minimum of 2.75 GPA

APPLICATION INFORMATION

Award Deadline: Apr

Instructions: For more information please visit the website or contact via email

CONTACT

University of Nevada, Reno
Office of International Students & Scholars
Fitzgerald Student Services Building, Room 120
Reno, NV 89557-0074
Tel: +1 (775) 784-6874
Fax: +1 (775) 327-5845
Email: international@unr.edu
Web: www.unr.edu/oiss

University of New Haven
University of New Haven International Student Scholarship (ISS) Program

PROGRAM INFORMATION

Description: The ISS program offers merit scholarships to academically-qualified students who wish to purse their bachelor's studies in the fields of arts, sciences, business, computers, engineering and criminal justice. Scholarships range from $6,000 to $20,000 per year. The ISS program also offers a $10,000 yearly scholarship for graduate students who wish to study engineering and computer science.

Levels of Study: Undergraduate, Graduate

Field of Study: All, Fine Arts

Nationality: Any Region

Location of Study: University of New Haven West Haven, CT

AWARD INFORMATION

Award Type: Scholarship

Average Amount: $6,000-$20,000

ELIGIBILITY REQUIREMENTS

- Must have a minimum GPA of 2.7 out of 4.0 at the time of application
- TOEFL 75 IBT/IELTS 6.0

APPLICATION INFORMATION

Award Deadline: Jun 1 for fall semester, Nov 1 for spring semester

CONTACT

University of New Haven
Senior Director of International Admissions
300 Boston Post Road
West Haven, CT 06516
Tel: +1 (203) 932-7441
Email: gradinternational@newhaven.edu
Web: www.newhaven.edu/admissions/internationaladmissions/11492/

University of New Mexico
University of New Mexico International Amigo Scholarship

PROGRAM INFORMATION

Description: The University of New Mexico welcomes applications from students all over the world who have earned distinguished academic records and have demonstrated English proficiency. At UNM we are proud to claim 1 of the most unique ethnically diverse student bodies among universities anywhere in the US. The University is committed to global engagement and provides a competitive scholarship package to selected international students. Scholarships are available for international students that apply and are admitted within the deadline for application.

Levels of Study: Undergraduate, Graduate, Doctorate, Post Doctorate

Field of Study: All

Nationality: Any Region

Location of Study: The University of New Mexico Albuquerque, NM

AWARD INFORMATION

Award Type: Scholarship
Average Amount: Varies
Number of Awards: 40 per year
Award Coverage: In-state tuition, stipend
Award Duration: 2 years or 4 years

ELIGIBILITY REQUIREMENTS

- Must be admitted to UNM by the deadline
- Must have degree-seeking status
- Must be enrolled full-time and not have other institutional awards
- Must hold non-immigrant visa status (F1 or J1 status and not permanent resident)
- Must have not previously attended or be currently attending UNM; must have a current and complete degree application on file with International Admissions

APPLICATION INFORMATION

Award Deadline: May 1 for fall; Oct 1 for spring
Instructions: No scholarship application is required, all eligible students will be considered for scholarships

CONTACT

The University of New Mexico
International Recruiter
1155 University Blvd. SE
Albuquerque, NM 87106
Email: mcramer@unm.edu
Web: www.unm.edu/admissions/newInternational/undergraduate.html

University of New Mexico
UNM Amigo Scholarship for International Students

PROGRAM INFORMATION

Description: The Amigo Scholarship for International Students entitles outstanding international students to a waiver of non-resident tuition and a cash award of $200 per semester.
Levels of Study: Undergraduate, Graduate, Doctorate
Field of Study: All
Nationality: Any Region
Location of Study: University of New Mexico Albuquerque, NM

AWARD INFORMATION

Award Type: Scholarship
Average Amount: Varies
Number of Awards: Varies
Award Coverage: Tuition reduction, stipend
Award Duration: Varies

ELIGIBILITY REQUIREMENTS

- Must be non-resident with non-immigrant visa status (F1), must be admitted to UNM by deadline, must enroll in full-time degree-bearing program, cannot have other institutional awards, must not be currently attending or have previously attended UNM
- Undergraduates must have secondary school grade point average of 3.5 or higher
- Graduate students must hold bachelor's degree as approved by the Ministry of Education of their home country, must have undergraduate grade point average of 3.5
- Personal essay and letter of recommendation should be included in application

APPLICATION INFORMATION

Award Deadline: Priority Deadline: Jan 1st for fall semester, Aug 1st for the spring semester
Instructions: No separate application is required. All applicants will be considered, apply by Jan 1st (for the upcoming Fall semester) and Aug 1 (for the upcoming Spring semester) for best consideration as scholarships are limited in number

CONTACT

University of New Mexico
Global Education Office (GEO)
1 University of New Mexico, MSC06 3850
2120 Mesa Vista Hall
Albuquerque, NM 87131-0001
Tel: +1 (505) 277-5829
Fax: +1 (505) 277-1867
Email: goglobal@unm.edu
Web: geo.unm.edu/admission.html

University of North Dakota
University of North Dakota Undergraduate Tuition Scholarships for International Students

PROGRAM INFORMATION

Description: The University of North Dakota offers 3 tuition scholarships for undergraduate international degree-seeking students. Scholarship #1: $3,000 first-year scholarships. Scholarship #2: Up to $17,056 second, third, and fourth year scholarships. Scholarship #3: Up to $12,000 SAT/ACT scholarships spread over 4 years.
Levels of Study: Undergraduate
Field of Study: All
Nationality: Any Region
Location of Study: University of North Dakota Grand Forks, ND

AWARD INFORMATION

Award Type: Tuition Reduction
Average Amount: $3,000-$17,056
Award Coverage: Tuition
Award Duration: Maximum of 4 years

ELIGIBILITY REQUIREMENTS

- Must have an F-1 student visa in valid standing with the Department of Homeland Security
- Must not have earned a baccalaureate degree
- Scholarship #1: For full-time, undergraduate degree-seeking international students, first 2 semesters on campus only; must maintain 2.50 GPA and participate in campus service activities; must be billed at full, non-resident tuition rate
- Scholarship #2: Eligible after 2 semesters at UND; demonstrated academic success (minimum cumulative GPA of 2.75), demonstrated active service to UND community; application deadline Apr 1
- Scholarship #3: Must be admitted to UND by Feb 5; in top 10 percent of high school class; must have minimum combined SAT scores (Math + Critical Reading) of 1090 or minimum ACT score of 24 at time of admission

APPLICATION INFORMATION

Award Deadline: Varies
Instructions: More information is available at the website; for Scholarship No. 1, please print and submit a paper copy; for Scholarship No. 2, apply online; for Scholarship No. 3, submit SAT or ACT test scores and proof of class ranking at time of application for admission to UND

CONTACT

University of North Dakota
Director of International Programs
International Centre
2908 University Avenue Stop 7109
Grand Forks, ND 58202-7109
Tel: +1 (701) 777-2938
Fax: +1 (701) 777-4773
Email: raymond.lagasse@und.edu
Web: www.und.edu/academics/international-programs/prospective-international-students.cfm

University of North Texas
University of North Texas Scholarships for International Students

PROGRAM INFORMATION

Description: A variety of scholarships, research and teaching assistantships are available. International students receiving any SFAS Academic Scholarship with an amount of at least $1,000 for the academic year would have their out of state tuition waived.
Levels of Study: Undergraduate, Graduate, Doctorate
Nationality: Any Region
Location of Study: University of North Texas Denton, TX

AWARD INFORMATION

Award Type: Fellowship, Scholarship, Tuition Reduction
Average Amount: $1000-$10,000
Number of Awards: Multiple Awards
Award Coverage: Varies.
Award Duration: Students can apply every year

ELIGIBILITY REQUIREMENTS

- Students must be admitted into the University of North Texas to apply for scholarship opportunities
- General Academic Scholarships: in order to be considered for these scholarships, students must complete the General Scholarship Application annually
- UNT Excellence Scholarships: entering freshmen must provide high school rank and SAT/ACT test scores are used to determine UNT Excellence Scholarship award amounts
- UNT Texas Transfer Scholarship: students must be transferring at least 45 credit hours from a Texas community/junior college or Texas University and have at least a 3.5 cumulative GPA
- Departmental Scholarships: students can find out more information on those scholarships by visiting their college, department or school in which they plan to major

APPLICATION INFORMATION

Award Deadline: Most scholarship deadlines are Mar 1st for the next academic year

CONTACT

University of North Texas
Student Financial Aid and Scholarships
1155 Union Circle #311370
Denton, TX 76203-5017
USA
Tel: 940-369-7624
Email: studyatunt@unt.edu
Web: financialaid.unt.edu/scholarships-international-students

University of Northern Iowa

University of Northern Iowa International Undergraduate Scholarships/Graduate Assistantships

PROGRAM INFORMATION

Description: The University of Northern Iowa is a comprehensive public liberal arts institution with over 12,000 students from 43 US states and 60 countries. UNI offers bachelor, masters and doctoral degrees as well as an Intensive English program. International undergraduate students may qualify for merit-based scholarships. Assistantships are available for graduate students.

Levels of Study: Undergraduate, Graduate, Doctorate

Field of Study: All

Nationality: Any Region

Location of Study: University of Northern Iowa Cedar Falls, IA

AWARD INFORMATION

Award Type: Scholarship, Tuition Reduction

Average Amount: Varies

Number of Awards: Varies

Award Coverage: Partial tuition for undergraduates; up to full cost of tuition, fees, living expenses for graduate students

Award Duration: Duration of study

ELIGIBILITY REQUIREMENTS

- Must be an incoming freshman or transfer student and meet all academic requirements for admission plus examples of leadership and service
- For graduate students, admission and reward requirements are determined by each individual department

APPLICATION INFORMATION

Award Deadline: Undergraduate, rolling; graduate, Feb 1

Instructions: Please submit your international admission application and required admission documents via the website, Graduate students need to submit additional applications at the designated page on the website

CONTACT

University of Northern Iowa
Assistant Director of Admissions/International
002 Gilchrist Hall
Cedar Falls, IA 50614-0164
Tel: +1 (319) 273-2281
Fax: +1 (319) 273-2885
Email: kristi.Maresani@uni.edu
Web: www.uni.edu/intladm

University of Notre Dame, Kellogg Institute

Notre Dame - Kellogg Visiting Fellowships

PROGRAM INFORMATION

Description: Kellogg Visiting Fellows have the opportunity to pursue research in comparative international studies within a highly supportive and stimulating community of peers. Each year the Kellogg Institute for International Studies offers 1-semester research fellowships, as well as a few academic-year fellowships with teaching and research responsibilities.

Levels of Study: Post Doctorate

Field of Study: Democracy, International Relations, Public Policy, Religion/Theology, Social Justice, Social Movements

Nationality: Any Region

Location of Study: University of Notre Dame Notre Dame, IN

AWARD INFORMATION

Award Type: Fellowship

Average Amount: Varies

Number of Awards: 10-12

Award Coverage: Living stipend, travel, materials

Award Duration: 1-2 semesters

ELIGIBILITY REQUIREMENTS

- Must hold a PhD or equivalent degree in a social science discipline or in history prior to commencement of fellowship

APPLICATION INFORMATION

Award Deadline: Nov

Instructions: Apply online or download application materials on website

CONTACT

University of Notre Dame
Kellogg Institute for International Studies
130 Hesbergh Center
Notre Dame, IN 46556
Tel: +1 (574) 631-6580
Fax: +1 (574) 631-6717
Email: kellogg@nd.edu
Web: kellogg.nd.edu/vfellowships

University of Oregon

University of Oregon International Cultural Service Program (ICSP) Tuition Scholarships

PROGRAM INFORMATION

Description: Tuition waiver scholarships are available to new and current international students with financial need. This scholarship includes a cultural service component which requires a minimum of 80 hours of presentations about your home country and culture to schools, community organizations, and at on-campus events.

Levels of Study: Undergraduate, Graduate, Doctorate

Field of Study: All

Nationality: Any Region

Location of Study: University of Oregon Eugene, OR

AWARD INFORMATION

Award Type: Scholarship

Average Amount: $9,00-$27,000

Number of Awards: 10-20

Award Coverage: Tuition

Award Duration: Each academic year for duration of 1 degree

ELIGIBILITY REQUIREMENTS

- Must have a minimum GPA of 3.0
- Current UO international students must be enrolled in a full-time course of study with a nonimmigrant visa (F-1 or J-1)
- New UO international students must apply for admission to UO by Jan 15th in addition to submitting a scholarship application by Jan 15th
- Must demonstrate financial need

APPLICATION INFORMATION

Award Deadline: Jan 15

Instructions: Apply online at: international.uoregon.edu/isss/scholarships

CONTACT

University or Oregon
Office of International Affairs
333 Oregon Hall
5209 University of Oregon
Eugene, OR 97403
Tel: +1 (541) 346-3206
Fax: +1 (541) 346-1232
Email: issa@uoregon.edu
Web: international.uoregon.edu/isss/scholarships

University of Oregon

University of Oregon International Affairs Endowed Scholarships

PROGRAM INFORMATION

Description: International affairs grants 15-20 competitive cash-based scholarships each year to new and continuing University of Oregon international students who demonstrate financial need and academic merit.

Levels of Study: Undergraduate, Graduate, Doctorate

Field of Study: All

Nationality: Any Region

Location of Study: University of Oregon Eugene, OR

AWARD INFORMATION

Award Type: Scholarship

Average Amount: $800-$10,000

Number of Awards: 15-20 per academic year

Award Coverage: Varies

Award Duration: 1 academic year

ELIGIBILITY REQUIREMENTS

- Applicants may be new or current University of Oregon international students and must apply by the Jan 15th deadline
- New UO international students must apply for admission to UO by Jan 15th in addition to submitting a scholarship application by Jan 15th
- Current students must be enrolled in a full-time course of study at the UO with a nonimmigrant visa (F-1 or J-1) and have a minimum grade point average of 3.0
- Must demonstrate evidence of academic merit
- Must demonstrate evidence of financial need

APPLICATION INFORMATION

Award Deadline: Jan

Instructions: Visit website to apply

CONTACT

University of Oregon
Office of International Affairs
333 Oregon Hall
5209 University of Oregon
Eugene, OR 97403
Tel: +1 (541) 346-3206
Fax: +1 (541) 346-1232
Email: issa@uoregon.edu
Web: international.uoregon.edu/isss/scholarships

University of Oregon

University of Oregon International Dean's Excellence Award (IDEA)

PROGRAM INFORMATION

Description: The International Dean's Achievement Award (IDEA) is a merit-based, partial-tuition scholarship awarded to new international undergraduate applicants. An application is not required for consideration for the award.

Levels of Study: Undergraduate

Field of Study: All

Nationality: Any Region

Location of Study: University of Oregon Eugene, OR

AWARD INFORMATION

Award Type: Tuition Reduction

Average Amount: $6,000-$8,000

Award Coverage: Tuition

Award Duration: Academic year, renewable for 4 years

ELIGIBILITY REQUIREMENTS

- The scholarship is awarded based on academic merit
- Must be a new undergraduate applicant entering in the fall (Sep)

APPLICATION INFORMATION

Award Deadline: Feb

Instructions: Student must apply for admission by the priority application deadline; IDEA award recipients are selected by international affairs on the basis of official academic records submitted with the University of Oregon admissions application, visit our website for further information

CONTACT

University of Oregon
Office of International Affairs
333 Oregon Hall
5209 University of Oregon
Eugene, OR 97403
Tel: +1 (541) 346-3201
Fax: +1 (541) 346-1232
Email: intl@uoregon.edu
Web: admissions.uoregon.edu/international/index.html

University of Oregon

University of Oregon International Work Study Program

PROGRAM INFORMATION

Description: University of Oregon grants more than 50 work-study awards, ranging from $500–$3,000 each year, to eligible international students with financial need. Students who receive these awards can compete for on-campus work-study jobs during the academic year. Students are not guaranteed on-campus jobs, but opportunities for on-campus employment will increase.

Levels of Study: Undergraduate, Graduate, Doctorate

Field of Study: All

Nationality: Any Region

Location of Study: University of Oregon Eugene, OR

AWARD INFORMATION

Award Type: Award

Average Amount: $500-$3,000

Number of Awards: 80-100

Award Coverage: Possible on-campus employment

Award Duration: Academic year, renewable for 4 years

ELIGIBILITY REQUIREMENTS

- New and continuing international students with financial need may apply

APPLICATION INFORMATION

Award Deadline: Apr 15

Instructions: Complete the International Work Study Application, visit our website to apply

CONTACT

University of Oregon
Office of International Affairs
333 Oregon Hall
5209 University of Oregon
Eugene, OR 97403
Tel: +1 (541) 346-3206
Fax: +1 (541) 346-1232
Email: issa@uoregon.edu
Web: international.uoregon.edu/isss/scholarships

University of Pennsylvania

UPenn Thouron Awards for Postgraduate Study

PROGRAM INFORMATION

Description: The Thouron-University of Pennsylvania Fund for British-American Student Exchange exists for the promotion of better understanding and closer friendship between the people of the United Kingdom and the US. The Thouron Award provides support for British recipients to attend any of the graduate and professional schools of the University of Pennsylvania.

Levels of Study: Graduate

Field of Study: All

Nationality: United Kingdom

Location of Study: University of Pennsylvania Philadelphia, PA

AWARD INFORMATION

Award Type: Scholarship

Average Amount: $80,000

Number of Awards: Up to 10

Award Coverage: Tuition, living stipend, travel

Award Duration: 1-2 years depending on length of degree program

ELIGIBILITY REQUIREMENTS

- Must be British citizens normally residing in the UK
- Must have received a UK secondary school education in the UK
- Must be a graduate of a UK university or due to graduate in the summer preceding entry to the University of Pennsylvania
- Must wish to pursue a full-time postgraduate program that is wholly located at the University of Pennsylvania and leads toward a graduate degree
- The majority of graduate programs require GRE or GMAT scores to be submitted

APPLICATION INFORMATION

Award Deadline: Nov

Instructions: Applicants must complete application materials for Thouron Awards in addition to an application for admission to a graduate program at the University of Pennsylvania; admissions application deadlines vary by program, but the scholarship application deadline will be fixed

CONTACT

5.24 Waterloo Bridge Wing, Franklin-Wilkins Building
Research & Graduate School Support
Stamford Street, London SE1 9NH, United Kingdom
Tel: +44 (0) 2078-483376
Fax: +44 (0) 2078-483328
Email: jennie.eldridge@kcl.ac.uk
Web: www.thouronaward.org

University of Pennsylvania: Graduate School of Education

University of Pennsylvania
PhD Fellowships

PROGRAM INFORMATION

Description: GSE seeks students who are interested in promoting a deeper understanding of educational issues and contributing to societal change. The curriculum places a strong emphasis on the interactive relationship of theory, research, and practice, often focusing on urban education. Students engage in extensive fieldwork throughout their studies and are both learners and agents of change within the university and the surrounding Philadelphia neighborhoods. Areas of study include: Interdisciplinary Studies in Human Development; Education, Culture, & Society; Educational Linguistics; Education Policy; Higher Education; Quantitative Methods; Reading/Writing/Literacy; Teaching, Learning, and Teacher Education.

Levels of Study: Doctorate

Field of Study: Education, Linguistics, Policy Research

Nationality: Any Region

Location of Study: University of Pennsylvania Philadelphia, PA

AWARD INFORMATION

Award Type: Fellowship

Average Amount: Full tuition & fees, health insurance, living stipend.

Number of Awards: All PhD students

Award Coverage: Full tuition & fees, health insurance, and a living stipend

Award Duration: 4 years guaranteed

ELIGIBILITY REQUIREMENTS

- All applicants to our PhD programs are eligible to receive the Dean's Fellowship

APPLICATION INFORMATION

Award Deadline: Dec 15

Instructions: Students must complete their admissions application by Dec 15 to be considered for admission to a PhD program, all admitted PhD students are awarded a Dean's Fellowship

CONTACT

University of Pennsylvania
Graduate School of Education
3700 Walnut Street
Philadelphia, PA 19104
Tel: +1 (215) 898-6415
Fax: +1 (215) 746-6884
Email: finaid@gse.upenn.edu
Web: www.gse.upenn.edu

University of Pittsburgh

University of Pittsburg
Graduate Assistantships

PROGRAM INFORMATION

Description: A wide variety of graduate appointments for teaching and research are available to support masters and doctoral study in all offered disciplines.

Levels of Study: Graduate, Doctorate, Post Doctorate, Professional

Nationality: Any Region

AWARD INFORMATION

Award Type: Fellowship

Average Amount: Varies

Number of Awards: Varies by discipline and program

Award Coverage: Tuition waiver plus annual stipend

Award Duration: Varies

ELIGIBILITY REQUIREMENTS

- Must gain admission to graduate study
- Pending application for financial aid (graduate appointment)

APPLICATION INFORMATION

Award Deadline: Dec

Instructions: Please visit the website for application information

CONTACT

University of Pittsburgh
Office of the Provost
801 Cathedral of Learning
Pittsburgh, PA 15260
Email: graduate@pitt.edu
Web: www.pitt.edu/academics.html

University of Richmond

University of Richmond Scholars

PROGRAM INFORMATION

Description: The University of Richmond awards 50 full tuition scholarships to 50 exceptional first year students each year. The scholarship recognizes engaged scholarship and leadership.

Levels of Study: Undergraduate

Field of Study: All

Nationality: Any Region

Location of Study: University of Richmond Richmond, VA

AWARD INFORMATION

Award Type: Scholarship

Average Amount: $47,100

Number of Awards: 50

Award Coverage: Full tuition

Award Duration: Maximum of 4 years

ELIGIBILITY REQUIREMENTS

- Must have a strong "A" grade average in a rigorous secondary school curriculum
- Must have competitive SAT scores for first-year applicants

APPLICATION INFORMATION

Award Deadline: Dec

Instructions: Submit undergraduate application for admission to the University of Richmond and submit the required essay

CONTACT

University of Richmond
Senior Associate Director
28 Westhampton Way
Richmond, VA 23173
Tel: +1 (804) 289-8640
Fax: +1 (804) 287-6535
Email: intladm@richmond.edu
Web: www.richmond.edu/RichmondScholars

University of Rochester

University of Rochester Scholarship Program for Syrian Students

PROGRAM INFORMATION

Description: The University of Rochester is offering Syrian students impacted by the unfortunate circumstances in Syria an opportunity to apply for a scholarship to study at the College of Arts, Sciences and Engineering. For undergraduate students, the scholarship for Syrian students will cover tuition and room and board fees. For graduate students, the scholarship for Syrian students will cover full tuition and fees.

Levels of Study: Undergraduate, Graduate

Field of Study: All

Nationality: Syria

Location of Study: University of Rochester Rochester, NY

AWARD INFORMATION

Award Type: Scholarship

Average Amount: $46,000-$59,000

Number of Awards: 1-3

Award Coverage: Tuition, fees, room and board

Award Duration: 1 year, renewable

ELIGIBILITY REQUIREMENTS

- Minimum TOEFL: 600 PBT/100 IBT; minimum IELTS: 7.0

APPLICATION INFORMATION

Award Deadline: Mar 15

Instructions: To qualify, students will be required to apply to the University of Rochester, students must complete the Common Application or Universal College Application by Jan 5

CONTACT

University of Rochester
Admissions Office
500 Joseph C. Wilson Blvd.
PO BOX 270251
Rochester, NY 14627, US
Tel: +1 (585) 275-3221
Fax: +1 (585) 461-4595
Email: admit@admissions.rochester.edu
Web: www.rochester.edu

University of Rochester

University of Rochester International Baccalaureate Scholarship

PROGRAM INFORMATION

Description: The IB Scholarship is awarded to students who have excelled in 1 of the most rigorous college preparatory programs available. Your preparation through the IB Diploma Program makes you an ideal candidate to take advantage of the learning environment that makes the University of Rochester so unique. This award is an acknowledgment of your hard work and determination.

Levels of Study: Undergraduate

Field of Study: All

Nationality: Any Region

Location of Study: University of Rochester
Rochester, NY

AWARD INFORMATION

Award Type: Scholarship

Average Amount: $10,000-$15,000

Number of Awards: 25

Award Coverage: Partial tuition

Award Duration: Renewable all 4 years of undergrad study

ELIGIBILITY REQUIREMENTS

- Recipients must complete the full International Baccalaureate Diploma.

APPLICATION INFORMATION

Award Deadline: Jan 5

Instructions: To qualify, students will be required to apply to the University of Rochester, students must complete the Common Application or Universal College Application by Jan 5

CONTACT

University of Rochester
Admissions Office
PO Box 270251
Rochester, NY 14627
Tel: +1(585) 275-3221
Fax: +1 (585) 461-4595
Email: admit@admissions.rochester.edu
Web: www.enrollment.rochester.edu

University of Rochester

University of Rochester Renaissance & Global Scholarship

PROGRAM INFORMATION

Description: Renaissance & Global Scholars are an exceptional group of more than 100 students who come to Rochester from across the US and all around the world. Not only are they academic all-stars, but they also have unique backgrounds that add to the diversity of our student body and extraordinary life experiences that enhance the classes in which they are enrolled.

Levels of Study: Undergraduate

Field of Study: All

Nationality: Any Region

Location of Study: University of Rochester
Rochester, NY

AWARD INFORMATION

Award Type: Scholarship

Number of Awards: 20

Award Coverage: Full tuition

Award Duration: 4 years

APPLICATION INFORMATION

Award Deadline: Jan 5

Instructions: To qualify, students will be required to apply to the University of Rochester, students must complete the Common Application or Universal College Application by Jan 5

CONTACT

University of Rochester
Admissions Office
PO Box 270251
Rochester, NY 14627
Tel: +1 (585) 275-3221
Email: admit@admissions.rochester.edu
Web: www.enrollment.rochester.edu

University of Rochester

Davis United World College Scholars Program

PROGRAM INFORMATION

Description: Davis United World College (UWC) Scholars are exceptional young people who have graduated from a UWC school and then matriculate at selected US colleges or universities. The UWC experience—which brings students from around the world to live and learn together in 1 of 14 locations on 5 continents—has challenged them academically and personally, expanded their horizons exponentially, and shown them how to build understanding from diversity. Once UWC graduates enroll in 1 of our partner US colleges or universities, our program provides financial support for their college educations through institutional grants that support need-based scholarships for Davis UWC Scholars.

Levels of Study: Undergraduate

Field of Study: All

Nationality: Armenia, Bosnia & Herzegovina, Canada, Costa Rica, Germany, Hong Kong, India, Italy, Netherlands, Norway, Singapore, Swaziland, United Kingdom, US

Location of Study: University of Rochester
Rochester, NY

AWARD INFORMATION

Award Type: Scholarship

Average Amount: Fully funded by the University of Rochester

Number of Awards: 1+

Award Coverage: Tuition

Award Duration: All 4 years of study

ELIGIBILITY REQUIREMENTS

- Must graduate from 1 of the following schools to qualify: Waterford Kamhlaba UWC, Mbabane, Swaziland; Li Po Chun UWC, Hong Kong SAR, China; UWC Mahindra College Pune, India; UWC South East Asia, Singapore; UWC Adriatic Duino, Italy
- Must graduate from 1 of the following schools to qualify: UWC Mostar, Bosnia and Herzegovina; UWC Red Cross, Nordic Flekke, Norway; Pearson College UWC, Victoria, Canada; UWC-USA Montezuma, New Mexico, USA; UWC Costa Rica, Santa Ana, Costa Rica
- Must graduate from 1 of the following schools to qualify: UWC Robert Bosch College Freiburg, Germany, or UWC Dilijan Dilijan, Armenia; UWC Atlantic College Llantwit Major, UK; UWC Maastricht, Maastricht, the Netherlands

APPLICATION INFORMATION

Award Deadline: Jan 5

Instructions: To qualify, students will be required to apply to the University of Rochester; students must complete the Common Application or the Universal College Application by Jan 5; please see the Common Application at www.commonapp.org or the Universal College Application at www.universalcollegeapp.com for details; for general information about applying to the University, please visit the following website: www.enrollment.rochester.edu

CONTACT

University of Rochester
Admissions Office
PO Box 270251
Rochester, NY 14627
Tel: +1 (585) 275-3221
Email: admit@admissions.rochester.edu
Web: www.davisuwcscholars.org

University of Rochester

Hong Kong Schools Alumni Federation/Evans Lam Scholarship

PROGRAM INFORMATION

Description: This scholarship will be used to support Hong Kong students with high need and exceptional talent, for their long-term career and research ambitions.

Levels of Study: Undergraduate

Field of Study: All

Nationality: Hong Kong

Location of Study: University of Rochester
Rochester, NY

AWARD INFORMATION

Award Type: Scholarship

Average Amount: Full funding

Number of Awards: 5

Award Coverage: 5 exceptional students with demonstrated financial need matriculating in arts, sciences & engineering from a Hong Kong high school will receive full funding for a 4-year education at the University of Rochester

Award Duration: All 4 years

ELIGIBILITY REQUIREMENTS

- Must graduate from a Hong Kong high school to receive scholarship

APPLICATION INFORMATION

Award Deadline: Jan

Instructions: To qualify, students will be required to apply to the University of Rochester, students must complete the Common Application or Universal College Application by Jan 5

CONTACT

University of Rochester
Admissions Office
PO Box 270251
Rochester, NY 14627
Tel: +1(585) 275-3221
Email: Admit@admissions.rochester.edu
Web: www.enrollment.rochester.edu

University of Rochester
The Hope Fund

PROGRAM INFORMATION

Description: Founded in 2000, the Hope Fund secures and coordinates scholarships from US colleges for talented and driven Palestinian youth, predominantly from refugee camps in the Arab world for whom a higher education would otherwise be unattainable. We endeavor to enrich the lives of young people, creating hope out of despair while fostering familiarity and understanding between the 2 different cultures.

Levels of Study: Undergraduate

Field of Study: All

Nationality: Jordan, Lebanon, Palestinian Authority, Syria

Location of Study: University of Rochester Rochester, NY

AWARD INFORMATION

Award Type: Scholarship

Average Amount: Full tuition

Number of Awards: 1-2 per year

Award Coverage: Full tuition and other expenses

Award Duration: Covers all 4 years

ELIGIBILITY REQUIREMENTS

- Please visit the following link for more information: www.thehopefund.org

APPLICATION INFORMATION

Award Deadline: Jan

Instructions: To qualify, students will be required to apply to the University of Rochester, students must complete the Common Application or Universal College Application by Jan 5

CONTACT

The Hope Fund
752 Forge Road
Lexington, VA 24450
Tel: +1 (540) 319-4077
Email: applications@thehopefund.org
Web: www.thehopefund.org

University of Rochester
AHORA Scholarship

PROGRAM INFORMATION

Description: AHORA scholarship recipients are academically excellent students from Latin America and the Caribbean who will bring unique experiences and perspectives to our campus community.

Levels of Study: Undergraduate

Field of Study: All

Nationality: Latin America

Location of Study: University of Rochester Rochester, NY

AWARD INFORMATION

Award Type: Scholarship

Average Amount: $8,000 - $12,000

Number of Awards: 10

Award Coverage: Partial tuition

Award Duration: 4 years

ELIGIBILITY REQUIREMENTS

- Recipients of the AHORA Scholarship must graduate from a secondary school located in Latin America or the Caribbean

APPLICATION INFORMATION

Award Deadline: Jan 5

Instructions: To qualify, students will be required to apply to the University of Rochester, students must complete the Common Application or Universal College Application by Jan 5

CONTACT

University of Rochester
Admissions Office
PO Box 270251
Rochester, NY 14627
Tel: +1 (585) 275-3221
Fax: +1 (585) 461-4595
Email: admit@admissions.rochester.edu
Web: enrollment.rochester.edu

University of Rochester
Sutton Trust US Programme

PROGRAM INFORMATION

Description: The aim of the US Programme is to identify the UK's most talented state school students and to provide them with the opportunity to experience US culture and higher education first hand. Those interested in applying for a full undergraduate degree in the States receive guidance from the Fulbright staff and a volunteer mentor during the admissions cycle. The programme is committed to ensuring that the cost of applying to American universities is not a barrier to their interest in US higher education and also provides students with free books and resources, test prep, waivers for admissions test fees and covers travel and accommodation costs for an application "boot camp" in London.

Levels of Study: Undergraduate

Field of Study: All

Nationality: United Kingdom

Location of Study: University of Rochester Rochester, NY

AWARD INFORMATION

Award Type: Award, Grant, Scholarship

Average Amount: Meets full demonstrated need

Number of Awards: 2-5

Award Coverage: Recipients will have their demonstrated need (as determined by the CSS PROFILE) met through scholarships, grants, on-campus employment

Award Duration: 4 years

ELIGIBILITY REQUIREMENTS

- Recipients must be a Citizen of the UK with significant financial need, will have completed secondary school level studies, apply through the Sutton Trust US Programme

APPLICATION INFORMATION

Award Deadline: Jan 5

Instructions: To qualify, students will be required to apply to the University of Rochester. Students must complete the Common Application or Universal College Application by Jan 5

CONTACT

University of Rochester
Admissions Office
PO Box 270251
Rochester, NY14627
Tel: +1 (585) 275-3221
Fax: +1 (585) 461-4595
Email: admit@admissions.rochester.edu
Web: www.suttontrust.com

University of San Diego School of Law
University of San Diego School of Law Merit Scholarship

PROGRAM INFORMATION

Description: The University of San Diego School of Law awards merit scholarships to full-time students admitted to the LLM in Comparative Law program, based on the merits of the applicant's scholastic and professional experience. Applicants accepted to the LLM program at the School of Law are automatically considered for a Merit Scholarship award.

Levels of Study: Graduate

Field of Study: Business Law, Comparative Law, Corporate Law, International Law, Law, Tax Law

Nationality: Any Region

Location of Study: University of San Diego School of Law San Diego, CA

AWARD INFORMATION

Award Type: Scholarship

Average Amount: $6,000-$15,000

Number of Awards: Varies

Award Coverage: Partial tuition

Award Duration: Academic year

ELIGIBILITY REQUIREMENTS

- Must have a minimum TOEFL score of 93 IBT or minimum IELTS score of 7.0
- Must have a degree in law

APPLICATION INFORMATION

Award Deadline: Jun

Instructions: Full time applicants accepted to an LLM program at the University of San Diego School of Law are automatically considered for a Merit Scholarship award, no additional scholarship application is necessary

CONTACT

University of San Diego School of Law
Assistant Director, Graduate and International Programs
5998 Alcala Park
Warren Hall, Room 207
San Diego, CA 92110
Tel: +1 (619) 260-4596
Fax: +1 (619) 260-4515
Email: llminfo@sandiego.edu
Web: www.sandiego.edu/law/grad

University of Scranton

University of Scranton Pakistani Student Scholarship

PROGRAM INFORMATION

Description: At present, the program provides financial assistance to the students from Pakistan and Bangladesh who want to pursue graduate study in business administration (MBA) or health administration (MHA). It is expected that the program will provide financial aid in any area of study.

Levels of Study: Graduate

Field of Study: All, Accounting, Business and Management, Business Law, Chemistry, Computer and Information Sciences, Computer Science, Economics, Finance, Health Studies, Information Technology, Marketing, Master of Business Administration (MBA)

Nationality: Bangladesh, Pakistan

Location of Study: University of Scranton Scranton, PA

AWARD INFORMATION

Award Type: Scholarship

Average Amount: $11,056

Number of Awards: Several

Award Coverage: 12 credit hours + $100. Coverage of housing costs is also possible

Award Duration: Varies

ELIGIBILITY REQUIREMENTS

- Must be an entering student from Pakistan or Bangladesh who is not a permanent resident of US
- Must enroll in the on-campus MBA or MHA program at the University
- For MBA: should have a score of at least 550 in GMAT
- For MHA: should have MBBS degree from a recognized medical college in Pakistan or Bangladesh
- Must show a commitment to help others

APPLICATION INFORMATION

Award Deadline: Varies

Instructions: Visit our website for more information: www.scranton.edu/faculty/hussai.

CONTACT

University of Scranton
Department of Economics/Finance
800 Linden Street
Scranton, PA 18510
Tel: +1 (570) 347-8077
Email: hussain@scranton.edu
Web: www.scranton.edu

University of South Carolina Upstate

USC Upstate Undergraduate Academic Scholarship

PROGRAM INFORMATION

Description: USC Upstate is proud to be home to many international students from over 71 nations. Scholarships are available to new international students based on academic merit.

Levels of Study: Undergraduate

Field of Study: All

Nationality: Any Region

Location of Study: University of South Carolina Upstate Spartanburg, SC

AWARD INFORMATION

Award Type: Scholarship

Average Amount: Varies

Number of Awards: 8-10

Award Coverage: Partial tuition

Award Duration: Academic year, renewable for up to 4 years

ELIGIBILITY REQUIREMENTS

- Must have a minimum combined SAT score of 1000
- Must have a minimum TOEFL score of 173 CBT

APPLICATION INFORMATION

Award Deadline: May

Instructions: Apply online

CONTACT

University of South Carolina Upstate
Office of Financial Aid
800 University Way
Health Education Complex, Suite 2081
Spartanburg, SC 29303
Tel: +1 (864) 503-5340
Fax: +1 (864) 503-5974
Email: finaid@uscupstate.edu
Web: www.uscupstate.edu

University of South Carolina, The Darla Moore School of Business

Moore School of Business
IMBA Fellowships

PROGRAM INFORMATION

Description: The Moore School of Business International MBA (IMBA) is a comprehensive full-time master's program with a global focus. The program prepares students for today's competitive business world through a blend of academic and real-world experience. In addition to an internationalized core curriculum, students gain practical experience during a required 4- to 6-month internship with a global company, typically overseas.

Levels of Study: Graduate

Field of Study: International Management, Master of Business Administration (MBA)

Nationality: Any Region

Location of Study: University of South Carolina
Columbia, SC

AWARD INFORMATION

Award Type: Fellowship, Scholarship

Average Amount: $2,000-$52,000

Number of Awards: Varies

Award Duration: Length of program

ELIGIBILITY REQUIREMENTS

- Must be an incoming International IMBA student with outstanding academic and/or professional accomplishments
- Selection criteria include leadership potential based on community service and extracurricular activities, GMAT scores, academic background, work experience

APPLICATION INFORMATION

Instructions: Please visit our website for instructions

CONTACT

University of South Carolina
Assistant Director of Recruitment
1705 College Street
Columbia, SC 29208
Tel: +1 (803) 777-7903
Email: jeff@moore.sc.edu
Web: www.moore.sc.edu/academicprograms/internationalmba.aspx

University of South Florida

University of South Florida
Undergraduate Admissions
Freshman Scholarships

PROGRAM INFORMATION

Description: The Office of Undergraduate Admissions at USF offers a number of competitive, merit-based awards to freshmen international students entering USF for the first time in the summer or fall semester. Award amounts range from $500 up to 100 percent tuition. The criteria noted for the various scholarships are used as minimum starting points for consideration; meeting or exceeding the minimum requirements will not guarantee selection.

Levels of Study: Undergraduate

Field of Study: All

Nationality: Any Region

Location of Study: University of South Florida
Tampa, FL

AWARD INFORMATION

Award Type: Scholarship

Average Amount: $500 to full tuition

Number of Awards: Varies

Award Coverage: Educational expenses

Award Duration: Up to 4 years, renewable as long as academic requirements are met

ELIGIBILITY REQUIREMENTS

- Must be a freshman (first time in college) planning to enter USF for the first time in the summer or fall semester
- Must complete the undergraduate admissions application to USF by the priority date of Jan 2
- Must meet minimum GPA and SAT/ACT requirements for consideration; see individual scholarship criteria for additional requirements, meeting or exceeding the minimum requirements will not guarantee selection
- Must submit appropriate immigration documents to support residency (in-state or out-of-state) classification

APPLICATION INFORMATION

Award Deadline: Jan

Instructions: For a list of scholarships and the minimum GPA and SAT/ACT requirements, please visit our website

CONTACT

University of South Florida
International Admissions
4202 E. Fowler Ave, SVC 1036
Tampa, FL 33620-6900
Tel: +1 (813) 974-3350
Fax: +1 (813) 974-9689
Email: scholarship@admin.usf.edu
Web: usfweb2.usf.edu/admissions/scholarships

University of South Florida

University of South Florida
Undergraduate Admissions
Transfer Scholarships

PROGRAM INFORMATION

Description: The office of undergraduate admissions at USF offers a number of competitive, merit-based awards to upper-division (at least 60 transferable credit hours) international transfer students entering USF for the first time in the fall or spring semester. The criteria noted for the various scholarships are used as minimum starting points for consideration; meeting or exceeding the minimum requirements will not guarantee selection.

Levels of Study: Undergraduate

Field of Study: All

Nationality: Any Region

Location of Study: University of South Florida
Tampa, FL

AWARD INFORMATION

Award Type: Scholarship

Average Amount: $1,000-$5,000

Number of Awards: Varies

Award Coverage: Educational expenses

Award Duration: 2 years, renewable as long as academic requirements are met

ELIGIBILITY REQUIREMENTS

- Must be an upper-division transfer student (at least 60 transferable credit hours or an AA degree from a Florida public community college) planning to enter USF for the first time in the fall or spring semester
- Must complete the undergraduate admissions application and be accepted to USF by the priority date
- Must meet the minimum GPA requirements for consideration; see individual scholarship criteria for additional requirements.
- Must submit appropriate immigration documents to support residency (in-state or out-of-state) classification
- Awards are renewable for up to 2 years of undergraduate coursework as long as the recipient maintains the scholarship renewal criteria outlined in the terms & conditions

APPLICATION INFORMATION

Award Deadline: Summer/fall: Mar 1; spring: Oct 1

Instructions: For a list of scholarships and minimum requirements, please visit our website.

CONTACT

University of South Florida
International Admissions
4202 E. Fowler Ave, SVC 1036
Tampa, FL 33620-6900
Tel: +1 (813) 974-3350
Fax: +1 (813) 974-9689
Email: scholarship@admin.usf.edu
Web: usfweb2.usf.edu/admissions/scholarships/

University of Southern California - Viterbi School of Engineering
Viterbi School of Engineering

PROGRAM INFORMATION

Description: The USC Viterbi School of Engineering's graduate program is ranked among the top 10 in the nation by US News and World Report. The school has over 30 faculty members elected to the National Academy of Engineering; over 60 who have earned Presidential Early Career, Presidential Young Investigator or NSF/NIH Young Investigator awards, and more than a third of its 169 faculty members are fellows in their respective professional societies. The School's newest MS programs are in cyber security, wireless health technology, data science, sustainable infrastructure, and petroleum geoscience technologies.

Levels of Study: Graduate

Field of Study: Aerospace, Aviation/Aerospace, Computer Science, Engineering, Engineering-Related Technologies

Nationality: Any Region

Location of Study: University of Southern California Los Angeles, CA

AWARD INFORMATION

Award Type: Scholarship

Average Amount: $5,000 - $10,200

Number of Awards: Varies

Award Coverage: Tuition

ELIGIBILITY REQUIREMENTS

- GPA of 3.4 or higher
- Must be pursuing a master's degree at the Viterbi School

APPLICATION INFORMATION

Award Deadline: Dec

Instructions: Contact recruitment officer

CONTACT

University of Southern California
Graduate Recruitment
3650 McClintock Ave
OHE 106
Los Angeles, CA 90089-1455
Tel: +1 (213) 740-0123
Fax: +1 (213) 821-0851
Email: viterbi.gradprograms@usc.edu
Web: viterbi.usc.edu/gapp

University of Southern Mississippi
USM Graduate Teaching and Research Assistantships

PROGRAM INFORMATION

Description: Assistantships are competitively awarded by the department or school to which you are applying. Please send a letter indicating that you are interested in an assistantship to the department or school to which you are applying.

Levels of Study: Graduate, Doctorate

Field of Study: All

Nationality: Any Region

Location of Study: University of Southern Mississippi Hattiesburg, MS

AWARD INFORMATION

Award Type: Associateship

Average Amount: Varies

Number of Awards: Varies

Award Coverage: Varies.

Award Duration: Academic year

ELIGIBILITY REQUIREMENTS

- Must meet admissions requirements

APPLICATION INFORMATION

Instructions: Contact department or view departmental websites for further details and requirements; apply for admission online or download application materials, indicate on your application for admission that you wish to be considered for an assistantship

CONTACT

The University of Southern Mississippi
Dean of The Graduate School
118 College Drive #5024
McCain Library Room 211
Hattiesburg, MS 39406
Tel: +1 (601) 266-4369
Fax: +1 (601) 266-5138
Email: Susan.Siltanen@usm.edu
Web: www.usm.edu/international-services

University of St. Thomas
International Undergraduate Student Scholarship

PROGRAM INFORMATION

Description: Merit based scholarships of up to 40% of undergraduate tuition are available international undergraduate students at St. Thomas.

Levels of Study: Undergraduate

Field of Study: Accounting, Art History, Biochemistry, Biology, Business and Management, Chemistry, Communications and Journalism, Computer Science, Creative Writing, Economics, Education, Engineering, Family and Consumer Sciences/Human Sciences, Geography, Health Studies, History, Liberal/General Studies, Mathematics, Music, Neuroscience, Physics, Psychology, Social Service, Spanish, Statistics, Women's Studies

Nationality: Any Region

Location of Study: University of Saint Thomas Saint Paul, MN

AWARD INFORMATION

Award Type: Scholarship

Average Amount: $14,000

Award Coverage: Tuition

Award Duration: 4 years

ELIGIBILITY REQUIREMENTS

- Complete online application for undergraduate admission
- Completed and submitted scholarship application form
- Submit additional 1 page scholarship application essay

APPLICATION INFORMATION

Instructions: Visit our website for the application: www.stthomas.edu/media/internationaladmissions/pdf/UGScholApp.pdf

CONTACT

University of St. Thomas
Director, International Admissions
Mail 44C
2115 Summit Avenue
St. Paul, MN 55105
Tel: +1 (651) 962-6880
Fax: +1 (651) 962-5199
Email: international@stthomas.edu
Web: www.stthomas.edu

University of Texas at El Paso
University of Texas at El Paso Programa de Asistencia Estudiantil (PASE)

PROGRAM INFORMATION

Description: PASE is a financial assistance program for Mexican students who cannot afford to pay out of state tuition. This program allows them to pay the same tuition rate as Texas residents.

Levels of Study: Undergraduate

Field of Study: All

Nationality: Mexico

Location of Study: University of Texas at El Paso El Paso, TX

AWARD INFORMATION

Award Type: Tuition Reduction

Average Amount: Difference between in-state and out-of-state tuition

Number of Awards: Unlimited

Award Duration: Academic year, renewable for additional years

ELIGIBILITY REQUIREMENTS

- Must be a Mexican citizen or permanent resident
- Must meet UTEP admission requirements
- Must prove that you can afford in-state cost of attendance, but cannot afford out-of-state cost of attendance
- Must turn in a complete PASE application

APPLICATION INFORMATION

Instructions: Please visit our website for application information

CONTACT

University of Texas at El Paso
Office of International Programs
203 Union East Bldg
El Paso, TX 79968
Tel: +1 (915) 747-5664
Email: oip@utep.edu
Web: www.sa.utep.edu/oip/pase-program

University of the Incarnate Word

University of the Incarnate Word Freshman Scholarship Program

PROGRAM INFORMATION

Description: Students applying from high school that have taken the SAT or ACT exam may be eligible for an academic scholarship. The scholarship is awarded based on high school grades and SAT/ACT test scores. It is renewable for 4 years, as long as a minimum grade average of 3.0 is maintained.

Levels of Study: Undergraduate

Field of Study: All

Nationality: Any Region

Location of Study: University of the Incarnate Word San Antonio, TX

AWARD INFORMATION

Award Type: Scholarship

Average Amount: Varies

Number of Awards: Unlimited

Award Coverage: Tuition

Award Duration: Maximum of 4 years

ELIGIBILITY REQUIREMENTS

- Presidential Scholarship: $12,000; the average profile is a high school GPA of 3.9 with an SAT average of 1205 or ACT average of 26
- Dean's Scholarship: $10,000; the average profile is a high school GPA of 3.72 with an ACT average of 22 or SAT average of 1053
- Distinguished Scholarship: $10,000; the average profile is a 3.53 GPA with an ACT average of 19 or SAT average of 946
- Achievement Award: $8,000; the average profile is a 3.25 GPA with an ACT average of 17 or SAT average of 881
- Incentive Award: $2,000; students that score at or above an SAT score of 1100 or an ACT composite score of 24

APPLICATION INFORMATION

Instructions: Submit ACT and SAT scores to University of the Incarnate Word when registering for the exam or applying

CONTACT

University of the Incarnate Word
International Admissions Counselor
847 East Hildebrand
San Antonio, TX 78212
Tel: +1 (210) 805-5707
Email: intladmis@uiwtx.edu
Web: www.uiw.edu/internationaladmissions

University of the Incarnate Word

University of the Incarnate Word International Transfer Students Scholarship Program

PROGRAM INFORMATION

Description: A student who has completed 24 or more hours of college credit is considered a transfer applicant. Cumulative college GPA is used to determine merit awards.

Levels of Study: Undergraduate

Field of Study: All

Nationality: Any Region

Location of Study: University of the Incarnate Word San Antonio, TX

AWARD INFORMATION

Award Type: Scholarship

Average Amount: $6,000-$10,000

Number of Awards: Varies

Award Coverage: Tuition

Award Duration: 4 years maximum

ELIGIBILITY REQUIREMENTS

- Presidential Scholarship: $10,000 per year; cumulative GPA of 3.5 or greater
- Dean's Scholarship: $8,000 per year; cumulative GPA 2.9-3.49
- Distinguished Scholar Award: $8,000 per year; cumulative GPA of 2.5-2.89
- Achievement Award: $6,000 per year; cumulative GPA of 2.49 or below

APPLICATION INFORMATION

Award Deadline: Rolling

Instructions: For more information on how to apply, please visit the website

CONTACT

University of the Incarnate Word
International Admissions Counselor
847 East Hildebrand
San Antonio, TX 78212
Tel: +1 (210) 805-5707
Email: intladmis@uiwtx.edu
Web: www.uiw.edu/internationaladmissions

University of the Pacific, McGeorge School of Law

Pacific McGeorge International LLM Program Fund: Young Lawyers

PROGRAM INFORMATION

Description: The Young Lawyers Scholarship offers 2-4 tuition scholarships annually to admitted LLM in Transnational Business Practice students at University of the Pacific, McGeorge School of Law.

Levels of Study: Graduate

Field of Study: Business Law, International Law, Law

Nationality: Asia

Location of Study: University of the Pacific Sacramento, CA

AWARD INFORMATION

Award Type: Scholarship

Average Amount: $10,00 - $28,000

Number of Awards: 2-4 per academic year

Award Coverage: Full or partial tuition

Award Duration: Academic Year

ELIGIBILITY REQUIREMENTS

- Must be newly admitted to the LLM in Transnational Business Practice program
- Must have a minimum TOEFL score of 88 IBT or minimum IELTS score of 6.5

APPLICATION INFORMATION

Award Deadline: Mar

Instructions: Submit an email request to the Graduate and International Programs Office

CONTACT

University of the Pacific, McGeorge School of Law
3200 Fifth Avenue
Sacramento, CA 95817
Tel: +1 (916) 739-7353
Fax: +1 (916) 739-7363
Email: graduatelaw@pacific.edu
Web: www.mcgeorge.edu/Future_Students/LLM_and_JSD_Programs/LLM_Programs/LLM_in_Transnational_Business_Practice.htm

University of the Pacific, McGeorge School of Law

Pacific McGeorge LLM Program Endowed Scholarship

PROGRAM INFORMATION

Description: The LLM Programs Scholarships offers 1 scholarship every year to a newly-admitted LLM in Transnational Business Practice student. The recipient is selected on the basis of academic achievement, financial need, and career intent.

Levels of Study: Graduate

Field of Study: Business Law, International Law, Law

Nationality: Any Region

Location of Study: University of the Pacific Sacramento, CA

AWARD INFORMATION

Award Type: Scholarship

Average Amount: $7,500

Number of Awards: 1 per academic year

Award Coverage: Tuition

Award Duration: 1 Academic year

ELIGIBILITY REQUIREMENTS

- Must be newly admitted to the LLM in Transnational Business Practice program
- Must have a minimum TOEFL score of 88 IBT or minimum IELTS score of 6.5

APPLICATION INFORMATION

Award Deadline: Mar

Instructions: Please submit an email request to the Graduate and International Programs Office

CONTACT
University of the Pacific, McGeorge School of Law
3200 Fifth Avenue
Sacramento, CA 95817
Tel: +1 (916) 739-7353
Fax: +1 (916) 739-7363
Email: graduatelaw@pacific.edu
Web: www.mcgeorge.edu/Future_Students/LLM_and_JSD_Programs/LLM_Programs/LLM_in_Transnational_Business_Practice.htm

University of the Pacific, McGeorge School of Law
Pacific McGeorge Emil Schnellbacher Memorial Scholarship

PROGRAM INFORMATION

Description: The Emil Schnellbacher Memorial Scholarship offers 1 scholarship to a newly-admitted student in the LLM in Transnational Business Practice. The recipient is selected on the basis of academic achievement, financial need, and career intent.

Levels of Study: Graduate

Field of Study: Business Law, International Law, Law

Nationality: Any Region

Location of Study: University of the Pacific
Sacramento, CA

AWARD INFORMATION

Award Type: Scholarship

Average Amount: $3,500

Number of Awards: 1 per academic year

Award Coverage: Partial tuition

Award Duration: Academic Year

ELIGIBILITY REQUIREMENTS

- Must be newly admitted to the LLM in Transnational Business Practice
- Must have a minimum TOEFL score of 88 IBT or minimum IELTS score of 6.5

APPLICATION INFORMATION

Award Deadline: Mar

Instructions: Submit an email request to the Graduate and International Programs Office

CONTACT
University of the Pacific, McGeorge School of Law
3200 Fifth Avenue
Sacramento, CA 95817
Tel: +1 (916) 739-7353
Fax: +1 (916) 739-7363
Email: graduatelaw@pacific.edu
Web: www.mcgeorge.edu/Future_Students/LLM_and_JSD_Programs/LLM_Programs/LLM_in_Transnational_Business_Practice.htm

University of the Pacific, McGeorge School of Law
Pacific McGeorge LLM Programs Scholarships

PROGRAM INFORMATION

Description: Pacific McGeorge LLM Programs Scholarships offers tuition scholarships to newly admitted LLM students. Recipient are selected on the basis of academic achievement, financial need, and career intent.

Levels of Study: Graduate

Field of Study: Business Law, International Law, Law, Public Law, Public Policy

Nationality: Any Region

Location of Study: University of the Pacific
Sacramento, CA

AWARD INFORMATION

Award Type: Scholarship

Average Amount: Varies

Number of Awards: Varies

Award Coverage: Full or partial tuition

Award Duration: Academic Year

ELIGIBILITY REQUIREMENTS

- Must be newly admitted to the LLM in Transnational Business Practice program
- Must have a minimum TOEFL score of 88 IBT or minimum IELTS score of 6.5

APPLICATION INFORMATION

Award Deadline: Mar

Instructions: Please submit an email request to the Graduate and International Programs Office

CONTACT
University of the Pacific, McGeorge School of Law
3200 Fifth Avenue
Sacramento, CA 95817, US
Tel: +1 (916) 739-7353
Fax: +1 (916) 739-7363
Email: graduatelaw@pacific.edu
Web: www.mcgeorge.edu/Future_Students/LLM_and_JSD_Programs.htm

University of Toledo
University of Toledo Sister Cities Award

PROGRAM INFORMATION

Description: This award covers the out-of-state surcharge for students whose permanent address is within 1 of the Toledo Sister Cities/Regions, which include Toledo, Spain; Londrina, Brazil; Qinhuangdao, China; Csongrad County, Hungary; Delmenhorst, Germany; Toyohashi, Japan; Tanga, Tanzania; Bekaa Valley, Lebanon; Poznan, Poland; Coimbatore, India; and Hyderabad, Pakistan.

Levels of Study: Undergraduate, Graduate

Field of Study: All

Nationality: Brazil, China, Germany, Hungary, India, Japan, Lebanon, Poland, Spain, Tanzania

Location of Study: University of Toledo
Toledo, OH

AWARD INFORMATION

Award Type: Scholarship

Average Amount: $9,120

Number of Awards: Unlimited

Award Coverage: Non-resident portion of tuition

Award Duration: Academic year, renewable for duration of degree program

ELIGIBILITY REQUIREMENTS

- Must meet admissions requirements and be a student from 1 of the approved sister cities
- Must have minimum TOEFL score of 500 PBT/173 CBT/61 IBT or complete our English Language Program
- Must enroll in at least 15 credit hours per semester and complete 30 credit hours per year

APPLICATION INFORMATION

Award Deadline: Rolling

Instructions: Apply online for admission

CONTACT
University of Toledo
Undergraduate Admission
Mail Stop #300
Toledo, OH 43606
Tel: +1 (419) 530-1213
Fax: +1 (419) 530-1202
Email: mschroe5@utnet.utoledo.edu
Web: www.utoledo.edu

University of Toledo
Phi Theta Kappa Scholarship

PROGRAM INFORMATION

Description: Scholarship for students who have been inducted into the Phi Theta Kappa international honor society.

Levels of Study: Undergraduate

Field of Study: All

Nationality: Any Region

Location of Study: The University of Toledo
Toledo, OH

AWARD INFORMATION

Award Type: Scholarship

Average Amount: $1,000

Number of Awards: Unlimited

Award Duration: Maximum of 2 years

ELIGIBILITY REQUIREMENTS

- Student must be a certified member of the Phi Theta Kappa honor society and can provide a copy of membership certification

APPLICATION INFORMATION

Award Deadline: Rolling

Instructions: Submit PTK member certification with application support documentation for verification

CONTACT

The University of Toledo
Director, International Admission
2801 West Bancroft Street
Rocket Hall Suite 1350
Toledo, OH 43606, US
Tel: +1 (419) 530-1211
Fax: +1 (419) 530-1202
Email: mark.schroeder5@utoledo.edu
Web: ptk.org

University of Toledo

University of Toledo International Student Scholarship

PROGRAM INFORMATION

Description: For F-1 international students with a passing TOEFL score who have the equivalent of a 3.0 or higher cumulative average. Available for both direct from high school and transfer students.

Levels of Study: Undergraduate

Field of Study: All

Nationality: Any Region

Location of Study: The University of Toledo
Toledo, OH

AWARD INFORMATION

Award Type: Scholarship

Average Amount: $9,120

Number of Awards: Unlimited

Award Coverage: Non-resident portion of tuition

Award Duration: Maximum of 5 years

ELIGIBILITY REQUIREMENTS

- Must have a minimum GPA of 3.0 on a 4.0 scale
- Must have a minimum of a 500 PBT/173 CBT/61 IBT on international TOEFL or have completed University of Toledo's English language program.
- Must have an F-1 International Student Visa

APPLICATION INFORMATION

Award Deadline: Rolling

Instructions: Visit website to apply online for admission, the completed admission application serves as the scholarship application

CONTACT

The University of Toledo
Undergraduate Admission
2801 W. Bancroft St
Mail Stop #300
Toledo, OH 43606
Tel: +1 (419) 530-1213
Fax: +1 (419) 530-5745
Email: mark.schroeder5@utoledo.edu
Web: www.utoledo.edu

University of West Georgia

University of West Georgia International Out-of-State Tuition Waiver Program

PROGRAM INFORMATION

Description: For qualifying students (based on test scores of SAT/ACT, and TOEFL/IELTS and grades), UWG offers an out-of-state tuition waiver for a significant portion of the international student population. Can be granted upon admittance or earned after 2 full semesters. Students with this waiver will pay reduced tuition at the same rate as in-state students, a savings of approximately $12,000 a year. Availability is limited, and those interested in the waiver should complete their application well in advance of the deadline for the term they wish to enter UWG. This program is valid for use at UWG only.

Levels of Study: Undergraduate, Graduate

Field of Study: All

Nationality: Any Region

Location of Study: University of West Georgia
Carrollton, GA

AWARD INFORMATION

Award Type: Tuition Reduction

Average Amount: $12,000 +

Number of Awards: Varies

Award Coverage: Tuition reduction

Award Duration: Renewable for duration of academic program

ELIGIBILITY REQUIREMENTS

- Eligibility from Application with proper SAT/ACT & TOEFL/IELTS scores
- Student will need to sign a waiver acceptance form
- Must maintain a minimum cumulative 2.8 GPA on a yearly basis
- Must demonstrate active participation in key events organized by the ISP Office and the International Student Club
- Must be a student in good standing with SEVIS and the University

APPLICATION INFORMATION

Instructions: Applicants must submit a completed admissions application for the term they wish to enter, waivers are available on a first-come, first-served basis, so apply early

CONTACT

University of West Georgia
Assistant Director
1601 Maple Drive
Carrollton, GA 30118
Tel: +1 (678) 839-4780
Fax: +1(678) 839-5509
Email: bmcguinn@westga.edu
Web: www.westga.edu/admissions/international.php

University of Wisconsin - Eau Claire

University of Wisconsin - Eau Claire Incoming International Student Scholarship

PROGRAM INFORMATION

Description: The University of Wisconsin - Eau Claire encourages admitted international students to apply for an Incoming International Student Scholarship.

Levels of Study: Undergraduate

Field of Study: All

Nationality: Any Region

Location of Study: University of Wisconsin-Eau Claire
Eau Claire, WI

AWARD INFORMATION

Award Type: Tuition Reduction

Average Amount: $1,000-$5,000

Number of Awards: Varies

Award Coverage: Tuition remission

Award Duration: Renewable for up to 9 semesters

ELIGIBILITY REQUIREMENTS

- Must demonstrate academic achievement and proof of financial need
- Must be admitted to the University of Wisconsin - Eau Claire
- Must indicate expected contributions to university cultural diversity and programs

APPLICATION INFORMATION

Award Deadline: rolling deadline; priority deadline: Apr for fall semester; Dec for spring semester

Instructions: Degree seeking students can apply to the university online, scholarships application available on the website

CONTACT

University of Wisconsin-Eau Claire
International Admissions Officer
105 Garfield Ave.
Eau Claire, WI 54702-4004
Tel: +1 (715) 836-5415
Fax: +1 (715) 836-2409
Email: intladm@uwec.edu
Web: www.uwec.edu

University of Wisconsin - Green Bay

University of Wisconsin - Green Bay Tuition Remission Scholarship

PROGRAM INFORMATION

Description: Tuition remission scholarship are available for international students.

Levels of Study: Undergraduate

Field of Study: All

Nationality: Any Region

Location of Study: University of Wisconsin - Green Bay
Green Bay, WI

AWARD INFORMATION

Award Type: Tuition Reduction
Average Amount: Varies
Number of Awards: Varies
Award Coverage: Partial tuition
Award Duration: 1-5 years

ELIGIBILITY REQUIREMENTS

- Must have a minimum 2.5 GPA on a 4.0 scale
- Must demonstrate financial need
- Must show previous service to the community and continued service once at the university

APPLICATION INFORMATION

Award Deadline: Apr and Oct
Instructions: Please visit the admissions page on our website for more information

CONTACT

University of Wisconsin - Green Bay
Cofrin Library 207
2420 Nicolet Drive
Green Bay, WI 54311
Tel: +1 (920) 465-5164
Fax: +1 (920) 465-2949
Email: aokik@uwgb.edu
Web: www.uwgb.edu/international

University of Wisconsin - LaCrosse

University of Wisconsin - La Crosse Global Link Scholarship for New International Students

PROGRAM INFORMATION

Description: Scholarship is awarded based on academic merit.
Levels of Study: Undergraduate, Graduate
Field of Study: All
Nationality: Any Region
Location of Study: University of Wisconsin - LaCrosse La Crosse, WI

AWARD INFORMATION

Award Type: Scholarship
Average Amount: $2,000-$4,000
Number of Awards: 10
Award Coverage: Tuition
Award Duration: Academic year, renewable for additional years

ELIGIBILITY REQUIREMENTS

- Undergraduate applicants must have a minimum TOEFL score of 73 IBT; graduate applicants must have a minimum score of 79 IBT
- Must have GPA of 3.0 on 4.0 scale
- Must meet admission requirements

APPLICATION INFORMATION

Award Deadline: May for fall semester; Nov for spring semester
Instructions: Apply online; download or contact to request applications for scholarship: www.uwlax.edu/oie/ia/Forms/scholarship.pdf

CONTACT

University of Wisconsin - LaCrosse
Office of International Education
1725 State Street, 1209 Centennial Hall
La Crosse, WI 54601
Tel: +1 (608) 785-8016
Fax: +1 (608) 785-8923
Email: uwlworld@uwlax.edu
Web: www.uwlax.edu/oie

University of Wisconsin - Oshkosh

University of Wisconsin - Oshkosh International Student Tuition Waiver

PROGRAM INFORMATION

Description: The University of Wisconsin Oshkosh provides a limited number of partial tuition waiver awards which allow students to pay in-state tuition rather than out-of-state tuition. The decision to award the partial tuition waiver is based on financial need and superior academic achievement.
Levels of Study: Undergraduate, Graduate
Field of Study: All
Nationality: Any Region
Location of Study: University of Wisconsin - Oshkosh Oshkosh, WI

AWARD INFORMATION

Award Type: Scholarship
Average Amount: Varies
Number of Awards: Varies
Award Coverage: Tuition reduction
Award Duration: Academic year, renewable for additional years

ELIGIBILITY REQUIREMENTS

- Must be eligible for F-1 visa status
- Academic requirements must be met in order for award to be renewed

APPLICATION INFORMATION

Award Deadline: Jun for fall semester; Nov for spring semester
Instructions: For more information on how to apply, please visit the website

CONTACT

University of Wisconsin Oshkosh
International Student Services
Office of International Education
800 Algoma Blvd., Dempsey Hall 202
Oshkosh, WI 54901
Tel: +1 (920) 424-0775
Fax: +1 (920) 424-0185
Email: iss@uwosh.edu
Web: www.uwosh.edu/oie/iss

University of Wisconsin - Stout

University of Wisconsin-Stout Tuition Remission Scholarship

PROGRAM INFORMATION

Levels of Study: Undergraduate, Graduate
Field of Study: All
Nationality: Any Region
Location of Study: University of Wisconsin-Stout Menomonie, WI

AWARD INFORMATION

Award Type: Tuition Reduction
Average Amount: Up to $5,000
Award Coverage: Tuition

ELIGIBILITY REQUIREMENTS

- Based on grade point average

CONTACT

University of Wisconsin – Stout
Associate Director
200 Main St. E
Menomonie, WI 54751, US
Tel: +1 (715) 232-2132
Email: globaled@uwstout.edu
Web: www.uwstout.edu/oie/isa/finances.cfm

University of Wisconsin System

Hessen-Wisconsin Exchange Program

PROGRAM INFORMATION

Description: The program provides students with 1 semester of study abroad experience. Students are entitled to take courses at 1 of the 13 4-year universities in the University of Wisconsin system. Students will not be permitted to receive diplomas or degrees from the host institution.
Levels of Study: Undergraduate, Graduate
Field of Study: All
Nationality: Germany
Location of Study: University of Wisconsin, WI

AWARD INFORMATION

Award Type: Grant
Average Amount: Varies
Number of Awards: 30 awards per semester
Award Coverage: Tuition
Award Duration: 1 semester

ELIGIBILITY REQUIREMENTS

- Must have a minimum TOEFL score of 79 IBT
- Must have completed 2 semesters of study
- Must be enrolled in a university in Hessen

APPLICATION INFORMATION

Award Deadline: Oct

Instructions: Download application materials from our website

CONTACT

Justus-Liebig-Universität Gießen
Hessen-Wisconsin Landesprogramm
Akademisches Auslandsamt
Goethestr. 58
35390 Gießen
Germany
Tel: +49 (641) 99-12170
Fax: +49 (641) 99-12133
Email: info@wisconsin.hessen.de
Web: www.wisconsin.hessen.de

University of Wisconsin-Platteville

University of Wisconsin-Platteville Undergraduate Program

PROGRAM INFORMATION

Description: UW-Platteville is home to over 8000 students. Our students are from across Wisconsin, the US and beyond…. including degree seeking international students from 19 different countries and visiting/exchange students from 12 different countries. UW-Platteville offers a tuition scholarship to full-time undergraduate international students. The maximum award is $5000 per year ($2500 per semester).

Levels of Study: Undergraduate

Field of Study: Accounting, Agriculture and Related Sciences, Arts and Culture, Biology, Business and Management, Chemistry, Computer Science, Engineering, English as a Second Language, Law, Liberal/General Studies, Mathematics, Music, Philosophy and Religion, Spanish, TESOL, Theater

Nationality: Any Region

Location of Study: University of Wisconsin-Platteville Platteville, WI

AWARD INFORMATION

Award Type: Tuition Reduction

Average Amount: $5,000

Number of Awards: Varies

Award Coverage: Tuition reduction

Award Duration: Maximum 4 years

ELIGIBILITY REQUIREMENTS

- Students educational background (performance)
- English proficiency (TOEFL/IELTS score)
- Extracurricular activities

APPLICATION INFORMATION

Award Deadline: Varies

Instructions: Additional information can be received by emailing to amin@uwplatt.edu

CONTACT

University of Wisconsin-Platteville
Student Services Program Manager
1300 Ullsvik Hall
Platteville, Wisconsin 53818
Tel: +1 (608) 342-1125
Fax: +1 (608) 342-1122
Email: amin@uwplatt.edu
Web: www3.uwplatt.edu/international-admission

University of Wisconsin-Platteville

University of Wisconsin-Platteville Student Tuition Waiver and Scholarship

PROGRAM INFORMATION

Description: UW-Platteville encourages international students to apply for both tuition waiver and scholarship.

Levels of Study: Undergraduate

Field of Study: All

Nationality: Any Region

Location of Study: The University of Wisconsin-Platteville Platteville, WI

AWARD INFORMATION

Award Type: Scholarship, Tuition Reduction

Average Amount: The maximum award is $5,000 per year ($2,500 per semester)

Number of Awards: Varies

Award Coverage: tuition

Award Duration: Maximum of 8 semesters

ELIGIBILITY REQUIREMENTS

- Strong academic achievements, comparable to other UW-Platteville applicants, especially in the areas of mathematics, natural science (chemistry, biology or physics), social sciences and the humanities.
- Proficiency in English: 500 (paper based) or 61 (Internet based) minimum on TOEFL, or an IELTS score of at least 5.5
- To continue receiving the scholarship after the first semester, students must be full-time, make good academic progress, maintain good academic standing (above a 2.0 GPA), and demonstrate involvement in a variety of campus activities and leadership opportunities each semester.

APPLICATION INFORMATION

Award Deadline: Fall: Jun 1; Spring: Nov 1

Instructions: More details about the eligibility criteria for receiving this waiver after the student's first semester can be requested by emailing intlinfo@uwplatt.edu

CONTACT

International Admission
105 Royce Hall, University Plaza
Platteville, WI 53818
Tel: 00.1.608.342.1125
Email: intlinfo@uwplatt.edu
Web: www.uwplatt.edu/international-admission/apply

University of Wisconsin-Superior

University of Wisconsin-Superior Non-Resident Tuition Waiver (NTW) Program

PROGRAM INFORMATION

Description: The University of Wisconsin-Superior seeks to promote diversity on its campus. To this end, the university has established the Non-Resident Tuition Waiver (NTW) Program, which grants qualified international degree-seeking students a partial waiver on their non-resident tuition expenses. Through NTW Awards, the University hopes to make the cost of studying at UW-Superior affordable to a wider range of qualified students from diverse backgrounds. Both undergraduate and graduate international students may apply for NTW Awards.

Levels of Study: Undergraduate

Field of Study: All, Accounting, American Politics, Art History, Arts and Culture, Behavioral Sciences, Biochemistry, Biology, Business and Management, Chemistry, Communications and Journalism, Computer Science, Conflict Resolution, Finance, Fine Arts, History, International Management, International Relations, Journalism, Life Sciences, Management, Marketing, Mathematics, Molecular Biology, Music, Natural Sciences, Peace Studies, Political Science, Psychology, Science, Social Science, Sociology, Theater, Transportation and Material Moving, Visual and Performing Arts

Nationality: Any Region

Location of Study: University of Wisconsin-Superior Superior, WI

AWARD INFORMATION

Award Type: Award, Grant, Scholarship, Tuition Reduction

Average Amount: $5,600-$7,500

Number of Awards: 200

Award Coverage: Tuition

Award Duration: Maximum of 5 years

ELIGIBILITY REQUIREMENTS

- International students who apply and qualify for academic admission will have a high probability of receiving an NTW Award of $5,600 per year.

APPLICATION INFORMATION

Award Deadline: Jul 1

Instructions: All students who apply for admission and submit an NTW application will be considered for an award, students may receive either the NTW Award or the NTW Scholar Award, but not both

CONTACT

University of Wisconsin-Superior; Old Main 337
Office of International Programs
Belknap & Catlin
Superior, WI 54880
Tel: +1 (715) 394-8052
Fax: +1 (715) 394-8363
Email: international@uwsuper.edu
Web: www.uwsuper.edu/international

Upper Iowa University

Upper Iowa University International Student Scholarships

PROGRAM INFORMATION

Description: A program for students learning English as a second language. We accept students with no previous English language experience. Our undergraduate programs vary and we have 2 graduate level programs.

Levels of Study: Undergraduate

Field of Study: All

Nationality: Any Region

Location of Study: Upper Iowa University
Fayette, IA

AWARD INFORMATION

Award Type: Scholarship

Average Amount: $7,000-$17,000

Number of Awards: Unlimited

Award Coverage: All scholarships go toward the cost of tuition

Award Duration: Up to 4 years of study

ELIGIBILITY REQUIREMENTS

- Must have over a 2.0 GPA
- Degree-seeking international students must have an I-20 in order to attend Upper Iowa University, domestic scholarships are available as well

APPLICATION INFORMATION

Award Deadline: No deadline

Instructions: All students are considered for scholarships when they are considered for admission

CONTACT

Upper Iowa University
605 Washington Street
Fayette, Iowa 52142
Tel: +1 (563) 425-5251
Fax: +1 (563) 425-5833
Email: international@uiu.edu
Web: www.uiu.edu

Utica College

Utica International Academic Achievement Award

PROGRAM INFORMATION

Description: Awarded to prospective students at the undergraduate level who have demonstrated outstanding academic achievement.

Levels of Study: Undergraduate

Field of Study: All

Nationality: Any Region

Location of Study: Utica College
Utica, NY

AWARD INFORMATION

Award Type: Scholarship

Average Amount: $2,000 - $6,000

Award Coverage: Partial tuition

Award Duration: Academic year, renewable for duration of degree as long as requirements are met

ELIGIBILITY REQUIREMENTS

- Must have secondary school diploma or 2-year college degree
- Must have proof of English proficiency (TOEFL, IELTS, SAT)
- Must have GPA between 2.8 and 4.0

APPLICATION INFORMATION

Award Deadline: Rolling

Instructions: Apply for admission online or contact to request application materials

CONTACT

Utica College
Office of International Education
1600 Burrstone Road
Utica, NY 13502
Tel: +1 (315) 792-3082
Fax: +1 (315) 792-3061
Email: intlpro@utica.edu
Web: www.utica.edu

Valdosta State University

Valdosta State University Center for International Programs Funding

PROGRAM INFORMATION

Description: Intensive English Language Program for TOEFL at the English Language Institute; out-of-state tuition waver for qualifying international students; graduate assistantships and athletic scholarships available.

Levels of Study: Undergraduate, Graduate

Field of Study: All

Nationality: Any Region

Location of Study: Valdosta State University
Valdosta, GA

AWARD INFORMATION

Award Type: Scholarship, Student Exchange, Study Abroad, Tuition Reduction

Average Amount: Varies

Number of Awards: Varies

Award Coverage: Tuition

Award Duration: 4 academic years

ELIGIBILITY REQUIREMENTS

- Must have a minimum GPA 3.0
- Must participate in community service via programs working with local schools and community organizations
- Must demonstrate active participation in key events organized by VSU Society of International Students
- Must be a student in good standing (minimum 12 credit hours per semester)
- Must demonstrate good conduct

APPLICATION INFORMATION

Instructions: For all scholarship applications, visit the website

CONTACT

Valdosta State University
1500 N. Patterson Street
Center for International Programs
Valdosta, GA 31698
Tel: +1 (229) 333-7410
Fax: +1 (229) 245-3849
Email: dstarlin@valdosta.edu
Web: www.valdosta.edu/cip

Valparaiso University

Valparaiso University International Scholarships - Founders & Board of Directors

PROGRAM INFORMATION

Description: Valparaiso University is pleased to reward international students demonstrating exceptional achievement with academic scholarships. All admitted students will be automatically considered.
Levels of Study: Undergraduate
Field of Study: All
Nationality: Any Region
Location of Study: Valparaiso University Valparaiso, IN

AWARD INFORMATION

Award Type: Scholarship
Average Amount: $21,500 per year
Number of Awards: 10
Award Coverage: Tuition
Award Duration: 4 years

ELIGIBILITY REQUIREMENTS

- Based on GPA and SAT/ACT scores

APPLICATION INFORMATION

Award Deadline: Dec 1
Instructions: Apply to Valparaiso and turn in necessary admission documents

CONTACT

Welcome Center
Undergraduate Admission Duesenberg
1620 Chapel Dr
Valparaiso, IN 46383
Tel: +1 (219) 464-5011
Fax: +1 (219) 464-6898
Email: undergrad.admission@valpo.edu
Web: www.valpo.edu/financialaid/scholarships/academicscholarships.php

Valparaiso University

Valparaiso University International Scholarships - Presidential and Honors Scholarship

PROGRAM INFORMATION

Description: Valparaiso University is pleased to reward international students demonstrating exceptional achievement with academic scholarships. All admitted students will be automatically considered.
Levels of Study: Undergraduate
Field of Study: All
Nationality: Any Region
Location of Study: Valparaiso University Valparaiso, IN

AWARD INFORMATION

Award Type: Scholarship
Average Amount: $12,000-$17,000
Number of Awards: Unlimited
Award Coverage: Tuition
Award Duration: 4 years

ELIGIBILITY REQUIREMENTS

- Based on GPA and extracurricular activities

APPLICATION INFORMATION

Award Deadline: Rolling
Instructions: Apply to Valparaiso and turn in required admission documents

CONTACT

Valparaiso University
Undergraduate Admission Duesenberg
Welcome Center
1620 Chapel Dr
Valparaiso, IN 46383
Tel: +1 (219) 464-5011
Fax: +1 (219) 464-6898
Email: undergrad.admission@valpo.edu
Web: www.valpo.edu/financialaid/scholarships/academicscholarships.php

Villanova University

Villanova University Graduate Arts and Sciences

PROGRAM INFORMATION

Description: Masters programs in the humanities, social sciences, mathematics, statistics, and natural sciences, and PhD program in philosophy.
Levels of Study: Graduate, Doctorate
Field of Study: American History, American Literature, American Politics, American Studies, Biochemistry, Biology, Chemistry, Classics, Communications and Journalism, Computer and Information Sciences, Computer Science, Education, Government, History, Human Resource Development, International Relations, Liberal/General Studies, Peace Studies, Philosophy and Religion, Political Science, Public Administration, Religion/Theology, Spanish, Statistics, Theater
Nationality: Any Region
Location of Study: Villanova University Villanova, PA

AWARD INFORMATION

Award Type: Scholarship
Average Amount: $15,270 plus tuition
Number of Awards: Varies by program
Award Coverage: Tuition and living expenses
Award Duration: 2 years for masters, 4 years for PhD

ELIGIBILITY REQUIREMENTS

- Baccalaureate degree from a US or foreign institution of higher education
- English language proficiency
- 3 letters of recommendation
- GRE scores
- Credentials evaluation

APPLICATION INFORMATION

Award Deadline: Feb 1
Instructions: Online application is available at www.gradartsci.villanova.edu

CONTACT

Villanova University
Dean of Graduate Studies
800 Lancaster Avenue
Villanova, PA 19085
Tel: +1 (610) 519-7090
Email: christine.palus@villlanova.edu
Web: www.gradartsci.villanova.edu

Virginia International University

Virginia International University Undergraduate/Graduate Scholarships

PROGRAM INFORMATION

Description: VIU provides an environment for international students to enlighten fellow international and American students about their traditions and ethics, and to gain valuable insight into the multicultural aspects of America society in return. By offering these scholarships, our aim is to attract the rare individual who will take these unparalleled experiences back to his or her home country, share the knowledge acquired with future generations, and launch successful careers as world leaders.
Levels of Study: Undergraduate, Graduate
Field of Study: All
Nationality: Any Region
Location of Study: Virginia International University Fairfax, VA

AWARD INFORMATION

Award Type: Scholarship
Average Amount: $500-$4,000
Award Coverage: Tuition
Award Duration: Academic year

ELIGIBILITY REQUIREMENTS

- Requirements differ based on scholarship; however, most require a minimum TOEFL or IELTS score, SAT and/or ACT score (GRE and/or GMAT score for graduates), previous outstanding academic success

APPLICATION INFORMATION

Award Deadline: Jul

Instructions: Contact or visit our website for more information

CONTACT

Virginia International University
Scholarship Program
4401 Village Drive
Fairfax, VA 22030
Tel: +1 (703) 591-7042
Fax: +1 (703) 591-7048
Email: scholarship@viu.edu
Web: www.viu.edu/future-students/about-scholarships.html

Viterbo University

Viterbo International Student Scholarship

PROGRAM INFORMATION

Description: The scholarship is based on high school GPA and TOEFL, SAT or ACT scores.

Levels of Study: Undergraduate

Field of Study: All

Nationality: Any Region

Location of Study: Viterbo University La Crosse, WI

AWARD INFORMATION

Award Type: Scholarship

Average Amount: Varies

Number of Awards: Varies

Award Coverage: Partial tuition

Award Duration: Maximum of 4 years

ELIGIBILITY REQUIREMENTS

- Must be an international undergraduate student, and see website for details

APPLICATION INFORMATION

Instructions: Download international student application from website and send with required documents

CONTACT

Viterbo University
Office of Global Education
900 Viterbo Drive
La Crosse, WI 54601
Tel: +1 (608) 796-3172
Fax: +1 (608) 796-3171
Email: globaled@viterbo.edu
Web: www.viterbo.edu/administration_and_services/global_education/International_Students.aspx

Wabash College

Wabash College Academic President's Scholarships

PROGRAM INFORMATION

Description: International Students are eligible for merit and need-based aid as well as Wabash College subsidized loans and on-campus employment

Levels of Study: Undergraduate

Field of Study: All

Nationality: Any Region

Location of Study: Wabash College Crawfordsville, IN

AWARD INFORMATION

Award Type: Grant, Loan, Scholarship, Student Exchange, Study Abroad

Average Amount: $15,000

Number of Awards: Approx 20 per year

Award Coverage: Varies.

Award Duration: Maximum of 4 years

ELIGIBILITY REQUIREMENTS

- Must have a high school degree
- Must demonstrate English language proficiency
- Must possess an excellent academic record
- Must have a good record of activities

APPLICATION INFORMATION

Award Deadline: Dec

Instructions: Please visit the website for application information

CONTACT

Wabash College
International Office Director
301 West Wabash Avenue
P.O. Box 352
Crawfordsville, IN 47933-0352
Tel: +1 (765) 361-6078
Fax: +1 (765) 361-6306
Email: clappd@wabash.edu
Web: www.wabash.edu/international/international

Wabash College

Wabash College Scholarships

PROGRAM INFORMATION

Levels of Study: Undergraduate

Field of Study: American Politics, Art History, Asian Studies, Biochemistry, Biology, Chemistry, Classics, Economics, Fine Arts, Foreign Languages, History, Life Sciences, Mathematics, Natural Sciences, Philosophy and Religion, Physics, Political Science, Psychology, Religion/Theology, Spanish, Speech and Debate, Theater

Nationality: Any Region

Location of Study: Wabash College Crawfordsville, IN

AWARD INFORMATION

Award Type: Grant, Internship, Loan, Scholarship, Student Exchange, Study Abroad

Average Amount: $20,000

Award Duration: Maximum of 4 years

APPLICATION INFORMATION

Award Deadline: Mar 15

Instructions: Please visit our website for more information www.wabash.edu/admissions/finances/sources

CONTACT

Wabash College
301 West Wabash Avenue
47933 Crawfordsville IN
Tel: +1 (765) 361-6000
Email: Admissions@wabash.edu

Waldorf College

Waldorf College International Financial Aid

PROGRAM INFORMATION

Description: Each international student is awarded an academic merit-based scholarship ranging from $1,000-$15,000 if arriving as a first-time college student. Transfers are awarded scholarships based on college transcripts and scholarships range from $1,000-$6,000. Athletic and Fine Art scholarships are also available, but students would need to contact the particular coach or director to discuss try-out/audition procedures.

Levels of Study: Undergraduate

Field of Study: All

Nationality: Any Region

Location of Study: Waldorf College Forest City, IA

AWARD INFORMATION

Award Type: Scholarship

Average Amount: $1,000-$15,000

Number of Awards: Every student is eligible

Award Coverage: Partial to full tuition

Award Duration: Duration of study

ELIGIBILITY REQUIREMENTS

- Must be accepted into Waldorf College and not be a US citizen
- Must score a minimum TOEFL of 500 PBT to be considered for any of the scholarships

APPLICATION INFORMATION

Instructions: See website

CONTACT

Waldorf College
106 S. 6th Street
Forest City, IA 50436
Tel: +1 (641) 585-2450
Email: admissions@waldorf.edu
Web: www.waldorf.edu/Residential/Future-Students/International-Student-Programs/International-Financial-Aid

Wartburg College
Wartburg College Ruppe International Scholarships

PROGRAM INFORMATION

Description: Students receiving the scholarships are awarded up to $25,000 per academic year, based on academic merit, financial need, and participation in co-curricular activities and community service.

Levels of Study: Undergraduate

Field of Study: All

Nationality: Any Region

Location of Study: Wartburg College
Waverly, IA

AWARD INFORMATION

Award Type: Scholarship

Average Amount: Maximum of $25,000

Number of Awards: Varies

Award Coverage: Tuition

Award Duration: Maximum of 4 years

ELIGIBILITY REQUIREMENTS

- Must be degree-seeking student at Wartburg College
- Must maintain at least a 2.0 cumulative GPA

APPLICATION INFORMATION

Award Deadline: Rolling

Instructions: No special application form or process; simply apply for admission to Wartburg College via our website, www.wartburg.edu/apply

CONTACT

Wartburg College
Associate Director of Global Admissions
100 Wartburg Boulevard
Waverly, IA 50677
Tel: +1 (319) 352-8511
Fax: +1 (319) 352-8579
Email: global.admissions@wartburg.edu
Web: www.wartburg.edu

Wartburg College
Davis UWC Scholarships

PROGRAM INFORMATION

Description: United Word College Scholars are eligible to receive scholarships from the Davis UWC Scholars Program. Wartburg College is 1 of the colleges and universities in the US who is a partner with this program. Wartburg College is dedicated to challenging and nurturing students for lives of leadership and service as a spirited expression of their faith and learning.

Levels of Study: Undergraduate

Field of Study: All

Nationality: Any Region

Location of Study: Wartburg College
Waverly, IA

AWARD INFORMATION

Award Type: Scholarship

Average Amount: Varies

Number of Awards: Varies

Award Coverage: Partial tuition, fees, room, board

Award Duration: Maximum of 4 years

ELIGIBILITY REQUIREMENTS

- Must be enrolled as a degree seeking student and have graduated from a United World College program

APPLICATION INFORMATION

Award Deadline: Rolling

Instructions: Indicate the name of your secondary school on your application when applying, no separate scholarship application is necessary

CONTACT

Wartburg College
Associate Director of Global Admissions
100 Wartburg Blvd
Waverly, IA 50677
Tel: +1 (319) 352-8511
Fax: +1 (319) 352-8579
Email: global.admissions@wartburg.edu
Web: www.wartburg.edu/global

Wartburg College
Meistersinger Music Scholarships

PROGRAM INFORMATION

Description: For vocal, instrumental, and keyboard musicians. Competition is open to music and non-music majors; selection is based on musical performance and ability, as demonstrated in an audition or audio/video recording. Auditions or audition CDs or DVDs must be submitted by Jan for the fall session.

Levels of Study: Undergraduate

Field of Study: All

Nationality: Any Region

Location of Study: Wartburg College
Waverly, IA

AWARD INFORMATION

Award Type: Scholarship

Average Amount: Maximum of $5,000

Number of Awards: Varies

Award Coverage: Partial tuition

Award Duration: Maximum of 4 years

ELIGIBILITY REQUIREMENTS

- Based on musical performance quality, must be a degree-seeking student

APPLICATION INFORMATION

Award Deadline: Jan

Instructions: Must either audition in person, or submit a CD or DVD; must be accepted to Wartburg College in order to apply

CONTACT

Wartburg College
Associate Director of Global Admissions
100 Wartburg Blvd
Waverly, IA 50677
Tel: +1 (319) 352-8511
Fax: +1 (319) 352-8579
Email: global.admissions@wartburg.edu
Web: www.wartburg.edu/music

Wartburg College
Wartburg College High Performance Scholarship

PROGRAM INFORMATION

Description: After completing 9 course credits at Wartburg (approximately 1 year of study), international students who participate in 2 or more campus activities and achieve a 3.0 grade point average or above may apply for a High Performance Scholarship.

Levels of Study: Undergraduate

Field of Study: All

Nationality: Any Region

Location of Study: Wartburg College
Waverly, IA

AWARD INFORMATION

Award Type: Scholarship

Average Amount: Maximum of $2,000

Number of Awards: Varies

Award Coverage: Some portion of tuition

Award Duration: Maximum of 3 years

ELIGIBILITY REQUIREMENTS

- Must be a degree-seeking student participating in 2 or more campus activities (such as sports, clubs, or volunteer organizations)
- Must achieve at least a 3.0 cumulative grade point average
- Must have completed at least 1 year of study at Wartburg

APPLICATION INFORMATION

Award Deadline: May

Instructions: You will be contacted each year that you study at Wartburg and meet the scholarship requirements; you will be required to submit recommendation letters and a personal statement; you can receive this award up to 3 times; awards are stackable

CONTACT

Wartburg College
Associate Director of Global Admissions
100 Wartburg Blvd
Waverly, IA 50677
Tel: +1 (319) 352-8511
Fax: +1 (319) 352-8579
Email: global.admissions@wartburg.edu
Web: www.wartburg.edu/global

Washington and Lee University

Washington and Lee University John M. Gunn International Scholarship

PROGRAM INFORMATION

Description: Scholarship for international students of exceptional academic, personal, and professional promise who wish to augment the UNDERGRADUATE studies in which they are engaged in their home academic institutions. Students with a background in politics, economics, and business development will be given preference. Financial need is considered in determining the amount of the award.

Levels of Study: Undergraduate

Field of Study: Business and Management, Economics, Liberal/General Studies, Political Science

Nationality: Any Region

Location of Study: Washington and Lee University Lexington, VA

AWARD INFORMATION

Award Type: Scholarship

Average Amount: $55,000

Number of Awards: 1

Award Coverage: Tuition and fees, room and board, books, health insurance

Award Duration: Academic year

ELIGIBILITY REQUIREMENTS

- Must currently be enrolled as an undergraduate student at a university outside of the US
- Must have minimum TOEFL score of 600 PBT/250 CBT/100 IBT
- Amount of award is based on demonstration of financial need

APPLICATION INFORMATION

Award Deadline: Mar

Instructions: Download application and brochure or contact to request application materials, applicant must complete International Student Financial Aid Application

CONTACT

Washington and Lee University
Assoc. Director, Center for International Education
21 University Place
Lexington, VA 24450
Tel: +1 (540) 458-8144
Fax: +1 (540) 458-8179
Email: arichwine@wlu.edu
Web: www.wlu.edu/x36714.xml

Washington College

Washington College Tuition Scholarships

PROGRAM INFORMATION

Description: Annual scholarships for international students admitted for undergraduate study at Washington range in amount from $7,500 to $20,000 per year. Scholarship amounts are based on academic credentials.

Levels of Study: Undergraduate

Field of Study: All

Nationality: Any Region

Location of Study: Washington College Chestertown, MD

AWARD INFORMATION

Award Type: Scholarship

Average Amount: $17,000

Number of Awards: 30 per year

Award Coverage: Partial tuition

Award Duration: Maximum of 4 years

ELIGIBILITY REQUIREMENTS

- Satisfactory completion of a college preparatory program of study
- Must have proficiency in the English language (TOEFL of 79 iBT or its equivalent; 6.5 IELTS)

APPLICATION INFORMATION

Award Deadline: Rolling

Instructions: All international applicants for admission will be reviewed to determine scholarship eligibility

CONTACT

Washington College
Senior Associate Director of Admissions
300 Washington Avenue
Chestertown, MD 21620
Tel: +1 (410) 778-7700
Fax: +1 (410) 778-7287
Email: tlittlefield2@washcoll.edu
Web: www.washcoll.edu/admissions/international-students.php

Washington Jefferson College

Washington Jefferson College Institutional Scholarships

PROGRAM INFORMATION

Description: Washington and Jefferson College offers partial merit scholarships to talented international students seeking to complete their bachelor's degree at Washington & Jefferson. W&J does not have full scholarships or meet full need.

Levels of Study: Undergraduate

Field of Study: Accounting, Biochemistry, Biology, Business and Management, Communications and Journalism, Computer and Information Sciences, Economics, Education, Engineering 3-2, Finance, Fine Arts, Foreign Languages, History, International Relations, Journalism, Law, Literature, Mathematics, Music, Physics, Political Science, Psychology, Spanish, Theater, Women's Studies

Nationality: Any Region

Location of Study: Washington & Jefferson College Washington, PA

AWARD INFORMATION

Award Type: Award, Grant, Scholarship, Student Exchange, Study Abroad, Tuition Reduction

Average Amount: $5,000-$17,000

Number of Awards: Unlimited

Award Coverage: Tuition

Award Duration: Maximum 4 years

ELIGIBILITY REQUIREMENTS

- Must be enrolled as a degree-seeking student at W&J and be in good academic standing

APPLICATION INFORMATION

Award Deadline: Rolling

Instructions: Apply online for admission at www.washjeff.edu, or at commonapp.org

CONTACT

Washington & Jefferson College
Director of International Recruitment
60 South Lincoln Street
Washington, PA 15301
Tel: +1 (724) 223-6025
Fax: +1 (724) 223-6534
Email: kcrosby@washjeff.edu
Web: www.washjeff.edu

Washington State University

Washington State University International Academic Awards

PROGRAM INFORMATION

Description: The International Freshman and Transfer Academic Awards reward students by offering tuition reductions based on academic excellence at previous institutions.

Levels of Study: Undergraduate

Field of Study: All

Nationality: Any Region

Location of Study: Washington State University Pullman, WA

AWARD INFORMATION

Award Type: Award

Average Amount: Varies

Number of Awards: Varies

Award Coverage: Partial tuition

Award Duration: Academic semester, renewable for additional years

ELIGIBILITY REQUIREMENTS

- Must have a freshman minimum GPA of 3.3 (on a 4.0 scale)
- Transfer students must have a minimum GPA of 3.3
- Renewable as long as requirements are met

APPLICATION INFORMATION

Award Deadline: Rolling

Instructions: Students who have completed the WSU international undergraduate application will automatically be notified if eligible

CONTACT

Washington State University
International Programs
PO Box 645121
Pullman, WA 99164
Tel: +1 (509) 335-8117
Fax: +1 (509) 335-2982
Email: international@wsu.edu
Web: www.international.wsu.edu

Webster University

WINS Travel Award

PROGRAM INFORMATION

Description: To support the university's mission of transforming students for global citizenship, monetary assistance is available to encourage participation of students from institutions members of the Webster International Network of Schools (WINS) consortium in study abroad courses at a Webster University international campus. Qualified students receive up to $1,000 toward a round-trip coach-class airline ticket to defray the cost of traveling abroad to attend a Webster international campus. Awards will be granted to qualified students who are academically eligible to enroll in the course.

Levels of Study: Undergraduate, Graduate

Field of Study: All

Nationality: US

Location of Study: Webster University

AWARD INFORMATION

Award Type: Award, Scholarship, Study Abroad

Average Amount: $1,000

Number of Awards: 80-100 per semester

Award Coverage: Airfare and travel agency fee

Award Duration: Semester

ELIGIBILITY REQUIREMENTS

- Complete application by deadline
- Be in good academic, social and financial standing
- Full-time student at an institution member of the Webster International Network of Schools (WINS)

APPLICATION INFORMATION

Award Deadline: Varies

Instructions: Submit application before its deadline to Webster University Office of Study Abroad

CONTACT

Webster University
Office of Study Abroad
470 E. Lockwood Avenue
St. Louis, MO 63119
Tel: +1 (314) 968-6988
Fax: +1 (314) 963-6019
Email: worldview@webster.edu
Web: www.webster.edu

Webster University

Webster University Walker Award

PROGRAM INFORMATION

Description: To support the university's mission of transforming students for global citizenship, monetary assistance is available to encourage participation in short-term study abroad courses by qualified students from the George Herbert Walker School of Business & Technology (The Walker School). Qualified students receive a $1,000 award to defray the cost of traveling abroad to participate in a HYBRID, short-term course. Awards will be granted to qualified undergraduate or graduate students who are academically eligible to enroll in the course.

Levels of Study: Undergraduate, Graduate

Field of Study: Accounting, Business and Management, Business Law, Corporate Law, Finance, Liberal/General Studies, Master of Business Administration (MBA), Tax Law

Nationality: Any Region

Location of Study: Webster University St. Louis, MO

AWARD INFORMATION

Award Type: Award, Study Abroad

Average Amount: $1,000

Award Coverage: Travel expenses

Award Duration: 1 month

ELIGIBILITY REQUIREMENTS

- Must be a degree-seeking student within the George Herbert Walker School of Business and Technology (Walker School)
- Must submit the form along with appropriate application deadline
- Must be in good academic, social, and financial standing
- Must not currently receive tuition remission or tuition exchange benefits from Webster University

APPLICATION INFORMATION

Award Deadline: Varies

Instructions: Complete the program application and submit to the Director of the program at the Walker School, students must also register for the course as per normal

CONTACT

Webster University
470 East Lockwood
East Academic Building 327
St. Louis, MO 63119
Tel: +1 (314) 246-8236
Email: annebrowning15@webster.edu
Web: www.webster.edu/depts/business/index_offer.php?page=study_abroad/walker_fund_student.php

Webster University

Webster World Traveler Program

PROGRAM INFORMATION

Description: The program awards 1 round-trip coach-class ticket to qualified Webster students from the student's home campus to another eligible Webster international site.

Levels of Study: Undergraduate, Graduate, Doctorate, Post Doctorate, Professional

Field of Study: All

Nationality: Any Region

Location of Study: Webster University Saint Louis, MO

AWARD INFORMATION

Award Type: Award

Average Amount: $1,000

Number of Awards: 110 per semester

Award Coverage: Round-trip, coach class airfare

Award Duration: Duration of study abroad program

ELIGIBILITY REQUIREMENTS

- Acceptance to a Webster University program
- Undergraduate students: must successfully complete a minimum of 15 credit hours at Webster University at time of international travel; graduate students: must successfully complete of a minimum of 9 credit hours at Webster University at the time of international travel
- English as a Second Language students: must be officially released from ESL at time of international travel and have completed at least 1 semester after such release
- Student cannot be on social or academic probation
- Student cannot have any account holds

APPLICATION INFORMATION

Award Deadline: Sep (spring), Feb (summer), Mar (fall)

Instructions: Contact Office of Study Abroad for application

CONTACT

Webster University
Office of Study Abroad
470 E. Lockwood Ave.
Sverdrup # 207
Saint Louis, MO 63119
Tel: +1 (314) 968-6988
Fax: +1 (314) 968-5938
Email: worldview@webster.edu
Web: www.webster.edu/studyabroad/wwtp.shtml

Webster University

Webster University International Undergraduate Scholarships

PROGRAM INFORMATION

Description: Undergraduate scholarships for international students that range from $5,000 to $15,000 per year.

Levels of Study: Undergraduate

Field of Study: All

Nationality: Any Region

Location of Study: Webster University St. Louis, MO

AWARD INFORMATION

Award Type: Scholarship

Average Amount: $9,000

Number of Awards: No Limit

Award Coverage: Scholarship renewable for 4 years so long as student maintains the requested GPA

Award Duration: 4 Years

ELIGIBILITY REQUIREMENTS

- Minimum GPA of 3.0 on a 4.0 scale

APPLICATION INFORMATION

Award Deadline: May

Instructions: All applicants are automatically considered for scholarships upon application

CONTACT

Webster University
Director of International Recruitment and Services
470 E. Lockwood Ave.
St. Louis, Missouri 63119
Tel: +1 (314) 246-7138
Fax: +1 (314) 246-7122
Email: smithca@webster.edu
Web: www.webster.edu

Wellesley College

Wellesley College Newhouse Faculty Fellowships

PROGRAM INFORMATION

Description: The Susan and Donald Newhouse Center for the Humanities at Wellesley College was established by a generous gift from Susan and Donald Newhouse in 2004. The Newhouse Center aims to promote excellence and innovation in humanistic studies. The Newhouse Center occupies a central space in the Wellesley campus.

Field of Study: Humanities

Nationality: Any Region

Location of Study: Wellesley College, The Newhouse Center for the Humanities
Wellesley, MA

AWARD INFORMATION

Award Type: Fellowship

Average Amount: Up to $50,000

Number of Awards: Varies

Award Coverage: Stipend, limited research expenses

Award Duration: 1 year

ELIGIBILITY REQUIREMENTS

- Open to both junior and senior faculty members at other institutions

APPLICATION INFORMATION

Award Deadline: Dec 1

Instructions: Applicants for Newhouse Faculty Fellowships should submit 1) a research proposal of no more than 1,250 words, describing the project and plan of research for the proposed residency; a brief bibliography may be appended; 2) a brief description of a broad programming vision in which to present his/her work while in residence; 3) a curriculum vitae; 4) the names and contact information of 3 referees; 5) a cover letter

CONTACT

Wellesley College
The Newhouse Center for the Humanities
106 Central St
Wellesley, MA 02481-8203
Tel: +1 (781) 283-2698
Fax: +1 (781) 283-3623
Email: nch@wellesley.edu
Web: www.newhouse-center.org/apply.php

Wesleyan University

Wesleyan Freeman Asian Scholars Program

PROGRAM INFORMATION

Description: Full-tuition scholarships are awarded to 1 student from each of 11 countries or regions in East and Southeast Asia in each entering class. The scholarships are for the 4 years required to earn the bachelor's degree at Wesleyan, one of the most selective institutions of liberal arts and sciences in the US Additional need-based financial aid is awarded to cover the remaining costs of room, board, books, supplies and travel. The goal of the program is to improve the relationship and understanding between the US and countries of the Pacific Rim. Our hope is that students will return home to become leaders, having gained an insight into the US culture and people. Of course, we benefit from the inclusion of Freeman Scholars sharing their perspective, traditions, and outlook while at Wesleyan.

Levels of Study: Undergraduate

Field of Study: All

Nationality: China, Hong Kong, Indonesia, Japan, Korea, Republic of, Malaysia, Philippines, Singapore, Taiwan, Thailand, Vietnam

Location of Study: Wesleyan University
Middletown, CT

AWARD INFORMATION

Award Type: Scholarship

Average Amount: Approx $46,000

Number of Awards: Varies

Award Coverage: Full tuition scholarship

Award Duration: 4 years

ELIGIBILITY REQUIREMENTS

- Must be a graduate from high school or equivalent, excellent student, and leader
- Not eligible if university studies have begun
- Must be a citizen or permanent resident of 1 of the countries included in the program and not a US citizen or US permanent resident
- Must be interested in sharing home culture
- It is expected that awardees return home after the scholarship period; preference to students currently in home countries; interviews of finalists take place in home country

APPLICATION INFORMATION

Award Deadline: Jan 1

Instructions: Complete the Common Application and Freeman Scholarship Addendum (supplemental material) and submit to Wesleyan by Jan 1; take SAT and TOEFL before Jan 1 and ask testing service to report scores

CONTACT

Wesleyan University
70 Wyllys Avenue
Middletown, CT 06459
Tel: +1 (860) 685-3000
Fax: +1 (860) 685-3001
Email: kshin@wesleyan.edu
Web: www.wesleyan.edu/admission/international_students/freeman.html

Wesleyan University

Wesleyan University Need-based Financial Aid for International Students

PROGRAM INFORMATION

Description: Wesleyan provides financial aid for approximately 15 international students in entering class who are citizens of countries not included in the Wesleyan Freeman Asian Scholars Program. We are one of the top institutions of liberal arts and sciences in the US

Levels of Study: Undergraduate

Field of Study: All

Nationality: Any Region

Location of Study: Wesleyan University
Middletown, CT

AWARD INFORMATION

Award Type: Grant, Loan

Average Amount: Varies

Number of Awards: Approx 15 per entering class

Award Coverage: Tuition, room, housing, travel expenses, books, supplies and miscellaneous expenses, based on need

Award Duration: 4 years

ELIGIBILITY REQUIREMENTS

- Must graduate from high school (or equivalent); excellent student, and participant in extracurricular activities
- Must be a first-time university student
- Admission for US citizens and US permanent residents, regardless of where they are living, is need blind and Wesleyan meets 100 percent of need through financial aid package
- Must take SAT or ACT, and TOEFL or IELTS (if English is not first language)

APPLICATION INFORMATION

Award Deadline: Jan 1

Instructions: Complete Common Application and submit to Wesleyan University

CONTACT

Wesleyan University
Associate Dean of Admission
70 Wyllys Avenue
Middletown, CT 06459
Tel: +1 (860) 685-3000
Fax: +1 (860) 685-3001
Email: toverton@wesleyan.edu
Web: www.wesleyan.edu/admission/international_students/expenses.html

Western Illinois University

Western Illinois University Scholarships Opportunities for International Violinists

PROGRAM INFORMATION

Description: Western Illinois University is pleased to announce 1 scholarship opportunity for an international undergraduate violinist.

Levels of Study: Undergraduate, Graduate

Field of Study: Music

Nationality: Any Region

Location of Study: Western Illinois University School of Music
Macomb, IL

AWARD INFORMATION

Award Type: Fellowship, Scholarship
Average Amount: Varies
Number of Awards: 1
Award Coverage: Full coverage of tuition, room and board

ELIGIBILITY REQUIREMENTS

- Must have a completed high school degree or equivalent
- Must submit 1 video of the candidate performing 2 contrasting works. DVD or video cassette is acceptable
- Must submit a completed school of music application form
- Must have successfully completed the TOEFL in internet, computer or traditional form

APPLICATION INFORMATION

Instructions: Contact or visit our website for further information

CONTACT

Western Illinois School University of Music
1 University Circle
Macomb, IL 61455
Tel: +1 (309) 298-2165
Fax: +1 (309) 298-1968
Email: music@wiu.edu
Web: www.wiu.edu/cofac/music/international_string_scholarship.php

Western Illinois University
Center for International Studies
Merit Scholarship

PROGRAM INFORMATION

Description: Western Illinois University offers the International Merit Scholarship to qualified undergraduate and graduate students (students who are not US citizens). Awards are based upon GPA and full time enrollment in a degree program at WIU. Students must be newly admitted, non-sponsored international students enrolling at WIU for the first time. Scholarship is only applied to WIU tuition. Students who have graduate assistantships or are sponsored are not eligible.
Levels of Study: Undergraduate, Graduate
Nationality: Any Region
Location of Study: Western Illinois University Macomb, IL

AWARD INFORMATION

Award Type: Scholarship
Average Amount: $3,000
Number of Awards: 20
Award Coverage: $3,000
Award Duration: Renewable yearly

ELIGIBILITY REQUIREMENTS

- Must complete the application process and be accepted into a degree program at Western Illinois University
- Must have a minimum 3.0 Grade Point Average (confirmed by WIU International Admissions Office)
- Full-time enrollment (a minimum of 12 semester hours undergraduate and 9 semester hours graduate) per semester
- Required to use University Housing options (some exceptions may apply)
- Must be newly admitted undergraduate or graduate, non-sponsored international student enrolling in WIU for the first time

APPLICATION INFORMATION

Award Deadline: May 1 and Oct 1
Instructions: Students must submit a completed Merit Scholarship application

CONTACT

Western Illinois University
Assistant Director Center for International Studies
1 University Circle
Macomb, IL 61455
Email: cis-activities@wiu.edu
Web: www.wiu.edu/international

Western Illinois University
Western's English as a Second Language Institute New Student Scholarship

PROGRAM INFORMATION

Description: Western Illinois University Western's English as a Second Language Institute New Student Scholarship is offered to ALL new, non-government sponsored international students who are enrolled in the WESL program. The scholarship is applied to the students tuition.
Levels of Study: Undergraduate, Graduate
Field of Study: English as a Second Language
Nationality: Any Region
Location of Study: Western Illinois University Macomb, IL

AWARD INFORMATION

Award Type: Scholarship
Average Amount: $1,000
Award Coverage: Tuition - $1,000 per academic year ($500 in Fall semester and $500 in Spring semester)
Award Duration: Maximum of 1 year

ELIGIBILITY REQUIREMENTS

- Must be enrolled in the WESL program at WIU
- Scholarship is automatically given to students who are not government sponsored
- Scholarship is applied for tuition only and is applied directly to the student's account
- Must be newly admitted to WIU and WESL for first time enrollment

APPLICATION INFORMATION

Award Deadline: Rolling
Instructions: No application necessary, scholarship is automatically given to international students who are newly admitted to WIU and WESL and are not government sponsored

CONTACT

Western Illinois University
Director, WESL
1 University Circle
Macomb 61455
Tel: +1 (309) 298-1107
Fax: +1 (309) 298-2405
Email: international-ed@wiu.edu
Web: www.wiu.edu/international_studies/wesl/scholarship.php

Western Illinois University
Rodney and Bertha Fink International Scholarship

PROGRAM INFORMATION

Description: This scholarship is for currently enrolled WIU female international students.
Levels of Study: Undergraduate
Field of Study: Agriculture and Related Sciences
Nationality: Any Region
Location of Study: Western Illinois University Macomb, IL

AWARD INFORMATION

Award Type: Scholarship
Average Amount: $1,000
Number of Awards: 1 per semester
Award Coverage: $1,000 ($500 awarded in fall, $500 awarded in spring)
Award Duration: Academic year

ELIGIBILITY REQUIREMENTS

- Student must be currently enrolled WIU female international student
- Financial need will be regarded as an important requisite
- Preference may be given to applicants based on academic performance and/or demonstrated campus/community involvement
- Preference will be given to a female student from an emerging/developing country majoring in Agriculture or Agriculture Business

CONTACT

Western Illinois University
Assistant Director Center for International Studies
1 University Circle
Macomb, IL 61455
Email: cis-activities@wiu.edu
Web: wiu.edu/international

Western Kentucky University
Western Kentucky University International Academic Scholarship

PROGRAM INFORMATION

Description: Beginning freshmen with a 3.4 unweighted GPA and a 24 ACT/1090 SAT score are eligible to receive the International Academic Scholarship that will pay the difference between the non-resident tuition rate and the Tuition Incentive program (TIP) rate.
Levels of Study: Undergraduate
Field of Study: All
Nationality: Any Region
Location of Study: Western Kentucky University Bowling Green, KY

AWARD INFORMATION

Award Type: Scholarship
Average Amount: Varies
Number of Awards: Unlimited
Award Coverage: The difference between the non-resident tuition rate and the Tuition Incentive program (TIP) rate
Award Duration: Renewable for entire academic program

ELIGIBILITY REQUIREMENTS

- Beginning freshmen must have a 3.4 (on a scale of 4.0) unweighted GPA and a 1090 SAT (Critical Reading and Math Scores)
- Transfer students must have 24 (approx 1 year) earned hours and a 3.4 (on a scale of 4.0) unweighted GPA
- Students must meet all regular admission requirements

APPLICATION INFORMATION

Award Deadline: Rolling

Instructions: Apply for regular undergraduate admission. Scholarship awarded automatically to eligible students

CONTACT

Office of Admissions, Western Kentucky University
1906 College Heights Blvd. #11018
Bowling Green, KY 42101
Tel: +1 (270) 745-2755, option 3
Email: scholarships@wku.edu
Web: www.wku.edu

Western Kentucky University

Western Kentucky University Non-Resident International Student Scholarship

PROGRAM INFORMATION

Description: All international graduate students who meet our admission requirements are given a special tuition scholarship each semester.

Levels of Study: Graduate

Field of Study: All

Nationality: Any Region

Location of Study: Western Kentucky University Bowling Green, KY

AWARD INFORMATION

Award Type: Scholarship

Average Amount: Varies

Number of Awards: Unlimited

Award Coverage: Tuition, research, travel expense.

Award Duration: Academic year, renewable for additional years

ELIGIBILITY REQUIREMENTS

- Must hold bachelor's degree or equivalent
- Must submit GRE or GMAT scores
- Must provide evidence of adequate financial resources
- Renewable as long as academic requirements are met

APPLICATION INFORMATION

Award Deadline: Apr for fall semester; Sep for spring semester

Instructions: Download or contact to request application materials

CONTACT

Western Kentucky University
Graduate School
1906 College Heights Blvd.
Bowling Green, KY 42101
Tel: +1 (270) 745-2446
Email: graduate.studies@wku.edu
Web: www.wku.edu/graduate/aid/

Western Michigan University

Diether H. Haenicke Scholarship for Undergraduate Students

PROGRAM INFORMATION

Description: The WMU Diether H. Haenicke Scholarship is a merit-based award available to undergraduate international students who meet the selection criteria.

Levels of Study: Undergraduate

Nationality: Any Region

Location of Study: Western Michigan University Kalamazoo, MI

AWARD INFORMATION

Award Type: Scholarship

Average Amount: $4,000-16,000

Number of Awards: Awarded to all those who meet the criteria (No Limit)

Award Coverage: Tuition

Award Duration: Maximum of 8 consecutive semesters

ELIGIBILITY REQUIREMENTS

- Undergraduate degree-seeking international student, entering WMU for the first time
- Cumulative GPA of 3.0 and above on a 4.0 scale
- Must be admissible to WMU
- Enroll fall term immediately after secondary school or transfer from another university
- Must maintain a cumulative WMU GPA of 2.5 for renewal and be a full time student (12 credits each semester), as well as successfully complete a minimum of 24 credit hours each academic year and remain a non-Michigan resident

APPLICATION INFORMATION

Award Deadline: Apr 1

Instructions: The International Admissions and Services office will automatically consider all entering freshmen and transferring students for this scholarship; no additional application is required

CONTACT

Western Michigan University
General Manager of International Enrollment, International Admissions and Services
1903 W. Michigan Ave
Ellsworth Hall
Kalamazoo, MI 49008-5246
Tel: +1 (269) 387-5866
Fax: +1 (269) 387-5899
Email: juan.tavares@wmich.edu
Web: international.wmich.edu/content/view/646/2/

Western Michigan University

Western Michigan University President's Incentive Scholarships for Graduate Students

PROGRAM INFORMATION

Description: The WMU President's Incentive Scholarships are awards available to new international graduate students from Spain and Mexico who meet the selection criteria.

Levels of Study: Graduate

Field of Study: All

Nationality: Mexico, Spain

Location of Study: Western Michigan University Kalamazoo, MI

AWARD INFORMATION

Award Type: Scholarship

Average Amount: $4,000

Number of Awards: Varies

Award Coverage: Tuition

Award Duration: Maximum of 4 semesters

ELIGIBILITY REQUIREMENTS

- Must be a graduate degree-seeking student entering WMU in the fall semester.
- Must be admitted to a WMU graduate program.
- Priority will be given to students from partner institutions in Spain and Mexico.
- At least 1 scholarship will be awarded to a student entering the MA or PhD program in Spanish.
- Criteria for renewal include: maintaining a cumulative WMU graduate GPA of 3.0; being a full-time student (minimum of 6 credits per semester); successfully completing a minimum of 12 graduate credit hours per academic year, remaining a non-Michigan resident.

APPLICATION INFORMATION

Award Deadline: Apr 1

Instructions: To be considered application for admission must be received by Apr 1 each year

CONTACT

Western Michigan University
Director, International Admissions and Services
1903 W. Michigan Ave
Ellsworth Hall
Kalamazoo, MI 49008-5245
Tel: +1 (269) 387-5866
Fax: +1 (269) 387-5899
Email: juan.tavares@wmich.edu
Web: wmich.edu/internationaladmissions/assistantships-scholarships/president

Western New England University

Western New England University Undergraduate International Scholarships

PROGRAM INFORMATION

Description: Western New England University is a small, private school offering programs through our Colleges of Business, Engineering, and Arts & Sciences. In order to provide international students with the opportunity to experience all that we offer, freshman and transfer students are eligible for our international student scholarship.

Levels of Study: Undergraduate

Field of Study: All

Nationality: Any Region

Location of Study: Western New England University Springfield, MA

AWARD INFORMATION

Award Type: Scholarship

Average Amount: $9,000-$14,000

Number of Awards: Unlimited

Award Coverage: Tuition

Award Duration: Up to 4 years

ELIGIBILITY REQUIREMENTS

- Must demonstrate academic merit
- Must meet minimum English requirement for admission
- Must be admitted into a degree program at the University

APPLICATION INFORMATION

Award Deadline: Rolling

Instructions: Rolling admissions, no additional documents required to apply for the scholarship

CONTACT

Western New England University
Director of International Admissions
1215 Wilbraham Road
Springfield, MA 01119
Tel: +1 (413) 782-1321
Fax: +1 (413) 782-1777
Email: mkowalsk@wne.edu
Web: www.wne.edu

Western Wyoming Community College

WWCC Academic Scholarships

PROGRAM INFORMATION

Description: International students may be awarded academic scholarships to attend Western Wyoming Community College in Rock Springs, Wyoming. Scholarships can pay 10-50 percent of the annual cost of attendance. Academic scholarship awards vary in amount and are based on official SAT or ACT score reports and academic transcripts. New college students and transfer students may be awarded academic scholarships. The priority award date is Apr 1 for the fall semester. Contact Admissions for program details.

Levels of Study: Undergraduate

Field of Study: All

Nationality: Any Region

Location of Study: Western Wyoming Community College Rock Springs, WY

AWARD INFORMATION

Award Type: Scholarship

Average Amount: Varies

Number of Awards: Varies

Award Coverage: Varies

Award Duration: 2 academic years

ELIGIBILITY REQUIREMENTS

- Opportunity Scholarship: minimum ACT composite of 19 and high school GPA of 3.0 are required. $1,600 per year
- Performance Scholarship: minimum ACT composite of 21 or SAT score of 1500 (Critical Math, Reading and Writing scores) is required, $3,200 per year
- Honors Scholarship: minimum ACT composite of 25 and high school GPA of 3.5 are required, $4,400 per year
- Superior Scholarship: minimum ACT composite of 27 and high school GPA of 3.75 are required, $6,200 per year

APPLICATION INFORMATION

Award Deadline: Rolling, Apr 1 priority date for fall semester

Instructions: Apply for admission online and provide official ACT or SAT scores, generally, awards are made as students are accepted for admission

CONTACT

Western Wyoming Community College
2500 College Drive
Rock Springs, WY 82901
Tel: +1 (307) 382-1633
Fax: +1 (307) 382-1636
Email: admissions@wwcc.wy.edu
Web: www.wwcc.wy.edu

Widener University

Widener University Undergraduate Academic Scholarships

PROGRAM INFORMATION

Description: There is no separate application necessary to qualify for these scholarships. The award amounts are based primarily on a student's performance in secondary school. Submitting standardized test scores (SAT or ACT) is recommend, but not necessary, for students seeking scholarship. The awards are based on a combination of impressive grades, challenging high school coursework, and standardized test scores when available.

Levels of Study: Undergraduate

Field of Study: All

Nationality: Any Region **Location of Study:** Widener University Chester, PA

AWARD INFORMATION

Award Type: Scholarship

Average Amount: Varies

Number of Awards: Varies

Award Coverage: Tuition

Award Duration: 4 years

ELIGIBILITY REQUIREMENTS

- Must be accepted to Widener University as an undergraduate

APPLICATION INFORMATION

Instructions: Complete the Widener University undergraduate admissions process, no additional application is necessary

CONTACT

Widener University
One University Place
Chester, PA 19013
Tel: +1 (610) 499-4161
Fax: +1 (610) 499-4687
Email: finaidmc@mail.widener.edu
Web: www.widener.edu/admissions/undergraduate/scholarships_aid/scholarships.aspx

Widener University

Widener University Presidential Service Corps (PSC) Leadership Award

PROGRAM INFORMATION

Description: Students invited to join the Presidential Service Corps are eligible for an award in addition to any other merit-based scholarships or awards they have received. To win this award, students must be highly active in service and leadership within school and in their communities outside of the classroom, while also maintaining strong academics.

Levels of Study: Undergraduate

Field of Study: All

Nationality: Any Region

Location of Study: Widener University Chester, PA

AWARD INFORMATION

Award Type: Award, Grant, Scholarship

Average Amount: $5,000 per year

Number of Awards: 60

Award Coverage: Tuition

Award Duration: 4 years

ELIGIBILITY REQUIREMENTS

- Must apply for admissions to Widener University by Jan, and must apply for the PSC award by Feb
- The Presidential Service Corps award is given to students who are highly involved in service and outreach activities that award winners must continue when attending Widener

APPLICATION INFORMATION

Award Deadline: Feb

Instructions: Visit the Presidential Service Corps website to download the award application and to view complete application instructions

CONTACT

Widener University
One University Place
Chester, PA 19013
Tel: +1 (610) 499-4596
Email: eahousholder@widener.edu
Web: www.widener.edu/civic_engagement/presidential_service_corps_scholarships.aspx

Widener University

Widener University Undergraduate Academic Scholarships for Transfer Students

PROGRAM INFORMATION

Description: Undergraduate transfer students, those who have attended another university but have not completed a bachelor's degree, qualify for merit-based scholarships. These awards range are given based on a student's cumulative university grade point average and chosen major. No separate application is necessary, and students will be evaluated for scholarship as part of the admissions process. The award structure is based solely on major and grade point average based on a 4.0 scale.

Levels of Study: Undergraduate

Field of Study: All

Nationality: Any Region

Location of Study: Widener University
Chester, PA

AWARD INFORMATION

Award Type: Scholarship

Average Amount: Varies

Number of Awards: Varies

Award Coverage: Tuition

Award Duration: 2-3 years

ELIGIBILITY REQUIREMENTS

- Must complete the undergraduate transfer application process, applicants will be evaluated for scholarship along with their application for admission, so no additional application is necessary
- Awards are given based on cumulative grade point average from any and all university level education completed.
- Students who already hold a bachelor's degree are not eligible for transfer scholarship

APPLICATION INFORMATION

Award Deadline: Aug for fall semester; Dec for spring semester

Instructions: Complete the undergraduate transfer admissions process, visit our website for more information

CONTACT

Widener University
One University Place
Chester, PA 19013
Tel: +1 (610) 499-4161
Fax: +1 (610) 499-4687
Email: finaidmc@mail.widener.edu
Web: www.widener.edu/admissions/undergraduate/scholarships_aid/scholarships.aspx

Willamette University MBA

Early Career and Career Change MBA - International Student Scholarships

PROGRAM INFORMATION

Description: Willamette University's Early Career and Career Change MBA program is designed for students who are recent college graduates, those with limited work experience or those looking for a change in their career. As a leader in experiential learning, Willamette MBA builds knowledge, real-world experience and career management skills.

Levels of Study: Graduate

Field of Study: Master of Business Administration (MBA)

Nationality: Any Region

Location of Study: Willamette University
Salem, OR

AWARD INFORMATION

Award Type: Scholarship

Average Amount: $10,000

Number of Awards: 60 percent of admitted students receive scholarships

Award Coverage: Merit-based scholarships range from 10 percent to 100 percent of tuition, all applicants admitted to the full-time Willamette MBA program are automatically considered for merit-based scholarships based on GMAT or GRE score, undergraduate grade point average, experience, potential, and ability to contribute to the learning experience of the Atkinson School

Award Duration: Maximum of 21 months

ELIGIBILITY REQUIREMENTS

- Complete online application and submit all required documents

APPLICATION INFORMATION

Award Deadline: May 1

Instructions: Application instructions for international applicants can be found here: www.willamette.edu/agsm/full-time/admission/international_applicants/index.html

CONTACT

Willamette University MBA
Director of Recruitment
900 State St.
Salem, OR 97301
Tel: +1 (503) 370-6167
Fax: +1 (503) 370-3011
Email: aakimoff@willamette.edu
Web: www.willamette.edu/mba

Willamette University MBA

Willamette University Early Career and Career Change MBA - Syrian Student Scholarships

PROGRAM INFORMATION

Description: Willamette University MBA will award each Syrian student who is admitted and matriculates as a full-time student in the 21 month Early Career and Career Change MBA program a scholarship in the amount equal to 20 percent of the tuition rate of the first-year of study.

Levels of Study: Graduate

Field of Study: Master of Business Administration (MBA)

Nationality: Syria

Location of Study: Willamette University
Salem, OR

AWARD INFORMATION

Award Type: Scholarship

Number of Awards: 5

Award Duration: Maximum of 21 months

ELIGIBILITY REQUIREMENTS

- Complete online application and submit all required application documents, including GMAT or GRE score, 2 letters of recommendation, official transcripts and TOEFL or IELTS score

APPLICATION INFORMATION

Award Deadline: May 1

Instructions: Visit our website at www.willamette.edu/agsm/full-time/admission/international_applicants/index.html for more information

CONTACT

Willamette University MBA
Director of Recruitment
900 State St.
Salem, OR 97301
Tel: +1 (503) 370-6167
Fax: +1 (503) 370-3011
Email: aakimoff@willamette.edu
Web: www.willamette.edu/mba

Willamette University MBA

Willamette University MBA Merit-Based Scholarships for International Students

PROGRAM INFORMATION

Description: The Willamette University MBA is located in Oregon, in the beautiful Pacific Northwest of the US. With nearly 40 percent of students coming from outside of the US, the Willamette MBA is truly a global community. All applicants admitted to the full-time Willamette MBA program are automatically considered for merit-based scholarships that range from 10 percent to 100 percent of tuition.

Levels of Study: Graduate, Professional

Field of Study: Master of Business Administration (MBA)

Nationality: Any Region

Location of Study: Willamette University MBA
Salem, OR

AWARD INFORMATION

Award Type: Scholarship

Average Amount: Varies

Number of Awards: Varies

Award Coverage: Partial to full tuition

Award Duration: Academic year, renewable for remainder of program

ELIGIBILITY REQUIREMENTS

- Must be admitted to full-time Willamette MBA program
- Scholarships are based on GMAT or GRE score, undergraduate grade point average, experience and potential

APPLICATION INFORMATION

Award Deadline: May 1

Instructions: All applicants admitted to a full-time format are automatically considered for merit-based scholarships, no additional application is required. Visit our website for more information

CONTACT

Willamette University
Director of Recruitment
900 State Street
Salem, OR 97301
Tel: +1 (503) 370-6167
Fax: +1 (503) 370-3011
Email: aakimoff@willamette.edu
Web: www.willamette.edu/mba/full-time/index.html

Wilson College

Wilson College Bogigian Scholarship for Armenian Students

PROGRAM INFORMATION

Description: Women of Armenian descent can apply for full-tuition scholarships at Wilson College under the Hagop Bogigian Scholarship. Scholarships are available for 2 women each year for up to 4 years, as long as they maintain satisfactory academic progress as defined by the college. To receive a scholarship, a student must meet all entrance qualifications and be accepted for admission to a bachelor's degree program. Wilson officials will make the final decision as to which applicants receive the award. Scholarship recipients are responsible for paying for room and board and all some fees and personal expenses.

Levels of Study: Undergraduate

Field of Study: All

Nationality: Armenia

Location of Study: Wilson College Chambersburg, PA

AWARD INFORMATION

Award Type: Scholarship

Average Amount: Full tuition

Number of Awards: 2

Award Coverage: Tuition, fees, some additional funds

Award Duration: Maximum of 4 years.

ELIGIBILITY REQUIREMENTS

- Must complete application process: application, teacher recommendation, secondary school academic transcript with marks including English translation, essay, English proficiency test
- Must submit a TOEFL of at least 500 PBT/61 IBT; IELTS at least 5.0
- Must be a female student from Armenia or of Armenian descent

APPLICATION INFORMATION

Award Deadline: Apr 1

Instructions: Apply for admission online at www.wilson.edu/apply or complete the Common Application or the Universal College Application

CONTACT

Wilson College
Admissions Office
1015 Philadelphia Ave.
Chambersburg, PA 17201-1285
Tel: +1 (717) 262-2002
Fax: +1 (717) 262-2546
Email: admissions@wilson.edu
Web: www.wilson.edu/www.wilson.eduwww.wilson.edu/admissions/undergraduate-college/scholarships/index.aspx

Wilson College

Wilson College International Student Scholarship Program

PROGRAM INFORMATION

Description: Wilson College offers significant scholarship opportunities, ranging from $3,000 to $12,000, for international students. Located within driving distance of cities such as Philadelphia, Baltimore, Washington D.C., Pittsburgh and New York City, Wilson College is set in an ideal location for international students looking to experience both the advantages of a safe and secure residential town surrounded by major metropolitan areas. 10 percent of full time bachelor's degree students are international students representing over 18 countries. Wilson College is recognized by US News & World Report as being one of the best Bachelor's degree institutions in the region. We offer rigorous and challenging academic programs, as well as research and internship opportunities. International students are automatically reviewed for scholarships upon application and submission of all requested documents. Students who complete A-Levels or IB curricula may be able to receive academic credit towards their degree.

Levels of Study: Undergraduate

Field of Study: All

Nationality: Any Region

Location of Study: Wilson College Chambersburg, PA

AWARD INFORMATION

Award Type: Scholarship

Average Amount: Varies

Number of Awards: Varies

Award Coverage: Academic scholarships range from $3,000 - $12,000

Award Duration: Maximum of 4 years

ELIGIBILITY REQUIREMENTS

- Must have a minimum TOEFL of 500 PBT/61 IBT; or IELTS 5.0; or STEP test Pre-1st
- Undergraduate first-year or transfer students are eligible
- Must have a strong academic background

APPLICATION INFORMATION

Award Deadline: Apr, Sep

Instructions: Complete international student admission process at www.wilson.edu/apply, Wilson College also accepts the Common Application or Universal College Application, financial documentation must also be submitted; visit our website for more information

CONTACT

Wilson College
International Admissions
1015 Philadelphia Avenue
Chambersburg, PA 17241-1285
Tel: +1 (717) 262-2002
Fax: +1 (717) 262-2546
Email: admissions@wilson.edu
Web: www.wilson.edu/international

Worcester Polytechnic Institute

Worcester Polytechnic Institute School of Business Merit-Based Aid

PROGRAM INFORMATION

Description: WPI, one of the nation's premier technological universities, delivers innovative management programs integrating business and technology. The Graduate Business Programs at WPI merge conceptual theory with real-world practice. Hands-on, active learning creates graduates who stand apart because of their ability to apply the fundamentals of technology and management to solve challenging, real-world problems. Every aspect of WPI's Graduate Management Programs recognizes the importance of this intersection of business and technology. WPI graduates gain the resources and experience to succeed in an increasingly complex world. With a world-class faculty, outstanding facilities, and international recognition, WPI graduates learn not only how to manage technological resources, but understand how the solutions to these business challenges impact the world around them.

Levels of Study: Graduate

Field of Study: Business and Management, Information Technology, Leadership, Management, Marketing, Master of Business Administration (MBA)

Nationality: Any Region

Location of Study: Worcester Polytechnic Institute Worcester, MA

AWARD INFORMATION

Award Type: Fellowship
Average Amount: $4,800
Number of Awards: 30 per semester
Award Coverage: Living stipend
Award Duration: Length of program

ELIGIBILITY REQUIREMENTS

- Must enroll in full-time study and work 15 hours per week with School of Business faculty
- Must remain in good academic standing (minimum 3.0 GPA)

APPLICATION INFORMATION

Award Deadline: Rolling
Instructions: Application materials and additional information are available on the website

CONTACT

Worcester Polytechnic Institute
Director of Admissions, WPI School of Business
100 Institute Road
Worcester, MA 01609-2280
Tel: +1 (508) 831-4674
Fax: +1 (508) 831-5866
Email: business@wpi.edu
Web: www.wpi.edu/academics/business/

Worcester Polytechnic Institute

Worcester Polytechnic Institute Graduate Science and Engineering Programs

PROGRAM INFORMATION

Description: WPI's 18 academic departments offer 35 master's and 15 PhD degree programs in science, engineering, technology, and business, leading to graduate, professional and doctoral degrees. In support of research endeavors, the university maintains numerous labs, research centers, and advanced research institutes, as well as a renowned information technology infrastructure.
Levels of Study: Graduate, Doctorate, Post Doctorate
Field of Study: All
Nationality: Any Region
Location of Study: Worcester Polytechnic Institute Worcester, MA

AWARD INFORMATION

Award Type: Associateship
Average Amount: $18,000-$22,000
Number of Awards: Varies
Award Coverage: Tuition (18-20 credits per year), monthly stipend (approx $1,900 per month)
Award Duration: 9-12 months

ELIGIBILITY REQUIREMENTS

- For admission, must have a minimum TOEFL score of 84 IBT or equivalent, or IELTS minimum overall score of 7.0 with no band score below 6.5; for TA funding, TOEFL minimum is 100 in most departments
- GRE scores required for most departments
- Must send 3 letters of recommendation
- Must send official transcripts from all previously attended universities
- Be sure to check specific departmental requirements at www.wpi.edu/admissions/graduate/appl-requirements.html

APPLICATION INFORMATION

Award Deadline: Oct, Jan
Instructions: Online application available at www.wpi.edu/+gradapp, admissions requirements are available on the website at grad.wpi.edu

CONTACT

Worcester Polytechnic Institute
Graduate Admissions Office
100 Institute Road
Worcester, MA 01609
Tel: +1 (508) 831-5301
Fax: +1 (508) 831-5717
Email: grad@wpi.edu
Web: grad.wpi.edu

Worcester Polytechnic Institute

Worcester Polytechnic Institute Undergraduate Programs

PROGRAM INFORMATION

Description: WPI offers several types of awards. Merit scholarships are available for freshman applicants based on academic performance and extracurricular involvement. WPI also offers a limited number of need-based scholarships. These awards range from $5,000 to $25,000. Awards will not exceed the cost of tuition. WPI allows international students to work part-time on campus. Students typically earn about $2,500 in an academic year. Students can choose to participate in 2 cooperative education programs while they are at WPI, during which they would be away from class working for a company/corporation for 6 to 8 months.
Levels of Study: Undergraduate
Field of Study: Aerospace, Biochemistry, Biology, Biotechnology, Business and Management, Chemistry, Computer Science, Economics, Engineering, Environmental Studies, Humanities, Information Technology, Life Sciences, Management, Mathematics, Multi/Interdisciplinary Studies, Natural Sciences, Physics, Science, Social Science
Nationality: Any Region
Location of Study: Worcester Polytechnic Institute Worcester, MA

AWARD INFORMATION

Award Type: Award, Scholarship, Study Abroad
Average Amount: $10,000-$20,000
Number of Awards: Varies
Award Coverage: Tuition
Award Duration: Academic year, renewable

ELIGIBILITY REQUIREMENTS

- All applicants for fall (Aug) enrollment who apply by Feb 1 are considered for a possible merit scholarship if admitted, no separate merit scholarship application is required
- Applicants for admission who wish to be considered for need-based International Scholarships must submit the International Student Financial Aid Application Form at the time that they apply for admission
- Must submit either SAT 1 or ACT scores, or Flex Path submission
- Applicants who are non-native English speakers must submit TOEFL, or IELTS, or PTE scores to prove English language proficiency

APPLICATION INFORMATION

Award Deadline: Feb 1

Instructions: Apply for admission using the Common Application

CONTACT

Worcester Polytechnic Institute
Office of Undergraduate Admissions
100 Institute Road
Worcester, MA 01609
Tel: +1 (508) 831-5286
Fax: +1 (508) 831-5875
Email: intl_admissions@wpi.edu
Web: www.admissions.wpi.edu

Yale University

Yale University Fox International Fellowships

PROGRAM INFORMATION

Description: The Fox International Fellowship Program is a direct, 2-way student exchange partnership between Yale University and 12 of the world's leading universities in Russia, England, Germany, China, Japan, France, India, Mexico, Turkey, Israel, Brazil, and South Africa. It was established to identify and support talented individuals who will be future leaders in their respective fields and who, by virtue of those leadership positions, will contribute to decisions affecting global policies and international relations.

Levels of Study: Undergraduate, Graduate, Professional

Field of Study: All

Nationality: Brazil, China, France, Germany, India, Israel, Japan, Mexico, Russia, South Africa, Turkey, United Kingdom

Location of Study: Yale University New Haven, CT

AWARD INFORMATION

Award Type: Fellowship

Average Amount: Varies

Number of Awards: Varies

Award Coverage: Airfare and housing expenses, and a stipend for living expenses

Award Duration: Academic year

ELIGIBILITY REQUIREMENTS

- Must be graduating seniors for undergraduate students
- Students in doctoral programs should have completed their coursework
- Must have administrative approval to interrupt their coursework for students in master's or graduate professional programs.
- Must demonstrate sufficient language proficiency to complete their research project at their host institution and to communicate directly with their hosts and peers
- Students may not apply for a fellowship to be conducted in a country where they currently hold citizenship (i.e., a US citizen studying at Bogazici in Istanbul cannot apply to go to Yale)

APPLICATION INFORMATION

Award Deadline: Varies

Instructions: Download application materials, submit application directly to home institution, see website for contact information at each partner university, do not submit directly to Yale, applicants must be enrolled at 1 of the 12 Fox Partner Institutions

CONTACT

The Fox International Fellowship Program
Yale University
P.O. Box 208206
New Haven, CT 06520
Fax: +1 (203) 432-5548
Email: Anne.Kellett@yale.edu
Web: www.yale.edu/macmillan/fif

Funding Resources by Field of Study

This index lists the funding opportunities available for specific fields of study. Please note that the majority of the scholarship listings are available for all fields of study.

All/Unrestricted

Accounting

Aerospace

Agriculture and Related Sciences

American History

American Jewish History

American Literature

American Politics

American Studies

Anthropology

Archaeology

Architecture and Environmental Design

Area and Ethnic Studies

Art History

Arts and Culture

Asian Studies

Astronomy

Aviation/Aerospace

Behavioral Sciences

Biochemistry

Biology

Biomedical Humanities

Biotechnology

Business and Management

Business Law

Chemistry

Classics

Cognitive Science

Communication Technologies

Communications and Journalism

Comparative Law

Computer and Information Sciences

Computer Science

Conflict Management

Conflict Resolution

Construction Trades

Corporate Law

Creative Writing

Dance

Democracy

Earth Science

Ecology

Economics

Education

Engineering

Engineering 3-2

Engineering-Related Technologies

English as a Second Language

Environmental Policy

Environmental Policy, Curatorial Studies, Master of Arts in Teaching

Environmental Studies

Equestrian Studies

European Studies/EU Studies

Family and Consumer Sciences/Human Sciences

Fashion Marketing & Management

Film

Finance

Fine Arts

Food Technologies

Foreign Languages

French

Geography

German-American Relations

Governance/Civil Society

Government

Greek Studies

Health Professions

Health Studies

History

Horticulture

Human Resource Development

Human Rights

Humanities

Imaging Science/Color Science

Information Technology

Intensive English

International Development

International Education

International Law

International Management

International Relations

Islamic Studies

Journalism

Law

Leadership

Liberal/General Studies

Life Sciences

Linguistics

Literacy

Literature

Management

Marine Engineering

Marketing

Master of Arts in Teaching

Master of Business Administration (MBA)

Mathematics

Medicine

Metal Mining

Metallurgy

Military Technologies

Minerals Industry

Minority Rights

Molecular Biology

Multi/Interdisciplinary Studies

Museum Studies

Music

Natural Disaster Research

Natural Resources and Conservation

Natural Sciences

Neuroscience

Physics

Policy Research

Political Science

Psychology

Psychometric

Public Administration

Public Health

Public Law

Public Policy

Religion/Theology

Residency Programs

Science

Science Technologies

Security and Protective Services

Social Justice

Social Movements

Social Science

Social Service

Sociology

Spanish

Statistics

Tax Law

TESOL

Theater

Translation and Interpretation

Transportation and Material Moving

U.S. Foreign Policy

Urban Planning

Veterinary Medical Technology

Visual and Performing Arts

Waste Minimization and Management

Women's Studies

Funding Resources by Country of Origin/Nationality

This index lists the funding opportunities that are available specifically to students or scholars from a particular country of origin/nationality. Please note that the majority of scholarship listings in this book are open to individuals from any country. The Fulbright Program is also available to students and scholars from any country. Please see the article on page 32 for more information on the Fulbright Program.

Category

Company .... Page No.

All

Afghanistan

Albania

Algeria

Andorra

Angola

Anguilla

Belarus

Belgium

Belize

Benin

Bhutan

Bolivia

Bosnia & Herzegovina

Botswana

Brazil

British Virgin Islands

Brunei

Bulgaria

Burkina Faso

Burundi

Cambodia

Cameroon

Canada

Cape Verde

Cayman Islands

Central African Republic

Chad

Chile

China

Colombia

Comoros

Cook Islands

Costa Rica

Côte d'Ivoire

Croatia

Cuba

Cyprus

Czech Republic

Democratic Republic of the Congo

Denmark

Djibouti

Dominica

France

French Guiana

French Polynesia

Gabon

Gambia

Georgia

Germany

Ghana

Gibraltar

Greece

Grenada

Guadeloupe

Guatemala

Guinea

Guinea-Bissau

Guyana

Haiti

Honduras

Hong Kong

Hungary

Iceland

India

Indonesia

Iran

Iraq

Ireland

Israel

Italy

Jamaica

Japan

Jordan

Kazakhstan

Kenya

Kiribati

Korea, Republic of

Kuwait

Kyrgyzstan

Laos

Latvia

Lebanon

Lesotho

Liberia

Libya

Liechtenstein

Lithuania

Luxembourg

Macao

Macedonia

Madagascar

Malawi

Malaysia

Mali

Malta

Marshall Islands

Martinique

Mauritania

Mauritius

Mexico

Moldova

Monaco

Mongolia

Montenegro

Montserrat

Morocco

Mozambique

Myanmar

Namibia

Nauru

Nepal

Netherlands

New Zealand

Nicaragua

Niger

Nigeria

Niue

Norway

Oman

Pakistan

Palau

Palestinian Authority

Panama

Papua New Guinea

Paraguay

Peru

Philippines

Poland

Portugal

Qatar

Republic of Maldives

Reunion

Romania

Russia

Rwanda

Samoa

San Marino

São Tomé & Príncipe

Saudi Arabia

Senegal

Serbia

Seychelles

Sierra Leone

Singapore

Slovakia

Slovenia

Solomon Islands

Somalia

South Africa

Spain

Sri Lanka

St. Helena

St. Kitts-Nevis

St. Lucia

St. Vincent

Sudan

Suriname

Swaziland

Sweden

Switzerland

Syria

Tajikistan

Tanzania

Thailand

Togo

Tonga

Trinidad & Tobago

Tunisia

Turkey

Turkmenistan

Turks & Caicos Islands

Tuvalu

Uganda

Ukraine

United Arab Emirates

United Kingdom

Uruguay

Uzbekistan

Vanuatu

Vatican City

Venezuela

Vietnam

Windward Islands

Yemen

Zambia

Zimbabwe

Index of Advertisers

2015/2016 Calendar

2015

JANUARY

S	M	T	W	T	F	S
				1	2	3
4	5	6	7	8	9	10
11	12	13	14	15	16	17
18	19	20	21	22	23	24
25	26	27	28	29	30	31

FEBRUARY

S	M	T	W	T	F	S
1	2	3	4	5	6	7
8	9	10	11	12	13	14
15	16	17	18	19	20	21
22	23	24	25	26	27	28

MARCH

S	M	T	W	T	F	S
1	2	3	4	5	6	7
8	9	10	11	12	13	14
15	16	17	18	19	20	21
22	23	24	25	26	27	28
29	30	31				

APRIL

S	M	T	W	T	F	S
			1	2	3	4
5	6	7	8	9	10	11
12	13	14	15	16	17	18
19	20	21	22	23	24	25
26	27	28	29	30		

MAY

S	M	T	W	T	F	S
					1	2
3	4	5	6	7	8	9
10	11	12	13	14	15	16
17	18	19	20	21	22	23
24/31	25	26	27	28	29	30

JUNE

S	M	T	W	T	F	S
	1	2	3	4	5	6
7	8	9	10	11	12	13
14	15	16	17	18	19	20
21	22	23	24	25	26	27
28	29	30				

JULY

S	M	T	W	T	F	S
			1	2	3	4
5	6	7	8	9	10	11
12	13	14	15	16	17	18
19	20	21	22	23	24	25
26	27	28	29	30	31	

AUGUST

S	M	T	W	T	F	S
						1
2	3	4	5	6	7	8
9	10	11	12	13	14	15
16	17	18	19	20	21	22
23/30	24/31	25	26	27	28	29

SEPTEMBER

S	M	T	W	T	F	S
		1	2	3	4	5
6	7	8	9	10	11	12
13	14	15	16	17	18	19
20	21	22	23	24	25	26
27	28	29	30			

OCTOBER

S	M	T	W	T	F	S
				1	2	3
4	5	6	7	8	9	10
11	12	13	14	15	16	17
18	19	20	21	22	23	24
25	26	27	28	29	30	31

NOVEMBER

S	M	T	W	T	F	S
1	2	3	4	5	6	7
8	9	10	11	12	13	14
15	16	17	18	19	20	21
22	23	24	25	26	27	28
29	30					

DECEMBER

S	M	T	W	T	F	S
		1	2	3	4	5
6	7	8	9	10	11	12
13	14	15	16	17	18	19
20	21	22	23	24	25	26
27	28	29	30	31		

2016

JANUARY

S	M	T	W	T	F	S
					1	2
3	4	5	6	7	8	9
10	11	12	13	14	15	16
17	18	19	20	21	22	23
24/31	25	26	27	28	29	30

FEBRUARY

S	M	T	W	T	F	S
	1	2	3	4	5	6
7	8	9	10	11	12	13
14	15	16	17	18	19	20
21	22	23	24	25	26	27
28	29					

MARCH

S	M	T	W	T	F	S
		1	2	3	4	5
6	7	8	9	10	11	12
13	14	15	16	17	18	19
20	21	22	23	24	25	26
27	28	29	30	31		

APRIL

S	M	T	W	T	F	S
					1	2
3	4	5	6	7	8	9
10	11	12	13	14	15	16
17	18	19	20	21	22	23
24	25	26	27	28	29	30

MAY

S	M	T	W	T	F	S
1	2	3	4	5	6	7
8	9	10	11	12	13	14
15	16	17	18	19	20	21
22	23	24	25	26	27	28
29	30	31				

JUNE

S	M	T	W	T	F	S
			1	2	3	4
5	6	7	8	9	10	11
12	13	14	15	16	17	18
19	20	21	22	23	24	25
26	27	28	29	30		

JULY

S	M	T	W	T	F	S
					1	2
3	4	5	6	7	8	9
10	11	12	13	14	15	16
17	18	19	20	21	22	23
24/31	25	26	27	28	29	30

AUGUST

S	M	T	W	T	F	S
	1	2	3	4	5	6
7	8	9	10	11	12	13
14	15	16	17	18	19	20
21	22	23	24	25	26	27
28	29	30	31			

SEPTEMBER

S	M	T	W	T	F	S
				1	2	3
4	5	6	7	8	9	10
11	12	13	14	15	16	17
18	19	20	21	22	23	24
25	26	27	28	29	30	

OCTOBER

S	M	T	W	T	F	S
						1
2	3	4	5	6	7	8
9	10	11	12	13	14	15
16	17	18	19	20	21	22
23/30	24/31	25	26	27	28	29

NOVEMBER

S	M	T	W	T	F	S
		1	2	3	4	5
6	7	8	9	10	11	12
13	14	15	16	17	18	19
20	21	22	23	24	25	26
27	28	29	30			

DECEMBER

S	M	T	W	T	F	S
				1	2	3
4	5	6	7	8	9	10
11	12	13	14	15	16	17
18	19	20	21	22	23	24
25	26	27	28	29	30	31